saturday kitchen

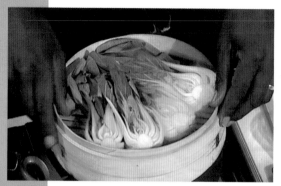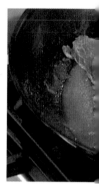

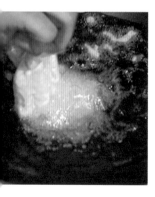

saturday kitchen

Over 100 simple but impressive recipes
From the country's top chefs

10 9 8 7 6 5 4 3 2 1

Published in 2007 by BBC Books,
an imprint of Ebury Publishing.
A Random House Group Company.

Copyright © Cactus TV 2007

Photography on pages 10, 11, 13, 16, 20, 24, 27, 30,
35, 38, 43, 46, 51, 55, 59, 75, 76, 77, 81, 84, 90, 91,
92, 98, 104, 118, 130, 136, 144, 154, 160, 170
by Will Heap, © Woodlands Books Limited 2007

The Random House Group Limited Reg. No. 954009

Addresses for companies within the Random House
Group can be found at www.randomhouse.co.uk

A CIP catalogue record for this book is available from
the British Library.

ISBN 978 1 8460 7223 9

The Random House Group Limited makes every effort
to ensure that the papers used in our books are made
from trees that have been legally sourced from
well-managed and credibly certified forests.
Our paper procurement policy can be found on
www.randomhouse.co.uk

Design by Grade Design Limited
Home Economy by Janet Brinkworth
Set in Berthold Akzidenz Grotesk
Colour Reproduction by Dot Gradations Ltd, UK
Printed and bound in England by Butler & Tanner Ltd

contents

introduction
James Martin

Hello and welcome to the first new *Saturday Kitchen* book. I love working on the show with so many passionate foodies in front of and behind the camera, as well as the viewers at home who give us so much great feedback. You've got to love this job as otherwise you'd never get up in time every Saturday at 5am. We have a great laugh in the studio, working with such a diverse and brilliant range of chefs. It's great to have the chance to put together some of their and my recipes so you can enjoy them at home again and again.

This is a book not just for Saturdays, it's full of inspiration for every day. Most people have very busy lives so it's hard to fit in cooking during the week, but some of these recipes are quick enough to try anytime and especially good to give you a mid-week lift! Hidden in there too are some that are slightly more challenging and will make a great weekend treat.

We've tried to make the book a true reflection of the show, so we've included all the elements that our viewers say they enjoy. We're privileged to have an amazing range of really high calibre guest chefs cooking for us every week. In between all the friendly chef banter they manage to knock up some fantastic food! Their recipes are purposefully straightforward, so you'll have no trouble turning them out successfully, but at the same time they're aspirational as the recipes are created especially for us by talented chefs. We've got some amazing dishes from some amazing people. Antonio Carluccio made a rare TV appearance to cook 'Stuffed lamb cutlets', and we were delighted to welcome Ken Hom who made us 'Stir-fried beef with onions and mint, and hot bean thread noodles'. It's been great to showcase chefs new to television like Chris Galvin and Tana Ramsay as well as seasoned TV professionals like Bill Granger, Rachel Allen and John Torode.

I'm very impressed by our wine experts on the show. Week after week they come up with amazing food matches that are not only interesting, but affordable and widely available. We thought it was really important to include wine tips from our wonderful experts so you can easily enjoy the same perfect marriage of food and wine at home.

They pick out the qualities of the ingredients and find wines and grapes that complement the dishes beautifully. They tell us why they match the grapes with the food in an easy to understand style, which makes it easy to learn about wine. These tips will help you choose great wines for your dishes time after time – they really give me the confidence to experiment.

An element of the show I personally love is cooking for the celebrities. I have to create recipes inspired by their ideas of food heaven and food hell, and the viewers decide what they get to eat. My recipes for food heaven try to give them a twist on their favourite ingredient, so they see their favourite foods in a new way. My food hell recipes are an attempt to change their minds about a nightmare ingredient, something they really hate – it can be a bit of a challenge sometimes! Everyone is so different, people can be turned off from the simplest of foods for the strangest reasons, and I do my best to make them see food differently. I think it will give your home cooking a bit of an extra twist knowing the recipes were inspired by the likes of Ronan Keating, Myleene Klass and Rupert Everett! Ronan was one of our most enthusiastic guests and took home copies of all the studio recipes so he could try them out himself.

Sprinkled throughout the book are some of my quick recipes that can be easily made at any time. Not surprisingly, my personal favourites are the puddings. I've included a wide variety from English classics like 'Steamed sponge pudding with custard' or 'Madeira trifle with raspberries', to the Russian classic 'sharlotka'. But there are some great quick savoury dishes, too, like 'Chilled melon soup with langoustines and mint' or 'Cob nut, wild mushroom and chestnut stir-fry with roast chicken' for tasty mid-week suppers.

I really hope you enjoy eating this food and drinking the wine as much as I have, and enjoy a book by people who I can now say aren't just chefs to me, but great friends also.

Happy cooking!

James Martin

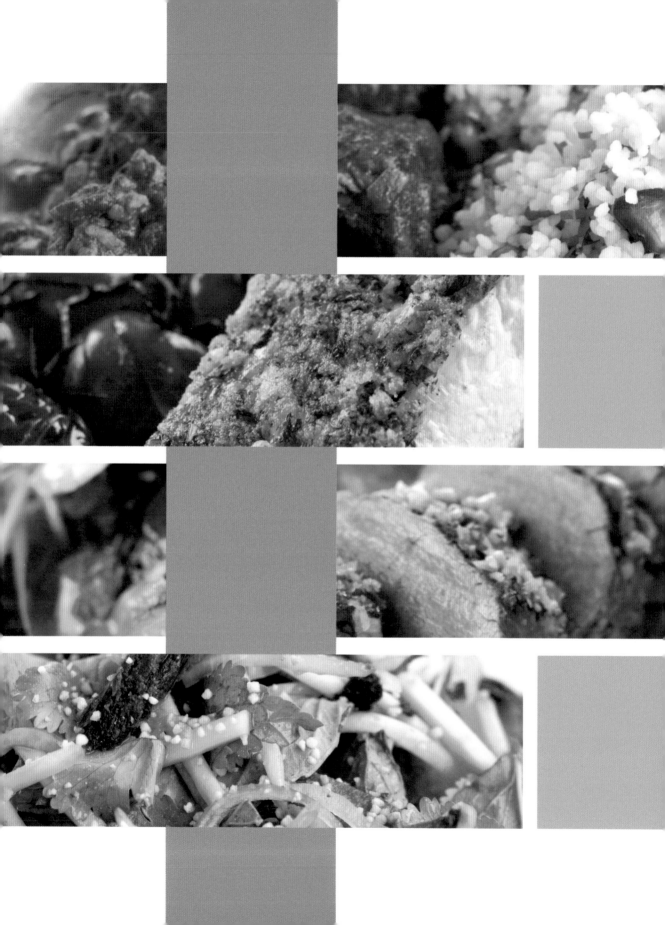

main courses

spiced salad of braised beef with roasted rice and almonds

John Torode

Serves 2

Ingredients

For the braised beef

300g (10½oz) beef skirt (or shin
  or strap from the fillet or sirloin)
2 tablespoons fish sauce
400ml (14fl oz) coconut milk
1 large piece galangal, roughly
  chopped
2 lemongrass stems, pounded
1 large piece ginger, roughly chopped
6 lime leaves

For the dressing

2 dried red chillies, deseeded,
  roasted and crushed
juice of 1 large lime
2 tablespoons fish sauce
2 tablespoons palm sugar

For the salad

1 sour green mango (or ½ green
  papaya), peeled and shredded
2 handfuls of beansprouts
4 Thai shallots, thinly sliced
1 small bunch of coriander leaves
1 small bunch of mint leaves, torn
1 small bunch of Thai basil leaves
100g (3½oz) basmati rice, soaked

Method

- Place the beef trimmings into a bowl, add the fish sauce and toss.
- Cover and place in the fridge overnight.
- Preheat the oven to 200°C/400°F/Gas Mark 6.
- Draining off any excess fish sauce, place the beef in a roasting tray.
- Add the coconut milk, galangal, lemongrass, ginger and lime leaves.
- Stir to combine and cover with foil.
- Place in the oven for 40 minutes.
- Take out of the oven and remove the foil.
- Turn the oven up to 220°C/425°F/Gas Mark 7.
- Turn the meat over and return to the oven for another hour, turning it over occasionally. By the end of the cooking time the liquid should have evaporated and the meat browned.
- Remove from the oven and place the meat on a plate to cool. Do not refrigerate if possible, as it is better served at room temperature.
- When cool, slice the beef thickly.
- To make the dressing, pound the chillies, lime juice, fish sauce and palm sugar in a pestle and mortar.
- Combine the mango or papaya with the beansprouts and shallots in a large bowl.
- Add a good dollop of dressing and the sliced beef and toss to combine. Leave to marinate for 5 minutes, and add the herbs.
- Heat a frying pan until hot. Add rice and toast until golden.
- Place on a serving dish and top with the roasted rice.

Wine expert Susie Barrie's choice
Care Rosado Cabernet Tempranillo

This rosé has bold cherry flavours to go with the beef and there's a touch of sweetness which is important when matching wines with chilli.

pan-roast chicken with crème fraîche spätzle

Oliver Rowe

Serves 4

Ingredients

For the chicken

4 chicken legs, boned out, skin on

2 chicken breasts,
    wing bone on, skin on

zest of 1 lemon

2 cloves garlic, crushed

2 sprigs of thyme

75ml (2½fl oz) white wine

2 tablespoons rapeseed oil

For the spätzle

250g (9oz) plain flour

½ teaspoon celery seed

½ teaspoon salt

pinch of black pepper

7 large eggs

1 teaspoon olive oil

2 shallots, finely diced

100ml (4fl oz) white wine

350ml (12fl oz) crème fraîche

For the cabbage

½ Hispi cabbage, or a round white
    cabbage, finely sliced

juice of 1 lemon

1 clove garlic, crushed

150ml (5fl oz) rapeseed oil

1 bunch of dill, roughly chopped

Method

- Mix the lemon zest, garlic, thyme and wine together.
- Smear the mixture over the chicken pieces, then place them flesh side down in a dish and leave in the fridge for at least 1 hour.
- Preheat the oven to 245°C/475°F/Gas Mark 9.
- Heat a frying pan. Add the rapeseed oil and chicken, skin side down.
- Fry for 3–4 minutes until golden-brown and crispy. Turn the chicken over and place in the oven for 6–8 minutes until cooked through.
- Meanwhile, make the spätzle by blending the flour, celery seed, salt, pepper and eggs in a food processor until you have a smooth batter.
- Spoon the batter into a piping bag.
- Heat a saucepan of salted, oiled water to boiling. Trim the end off the bag, drizzle the batter across the water and cook for 2–3 minutes.
- Drain and toss straight into a hot frying pan with a little rapeseed oil. Cook for 1–2 minutes until just coloured.
- To make the sauce, heat a small frying pan, add the olive oil and shallots and cook for 4–5 minutes until softened.
- Add the wine and reduce by ⅓. Add the crème fraîche and warm through.
- Spoon half the sauce over the spätzle and stir to combine.
- Whisk the lemon juice and garlic together and season with salt and pepper. Then whisk in the oil.
- Pour the dressing over the cabbage, add the dill and stir.
- Carve and serve with a spoonful of spätzle and cabbage.

> **Wine expert Pip Martin's choice**
> *Hautes Côtes de Nuits Pinot Noir*
>
> This wine has a good, crisp acidity that partners the lemon in this dish well, yet will not overpower the chicken.

chilled melon soup
with langoustines and mint

James Martin

Serves 8

Ingredients

2 Cantaloupe melons, diced
¼ watermelon, diced
110ml (4fl oz) white wine
juice of 1 lime
2 tablespoons white wine vinegar
6 tablespoons extra virgin olive oil
salt and freshly ground black pepper
16 cooked langoustines
1 bunch of mint leaves, shredded
200ml (7fl oz) double cream

Method

- Place the diced melon, white wine and lime juice in a blender and purée.
- Pass through a sieve and chill until ready to use.
- Whisk the vinegar and olive oil together and season well.
- Toss the langoustines in the dressing with 2 tablespoons of the shredded mint and place in the centre of a soup bowl.
- Whip the cream lightly, then fold in the remaining mint and season.
- Spoon the chilled soup around the langoustines and top with a quenelle of the mint cream.

moroccan lamb tagine
with lemon and pomegranate couscous

Rachel Allen

Serves 12–14

Ingredients

For the tagine

4 tablespoons olive oil

8 cloves garlic, crushed

4 onions, chopped

4 teaspoons grated ginger

1½ tablespoons crushed coriander
 seeds

3 teaspoons ground cinnamon

salt and freshly ground black pepper

3kg (6½lb) shoulder of lamb, boned,
 fat discarded and cut into 4cm
 (1½in) cubes

2 tablespoons tomato paste

2kg (4lb) ripe tomatoes or 4 x 400g
 (14oz) tins tomatoes, coarsely
 chopped

4–5 tablespoons honey

wedges of lime and a bowl of
 Greek yoghurt, to serve

For the couscous

1 large or 2 small pomegranates

800g (1¾lb) couscous

6 tablespoons olive oil

juice of 2 lemons

1 litre (1¾ pints) boiling chicken
 stock or water

4 tablespoons chopped fresh mint
 or coriander

Method

· Preheat the oven to 165°C/325°F/Gas Mark 3.

· Heat a large flameproof casserole or heavy saucepan, add the olive
 oil, garlic, onions, ginger and spices.

· Season with salt and pepper, stir and cook on a low heat with the lid
 on for about 10 minutes until the onions are soft.

· Add the lamb, tomato paste, chopped tomatoes and honey.

· Stir, bring to a simmer and place in the oven for 1½ hours, removing
 the lid halfway through to let the liquid reduce and thicken. If it is still
 a bit thin, put the pan on the hob on a medium heat, without the lid,
 stirring occasionally until the liquid thickens.

· Season to taste.

· Cut the pomegranate in half and scoop out the seeds using a
 teaspoon, discarding the white membrane.

· Place the couscous in a bowl and mix in the olive oil and lemon juice.

· Pour in the boiling stock or water and season.

· Allow to sit in a warm place for 5–10 minutes until the liquid is
 absorbed.

· Stir in the chopped herbs and pomegranate seeds.

· Spoon the tagine onto serving plates with the couscous and wedges
 of lime, and serve with a bowl of thick Greek yoghurt on the table.

Wine expert Susy Atkins' choice
Ravenswood California Red Zinfandel

This wine has a wonderful aroma, hints of raspberry and black pepper and
a sweet ripeness, almost like a fruit pastille. The lightness of the red-fruit
flavour goes really well with the spices in the lamb tagine.

summer salad roscoff
Paul Rankin

Serves 4

Ingredients

For the salmon

200ml (7fl oz) white wine

200ml (7fl oz) water

2 tablespoons white wine vinegar

1 bouquet garni of flat-leaf parsley,
  bay leaves and thyme

1 teaspoon salt

450g (1lb) boneless salmon fillet

For the salad

120g (4oz) green beans, cut into
  2cm (¾in) lengths

4 tablespoons mayonnaise

1 tablespoon chopped fresh basil
  leaves

2 anchovy fillets, finely minced

2 tablespoons poaching liquid

salt and freshly ground black pepper

120g (4oz) mixed salad leaves

4 tablespoons vinaigrette

½ cucumber, peeled, quartered
  lengthwise and chopped

250g (9oz) salad tomatoes, cut
  into wedges

4 hard boiled eggs (cooked for
  9 minutes), peeled and quartered

12 black olives, stones removed

Method

· Pour the wine, water and white wine vinegar into a large pan.

· Add the bouquet garni and the salt and bring to the boil.

· Immerse the salmon fillet in the liquid and simmer very gently for
  2 minutes.

· Remove from the heat, cover and allow to cool.

· Cook the green beans in salted boiling water for 6 minutes and then
  drain. Refresh in cold water and drain again.

· To make the dressing, whisk the mayonnaise, chopped basil and
  minced anchovies together in a small bowl.

· Thin with the poaching liquid from cooking the salmon, whisking
  continually. Add salt and pepper to taste.

· Toss the salad leaves and green beans with the vinaigrette and
  arrange attractively in the centre of each plate, surrounded by the
  cucumber, tomato, egg and olive garnishes.

· Remove the salmon from the poaching liquid and flake some carefully
  onto each plate.

· Drizzle with some of the anchovy and basil dressing.

Wine expert Peter Richards' choice
Casillero del Diablo Riesling

We need a wine that will match the fattiness of the egg and mayonnaise
and the saltiness and fishiness of the anchovies and salmon. The wine will
need to be light and summery but have body and tang. Rosé would work
well, but here we have gone for a Riesling. This Chilean wine has a
citrusy lemon–lime tang to go with the fish, creaminess to complement
the mayonnaise and a salty character that goes well with the olives.

cob nut, wild mushroom and chestnut stir-fry with roast chicken

James Martin

Serves 2

Ingredients

25g (1oz) butter

1 onion, finely sliced

2 sprigs of thyme

150g (5oz) mixed wild mushrooms, sliced

50g (2oz) shelled fresh cob nuts

150g (5oz) cooked chestnuts

salt and freshly ground black pepper

1 roast chicken

Method

- Heat a frying pan and add the butter and onion.
- Fry for 2–3 minutes until softened, then add the thyme and wild mushrooms.
- Sauté for another 2–3 minutes until tender.
- Add the cob nuts and cooked chestnuts and fry for 1–2 minutes.
- Season to taste.
- Serve with a slice of roast chicken.

grilled red mullet
with squid, flat-leaf parsley and capers

Chris Galvin

Serves 4

Ingredients

1 bunch of flat-leaf parsley, leaves
   picked
2 shallots, thinly sliced
25g (1oz) black olives
25g (1oz) Piquello peppers, peeled
   and cut into strips
10g (½ oz) fine capers
1 lemon, peeled and cut into
   segments
20g (½ oz) orzo pasta, cooked in
   water with a few strands of saffron
   and cooled
1 tablespoon extra virgin olive oil
salt and freshly ground black pepper
8 red mullet fillets, scaled and
   pin-boned
200g (7oz) baby squid, cleaned
3 cloves garlic, peeled, sliced
   and blanched
50ml (2fl oz) extra virgin olive oil
175ml (6fl oz) three-year-old Banyuls
   wine or any red wine, reduced
   to 1 tablespoon

Method

- Preheat the grill.
- Mix the parsley, shallots, olives, peppers, capers, lemon and orzo together.
- Toss in the extra virgin olive oil and season to taste.
- Brush the red mullet fillets with a little olive oil, season and place on a baking tray.
- Place under the grill and cook for 1–2 minutes.
- Heat a little olive oil in a heavy pan until smoking, then quickly sear the squid and garlic slices.
- Season, remove from the heat onto some kitchen paper to drain and add to the parsley salad.
- To serve, place some salad on each plate with two fillets resting on it. Drizzle some extra virgin olive oil around each plate and finally spoon on some of the reduced wine.

Wine expert Olly Smith's choice
Sileni Sauvignon Blanc 2005

For this dish, I am after a wine with enough zip to cope with the dressing and capers, but will also allow those fresh fish flavours to come through.
   My top choice is the Sileni Sauvignon Blanc 2005. It has all the acidity needed to match up with the capers and will allow the flavours of the fish to come through beautifully. Lime and gooseberry flavours burst from the glass and it has a bit of a herby twist. It is so fresh and crisp – perfect for fish.

braised chicken with lemon and honey and shepherd's salad with feta

Bill Granger

Serves 4

Ingredients

For the chicken

1 tablespoon olive oil

1.6kg (3lb 8oz) chicken, cut into
   8 pieces

1 red onion, sliced

12 cloves garlic, peeled but left whole

1 lemon, cut into chunks

175ml (6fl oz) chicken stock

125g (4½oz) honey

1 small handful of fresh oregano
   leaves

For the salad

400g (14oz) tinned chickpeas, rinsed
   and drained

150g (5oz) feta cheese, crumbled

1 small handful of fresh flat-leaf parsley

2 Lebanese cucumbers, or small
   regular cucumbers, chopped

1 green pepper, chopped

50g (2oz) black olives, halved
   and pitted

3 tablespoons olive oil

1 tablespoon lemon juice

salt and freshly ground black pepper

Method

· Heat a large frying pan over high heat, add the oil and chicken and cook for 5 minutes until golden.

· Remove and set aside.

· Reduce the heat to medium–high, add the onion and cook for 1 minute.

· Add the garlic and cook for 1 minute.

· Return the chicken to the pan with the lemon, chicken stock and honey, reduce the heat, cover the pan and simmer for 20 minutes or until the chicken is cooked through.

· Lift out the chicken and put on a baking tray.

· Increase the heat under the sauce and simmer, uncovered, for another 15 minutes to thicken.

· Place the chicken under a hot grill for 5 minutes until crisp.

· Arrange the chicken on a platter, drizzle with the sauce and sprinkle with oregano.

· To make the salad, gently mix together the chickpeas, feta, parsley, cucumber, green pepper and olives in a large bowl.

· Whisk the olive oil and lemon juice together and season with salt and pepper.

· Toss the salad with the dressing.

Wine expert Susie Barrie's choice
Cusumano Grecanico

Bill's chicken dish is filled with fantastic Mediterranean flavours – and it needs a Mediterranean-style wine. As this is a dish I can imagine myself eating as I am sitting on a sunny terrace, I chose a cool, crisp white wine. The Grecanico grape variety can retain high levels of acidity so it is able to match the lemon and the nutty note goes well with the chicken.

prune rösti and honey-roasted pork fillet

James Martin

Serves 4

Ingredients

For the pork

2 pork tenderloins

salt and freshly ground black pepper

2 tablespoons honey

25g (1oz) butter

For the rösti

2 medium Estima potatoes, peeled

1 apple, peeled

4 tablespoons crème fraîche

4 egg yolks

salt and freshly ground black pepper

4 prunes, stoned

25g (1oz) butter

Method

· Preheat the oven to 220°C/425°F/Gas Mark 7.

· Season the pork fillets and brush with honey.

· Heat a frying pan and add the butter and pork.

· Seal on each side until golden-brown.

· Place in the oven for 8–10 minutes until just cooked through.

· Remove from the oven and rest for 5 minutes.

· To make the rösti, grate the potatoes and apple with a large grater into a tea towel.

· Twist the tea towel to squeeze out any water and starch.

· Place the dry potato mix into a bowl, add the crème fraîche and egg yolks and season.

· Take 4 x 8cm (3in) rings and fill to halfway up with the potato mix.

· Place a prune on top of each one.

· Fill to the top with the remaining potato mix and press down firmly.

· Heat a frying pan, add the butter and place the röstis into the pan.

· Remove the rings and cook for 2–3 minutes on either side until golden–brown and crispy.

· Slice the pork and serve with the röstis.

braised salmon with mustard and a Gruyère herb crust

James Tanner

Serves 4

Ingredients

For the crust

1 slice white bread, crumbed

25g (1oz) Gruyère cheese, grated

15g Cheddar cheese (½oz), grated

4 sprigs of thyme, leaves picked

4 tablespoons roughly chopped
curly parsley

50g (2oz) soft butter

For the salmon

4 x 150g (5oz) salmon fillets

50ml (2fl oz) fish stock

50ml (2fl oz) white wine

salt and freshly ground pepper

50g (2oz) Dijon mustard

150g (5oz) vine tomatoes

2 tablespoons balsamic vinegar

1 tablespoon olive oil

25g (1oz) butter

4 handfuls of spinach leaves

Method

- Blend the breadcrumbs, cheese, thyme, parsley and butter in a food processor until smooth.
- Spread the crust mixture onto a lined baking tray and chill until set.
- Preheat the oven to 200°C/400°F/Gas Mark 6.
- Pour the fish stock and wine into an oven-proof dish.
- Place the salmon fillets into the dish and season with salt and pepper.
- Brush the fillets with the mustard.
- Cut the crust into rectangles large enough to cover the salmon and place on top.
- Place in the oven for 10 minutes.
- Put the tomatoes on a baking tray, pour over the vinegar and oil, season and roast in the oven for 8 minutes.
- Heat a frying pan, then add the butter and spinach and sauté for 2 minutes until wilted.
- To serve, place the spinach in the centre of the plate, the salmon on top and the roasted tomatoes on the side.

Wine expert Tim Atkin's choice

Vidal East Coast Sauvignon Blanc

There is a lot of cheese in this recipe so opt for something white and quite high in acid, which will cut through it. I'm going to go with a Sauvignon from New Zealand which has masses of flavour and a tiny bit of sweetness that will go well with the roasted vine tomatoes. This New World wine is a lot more flavoursome than many from the Loire Valley or Bordeaux. It has beautiful gooseberry, passion fruit and elderflower aromas – just what you would expect from a Sauvignon Blanc.

chicken saltimbocca with rosemary, Fontina and prosciutto

Gennaro Contaldo

Serves 2

Ingredients

For the chicken

2 sprigs of rosemary, the same length
   as the chicken breast

1 chicken breast, skinless and
   boneless, cut in half lengthways

salt and freshly ground black pepper

2 slices Fontina cheese, 3mm thick
   and the same length as the chicken
   breast

2 x 30g (1oz) slices prosciutto ham,
   2mm thick and the same length as
   the chicken breast

plain flour for dusting

10g (½oz) butter

2 tablespoons olive oil

¼ glass white wine

For the vegetables

3 tablespoons extra virgin olive oil

2 courgettes, cut into 6mm thick slices

2 tomatoes, cut into 6mm thick slices

2 sprigs of marjoram, leaves picked

2 tablespoons grated Parmesan
   cheese

salt and freshly ground black pepper

Method

- Remove the needles from the rosemary, setting the branches to one side, and chop finely.
- Sharpen one end of each branch, to make skewers.
- Flatten the chicken pieces slightly, then season with salt, pepper and the chopped rosemary needles.
- Place one slice of Fontina on top of each chicken piece, followed by the Prosciutto and secure with the rosemary branches.
- Dust the chicken side with plain flour, shaking off any excess.
- Heat the butter and olive oil in a frying pan, then add the meat, chicken side down, and cook on a medium heat for about 2 minutes or until sealed. Turn over and cook for a minute.
- Turn over again, add the wine and reduce to nearly nothing.
- Remove the chicken to a serving plate, leaving the pan on the heat.
- Add a small knob of butter to the pan to thicken the sauce.
- Preheat the oven to 250°C/500°F/Gas Mark 9.
- Arrange slices of courgettes and tomatoes on a small dish, drizzle with olive oil, marjoram and Parmesan, and bake for 4–5 minutes.
- Pour the sauce over the chicken and serve immediately with the baked courgettes and tomatoes.

Wine expert Olly Smith's choice
Verdicchio dei Castelli di Jesi

This is a lemony, spritzy wine with a bitter herby twist that will pick up on the rosemary. It has enough zing to match up to the acidity of the tomatoes but has a subtlety which allows the flavour of the courgettes to come through.

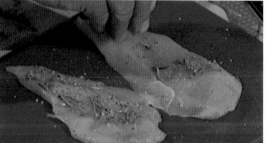
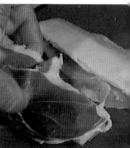

seared tuna with avocado purée and radish and apple salad

Bryn Williams

Serves 2

Ingredients

For the tuna

½ teaspoon cloves

½ teaspoon nutmeg

½ teaspoon ground ginger

½ teaspoon white peppercorns

½ teaspoon black peppercorns

200g (7oz) fresh tuna

For the salad

1 avocado

juice of 1 lime

2–3 drops Tabasco

salt and freshly ground black pepper

1 apple, thinly sliced and cut into matchsticks

2 red radishes, finely sliced

1 punnet Shizo cress

1 punnet Daikon cress

1 tablespoon extra virgin olive oil

Method

- Place all the spices in a grinder and grind to a fine mix.
- Roll the tuna in the spice mix, coating well.
- Heat a frying pan, then sear the tuna on each side for 30 seconds.
- Remove the tuna from the pan, roll tightly in cling film and place in the fridge.
- Blend the avocado, lime juice and Tabasco in a blender until smooth, then season with salt and pepper and keep to one side.
- Place the apple, radishes, Shizo and Daikon cress and olive oil in a bowl, toss to combine and season to taste.
- To serve, place the avocado purée on a plate. Cut the tuna into 5mm (¼in) thick slices, season with salt and pepper and place three or four slices on each plate. Pile the salad to one side.

Wine expert Susie Barrie's choice

Leasingham Magnus Riesling

Tuna works well with both red and white wines. If I was going for red then a New World Pinot Noir would work well, but when matching you need to look at the overall flavours, not just the main ingredient.

The tuna is surrounded by hot flavours, so a white works better. The Leasingham Riesling is zippy, with lots of concentration and refreshing lime flavours. Riesling works well with food as it is packed with flavour and acidity, but you should be careful to choose a dry one. This example is powerful enough to match the tuna, refreshing enough to complement the zesty avocado and aromatic enough to cope with the crunchy salad.

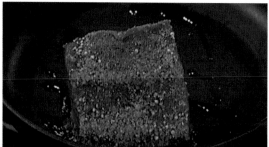

jugged fresh kippers with cider and lime butter

James Martin

Serves 2

Ingredients

2 fresh kippers
100g (4oz) butter, softened
3 tablespoons chopped fresh parsley
50ml (2fl oz) cider
¼ apple, grated
juice and zest of 1 lime

Method

- Place the kippers in a tall jug with the tails sticking out of the top and pour boiling water carefully into the jug, right up to the top.
- Put the softened butter (not melted) into a bowl and mix with the chopped parsley.
- Slowly combine the grated apple and cider with the butter and leave to one side.
- After the kippers have been in the water for about 2–3 minutes, pour off the water and place the kippers onto a plate.
- Put half the butter on each kipper, add the juice and zest of the lime and eat either on its own or with some sliced bread.

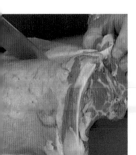

hazelnut crusted lamb with new potatoes and a hazelnut dressing

Brian Turner

Serves 4

Ingredients

For the dressing

50g (2oz) whole skinned hazelnuts

1 teaspoon mustard

1 tablespoon white wine vinegar

2 tablespoons ground nut oil

2 tablespoons olive oil

1 teaspoon chopped parsley

salt and freshly ground black pepper

For the lamb

2 lamb fillets (from best end of lamb)

1 tablespoon olive oil

20g (¾oz) butter

1 teaspoon mustard

1 tablespoon white wine

For the new potatoes

350g (12oz) new potatoes, skin on, cooked and sliced

50g (2oz) butter

50g (2oz) shallots, finely chopped

75g (3oz) soft salad leaves

Method

- Preheat the oven to 200°C/400°/Gas Mark 6.
- Chop half the hazelnuts finely and put to one side.
- Chop the rest not quite so finely and put into a bowl.
- Add the mustard, white wine vinegar, oils and parsley and whisk to incorporate.
- Season with salt and pepper.
- Heat a frying pan, add the oil and butter and sear the lamb for 1–2 minutes.
- Remove from the pan and cool.
- Mix the mustard and white wine together and brush over the lamb.
- Roll the lamb in the finely chopped hazelnuts to coat.
- Place on a wire rack in a roasting tray and put in the oven for 8–10 minutes until just pink.
- Remove and rest for 5 minutes.
- Heat a frying pan, add the butter and potatoes and cook until golden-brown.
- Sprinkle with the chopped shallots and season with salt and pepper.
- To serve, slice the lamb and lay on top of the potatoes. Toss the salad leaves with the dressing and pile in the centre.

Wine expert Tim Atkin's choice

Torres De Casta Rosado

Brian's lamb salad has quite difficult ingredients, such as white wine vinegar, mustard, shallots, potato and salad. You could go for a weighty white wine such as Chardonnay or Viognier, a lighter red such as a Pinot Noir, or a dry, fruity rosé. I am going for the Torres De Casta Rosado, which is full-bodied and has lovely strawberry characters. This rosé has enough body and tannin to match the lamb.

chicken and butter bean casserole with basmati rice

Tana Ramsay

Serves 4–6

Ingredients

drizzle of olive oil

4 small red onions, finely chopped

1 clove garlic, crushed

2 sticks celery, finely sliced

1 sweet red pepper, deseeded and
finely sliced

6 baby leeks, finely sliced

6 Portabellini mushrooms (or any
large, flat mushrooms)

3 litres (5 pints) chicken stock

2 tablespoons soy sauce

1 x 400g (14oz) tin chopped tomatoes

2 carrots, finely diced

1 x 400g (14oz) tin butter beans

10 skinless chicken thighs
on the bone

salt

285g (10oz) basmati rice

Method

· Heat the olive oil in a large heavy-based saucepan.

· Add the onions and garlic and fry gently until softened.

· Add the celery, red pepper, leeks and mushrooms, gently stirring
together.

· Add the stock, soy sauce and tomatoes and bring to the boil, then
turn down to a gentle simmer.

· Add the carrots and butter beans.

· Add the chicken thighs and leave to simmer gently for approximately
1 hour.

· Bring to the boil a pan of water seasoned with a pinch of salt.

· Add the rice and cook according to the pack instructions.

· Take out one of the chicken thighs and gently break it open to check
that the meat is cooked through.

· Remove the chicken thighs once cooked and take them off the bone.
The chicken should literally fall off the bone. If desired, cut into bite-
sized pieces.

· Spoon the rice and chicken into bowls, add a generous ladle of
vegetables and sauce and serve.

Wine expert Olly Smith's choice

Barbera d'Asti

There are lots of vegetables in this dish, so a wine that will bring out that
earthy, rustic character is required. Barbera D'Asti is great and has the
perfect body to let those meaty chicken flavours flourish. It has lively,
bright, sour cherry flavours but the body is soft – it's like chewing on a
fluffy pillow!

vichy-glazed carrots with pan-fried chicken breast

James Martin
Serves 4

Ingredients

50ml (2fl oz) olive oil

50g (2oz) butter

4 chicken breasts, skin on

salt and freshly ground black pepper

500ml (17½fl oz) mineral water

25g (1oz) sugar

1 teaspoon salt

500g (1lb 2oz) chantannay carrots
 or baby carrots, washed

25g (1oz) flat-leaf parsley, chopped

25g (1oz) chervil, chopped

Method

- Preheat the oven to 190°C/375°F/Gas Mark 5.
- Heat a frying pan and add the olive oil and butter.
- Season the chicken and place in the pan, skin side down.
- Fry for 3 minutes until golden-brown, then turn over and place in the oven.
- Roast for 8 minutes until tender, then remove and rest for 5 minutes.
- Put the water, sugar, salt and butter in a saucepan, then add the carrots, bring to the boil, turn down to a simmer, cover the pan and cook for 5 minutes.
- Remove the lid and allow the liquid to reduce to a syrup on a high heat, then add the chopped herbs and serve with the chicken.

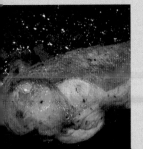
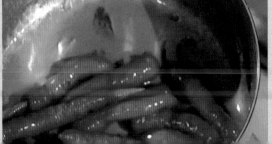

sichuan pepper beef with five-a-day vegetables and five-spice gravy

Ching He Huang

Serves 2

Ingredients

2 sirloin steaks, cut into strips

1 tablespoon Shaoxing rice wine or dry sherry

2 teaspoons ground Sichuan pepper

1 teaspoon dark soy sauce

½ teaspoon Chinese five-spice powder

2 cloves garlic, crushed and finely chopped

2 tablespoon groundnut oil

1 medium red chilli, deseeded and chopped

½ onion, chopped

1 small handful of broccoli, cut into small stems

1 small handful of mangetout, chopped

1 small handful of carrots, sliced into half-rounds

1 small handful of baby corn, cut in half

300ml (10½fl oz) hot fresh beef or vegetable stock

1 tablespoon light soy sauce.

1 tablespoon cornflour blended with 2 tablespoons cold water

1 spring onion, finely sliced

salt and freshly ground white pepper

Method

· Mix the rice wine or sherry, ground Sichuan pepper, dark soy sauce, five-spice powder and garlic in a bowl and marinate the beef for as long as possible – overnight is best.

· Heat a wok over a high heat and add the oil.

· Stir-fry the marinated beef for 2 minutes.

· Add the red chilli and onion and stir-fry for less than 1 minute, then add the rest of the vegetables and stir-fry for 1 minute.

· Add the stock (it needs to be hot) and mix well.

· Season with light soy sauce.

· Bring to the boil, add the blended cornflour and stir well.

· Add the spring onion, season to taste and serve with some steamed jasmine rice.

Wine expert Olly Smith's choice

Casillero del Diablo Merlot 2005

For this dish you need a wine that is low in tannin because of the soy sauce, which tends to make tannic wines taste bitter. Yering Frog Pinot Noir might work, but it doesn't have quite the depth of flavour I am after. The Casillero del Diablo Merlot has the perfect balance of acidity and tannin, but also some luscious fruit to make it all blend in. This is a double-medal-winning wine – it's like going to the pet shop to buy a hamster, bringing it home and discovering you've bought a bear!

honey-baked chicken with hoisin, plantain and wilted garlic stems

Michael Moore

Serves 2

Ingredients

2 chicken breasts, skinless

salt and freshly ground black pepper

1 tablespoon olive oil

2 tablespoons butter

1 plantain, peeled and sliced
   lengthways

1 tablespoon ground cinnamon

20g (¼oz) honey

40g (1½oz) hoisin sauce

110g (4oz) wild garlic stems or garlic
chives blanched for 15 seconds

Method

- Preheat the oven to 200°C/400°F/Gas Mark 6.
- Season the chicken breasts with salt and pepper.
- Heat a frying pan and add the olive oil and half the butter.
- Add the chicken and seal on each side until golden-brown.
- Place in the oven for 6–8 minutes until cooked through.
- Remove from the oven and rest for 5 minutes.
- Heat a frying pan and add the remaining butter.
- Dust the plantain with the cinnamon and fry for 1–2 minutes until golden and tender.
- To serve, place the wilted garlic stems to one side of the plate and the plantain in the centre and drizzle with the hoisin sauce. Slice the chicken, place it across the plantain and drizzle with the honey.

Wine expert Susie Barrie's choice

Tesco's Finest South African Chenin Blanc Reserve 2005

For Michael's summery chicken dish, we need a nice, cool white with lots of crisp acidity and a focus on fruit rather than oak. Tesco's Finest South African Chenin Blanc Reserve has loads of lovely acidity and ripe red apple, honey and lemon flavours. I think this is the perfect match for the caramelized flavours of the chicken in Michael's dish.

duck rillettes

James Martin

Serves 4

Ingredients

4 duck legs

1 tablespoon salt per kilo of duck legs

2–3 sprigs fresh thyme,
  leaves stripped

300g (11 oz) duck fat

5 tablespoons roughly chopped flat-
  leaf parsley

salt and freshly ground black pepper

Method

- For the duck confit, weigh the duck legs and sprinkle with one tablespoon of salt per kilo of duck. Place onto a tray and sprinkle with thyme. Wrap with cling film and place in the fridge overnight.
- Heat a heavy pan and add the duck legs. Add the duck fat to completely cover the legs. Bring the fat to a gentle simmer and cook slowly for about two and a half hours, or until the duck meat is very tender.
- Remove and discard all skin, bone and tendons from the duck legs and set the duck fat aside.
- Place the meat in a bowl and mash with a fork.
- Slowly add 150–175g (5–6 oz) of the reserved duck fat.
- Add the chopped parsley and season with salt and black pepper.
- Spoon into individual ramekins and place in the fridge to set.
- Remove from the fridge 10 minutes before serving.

spiced pork burgers

Tony Tobin

Serves 4

Ingredients

1 small onion, minced

2 cloves garlic, minced

1 teaspoon coriander powder

1 teaspoon cumin powder

1 teaspoon chilli powder

1 teaspoon crushed pink peppercorns

600g (1¼lb) pork mince

200g (7oz) pork fat, minced

1 tablespoon chopped sage

2 eggs

salt and freshly ground black pepper

4 rings fresh pineapple

8 thin slices Gruyère cheese

2 hamburger buns

50g (2oz) rocket

2 vine-ripened tomatoes, sliced

1 Spanish onion, sliced into rings

250ml (9fl oz) beer

110g (4oz) flour

oil for frying

100ml (4fl oz) mayonnaise

1 teaspoon minced chillies

Method

- Sweat the onions and garlic with the coriander, cumin, chilli powder, peppercorns and a little olive oil for 2 minutes on a medium heat.
- Cool and place in a mixing bowl with the pork and pork fat minces, sage and eggs.
- Mix well and season.
- Form into 4 large patties, about 2–3cm (1in) thick.
- In a heavy frying pan, cook the patties in a little olive oil on a medium heat for 3 minutes each side.
- Grill the pineapple rings for 1–2 minutes and place 2 slices of Gruyère on each ring for the last 30 seconds to melt.
- Cut the hamburger buns in half and toast the halves on both sides.
- Put the flour in a bowl and whisk in the beer using a hand whisk.
- Dip the onion rings in the batter as soon as possible and deep-fry.
- To construct the burger, on each half-bun place a small amount of rocket, followed by slices of tomato, a pork patty, a cheesy pineapple ring and onion rings.
- Mix the mayonnaise and chillies together and drizzle over the burger.

Wine expert Jonathan Ray's choice
Sainsbury's Taste the Difference Douro 2004

This recipe has lots of competing flavours: grilled pineapple, chilli mayonnaise and the pork itself. If you are considering a white wine with this dish, think Viognier. Viognier is known for having apricoty, peachy, even slightly pineappley flavours, and I think that would work really well with the pineapple and help combat the spiciness.

Ultimately, we are going to go for a red wine. The Sainsbury's Taste the Difference Douro is made from the port grape varieties. It is big, soft, mellow, juicy and will work with all the competing flavours in the spicy pork burgers. The soft, gentle tannins in this wine will match the chilli and the rich, dark-berry fruit flavours will complement the pork perfectly.

crab and ginger tart with a chilli dressing
Lesley Waters

Serves 8–10

Ingredients

For the tart
450g (1lb) shortcrust pastry

10cm (4in) piece fresh ginger, peeled and roughly chopped

1 large bunch of flat-leaf parsley

2 tablespoons cold-pressed sunflower oil, or normal sunflower oil

350g (12oz) fresh white crab meat

2 eggs

2 egg yolks

325ml (11fl oz) crème fraîche

salt and freshly ground black pepper

For the dressing
4 spring onions, finely chopped

juice of 1 lime

1 red chilli, finely chopped

3 tablespoons soy sauce

6 tablespoons sunflower oil

1 teaspoon caster sugar

Method
- Preheat the oven to 200°C/400°F/Gas Mark 6.
- On a lightly floured surface, roll out the pastry and use to line a 25cm (10in) loose-bottomed tart tin. Cover and place in the fridge for 15 minutes.
- Line the tart tin with greaseproof paper and fill with baking beans.
- Bake in the oven for 10–15 minutes.
- Remove the greaseproof paper and beans and return the tart tin to the oven for a further 3–5 minutes until it is just cooked.
- Reduce the heat to 175°C/350°F/Gas Mark 4.
- In a small food processor, blend the ginger with the parsley and sunflower oil.
- Spread the mixture over the base of the tart tin and scatter the crab meat over the top.
- In a bowl combine the eggs and egg yolks with the crème frâiche and season.
- Pour into the tart case.
- Return the tart to the oven for 30–35 minutes or until just set.
- For the dressing, whisk together the onions, lime juice, chilli, soy sauce, sunflower oil and sugar with 1 tablespoon of water. Season to taste.
- Serve the tart warm with a drizzling of the chilli dressing.

Wine expert Susy Atkins' choice
Spier Sauvignon Blanc 2005

My tip at the moment for sheer value for money and quality is South African Sauvignon Blanc. They are doing terrifically well with this grape variety, which is zesty, crisp, dry and unoaked, with plenty of rich fruit flavours. Spier has a crisp, fresh acidity which will really go well with the ginger and cut through the rich crab meat.

bridies

James Martin

Serves 4

Ingredients

2 tablespoons olive oil

1 onion, finely chopped

3 sprigs of thyme, finely chopped

350g (12oz) lean minced beef

1 teaspoon dry mustard powder

75ml (2½fl oz) beef stock

salt and freshly ground black pepper

500g (1lb 2oz) puff pastry

2 eggs, beaten

Method

- Preheat the oven to 230°C/450°F/Gas Mark 8.
- Heat a frying pan, add the olive oil, onion and thyme and fry until golden and softened.
- Place the minced beef into a bowl along with the mustard powder and beef stock.
- Add the cooked onions and plenty of salt and pepper and mix to combine.
- Roll the pastry to 5mm (¼ in) thick and cut out 4 circles, 15cm (6in) in diameter each.
- Place a spoonful of the beef mixture in the centre of each pastry circle.
- Brush the outer edges with the beaten eggs.
- Fold over and crimp the edges together firmly.
- Brush with the egg wash and sprinkle with salt and pepper.
- Place on a lightly oiled baking tray in the oven for 15 minutes.
- Reduce the heat to 175°C/350°F/Gas Mark 4 and cook for another 45 minutes until golden-brown.
- Serve hot or warm, but never cold.

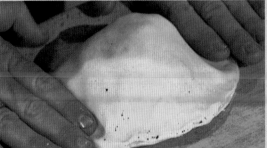

seared chicken livers with spinach, peas and sherry

Martin Blunos

Serves 2

Ingredients

25g (1oz) unsalted butter

1 tablespoon olive oil

250g (9oz) chicken livers, trimmed and cut into even-sized pieces

1 shallot, finely chopped

1 clove garlic, crushed

50ml (2fl oz) sherry

¼ teaspoon English mustard

500g (1lb 2oz) baby leaf spinach

50g (2oz) fresh peas, cooked and refreshed (or frozen peas, defrosted)

salt and freshly ground black pepper

pinch of grated nutmeg

juice of 1/2 lemon

200g (7oz) new potatoes, boiled and lightly crushed

Method

- Heat a non-stick frying pan and add the butter and oil.
- Season the chicken livers and toss into the hot pan along with the shallot and garlic.
- Cook for 3–4 minutes, turning occasionally to colour well.
- Pour in the sherry and stir in the mustard.
- Lift the livers out and set aside.
- Add the spinach to the pan with 1 tablespoon of water.
- After 1 minute add the peas and season with salt and black pepper and some grated nutmeg.
- Cook until the spinach has wilted, then add the lemon juice.
- Stir the livers back into the spinach.
- Check the seasoning, then serve with a bed of crushed new potatoes.

Wine expert Susy Atkins' choice
Tyrrell's Old Winery Pinot Noir 2004

Chicken livers and sherry are strong flavours that need a soft, fruity, easy-drinking red. Beaujolais is very easy to enjoy, as is the Burgundian Pinot Noir. Pinot Noirs are a possibility. However, I think we need a slightly riper style of Pinot, so let's pick from a hotter country. Tyrrell's Old Winery Pinot Noir has got all the easy-drinking, silky character I want for this dish, but it is relatively ripe and rich because it comes from warm vineyards in Australia. It has a lovely bright colour and is very aromatic and strawberryish – perfect for liver.

crisp-fried spicy fish in batter with salad

Atul Kochhar

Serves 4

Ingredients

For the fish

4 cod fillets weighing 100–120g
   (3½–4oz) each

1 tablespoon lime juice

salt to taste

oil for deep-frying

1 teaspoon chaat masala

For the batter

1 tablespoon ginger-garlic paste

½ teaspoon turmeric powder

½ teaspoon red chilli powder or
   crushed black pepper

¼ teaspoon garam masala powder

½ teaspoon mango powder

½ teaspoon ajwain seeds (optional)

100g (4½oz) chickpea or gram flour

1 tablespoon cornflour

1 drop orange food colouring
   (optional)

120ml (4fl oz) sparkling water

For the salad

1 teaspoon lime juice

½ teaspoon olive oil

salt and crushed black pepper

1 small cucumber, thickly sliced

2 medium tomatoes, sliced

½ medium red onion, sliced

10 sprigs of coriander, leaves picked

Method

- Marinate the fish in the lime juice and salt for 20 minutes.
- Meanwhile, make the batter by whisking all the ingredients together.
- Wipe the fish with kitchen paper to remove excess moisture.
- Marinate the fish in the batter for 10 minutes.
- Heat the oil in a wok and fry the fillets over a medium heat until crisp.
- Remove the fish from the wok, drain on some kitchen paper and sprinkle with chaat masala powder.
- To make the dressing mix the lime juice, oil and salt and pepper. Toss the salad ingredients with the dressing and serve with the crispy fish.

Wine expert Peter Richards' choice
Honey Tree Gewürztraminer Riesling

Two varieties that spring to mind when we talk about spicy dishes are Gewürztraminer and Riesling. A great tip when looking for good value versions of these varieties is to head to the New World, especially Australia.

The wonderful thing about Atul's fish dish is the combination of flavours. On the one hand, you've got the full-on and spicy flavours of the mango, ginger and chilli. On the other, you've got the delicacy and freshness of the cod and the lime. That's exactly what you get in this wine – the exotic, honeyed, spicy character of the Gewürztraminer, but also the lovely freshness and elegance of the Riesling.

tomato and apple chutney

James Martin

Ingredients

570ml (1 pint) malt vinegar

450g (1lb) soft brown sugar

300g (11oz) sultanas

15g (½oz) root ginger, peeled and chopped

4 red chillies, chopped

2kg (4lb 4oz) tomatoes, cut into 6 or 8 pieces each

500g (1lb 2oz) green apples, peeled and chopped

400g (14oz) shallots, roughly chopped

salt and freshly ground black pepper

Method

- To sterilize the jars wash and rinse thoroughly and then dry. Place in a preheated oven at 180°C/350°F/Gas Mark 4 for 5 minutes without rubber/plastic seal. Remove from the oven, leave to cool, replace seal, do not touch the inside of the jar. To make the chutney, place the vinegar and sugar in a large saucepan and bring to the boil.
- Cook for 3–4 minutes until just caramelized.
- Add the sultanas and cook until just reduced.
- Add all the other ingredients, bring to the boil and cook for 20–30 minutes, stirring all the time. The chutney should be chunky and not over cooked, as it will become a purée.
- Cool the chutney, place in jars and store in the fridge.

soy-poached chicken with pak choi, coconut rice and hot and sour sauce

Ainsley Harriott

Serves 4

Ingredients

For the rice
225g (8oz) basmati rice
150ml (5fl oz) coconut milk
300ml (10½ fl oz) water
pinch of salt

For the chicken
2 lime leaves, fresh or dried, finely
    shredded
2cm (¾in) piece fresh ginger, finely
    sliced
1 clove garlic, sliced
½ large red chilli, deseeded and
    roughly chopped
1 tablespoon light soy sauce
600ml (1 pint) water
4 chicken breasts, boneless and
    skinless
4 heads pak choi, cut in half
    lengthways
4 spring onions, chopped
1 tablespoon toasted sesame seeds

For the hot and sour sauce
4 tablespoons caster sugar
1 heaped teaspoon cornflour
4 tablespoons rice vinegar
4 tablespoons light soy sauce
2 tablespoons rice wine or dry sherry

Method

- Place the rice in a bowl, cover with cold water and soak for 15–20 minutes.
- Drain and rinse the rice and place into a saucepan. Add the coconut milk, water and salt.
- Bring to the boil and reduce the heat to a very gentle simmer. Cover and cook for 10 minutes until the rice is tender.
- While the rice is cooking, place the lime leaves, ginger, garlic and chilli into a saucepan. Add the soy sauce and water and bring to the boil.
- Add the chicken breasts, then cover and cook over a low heat for 4 minutes.
- Turn the chicken in the liquid, then place the pak choi in a steamer and set over the chicken pan for 3 minutes until tender.
- Meanwhile, place all the sauce ingredients in a small saucepan and bring to the boil.
- Simmer for 1 minute, stirring constantly until thickened and glossy.
- Slice the chicken and arrange on plates or in bowls with the coconut rice and pak choi. Drizzle with the sauce, scatter with the spring onions and sesame seeds and serve immediately.

Wine expert Olly Smith's choice
Leitz Rudesheimer Rosengarten Riesling

For this dish, I am looking for a white wine with enough zip to cope with the vinegar in the sauce and enough sweetness to match up to the spice, but without overwhelming the chicken. The Leitz Rudesheimer Rosengarten Riesling has a lovely texture, is packed with nectarine and lychee flavours and has got all the sugariness I'm after.

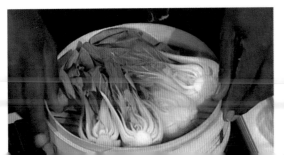

salmon kiev

Silvena Rowe

Serves 4

Ingredients

80g (3oz) butter, at room temperature
3 tablespoons chopped fresh dill
3 tablespoons chopped fresh chives
salt and freshly ground black pepper
300g (11oz) fresh sorrel leaves,
    washed and trimmed
400g (14oz) puff pastry block
4 x 150g (5oz) salmon fillets, skinless
    and boneless
1 egg yolk, beaten

Method

- Pre-heat the oven to 175°C/350°F/Gas Mark 4.
- Place the butter in a small bowl and add the dill and chives. Season to taste and mix together. Shape into a sausage and wrap in cling film. Place in the freezer and cut into 4 pieces when ready to use.
- Heat about 2–3 tablespoons of water in a saucepan and add the sorrel leaves. Cook for 2–3 minutes, swirling all the time, to wilt. Drain and keep aside.
- Divide the pastry block into 8 equal pieces. Roll each one into a rectangle about 18cm (7in) x 12cm (5in). Place a salmon fillet in the centre, then top with a piece of the frozen butter, then a handful of the wilted sorrel leaves. Brush the pastry edges liberally with the egg yolk and cover with another pastry piece, sealing the edges really well. Brush with some more egg. Trim the pastry parcel and decorate the top if desired. Repeat with the rest of the salmon fillets and pastry.
- Cook in the pre-heated oven for 25 minutes. Serve hot with salad leaves.

Wine expert Jonathan Ray's choice

Santa Rita Cabernet Sauvignon Rosé

An obvious choice for this dish would be a white wine, but we can afford to be a little more imaginative so let's think of something different.

Some reds go really well with salmon – Oyster Bay Pinot Noir for example, is light, soft and fresh and can be served chilled – but I'm going to go for a rosé. The Santa Rita Cabernet Sauvignon Rosé has lots of character and plenty of weight and you can chill it right down. It smells of wild strawberries and herbs and has a creaminess that goes really well with the salmon, while the herbal notes will match the dill and chives. I think it works perfectly with this dish.

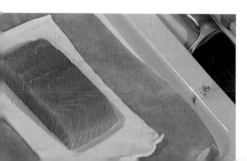

curly kale bubble and squeak
with poached eggs and Hollandaise sauce

James Martin

Serves 4

Ingredients

675g (1lb) Maris Piper potatoes, peeled and cut into chunks

225g (8oz) curly kale or spring cabbage, thinly sliced

25g (1oz) butter

1 leek or small onion, chopped

150ml (5fl oz) full-cream milk

freshly ground white pepper

6 rashers streaky bacon, cut into lardons

2 tablespoons white wine vinegar

4 eggs

Hollandaise sauce to serve (see page 93)

Method

- Put the potatoes in a large pan of water, salted with 1 teaspoon per 600ml (1 pint). Bring to the boil, simmer until tender and drain, leaving the steam to die down.
- Put 1cm (½in) of water in a large pan and bring to the boil. Add ½ teaspoon of salt and the cabbage and cook over a vigorous heat for 4–5 minutes until just tender, but not mushy. Drain well.
- Melt the butter in the pan in which you cooked the cabbage, then add the leek or onion and cook gently for 7–8 minutes until very soft, but not coloured.
- Pass the potatoes through a potato ricer (or you can use a masher) into the pan and add the cabbage, milk and white pepper to taste.
- Mix together well.
- Heat a frying pan, add the bacon and fry until crispy.
- Add the bacon to the potato mix and form into four patties.
- Place in the frying pan, cook for 2–3 minutes until golden-brown, then flip and cook for another 2–3 minutes.
- Meanwhile, bring a pan of salted water to the boil and add the vinegar.
- Whisk the water to create a whirlpool and once settled, crack an egg into it.
- Simmer for 2–3 minutes, remove the poached egg carefully with a slotted spoon onto some kitchen paper and repeat the process with the remaining eggs.
- Serve the bubble and squeak topped with the eggs and a spoonful of Hollandaise sauce.

roast fillet of lamb with pan-fried tomatoes, aubergines and courgettes and sauce vierge

Daniel Galmiche

Serves 2

Ingredients

For the lamb

1 lamb fillet, fully trimmed

salt and freshly ground black pepper

2 sprigs of rosemary

1 tablespoon olive oil

2 cloves garlic, skin on

For the vegetables

2 plum tomatoes, skinned

2 courgettes

1 small aubergine

2–3 tablespoons olive oil

For the sauce vierge

110ml (4fl oz) olive oil

juice of 1 lime

2 tomatoes, peeled, deseeded and diced

1 small sprig of rosemary, roughly chopped

1 small bunch of rocket

Method

· Preheat the oven to 220°C/425°F/Gas Mark 7.

· Season the lamb with salt and pepper and insert the rosemary into the side of the fillet.

· Heat a frying pan and add the olive oil and garlic.

· Add the lamb and seal on each side until browned, then place in the oven for 5–8 minutes.

· Remove and leave to rest.

· Meanwhile, slice the tomatoes, courgettes and aubergine into 5mm (¼in) thick rounds.

· Heat a frying pan and add the olive oil.

· Add the vegetables, a few at a time, season with salt and pepper and fry until just tender and golden.

· To make the sauce, place the olive oil in a saucepan and warm through.

· Add the lime juice, tomato and rosemary and season with salt and pepper.

· Place three slices of each vegetable, just overlapping, in the centre of the serving plate.

· Carve the lamb into thick slices on the angle and place on top of the vegetables. Spoon the sauce over the lamb and top with some rocket leaves.

Wine expert Susie Barrie's choice

Borie de Maurel Rêve de Carignan

In the summer I would probably choose a rosé to go with this, otherwise I would opt for this chunky red from the south of France. Soft, spicy and supple, Borie de Maurel Rêve de Carignan has just enough tannin to cut through the richness of the lamb. It is also packed with ripe, wild-berry fruits, which will complement the roasted vegetables, rosemary and olive oil. I can't imagine a better match for this dish.

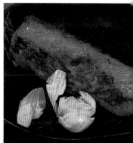

black fig and chilli tagliatelli

Ben O Donoghue

Serves 4

Ingredients

320g (11½oz) fresh egg tagliatelli
pasta
6 overripe black figs
2–3 tablespoons extra virgin olive oil
1 clove garlic, finely sliced
pinch of dried chilli
125ml (4½fl oz) double cream
salt and freshly ground black pepper
squeeze of lemon juice
1/2 bunch of purple basil
1/2 bunch of green sweet basil
4 long red chillies, grilled, peeled and
deseeded
200g (7oz) Parmesan cheese, shaved

Method

· Bring a large saucepan of salted water to the boil, drop in the pasta
and cook for 2–3 minutes.
· Remove the stems from the figs and chop each one into quarters and
then into eighths.
· Gently heat the oil in a heavy-based pan then add the garlic and
lightly fry until sticky and just golden.
· Add the dried chilli and chopped figs, then gently fry for about 1–2
minutes.
· Add the cream and lower the heat to a simmer.
· Season with salt, pepper and a squeeze of lemon juice.
· Add a few of each of the different basil leaves.
· Drain the pasta and add to the sauce.
· Toss to combine and coat the pasta.
· Taste for seasoning and divide between four bowls.
· Garnish with strips of the grilled chilli, a few basil leaves and
Parmesan shavings.

Wine expert Tim Atkin's choice
Domaine de Bionnay Beaujolais, 2005

If there's one ingredient that experts hate when matching wine to a dish it
is chilli. At least this dish isn't too spicy, as the chilli is deseeded. You
need a light, soft, fairly juicy red. I could have gone with a Dornfelder from
Germany, which is unusual as most German wines are white. However,
I have chosen something more traditional in the Beaujolais – 2005 was a
terrific year for it. This wine is lip-smacking, thirst-quenching and juicy.
It smells almost figgy and is not too tannic, so it won't clash with the chilli.
The acidity will cut through the cream and Parmesan.

lamb ragout
spring rolls with mango salsa

James Martin
Serves 4

Ingredients

For the ragout

1kg (2lb 2oz) lamb mince

2 tablespoons olive oil

1 onion, chopped

3 garlic cloves, finely chopped

250g tomatoes, roughly chopped

1 tablespoon tomato purée

1 tablespoon plain flour

150ml (5fl oz) red wine

300ml (10fl oz) chicken stock

2 sprigs thyme

2 bay leaves

150g (5oz) flageolet beans, tinned,
    rinsed and drained

For the spring rolls

20 wonton wrappers

For the mango salsa

1 mango, finely chopped

1 red chilli, finely chopped

1 small bunch mint leaves, finely
    chopped

1 lime, juiced

1 tablespoon extra virgin olive oil

Method

- To make the ragout heat a large pan until hot and add the lamb mince and fry until golden.
- Remove from the pan and drain off any excess oil.
- Add the oil to the pan and the onions and garlic, and fry until golden.
- Add the tomatoes and tomato purée and fry for 2 minutes.
- Stir in the flour and cook for a further 1–2 minutes.
- Return the mince to the pan and mix well.
- Add the wine, chicken stock and herbs and bring to the boil.
- Season with salt and black pepper.
- Reduce the heat to a simmer and cook for 1 hour until the sauce is thickened and the meat tender.
- Add the flageolet beans and cook for a further 5–10 minutes.
- Adjust the seasoning and serve with pasta.
- Allow the remaining ragout to cool totally.
- To make the spring rolls heat a deep fat fryer to 190°C.
- Place a wonton wrapper onto a board.
- Place a spoonful of cold ragout onto the centre of the wonton.
- Brush the outside of the wrapper around the mince with a little water.
- Fold the wrapper over either end then wrap up through the centre.
- Drop the wonton's into the hot oil and cook for 3–4 minutes until golden brown and cooked through. Drain onto kitchen paper.
- To make the salsa place all the ingredients into a bowl and mix to combine.
- To serve place spring rolls onto a plate with a small bowl of salsa for dipping.

smoked cockles on a bed of creamed corn with lemon salad

Kevin Dundon

Serves 4

Ingredients

For the smoked cockles

200g (7oz) oak wood chips

40g (1½oz) raspberries

500g (1lb 2oz) cockle meat, or 1kg (2lb 4oz) whole cockles, cooked then shelled

50g (2oz) semolina flour

olive oil for shallow-frying

For the creamed corn

2 tablespoons olive oil

1 shallot, finely chopped

110g (4oz) sweetcorn kernels

50ml (2fl oz) white wine

50ml (2fl oz) double cream

salt and black pepper

For the salad

2 lemons, peeled and segmented

1 small bunch of celery leaves

1 small bunch of flat-leaf parsley, leaves picked

50ml (2fl oz) olive oil

salt and black pepper

Method

- Place a wok on a high heat and add the oak wood chips. Once the wood starts to smoke, add the raspberries.
- Thread cockles onto a wooden skewer and lie across the inside of the wok leaving about a 2½cm (1in) gap above the smoking chips.
- Leave to smoke for about 5–6 minutes, then remove the cockles and take them off the skewer.
- Toss the cockles in the semolina flour.
- Heat a high-sided frying pan, then add enough olive oil to cover the bottom of the pan, about 2cm (¾in) deep.
- Add the cockles and shallow-fry for 1 minute.
- Remove and drain on kitchen paper.
- To prepare the creamed corn, heat a frying pan, then add the olive oil.
- Add the shallot and sweat for 1 minute until soft but not coloured.
- Add the sweetcorn and white wine.
- Cook until the wine is reduced by half.
- Add the double cream and again reduce by half.
- Season to taste and remove from the heat.
- Toss the lemon segments, celery leaves, parsley and olive oil together in a bowl and season to taste.
- Place the corn on a plate and top with the salad and smoked cockles.

Wine expert Olly Smith's choice

Domaine Petit Château Chardonnay

With Kevin's smoked cockles, what is needed is a white wine with enough zip to match up to the freshness of shellfish, enough body to cope with the creaminess of the dish and a little bit of spice to cope with that smoke. Domaine Petit Château Chardonnay has a wonderful element of spice because 10 per cent of it is oaked. It is a really subtle wine and has a creaminess that will go well with Kevin's creamed corn.

rib-eye steaks with tomatoes and olives

Angela Hartnett

Serves 4

Ingredients

For the steaks

300ml (10½fl oz) olive oil

30ml (1fl oz) Cabernet Sauvignon
  vinegar

2 tablespoons olive oil

4 x 250–300g (9–11oz) rib-eye steaks

4 plum tomatoes, peeled, deseeded
  and cut into quarters

20 black olives, pitted

2 tablespoons caperberries

splash of red wine

For the side dishes

2 tablespoons olive oil

30g (1oz) butter

300g (11oz) salad potatoes, cooked

2 cloves garlic, peeled but left whole

1 small handful of rosemary needles

200g (7oz) spinach

Method

- Make a vinaigrette by whisking together the olive oil and red wine vinegar and leave to one side.
- Heat a pan and add the butter and olive oil.
- Cook the steaks for about 5 minutes, turning once so both sides are coloured.
- When ready, remove from the pan and allow to rest for a few minutes.
- Add the tomato quarters and olives to the pan and quickly sauté.
- Deglaze the pan with the red wine and add the contents to the vinaigrette.
- Heat a frying pan, add the olive oil, potatoes, garlic cloves and rosemary and sauté until the potatoes are golden-brown.
- Wilt the spinach in a frying pan with the butter and olive oil.
- Remove the garlic from the potatoes and serve the steaks over the spinach with the potatoes, vinaigrette, tomatoes and olives.

Wine expert Olly Smith's choice

Feudo di Santa Tresa 'Nivuro' Nero d'Avola Cabernet Sauvignon

This dish demands a red wine with enough guts and structure to stand up to the mighty cow. But it also needs enough acidity in there to cope with the zing of the tomatoes. My top choice is the Feudo di Santa Tresa. It's got all the chunk needed to match up to the steak, plus the zing for the tomatoes. If you like big red wines like Shiraz, you will love this. It has everything. It's like the A-Team – the brawn of BA, the looks of Face, the longevity of Hannibal and the wild side of howling Mad Murdoch.

chunky green-pea dip with nachos

James Martin

Serves 4–6

Ingredients

450g (1lb) frozen petit pois or peas,
  defrosted and drained

½ red onion, finely chopped

1 clove garlic, finely chopped

1 small bunch of mint leaves

115g (4oz) natural yoghurt

½ red chilli, deseeded and finely
  chopped

1 teaspoon ground cumin

½ teaspoon ground coriander

juice of 1 lime

salt and freshly ground black pepper

2 tablespoons extra virgin olive oil

1 large bag nachos to serve

Method

- Place the peas in a food processor along with the onion, garlic and mint leaves and process until well mixed.
- Add the yoghurt and process once more, leaving the mix slightly chunky.
- Remove from the processor, stir in the chilli, cumin, coriander and lime juice and season to taste.
- Spoon into a serving bowl and top with the olive oil.
- Serve with nachos.

spice-rubbed pork fillet with tzatziki and Romesco sauce

James Tanner

Serves 2

Ingredients

For the pork fillet

200g (7oz) pork fillet

1 teaspoon ground turmeric

1 teaspoon ground paprika

1 teaspoon ground ginger

1 teaspoon ground cumin

splash of olive oil

splash of sesame oil

2 tablespoons brown sugar

1 tablespoon Worcestershire sauce

1 teaspoon chilli powder

1 teaspoon tomato paste

1 teaspoon salt

½ teaspoon pepper

For the tzatziki and Romesco sauce

1 cucumber, peeled, seeded and
 diced

1 teaspoon salt

200g (7oz) Greek yoghurt

1 clove garlic, chopped

1 handful of chopped mint leaves

salt and freshly ground black pepper

1 red pepper

1 red onion, chopped

2 chillies, split and deseeded

2 tablespoons olive oil

2 plum tomatoes, cut in half

4 anchovy fillets

125g (4½oz) ground roast almonds

1 tablespoon white wine vinegar

250g (9oz) toasted white bread,
 crusts removed

125ml (4½fl oz) olive oil

salt and freshly ground black pepper

Method

· Preheat the oven to 200°C/400°F/Gas Mark 6.

· To prepare the pork, place all the marinade ingredients in a bowl and mix well.

· Add the pork fillets and toss to combine, then leave to marinate for 20–30 minutes.

· Drain off the excess marinade.

· Heat a frying pan, add some olive oil and sear the fillet on either side.

· Place in the oven for 8–10 minutes until just firm to the touch.

· Leave to rest.

· To prepare the tzatziki, mix the cucumber and salt together and allow to sit for 1 hour.

· Rinse and pat dry.

· Place in a bowl with the yoghurt, garlic and mint, stir to combine and season with salt and black pepper.

· To prepare the Romesco sauce, preheat the oven to 175C°/350°F/Gas Mark 4.

· Place the pepper, onion, chillies and olive oil in a roasting tray and place in the oven for 10–15 minutes until soft and caramelized.

· Heat a frying pan, add the tomatoes, cut side down, and sear until blackened.

· Place the roasted vegetables, anchovy fillets, ground almonds, vinegar and bread in a food processor and blend for 2 minutes until smooth.

· With the food processor still on, gradually add the olive oil in a steady stream until well incorporated and season with salt and pepper.

· To serve, slice the pork and spoon the sauce and tzatziki to the side.

Wine expert Susie Barrie's choice

St Hallett Gamekeeper's Reserve Blend

St Hallett Gamekeeper's Reserve Blend is an unusual mix of Shiraz with the Grenache and Touriga. So we have the power and spice of the Shiraz to stand up to the chilli and garlic, tempered by the soft, gamey character of the Grenache and the floridity of the Touriga. When you put all that together, the wine will allow full rein to the flavours of the pork.

roast halibut with white beans and chorizo
John Torode

Serves 4

Ingredients

For the white beans
100ml (4fl oz) olive oil
2 small shallots, diced
1 onion, finely sliced
1 carrot, diced into 5mm (¼in) cubes
100g (3½oz) chorizo, diced
200g (7oz) tinned butter beans, drained
½ bunch of flat-leaf parsley, roughly chopped

For the halibut
4 hunks of halibut, bone in and skin on (classically called a tranche)
salt and freshly ground black pepper
100ml (4fl oz) olive oil

Method

· Preheat the oven to 220°C/425°F/Gas Mark 8.
· Heat a heavy-based pan, then add the olive oil, shallots and onion and sweat for 3–4 minutes.
· Add the carrot and cook for a further 4–5 minutes, until the onion is soft but still translucent.
· Add the chorizo and cook for 5 minutes, stirring well – the oil from the chorizo will be released, colouring and flavouring the vegetables.
· Add the beans and reduce the heat to nearly nothing, to just warm the beans through (you may need to add a little water or stock at this stage).
· Finish with the chopped parsley and adjust the seasoning.
· Heat a large heavy-based ovenproof pan.
· Take the halibut and score the dark side of the skin, then season all over with the salt and black pepper.
· Rub the fish with plenty of olive oil and place dark side down in the pan.
· Cook for 3 minutes, then place in the oven.
· Turn the fish over after 5 minutes and return to the oven for a further 5 minutes.
· Remove from the oven and serve with the warmed beans and a wedge of lemon.

Wine expert Pip Martin's choice
Marqués de Cáceres Rioja

The Marqués de Cáceres is a highly scented, aromatic wine that gives a light impression of sweetness, which draws out the sweetness of the halibut. The fresh acidity works well with the saltiness of the chorizo.

steak burger with Taleggio cheese
James Martin

Serves 2

Ingredients

300g (10½oz) minced beef

1 tablespoon chopped capers

2 shallots, finely chopped

2 tablespoons finely chopped flat-leaf parsley

1 tablespoon extra virgin olive oil

2 cornichons, finely chopped

3 dashes Tabasco

½ teaspoon salt

20 grinds of black pepper

2 medium egg yolks

2 slices Taleggio cheese

2 olive ciabatta rolls, split

50g (2oz) mixed salad leaves

Method

- Place the meat in a bowl along with all the ingredients except the cheese, rolls and salad leaves and combine well.
- Divide into two and form into patties.
- Place a piece of cheese in the centre of each burger and draw the meat over to cover, reforming the patties.
- Heat a griddle pan until very hot and drizzle with a little olive oil.
- Place the burgers on the griddle and cook for 3–4 minutes on each side.
- Remove and serve in the ciabatta roll with some salad leaves.

cumin and yoghurt chicken with cucumber and dill salad

Rachel Allen

Serves 4–6

Ingredients

For the chicken

1kg (2lb 2oz) organic chicken, spatchcocked

300ml (10½fl oz) natural yoghurt

2 tablespoons finely chopped mint or coriander

juice of 1 lemon

1 tablespoon crushed cumin seeds

2 tablespoons olive oil

2 cloves garlic, finely grated or crushed

good pinch of freshly ground pepper

For the cucumber salad

1 large or 2 medium cucumbers

juice of ½ lemon

4 tablespoons extra virgin olive oil

2 tablespoons chopped dill, mint or coriander

sea salt and freshly cracked black pepper

Method

- Mix the yoghurt, mint or coriander, lemon juice, cumin seeds, olive oil, garlic and pepper together in a bowl to make a marinade.
- Make slashes in the chicken and rub in the marinade, massaging well.
- Place on a plate in the fridge for at least 30 minutes, and if possible overnight.
- Preheat the oven to 200°C/400°F/Gas Mark 6.
- Heat a griddle pan until really hot.
- Remove the chicken from the marinade. Let the excess drip off, but do not wipe clean.
- Pour a little olive oil into the griddle pan, then add the chicken.
- Cook for 2–3 minutes each side until golden.
- Transfer to a roasting tin and place in the oven for 25–30 minutes until cooked through.
- Remove from the oven and rest for 5–10 minutes.
- Cut the cucumbers into halves lengthways, scoop out the watery seeds, cut into wedges and place in a bowl.
- Add the remaining salad ingredients and toss.
- Add more lemon juice and salt and pepper if necessary.
- Serve the chicken and salad with some freshly boiled new potatoes.

Wine expert Peter Richards' choice

Aramonte Catarratto 2005

This dish has creamy textures and flavours, with added freshness from the lemon, mint and dill and a spicy exotic edge from the cumin. The Aramonte has lovely Mediterranean lemon and dried herb flavours that go well with the lemon, mint and dill in the dish. It also has an attractive creaminess which should complement the yoghurt.

stuffed lamb cutlets
Antonio Carluccio

Serves 4

Ingredients

For the lamb

16 x 2.5cm (1in) thick lamb cutlets,
  French-trimmed

salt and freshly ground black pepper

75g (3oz) Fontina or Gruyère cheese,
  cut into slivers

16 large fresh sage leaves

8 slices of Parma ham

2 eggs, beaten with a pinch of salt

300g (11oz) fine dried breadcrumbs

olive oil for shallow-frying

For the salad

250g (9oz) mixed salad leaves,
  such as rocket, watercress and
  Little Gem lettuce

3 spring onions, finely sliced

1 bunch of mint leaves

2 sticks celery, finely sliced

3 tablespoons extra virgin olive oil

1 tablespoon white wine vinegar

Method

- Make a horizontal cut in the centre of each cutlet until almost through to the other side and open out.
- Season with salt and pepper, then place a sliver of Fontina or Gruyère cheese on one side of each cutlet, followed by a sage leaf and a little Parma ham.
- Fold over the other side of the meat. Dip the cutlets in the egg and then the breadcrumbs to completely coat the meat.
- Press the cutlets firmly together to seal and slightly flatten the meat.
- Shallow fry in moderately hot oil until golden on both sides.
- Toss the salad ingredients together, drizzle with the olive oil and vinegar and season. Serve with the lamb cutlets.

Wine expert Peter Richards' choice

Umani Ronchi Montepulciano d'Abruzzo

There is a lot happening in this Italian dish, so we need a wine that will match up to it but not overwhelm it – a smooth wine, with not too much tannin. This Italian wine is perfect. It has a herbiness, pepperiness and freshness which will complement this recipe wonderfully.

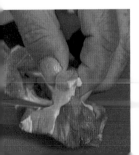

monkfish with mustard and cucumber sauce
Shaun Hill

Serves 4

Ingredients

1 small cucumber, peeled and thinly sliced
1 teaspoon salt
1 tablespoon caster sugar
1 tablespoon white wine vinegar
1 teaspoon ground black pepper
125ml (4½fl oz) fish stock or white wine
1 tablespoon crème fraîche
1 tablespoon wholegrain mustard
50g (2oz) unsalted butter
juice of 1 lemon
4 x 200g (7oz) monkfish tails
25ml (1fl oz) olive oil
salt and freshly ground black pepper

Method

- Mix the sliced cucumber with the salt and press for an hour. Placing a small plate or lid on the cucumber and putting a full tin or jar on top will do the job nicely.
- Squeeze as much liquid as possible from the cucumber.
- In a separate bowl, mix together the sugar, vinegar and black pepper, then toss the cucumber slices in it to coat well.
- Make the sauce by heating the stock, crème fraîche and mustard together, then whisking in the butter, a bit at a time.
- Season with a few drops of lemon juice.
- Brush the monkfish fillets with olive oil and fry in a dry, hot pan for 5 minutes.
- Add a knob of butter or few more drops of olive oil and continue to fry for about 1 minute until done, being careful not to burn the butter.
- Squeeze a few more drops of lemon juice over the cooked fish.
- Place the fish on warmed plates along with the cucumber and sauce.

Wine expert Tim Atkin's choice
Tesco's Finest Denman Vineyard Semillon

This is a pretty subtle recipe, so that rules out red wine. The obvious choice is a Sancerre, but that's too boring for this dish. The Semillon is an incredibly delicate wine with just 11 per cent alcohol. This grape variety is often blended with Sauvignon Blanc, but the Aussies have made it their speciality to use it on its own. This example is not oaked, which raises the acidity, and it has a herby edge which will work with the cucumber. The acidity will go well with the texture of the monkfish. The mustard worries me a little, but this wine has enough flavour to cope with it.

stuffed loin of pork wrapped in pancetta with parsnip purée

John Torode

Serves 6–8

Ingredients

For the pork

2kg (4lb 4oz) loin of pork, skin removed

salt and freshly ground black pepper

1 small bunch of sage, leaves picked

1 small bunch of oregano, leaves picked

1 small bunch of flat-leaf parsley, leaves picked

zest of 1 lemon

2 tablespoons olive oil

75g (3oz) fresh white breadcrumbs

12–16 slices pancetta

110ml (4fl oz) vegetable oil

For the parsnip purée

250g (9oz) parsnips, peeled and cut into chunks

250g (9oz) potatoes, peeled and cut into chunks

110ml (4fl oz) milk

salt and freshly ground black pepper

40g (1½oz) butter

50g (2oz) crème fraîche

Method

- Preheat the oven to 200°C/400°F/Gas Mark 6.
- Lay the pork, flesh side up, on a chopping board with the belly flap away from you.
- With a sharp knife make an incision in the meat halfway down, running parallel to the board, cutting almost all the way through.
- Open the loin up and season with salt and pepper.
- Chop the herbs roughly and place in a mixing bowl with the lemon zest and olive oil and mix well.
- Rub the herb mix onto the pork, then sprinkle over the breadcrumbs.
- Roll up tightly and leave to sit for 20 minutes.
- Take a piece of foil large enough to wrap the pork in and lay the pieces of pancetta on the foil (two abreast, overlapping slightly).
- Place the pork on top and roll.
- Bring the pancetta up to the edge covering the pork and then roll the foil around and twist the ends so that the parcel is very tight.
- Heat a large roasting tray on the hob and add the vegetable oil.
- Put the foil parcel in the tray and cook. Turn to make sure every part of the parcel has contact with the heat for 2 minutes.
- Put into the oven and roast for 1–1½ hours.
- Meanwhile, place the parsnips and potatoes in a saucepan with the milk and enough water to just cover.
- Season well, bring to the boil and simmer for 20 minutes until tender.
- Drain most of the liquid off and add the butter and crème fraîche.
- Purée in a blender until smooth, then taste and season well.
- Remove the pork from the oven and test it is cooked by inserting a skewer through the foil and into the centre of the meat. If the juice runs clear the pork is cooked.
- Leave to rest for 5 minutes, then gently unwrap and cut into slices.
- Serve a couple of slices with a spoonful of purée.

pot-roast pheasant with sweetcorn mash
Sophie Grigson

Serves 4–6

Ingredients

For the pot-roast

15g (½oz) butter

1 tablespoon sunflower oil

2 pheasants

1 onion, chopped

3 cloves garlic, sliced

500g (1lb 2oz) carrots, cut into batons

4 sprigs of tarragon

150ml (5fl oz) dry Riesling wine

salt and freshly ground black pepper

100ml (4fl oz) double cream

For the mash

1.2kg (2½lb) large baking potatoes,
baked until cooked through

200–250ml (7–9fl oz) milk

1–2 generous pinches of saffron

45g (1½oz) butter

180g (6½oz) lightly cooked
   sweetcorn kernels

salt and freshly ground black pepper

Method

- Heat the butter with the oil in a flameproof casserole large enough to take the pheasant and all the carrots.
- Brown the pheasant in the fat then remove from the casserole.
- Reduce the heat, then stir the onion and garlic into the fat and fry gently until tender.
- Add the carrots and tarragon and stir around for a few minutes, then return the pheasant to the pot, nestling it breast side down amongst the carrots.
- Pour over the Riesling and season with salt and pepper.
- Bring to the boil, then cover with a tight-fitting lid.
- Turn the heat down low and leave to cook gently for 1 hour, turning over after 30 minutes.
- To prepare the mash, place the milk in a saucepan and bring to the boil, then take off the heat, stir in the saffron and set aside.
- Cut the potatoes in half and scoop the flesh out into a saucepan.
- Mash with the butter and plenty of salt and set over a low heat.
- Beat the saffron milk in, a good slurp at a time. If you prefer it softer and runnier, add more milk.
- Stir in the sweetcorn, taste and adjust the seasoning.
- Once the pheasant is tender, lift it out onto a plate and keep warm.
- Stir the cream into the carrots and juices and simmer for 2 minutes, then taste and adjust the seasoning.
- Spoon around the pheasant and serve with the mash.

Wine expert Peter Richards' choice
Tesco's Finest Chablis 2005

This Chablis has got good acidity, but also a lingering creamy flavour that will go well with the butter and cream.

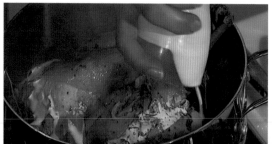
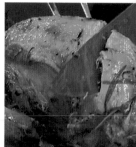

green prawn curry with cumin pilau
Cyrus Todiwala

Serves 4–6

Ingredients

2 tablespoons vegetable oil

1 onion, finely sliced

1 teaspoon cumin seeds

900ml (1 pint 12fl oz) water

500g (1lb 2oz) basmati rice, washed

salt and freshly ground black pepper

2 tablespoons vegetable oil

4 green cardamom pods, cracked

4 cloves

5cm (2in) piece cassia bark

1 medium onion, finely sliced

3 cloves garlic, crushed

4cm (1½in) piece ginger, finely grated

2 green chillies, deseeded and
    finely chopped

½ teaspoon turmeric

1 level tablespoon ground coriander

1 teaspoon ground cumin

150ml (5fl oz) water

1–1½ cans coconut milk

50g (2oz) cashew nuts, roughly
    chopped

110g (4oz) ground almonds

5–6 fresh curry leaves

salt

500g (1lb 2oz) raw tiger prawns,
    peeled

2 tablespoons roughly chopped
    coriander leaves

Method

· To prepare the pilau, preheat the oven to 150°C/300°F/Gas Mark 2.
· Heat an ovenproof saucepan and add the oil, onion and cumin seeds.
· Fry for 3–4 minutes until translucent and softened.
· Add the water and bring to a simmer. Add the rice and stir well.
· Bring to a simmer and cover.
· Place in the oven for 15 minutes.
· Remove from the oven, season with salt and black pepper.
· To prepare the curry, heat a saucepan and add the vegetable oil.
· When just hot, add the cracked cardamom, cloves and cassia bark
  and sauté for a minute on a medium heat.
· Add the sliced onions and sauté until translucent.
· Add the garlic, ginger and green chillies, again taking care not to
  brown. This whole process should not take more than 5 minutes.
· Mix the turmeric, coriander, cumin and water. Add to the saucepan.
· Blend the coconut milk, cashew nuts and ground almonds in a food
  processor until it is the consistency of single cream.
· As soon as the liquid in the saucepan has reduced down, add the
  coconut milk mixture and stir continuously for 1–2 minutes.
· Add the curry leaves.
· Bring the contents slowly to the boil, stirring gently.
· Add salt to taste and simmer for 1–2 minutes, then add the prawns.
· Continue to cook for a further 2 minutes, then remove from the heat.
· Latent heat will make the curry ready for serving within 5–6 minutes.

Wine expert Olly Smith's choice
Cono Sur Gewürztraminer 2005

This wine has enough zip to cut through the coconut and a delicious
aromatic quality to enhance the delicate spices.

sage-roasted chicken with goats' cheese gnocchi

Tony Tobin

Serves 4

Ingredients

For the gnocchi

2 large potatoes, unpeeled

200g (7oz) plain flour

150g (5oz) strong goats' cheese

For the chicken

4 x 200g–225g (7–8oz) chicken
    breasts, skin on

12 sage leaves

50g (2oz) butter

salt and freshly ground black pepper

200ml (7fl oz) fresh chicken stock

150ml (5fl oz) double cream

2 tablespoons of olive oil

1 bag spinach, washed

Method

- Place the potatoes in a saucepan with plenty of water, bring to the boil and simmer for 20–25 minutes until soft.
- Remove from the water into a bowl, peel and mash until smooth.
- Add half of the flour and gently work into the potato.
- Add the goats' cheese and mix gently.
- Add the remaining flour and mix gently to form a paste.
- Roll out the dough to form a sausage with a diameter of 2cm (¾in) and cut into 2cm (¾in) sections.
- Bring a large pan of salted water to the boil and drop in the gnocchi, removing them when they float to the surface.
- Cool the gnocchi in iced water and place on a tray.
- Preheat the oven to 200°C/400°F/Gas Mark 6.
- Gently lift up the skins of the chicken breasts, place 3 sage leaves under each one, rub with butter and season with salt and pepper.
- Place the chicken in a pan and roast in the oven for 10 minutes.
- Reduce the oven temperature to 150°C/300°F/Gas Mark 2 and continue roasting for a further 15 minutes.
- Remove the chicken from the pan and add the stock to the pan.
- Place over a high heat and reduce by half.
- Add the gnocchi and cream to the stock, return to the boil and allow to thicken slightly. Season with salt and pepper.
- Heat a frying pan and cook the olive oil and spinach for 1 minute.
- Serve the chicken with the spinach, gnocchi and creamy sauce.

Wine expert Olly Smith's choice

Vinha da Urze

Vinha da Urze has acidity to cut through the goats' cheese, but most importantly, it has got a touch of oak that will go well with the chicken.

Moroccan fish stew

Bill Granger

69

Serves 4

Ingredients

1 tablespoon olive oil
1 large onion, thinly sliced
1 clove garlic, crushed
2 teaspoons grated fresh ginger
1 teaspoon ground cumin
1 teaspoon turmeric
1 cinnamon stick
pinch of cayenne pepper
400g (14oz) tinned chopped tomatoes
pinch of sea salt
250ml (9fl oz) water
500g (1lb 2oz) firm white fish fillets
    (cod, snapper or ling), cut into
    chunks
400g (14oz) tinned chickpeas,
    drained and rinsed
2 teaspoons honey
salt and freshly ground black pepper
fresh coriander
flaked almonds, lightly toasted

Method

- Heat the olive oil in a large, heavy-based pan over a medium heat.
- Add the onion and cook, stirring occasionally, for 5 minutes, or until the onion is translucent.
- Add the garlic, ginger, cumin, turmeric and cinnamon and cook, stirring all the time, for 2 minutes.
- Add the cayenne, tomatoes, salt and water and cook, stirring frequently, for 10 minutes.
- Add the fish and simmer for 5 minutes, or until the fish is just tender.
- Add the chickpeas and honey and cook for a further 2–3 minutes.
- Season to taste and serve garnished with the coriander and flaked almonds.

Wine expert Peter Richards' choice
Radcliffe's Almenar Rioja Gran Reserva 1998

fusilli with walnuts
Gennaro Contaldo

Serves 4

Ingredients

75g (3oz) butter
300g (11oz) fusilli pasta
1 clove garlic, crushed
160g (5½oz) pancetta, roughly
  chopped
150g (5oz) walnuts (shelled weight),
  roughly chopped
1 egg, beaten
150ml (5fl oz) single cream
freshly ground black pepper
freshly grated Pecorino cheese
  (optional)
thyme leaves (optional)

Method

- Bring a large saucepan of lightly salted water to the boil for the fusilli.
- Meanwhile, heat the butter in a large frying pan, add the garlic and sauté until golden-brown.
- Remove the garlic clove and discard.
- Add the pancetta and walnuts to the pan and sauté until the pancetta turns a golden-brown colour, taking care not to let the walnuts burn.
- In a bowl, mix together the beaten egg and cream and set aside.
- Cook the fusilli until al dente and drain.
- Add to the walnuts and pancetta, then stir in the egg and cream mixture.
- Season well with freshly ground black pepper.
- Serve immediately with some freshly grated Pecorino cheese and garnish with a couple of thyme leaves if you like.

Wine expert Peter Richards' choice
Ravenswood Vintners Blend Chardonnay

italian and cypriot tiered bread
Paul Hollywood

Serves 8

Ingredients

For the dough

500g (1lb 2oz) strong white flour

2 teaspoons salt

50ml (2fl oz) olive oil

25g (1oz) fresh yeast

300ml (10½fl oz) cold water

For the Italian filling

150g (5oz) green olives, finely
  chopped

3–5 slices Parma ham

2–3 packs Buffalo Mozzarella,
  thickly sliced

20g (¾ oz) basil leaves, roughly torn

For the Cypriot filling

150g (5oz) black olives,
  finely chopped

3–5 slices Lounza ham

2–3 packs Halloumi cheese

1 tablespoon roughly chopped
  coriander

½ teaspoon dried mint

Method

- Lightly oil two round tins, 25cm (10in) in diameter and 10cm (4in)
  deep, with olive oil.
- Place the flour, salt, oil, yeast and water into a large bowl and mix
  together until all the flour has been used up by the water.
- Tip onto a floured surface and knead for 6 minutes, then place the
  dough back in the bowl and leave to rise for 1 hour.
- Preheat the oven to 220°C/425°F/Gas Mark 7.
- Divide the dough into eight equal pieces and roll each piece into a
  circle, so that it just fits into the tin.
- Place one dough circle in the bottom of each tin and spread the
  chopped green olives evenly over the top.
- Place another dough circle on top of the olives and cover with the
  Parma ham.
- Place another dough circle on top of the Parma ham and cover with
  the Mozzarella.
- Sprinkle the basil over the cheese.
- Place a final dough circle on top and leave to rise for 1 hour.
- Repeat with the Cypriot fillings and remaining dough circles.
- Place both tins in the oven for 30–40 minutes until golden-brown.
- Remove from the tins once cooled slightly, cut into wedges and serve
  warm or cold.

Wine expert Peter Richards' choice
Errazuriz Cabernet Sauvignon Rosé 2005

There is a lot going on in this dish: the saltiness of the olives, the herbs
and lots of oiliness. This Errazuriz Cabernet Sauvignon Rosé has loads of
flavour, but also the lovely, juicy freshness of a rosé. It has a deep colour,
almost like a red wine. It has a eucalyptus oil and herbal note, which
brings to mind the mint and basil in the dish, and while fresh and crisp on
the palate, it is also very big and full-on.

stir-fried beef with onions and mint and hot bean thread noodles

Ken Hom

Serves 4

Ingredients

For the beef

450g (1lb) lean beef fillet, cut into
    5mm (¼in) x 5cm (2in) slices

2 teaspoons light soy sauce

1 teaspoon rice wine or dry sherry

1 teaspoon cornflour

2 tablespoons groundnut oil

225g (8oz) onion, thickly sliced

3 tablespoons water

2 tablespoons oyster sauce

1 small handful of fresh mint leaves

Method

- Soak the noodles in a large bowl of warm water for 15 minutes until they are soft, then drain them and discard the water.
- Cut them into 7.5cm (3in) lengths using scissors or a knife.
- Place the beef in a bowl, add the light soy sauce, rice wine and cornflour and mix well.
- Heat a wok until very hot and pour in the oil.
- Add the beef and stir-fry for 1 minute to brown.
- Remove the beef with a slotted spoon and set aside.
- Add the onions to the wok and stir-fry for 1 minute.
- Pour in the water and cook for 3 minutes.
- Drain off the juices from the beef and add the oyster sauce.
- Return the beef to the wok, add the mint leaves and stir-fry for another minute. Set aside.

For the noodles

175g (6oz) bean thread (transparent)
noodles

1 tablespoon groundnut oil

2 tablespoons coarsely chopped
cooked black beans

3 tablespoons finely chopped spring
onions

2 tablespoons coarsely chopped garlic

1 tablespoon finely chopped ginger

110g (4oz) carrots, finely shredded

110g (4oz) bean curd, finely shredded

225g (8oz) Chinese flowering
cabbage or bok choy, finely
shredded

250ml (9fl oz) water

2 tablespoons Shaoxing rice wine or
dry sherry

1½ tablespoons chilli bean sauce

1 tablespoon whole yellow bean sauce

2 tablespoons light soy sauce

2 teaspoons dark soy sauce

½ teaspoon salt

½ teaspoon freshly ground black
pepper

2 teaspoons sesame oil

2 teaspoons finely chopped spring
onions

- To prepare the noodles, add the oil to the wok.
- When it is very hot and slightly smoking, add the black beans, spring onions, garlic and ginger and stir-fry quickly for 15 seconds.
- Add the carrots and stir-fry for 2 minutes.
- Add the bean curd and cabbage or bok choy, carefully mixing them together without breaking up the bean curd.
- Add all the rest of the ingredients except the sesame oil and spring onions and cook the mixture over a gentle heat for about 2 minutes.
- Now add the drained noodles and sesame oil and cook the mixture for a further 3 minutes.
- Ladle some noodles into individual bowls or into one large serving bowl, spoon the beef stir-fry over the top and garnish with the spring onion.

Wine expert Susie Barrie's choice
Duque de Viseu Tinto

Beef stir-fry is a challenge. We need something that stands up to the hot, salty flavours of the chilli and soy, but also complements the freshness of the mint and the simple, unfussy cooking.

One grape variety which goes well with oriental cuisine is Gewürztraminer, but I think the chilli and beef are crying out for a red wine. Duque de Viseu Tinto is soft and supple with lots of black- and red-berry fruit flavours which work well with beef and mint. Towards the end there is a twist of crushed black pepper – perfect for the spiciness of the dish.

Wexford strawberry salad with a peppered blackwater cheese basket

Kevin Dundon

Serves 4

Ingredients

For the salad

110g (4oz) mature, hard goats'
  cheese, such as Blackwater, grated
1 teaspoon cracked black pepper
2 x 110g (4oz) soft, rinded goats'
cheese, such as Mine-Gabhar,
  cut into chunks
110g (4oz) small strawberries, hulled
  and halved
110g (4oz) raspberries
1 good handful of mixed fresh
  summer herbs, such as chives, dill,
  mint and oregano
50g (2oz) mixed baby salad leaves
2–3 tablespoons raspberry vinaigrette

For the croutons

2 tablespoons olive oil
2 slices streaky bacon, cut into
  5mm (¼ in) thick slices
1 clove garlic, finely sliced
75g (3oz) sourdough bread,
  cut into 1cm (½ in) cubes

Method

- Heat a non-stick frying pan until searing hot. Sprinkle a quarter of the grated hard goats' cheese into the centre of the pan in a circle that is about 10cm (4in) in diameter.
- Add a sprinkling of the cracked black pepper and cook for 2–3 minutes until the fat starts to separate from the cheese and bubble.
- Remove from the heat and leave to cool for 1 minute.
- Using a spatula, remove the melted-cheese disc from the pan.
- Shape the cheese basket around the bottom of a straight-sided, tall glass and hold for 30 seconds to 1 minute until set.
- Transfer to a wire rack and cool completely.
- Repeat with the remaining hard goat's cheese and black pepper until you have four cheese baskets.
- To make the croutons, heat a frying pan, add the olive oil and bacon and fry for 1–2 minutes.
- Add the garlic and bread cubes and stir-fry for 3–4 minutes until golden-brown and crispy.
- Place the soft goat's cheese in a bowl with the strawberries, raspberries, herbs and mixed leaves.
- Drizzle over enough of the raspberry vinaigrette to coat the mixture.
- To serve, spoon in the dressed fruit and salad mixture to the baskets, and garnish with the bacon and garlic croutons.

Wine expert Olly Smith's choice
Val do Sosego Albariño 2005

Val do Sosego cuts through the goats' cheese and has enough zing to match up to the acidity of the strawberries.

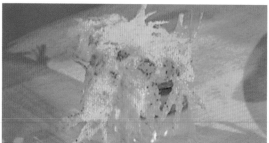

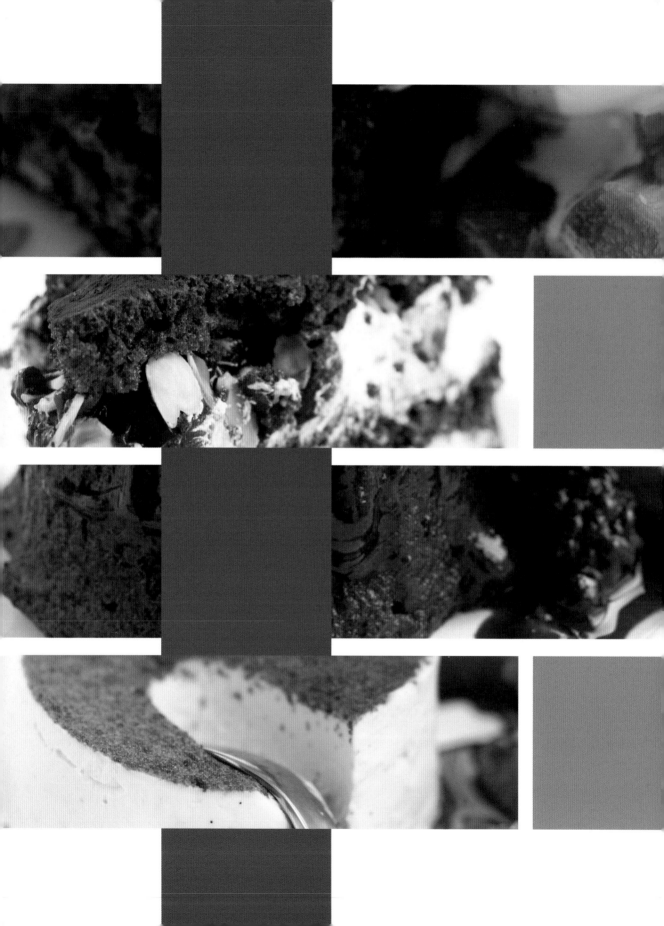

puddings

steamed sponge pudding with custard

James Martin

Serves 4

Ingredients

For the sponge

100g (4oz) self-raising flour

100g (4oz) caster sugar

100g (4oz) butter, softened

2 eggs

25ml (1fl oz) milk

4 tablespoons honey

1 teaspoon ground ginger

For the custard

4 egg yolks

40g (1½oz) caster sugar

150ml (5fl oz) milk

150ml (5fl oz) double cream

1 vanilla pod, split

Method

- Butter and lightly flour four ramekins.
- Place the flour, sugar, butter, eggs and milk in a blender and process to a smooth batter.
- Mix the honey and ground ginger together and place a spoonful in the base of each ramekin.
- Pour the batter over the top.
- Lightly place some cling film over the ramekins.
- Place in the microwave on a high setting for 2 minutes.
- To make the custard, place the egg yolks and sugar in a bowl and whisk until well blended.
- Place the milk and cream in a saucepan
- Scrape the inside of the vanilla pod into the milk and bring to the boil.
- Sit the bowl of beaten eggs over a pan of hot water and whisk the milk into the egg mix. As the egg yolks warm, the cream will thicken to create a custard – keep stirring until it coats the back of the spoon and remove the bowl from the heat.
- To serve, turn out the sponges onto plates and spoon over the custard.

apple and quince slices
with honey and walnut cream

James Martin

Serves 4

Ingredients

For the cream

150 ml (5fl oz) double cream

3 tablespoons clear honey

25g (1oz) diced walnuts

For the slices

450g (1lb) puff pastry

50g (2oz) melted butter

110g (4oz) quince jelly

6 Golden Delicious apples, peeled,
    cored and cut into thin slices

25g (1oz) caster sugar

4 sprigs of mint

Method

· Whip the double cream until thick, then fold in the honey and walnuts
  and place in the fridge.
· Preheat the oven to 200°C/400°F/Gas Mark 6.
· Roll out the puff pastry thinly and prick the surface with a fork.
· Cut out four rectangles, 10cm (4in) x 20cm (8in).
· Place the rectangles on a non-stick, buttered baking tray.
· Lightly brush the edges of the rectangles with melted butter and
  spread the quince jelly in the middle.
· Layer on the apple slices and drizzle some of the melted butter and
  the caster sugar over the top.
· Place in the oven for 5–6 minutes until golden-brown.
· Remove the slices from the oven and glaze with a little of the
  remaining butter.
· Serve with a spoonful of the honey and walnut cream and garnish
  with the sprigs of mint.

vanilla and gingerbread cheesecake
Stuart Gillies

Serves 8

Ingredients

50g (2oz) gingerbread, thinly sliced

450g (1lb) cream cheese

250g (9oz) caster sugar

250g (9oz) crème fraîche

475ml (17fl oz) double cream

2 vanilla pods

1 punnet English strawberries

2 teaspoons caster sugar

2 teaspoons balsamic vinegar

Method

· Lay the gingerbread on a tray and leave out overnight to dry.
· When dry and hard, place in a blender and process until fine crumbs are formed.
· Place the cream cheese, caster sugar, crème fraîche and double cream into a large bowl.
· Split the vanilla pods and scrape the seeds into the bowl.
· Whisk together until smooth.
· Place the mix in a piping bag and pipe carefully into ring moulds which are 5cm (2in) in diameter and 4cm (1½in) deep.
· Smooth the tops and bottoms with the back of a flat knife and place in the fridge for 2 hours to set.
· When set, remove from the fridge and leave at room temperature for 5 minutes.
· Dip each end of the cheesecakes in the gingerbread crumbs.
· Hold each of the ring moulds in your hands for 30 seconds to warm them and release the cheesecakes.
· Then, holding the ring moulds, lightly shake the cheesecakes out over a serving plate.
· Toss the strawberries in the sugar and drop them into a hot frying pan.
· Cook for 30–45 seconds until caramelised, then add the balsamic vinegar and heat through. Serve alongside the cheesecakes.

Wine expert Susy Atkins' choice
Brown Brothers Orange Muscat and Flora

For this dish, you might be tempted to choose a rosé, as some people think dry pink wine goes with red berries, but that is a mistake. You need more sweetness, something with a honeyed, luscious flavour and a good fresh finish.

This wine has a lovely, orangey, marmalade flavour at the beginning, but the end is really crisp and mouth-watering, and it's that tanginess that will complement the strawberries and balsamic vinegar in the dish.

mixed-berry gratin with basil sabayon
James Martin

Serves 4

Ingredients

For the sabayon

3 egg yolks

50g (2oz) caster sugar

110ml (4fl oz) Champagne

6 basil leaves, finely shredded

For the mixed berries

50g (2oz) raspberries

50g (2oz) strawberries

50g (2oz) blackberries

50g (2oz) blueberries

50g (2oz) caster sugar

Method

- Place a glass bowl over a pan of simmering water.
- Add the egg yolks and sugar and whisk until lightened.
- Add the Champagne and continue whisking until pale. The foam must be sufficiently thickened so that it won't break down on cooling.
- Remove from the heat and cool until tepid.
- Mix the berries together with the sugar and arrange in oven-proof ramekins.
- Mix the basil into the sabayon, then spoon over the berries.
- Glaze using a blow torch and serve immediately.

ginger butternut squash ice cream
James Martin

Serves 4

Ingredients
500ml (17½fl oz) double cream

2 tablespoons chopped fresh ginger

4 egg yolks

125g (4½oz) caster sugar

125g (4½oz) cooked butternut
    squash, puréed

dash of lemon juice

Method
- Fill a large bowl with ice and a little water.
- Place the cream and ginger in a saucepan and bring to the boil.
- Cover, remove from the heat and leave to steep for 30 minutes.
- Return the pan to the heat and bring to the boil.
- Place the egg yolks and sugar in a bowl and whisk together.
- Pour in some of the hot cream mixture and whisk to combine.
- Pour the egg mix into the remaining cream and continue to cook for 3–4 minutes, or until the mixture coats the back of a spoon and steam rises from the top.
- Place the saucepan in the ice water bath, stirring occasionally, until chilled.
- Stir in the squash, add the lemon juice to taste and strain through a fine-meshed sieve.
- Freeze in an ice-cream machine and keep frozen until ready to use.

crème brûlée with marinated autumn fruits and a mint broth

Michael Caines

Serves 8

Ingredients

For the crème brûlée

50g (2oz) caster sugar

5 egg yolks

75ml (2½fl oz) milk

3 vanilla pods, split and scraped

500ml (17½fl oz) whipping cream

100g (3½oz) Demerara sugar

For the marinated fruit

100g (3½oz) strawberries

100g (3½oz) raspberries

100g (3½oz) redcurrants

100g (3½oz) blackcurrants

100g (3½oz) blackberries

100g (3½oz) caster sugar

1 small bunch of fresh mint, chopped

For the mint broth

300ml (10½fl oz) milk

2 tablespoons Crème de Menthe

Method

- Place the caster sugar and egg yolks in a bowl and beat together.
- Place the milk in a saucepan with the vanilla and bring to the boil.
- Take the milk off the heat and add to the beaten eggs and sugar, then pour in the cream and whisk to combine.
- Place in the fridge and leave for 12 hours to infuse.
- Preheat the oven to 135°C/275°F/Gas Mark 1.
- Line the base of 8 small ring moulds with 2 layers of cling film then place onto a flat-bottomed baking tray.
- Fill the moulds with the crème brûlée mixture and place in the oven for 45 minutes until the mixture has set like an egg custard.
- Remove from the oven and leave to cool.
- Sprinkle the top of the crème brûlées with Demerara sugar, place on a plate and then remove from the mould.
- Heat the sugar topping with a blow torch until bubbling.
- Place 100g (3½oz) of the mixed fruit in a bowl and, using a fork, mash well with the caster sugar.
- Add to this the rest of the fruit and the mint and leave to stand for 5 minutes. Taste and add a little more sugar if the fruit is too sharp.
- To make the mint broth, place the milk and Crème de Menthe in a saucepan and heat to 80°C/176°F. Using a hand blender, froth to produce a cappuccino effect.
- To serve, place the brûlées and fruit onto plates and drizzle with the mint broth.

Wine expert Peter Richards' choice

Moscato d'Asti Saracco

This sparkling wine has a little bit of sweetness to match up to the crème brûlée, but it also has lively acidity which should go very well with the fruit.

lemon syllabub

James Martin

Serves 4

Ingredients

4 lemon shortbread biscuits
110ml (4fl oz) sweet vermouth
250ml (9fl oz) double cream
4 tablespoons icing sugar
8 tablespoons lemon curd
2 tablespoons flaked almonds, toasted
2 sprigs of fresh mint

Method

· Crumble a biscuit into the bottom of 4 sundae glasses.
· Drizzle over 1 tablespoon of sweet vermouth in each one.
· Pour the cream into a bowl and add the icing sugar.
· Whisk the cream until soft peaks form.
· Fold in the rest of the sweet vermouth.
· Add the lemon curd and lightly fold through, leaving a marbled effect.
· Spoon the syllabub into each of the glasses.
· Top with the flaked almonds and mint.
· Serve chilled.

Madeira trifle with raspberries

James Martin

Serves 4

Ingredients

225g (8oz) Madeira cake, sliced
70g (2½oz) raspberry jam
150ml (5fl oz) Madeira
200g (7oz) fresh raspberries
570ml (1 pint) milk
1 vanilla pod, split
50g (2oz) caster sugar
6 egg yolks
zest of 2 oranges
400ml (14fl oz) double cream
25g (1oz) flaked almonds, toasted

Method

- Spread the jam over the slices of Madeira cake and place in the bottom of a large glass dish or divide equally between 6 tall glasses.
- Pour the Madeira over the cake and sprinkle the fresh raspberries evenly over the top.
- To make the custard, bring the milk to the boil with the split vanilla pod and, in a separate bowl, whisk the egg yolks with the sugar.
- Once the milk is boiling, pour onto the egg mixture and return to the pan. Cook, stirring all the time, until it coats the back of a wooden spoon. Do not allow the mixture to boil or it will curdle.
- Pass the custard through a sieve, add the orange zest, allow to cool, then pour it over the Madeira cake and raspberries.
- Whip the double cream and either pipe it over the top of the trifle or spread it on and spike it with a fork.
- Refrigerate overnight and sprinkle with the toasted flaked almonds just before serving.

buttermilk pannacotta with lemon-roasted apricots

Paul Rankin

Serves 4

Ingredients

300ml (10½fl oz) double cream
1 vanilla pod, split lengthwise
100ml (4fl oz) condensed milk
2 gelatine leaves, soaked in cold
   water for at least 10 minutes
350ml (12fl oz) buttermilk, at room
   temperature
8 ripe apricots
juice of 1 lemon
50ml (2fl oz) water
juice of ½ orange
4 strips lemon peel
75g (3oz) sugar
8–12 biscotti biscuits

Method

· Heat the double cream in a small saucepan with the split vanilla pod.
· Bring to the boil, then remove from the heat and add the milk.
· Squeeze dry the gelatine leaves, add to the hot cream and stir until they have dissolved. When the cream mixture has cooled to near body temperature, add the buttermilk and stir gently.
· Remove the vanilla pod, scrape out the seeds into the cream mixture and stir.
· Divide the mixture into four ramekins and set in the fridge for 4 hours.
· Preheat the oven to 190°C/375°F/Gas Mark 5.
· Halve the apricots, stone them and gently roll them in the lemon juice to prevent discolouration.
· Place the water in an ovenproof dish with the remaining lemon juice, the orange juice and the lemon-peel strips, add the apricot halves, skin side down, and sprinkle the sugar over them.
· Cover loosely, but firmly, with foil and bake in the oven for about 10 minutes. The exact time will depend on the size and ripeness of the fruit – when cooked, the tip of a knife should easily pierce the flesh of the fruit with no resistance.
· Remove the fruit carefully with a slotted spoon, pour the juices into a small pan and reduce down to a syrup-like consistency.
· Take the syrup off the heat, return the fruit to the pan and allow to cool.
· To serve, dip the pannacotta moulds into hot water for a few seconds, then gently turn them out onto soup plates. Spoon the apricots and syrup carefully around the edge of the pannacotta.

Russian sharlotka or apple tart
James Martin

Serves 4–6

Ingredients
225g (8oz) caster sugar
165g (6oz) flour
3 eggs
1 tablespoon butter
1 tablespoon flour
2–3 Granny Smith apples, peeled, cored and sliced

Method
- Preheat the oven to 175°C/350°F/Gas Mark 4.
- Place the caster sugar and flour in a bowl, add the eggs and whisk together to form a thick batter.
- Butter and flour a deep baking dish.
- Arrange the apple slices on the bottom of the dish and spoon the batter over the top.
- Place in the oven for 30–40 minutes.
- To check if the pie is ready, insert a skewer into the top. If it comes out sticky, it needs to cook for another 5 minutes.

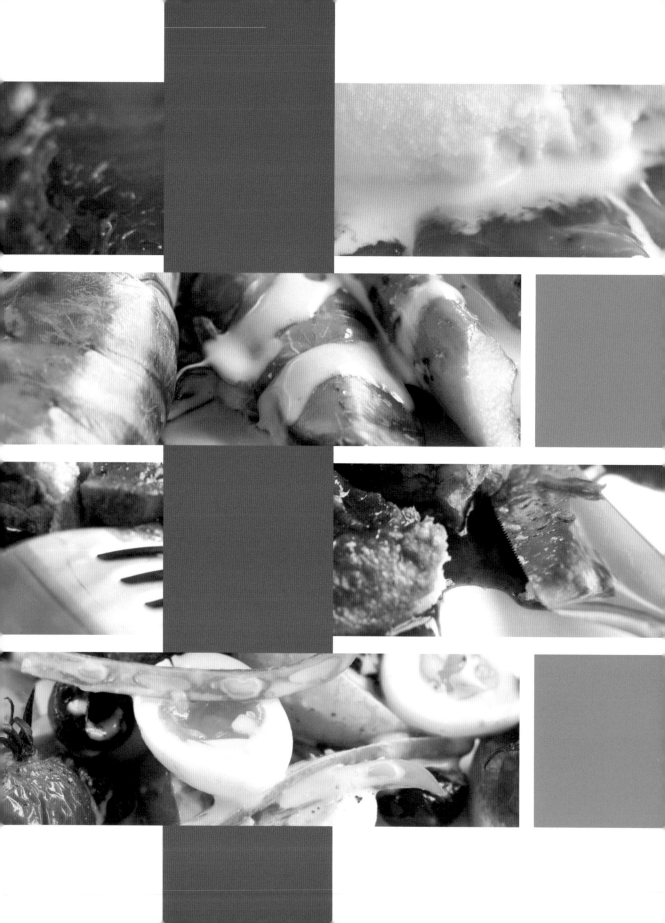

heaven

and

hell

food heaven

Natalie Cassidy

Natalie was brought up with traditional English food: 'I grew up on shepherd's pie, Sunday roasts, bangers and mash, and so on. I also love offal, which I think in this day and age people are scared to try. I love stuffed hearts and kidneys – they are flavoursome and different.' She also loves to eat out: 'I am not a clubby girl, and restaurants are my favourite places in the world.'

tiger prawns steamed in beer with Hollandaise sauce and griddled asparagus

Serves 4

Ingredients

For the prawns and asparagus

350ml (12fl oz) bottle of beer

8 large wild tiger prawns, shells on

salt and freshly ground black pepper

12 stems asparagus

1 tablespoon olive oil

For the Hollandaise

125g (4½oz) butter

2 teaspoons lemon juice

2 teaspoons white wine vinegar

2 large egg yolks

salt and freshly ground black pepper

Method

- Pour the beer into the base of a steamer.
- Place the prawns in a bowl, drizzle with a little olive oil and season.
- Place the prawns in the steamer basket, put the lid on and steam for 5–6 minutes until just cooked through.
- Meanwhile, heat a griddle pan.
- Toss the asparagus in the olive oil and season.
- Place on the griddle pan and grill for 3–4 minutes, turning once, until tender.
- To make the Hollandaise, place the butter in a saucepan and bring to a simmer.
- Place the lemon juice and vinegar in a separate small pan and heat until just boiling.
- Place the egg yolks in a food processor with a pinch of salt and turn on.
- With the motor running, add the hot lemon and vinegar, then slowly add the melted butter.
- Remove from the processor and season to taste.
- Serve two large prawns each with three asparagus spears and a drizzle of Hollandaise sauce.

Wine expert Peter Richards' choice
Secano Estate Sauvignon Blanc

'I love Italian food and spend quite a lot of time in Sicily. There is nothing I love more than Mediterranean king prawns. If I had to pick something for my last meal on this planet, it would be huge prawns.'

food hell

Natalie Cassidy

'I really hate polenta. I went to Verona and all they served me for four days was polenta. I had everything with polenta.'

lemon and polenta cake
with lemon-vodka cream

Serves 8–10

Ingredients

For the cake

1 tablespoon olive oil

2 lemons, thinly sliced

450g (1lb) butter

450g (1lb) caster sugar

6 eggs

150g (5oz) ground almonds

500g (1lb 2oz) quick-cook polenta

zest and juice of 2 lemons

For the lemon-vodka cream

150g (5oz) Mascarpone cheese

200ml (7fl oz) double cream

45ml (1½fl oz) lemon vodka

30g (1oz) icing sugar

juice of ½ lemon

Method

- Preheat the oven to 175°C/350°F/Gas Mark 4.
- Line a deep, 30cm (11in) cake tin with baking parchment.
- Heat a frying pan, then add the oil and lemon slices.
- Fry for 1–2 minutes until just caramelized.
- Remove and place, caramelized side down, in an even pattern on the baking parchment.
- Place the butter and sugar in a large bowl and whisk together until light and fluffy.
- Add the eggs, one at a time, mixing well.
- Fold in the ground almonds, polenta, lemon juice and zest and stir to combine.
- Pour the mixture over the lemon slices and spread evenly.
- Place in the oven for 25–30 minutes until just risen and golden.
- Allow to cool before turning out onto a plate, so that the lemon slices are at the top.
- To make the lemon cream, place the Mascarpone in a bowl and beat to soften.
- Add the double cream, vodka, icing sugar and lemon juice and whisk to soft peaks.
- Serve a wedge of cake with a dollop of cream, sprig of mint and sprinkle of lemon zest.

Wine expert Peter Richards' choice
Hermit's Hill Botrytis Semillon 2002

food heaven

Arlene Phillips

Arlene was born and brought up in Manchester, Lancashire. However, traditional Lancashire meals such as Lancashire hot pot were not part of her staple diet. Instead, her mother used to serve up lots of salads, which is probably where Arlene got her huge love of vegetables and fruit from.

As much as Arlene loves food, she professes to be a terrible cook. 'I am totally useless in the kitchen. Every time I cook, it is a complete disaster! I've been known to forget to put water in the saucepan when attempting to boil eggs.'

goats' cheese salad
with chicory-orange jam

Serves 4

Ingredients

For the chicory-orange jam

25g (1oz) butter

1 onion, roughly chopped

1 clove garlic, chopped

5 heads chicory, finely sliced

zest and juice of 2 oranges

150g (5oz) caster sugar

250ml (9fl oz) dry white wine

For the salad

4 Crottin goats' cheeses

4 slices white bread, lightly toasted

20g (¾oz) butter

1 apple, peeled, cored and cut
   into wedges

75g (3oz) cooked beetroot, cut
   into wedges

50g (2oz) rocket leaves

25g (1oz) walnuts, halved

2 tablespoons vinaigrette

Method

- Heat a large, heavy-based saucepan, then add the butter.
- Add the onion and garlic and fry for 2–3 minutes.
- Add the chicory and the remaining ingredients.
- Bring to the boil, reduce the heat and simmer for 45 minutes, stirring occasionally, until thick and caramelized.
- Preheat the grill until hot.
- Place one goats' cheese on each piece of toast and grill until golden and bubbling.
- Heat a frying pan, then add the butter and apple and sauté until golden brown. Set aside to cool.
- To serve, place the jam in the centre of a serving plate, top with the goats' cheese toast and spoon the apple, beetroot, rocket leaves and walnuts around. Drizzle the vinaigrette over the top.

Wine expert Pip Martin's choice
Montana Sauvignon Blanc

'When I'm on a diet, I always carry a bag of red and green chicory around with me. In the evenings, I like to pile it high on a plate, dressed with balsamic vinegar.'

food hell

Arlene Phillips

'I can't bear the texture and taste of slimy cooked onions. I hate onions with a passion and always have.'

yorkshire pudding with red onion gravy

Serves 2

Ingredients

For the Yorkshire puddings

225g (8oz) plain flour

8 medium free-range eggs

salt and freshly ground black pepper

570ml (1 pint) full-fat milk

100g (4oz) beef dripping

For the red onion gravy

30g (1oz) butter

2 red onions, thinly sliced

2 cloves garlic, grated

200ml (7fl oz) red wine

1 litre (2 pints) fresh beef stock

2 tablespoons balsamic vinegar

2 sprigs of thyme

salt and freshly ground black pepper

Method

· Place the flour and eggs in a food processor and season.

· Turn on and blend to a paste before adding the milk.

· Continue to process until a smooth batter is formed.

· Pour into a jug and place in the fridge to rest, preferably overnight.

· Preheat the oven to 230°C/450°F/Gas Mark 8.

· Place the Yorkshire pudding tins on a baking tray, then divide the beef dripping between them and place in the oven.

· Heat for 5–10 minutes until smoking hot.

· Pour the batter into the tins and bake for 10–15 minutes until golden-brown and risen around the edges.

· To make the gravy, heat a sauté pan, then add the butter, sliced onions and garlic and cook for 8–10 minutes until tender but not coloured.

· Add the red wine and reduce by half.

· Add the beef stock and bring to the boil.

· Reduce the heat to a simmer, add the balsamic vinegar and thyme and cook for 10–15 minutes.

· Season to taste and serve poured over the Yorkshire puddings.

Wine expert Pip Martin's choice

Penfolds Koonunga Hill Shiraz Cabernet

food heaven

Myleene Klass

Myleene's mother is Spanish/Filipino and her father is half Austrian, so she has been brought up eating a wide variety of cuisines: 'Being half Austrian, my grandmother made the best pastries and cakes in the world.'

She thinks she takes after the Austrian side of her family and classes herself as a baker rather than a cook: 'I make very good cherry pies and am good at cakes and biscuits, which probably has something to do with the fact that I have a very sweet tooth.'

crab cakes with chilli sauce

Serves 4

Ingredients

For the crab cakes

250g (9oz) King Edward potatoes,
   peeled and cut into large chunks
10g (½oz) butter
1 tablespoon double cream
½ teaspoon medium curry powder
1 tablespoon finely chopped coriander
½ large green chilli, deseeded and
   finely chopped
1 tablespoon grated red onion
salt and freshly ground black pepper
250g (9oz) white crab meat, flaked
1 tablespoon vegetable oil

For the chilli sauce

75g (3oz) caster sugar
2 red chillies, roughly chopped
3 plum tomatoes, roughly chopped
8 kaffir lime leaves
2 lemongrass stems, finely chopped
25g (1oz) ginger, roughly chopped
2 cloves garlic
2 shallots, roughly chopped
4 tablespoons fish sauce
40ml (1½fl oz) sesame oil
50ml (2fl oz) dark soy sauce
2 tablespoons clear honey
juice and zest of 3 limes

Method

- Boil the potatoes in a saucepan of lightly salted water for about 15 minutes, or until tender.
- Drain well, then return to the pan.
- Mash with a fork or potato masher until smooth, beating in the butter, cream, curry powder, coriander, chilli, onion and lots of seasoning, and leave to cool completely.
- Meanwhile, check the crab meat carefully and discard any flecks of shell.
- Mix the crab meat with the potato mixture, then shape into four neat round patties. If the mixture sticks to your hands, dip your hands in cold water.
- Heat some oil in a shallow frying pan, add the crab cakes and fry for about 3 minutes until crisp and golden-brown. Carefully turn them and fry for a further 3 minutes.
- Remove onto kitchen paper.
- To make the chilli sauce, place the sugar in a pan over a medium heat and melt to a light-brown caramel.
- Place the remaining ingredients in a food processor and blend to a smooth purée.
- Pour the puree into the pan with the caramelized sugar and mix well.
- Bring the mixture to the boil, then reduce the heat and simmer for about 5 minutes. Remove from the heat and allow to cool.
- Serve the crab cakes on a plate and the chilli sauce in a bowl for dipping.

Wine expert Tim Atkin's choice
Jacob's Creek Riesling

'I love fresh crab. My father used to be a diver and would bring back lobsters and crabs all the time.'

food hell
Myleene Klass

'I hate the taste and texture of beans. I hate all beans – kidney beans, butter beans, chickpeas, broad beans. The only beans I like are baked beans.

I remember eating a chilli con carne my dad made. My mum and dad thought that the kidney beans would be hidden in the dish, so I would unwittingly eat them. I tried to pay my brother to eat my kidney beans. My dad saw what I was doing, went mad and served me up some more. I was so desperate not to eat it, I threw it in the bin!'

salad of two beans, walnuts, radicchio and croutons with beef fillet

Serves 2

Ingredients

For the salad

3 tablespoons extra virgin olive oil

50g bread, cubed

3 sprigs of rosemary

150g (5oz) radicchio

50g (2oz) walnuts

100g (4oz) French beans, cooked

100g (4oz) broad beans, blanched
  and peeled

1 tablespoon chopped flat-leaf parsley

15g (½oz) Parmesan, shaved

For the dressing

2 slices white bread, torn into pieces

4 tablespoons milk

2 cloves garlic

juice and zest of 1 lemon

50g (2oz) walnuts

150ml (5fl oz) extra virgin olive oil

salt and freshly ground black pepper

For the beef

2 x 150g (5oz) beef fillets

Method

· Preheat the oven to 220°C/425°F/Gas Mark 7.

· Heat a frying pan, then add the olive oil, cubed bread and rosemary.

· Toss to combine and fry until just golden.

· Transfer onto a baking tray and place in the oven for 5 minutes until crispy.

· Meanwhile, heat a frying pan, then add a little oil and the beef fillet.

· Sear on each side for 2 minutes, then place in the oven for 5 minutes.

· To make the dressing, place the bread in a food processor and moisten with the milk.

· Add the garlic, lemon and walnuts and blend to a paste.

· Add the olive oil, season to taste and blend to combine.

· Place the radicchio, walnuts and beans in a bowl and pour the dressing over.

· Add the parsley and croutons, season and mix well.

· Place on a serving plate, drizzle with olive oil, top with shaved Parmesan and serve with the beef fillet.

Wine expert Tim Atkin's choice
Cono Sur Pinot Noir

food heaven

Nick Knowles

'My mother cooked very traditional English meals for us all – meat and two veg, that sort of thing. I learnt to scoff pretty much anything down very quickly. I have four siblings, one brother and three sisters, so you had to eat quickly to ensure you got anything at all!'

He loves cooking and gets his inspiration from his extensive travels around the world. In 1988, Nick worked for a TV station in Australia and lived with a family on an Aboriginal reserve: 'They used to eat a lot of witchetty grubs. I preferred them barbequed, in which case they are similar to sausages. When raw, they are very unpleasant and bitter.'

basil and summer-fruit pudding
with basil syrup

Serves 4

Ingredients

For the pudding

300g (11oz) mixed frozen fruits, defrosted

1 punnet mixed strawberries, blackberries and raspberries, the strawberries hulled and cut into quarters

50g (2oz) caster sugar

10 basil leaves, roughly torn

14 thin slices white bread

For the basil syrup

200g (7oz) caster sugar

110ml (4fl oz) water

1 large bunch of basil

Method

- Place half the mixed frozen fruit in a bowl.
- Add half the fresh berries, half the caster sugar and the basil leaves, stir to combine and set to one side.
- Place the remainder of the frozen fruit in a blender and puree well.
- Add the remaining sugar and pass the sauce through a sieve.
- Remove the crusts from the bread and cut out four small circles to fit the bottom of four small moulds.
- Cut out four larger circles to cover.
- Cut the remaining bread to fit the sides of the moulds.
- Lightly oil the inside of each mould, then line them with cling film.
- Dip one side of the small bread circles in the sauce and place in the bottom of the mould, dipped side down.
- Repeat with the slices for the sides. The dipped sides should be against the moulds and they should overlap slightly.
- Fill the centres with the reserved basil-infused fruit and some of the sauce and press down well.
- Top with the larger circles of bread, dipped in the remaining sauce, dipped side up. Place in the fridge until ready to serve.
- To make the syrup, place the sugar and water in a saucepan and bring to a simmer.
- Cook for 6–8 minutes until a thick, colourless syrup is formed.
- Add the basil leaves, leave to cool, then place in a blender and puree.
- Strain through a muslin-lined sieve into a jug.
- Turn the puddings out onto plates, garnish with the remaining berries and the syrup.

Wine expert Susie Barrie's choice
Moscato d'Asti 'Nivole'

'I love basil. It is such a flavoursome herb and is used a lot in my favourite type of food – Italian dishes.'

food hell
Nick Knowles

'Southall, where I grew up, has huge Indian, Pakistani, African and Caribbean communities, so all my friends ate fantastically exotic food. I loved all of it apart from okra, which I think is so slimy. It has a texture like someone has sneezed on the back of a turtle.'

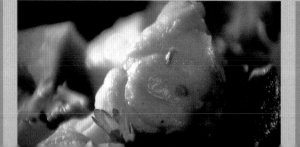

Thai monkfish and okra curry

Serves 4

Ingredients

2 tablespoons vegetable oil

1–2 tablespoons Thai green
    curry paste

2 large cloves garlic, mashed to a
    paste with a little salt

2 stalks lemongrass, tender part only,
    finely chopped

2 lime leaves, shredded

750ml (1¼ pints) coconut milk

4 tablespoons chopped coriander,
    leaves and stalks

2–3 green chillies, deseeded and
    finely chopped

400g (14oz) monkfish tails, cut into
    large chunks

200g (7oz) okra

4 tablespoons roughly torn basil
    leaves

30ml (1fl oz) Thai fish sauce

1 tablespoon freshly squeezed
    lime juice

Method

· Heat a large wok, add the vegetable oil and curry paste and cook
  over a high heat for 3 minutes.

· Add the garlic, lemongrass, lime leaves and half the coconut milk and
  cook until the sauce starts to split, about 5 minutes.

· Add the coriander and chillies and simmer for 10 minutes.

· Add the remaining coconut milk and cook for a further 3 minutes.

· Add the monkfish and okra and cook for further 4–5 minutes until just
  tender.

· Fold in the basil leaves, fish sauce and lime juice.

· Serve with Thai jasmine rice and garnish with coriander leaves.

Wine expert Susie Barrie's choice
Stoneleigh Sauvignon Blanc

food heaven

Sian Reeves

'I was brought up in the Midlands and never had any foreign cuisine when I was growing up. I didn't have a curry until I was twenty-two, and I was twenty-five before I tried pasta or pizza. It is actually only in the last few years that I have really started going out more and trying different foods. I had led quite a sheltered life before that. I am much more adventurous now than I have ever been.'

deep-fried Mozzarella with tomato and rocket sauce

Serves 4

Ingredients

For the sauce

1 medium onion, finely chopped

1 clove garlic, finely chopped

1½kg (3lb 4oz) tomatoes, chopped

3 tablespoons extra virgin olive oil

8 basil leaves

50g (2oz) rocket leaves

salt and freshly ground black pepper

For the Mozzarella

200g (7oz) Buffalo Mozzarella

8 thin slices of white bread

2 medium eggs

salt and freshly ground black pepper

125ml (4½fl oz) milk

6 tablespoons plain flour

Method

- To make the sauce, heat the olive oil in a pan and fry the onion and garlic for 4–5 minutes.
- Add the tomatoes, bring to the boil, reduce the heat and cook for 25–30 minutes.
- Halfway through the cooking, add the basil leaves and rocket.
- Season and blend to a sauce, then pass through a sieve and leave to one side.
- Heat a deep-fat fryer to 175°C/350°F.
- Slice the Mozzarella into four slices, about 1cm (½in) thick.
- Cut the crusts off the bread and cut into slightly larger discs than the mozzarella slices.
- Beat the eggs lightly and season.
- Dip one side of the slices of bread into the milk, then place a slice of the Mozzarella on four of the dry sides.
- Season the Mozzarella and make sandwiches with the other four slices of bread, with the milk-soaked sides on the outside.
- Dust the sandwiches with flour, then dip them in the beaten egg.
- Deep-fry the sandwiches in the fryer until golden and crisp on the outside.
- Drain onto kitchen paper and serve with the hot sauce.

Wine expert Olly Smith's choice
Southbank Estate Marlborough Sauvignon Blanc

'My favourite ingredient is Mozzarella.
It is bad for you, but I love it.'

food hell

Sian Reeves

'When I was growing up, we would have things like roast beef dinners, chicken and potatoes and egg and chips – which is my favourite meal ever! Fish was never part of my diet, which is probably why I have such an aversion to it now. I particularly hate the texture of sea bass.'

sea bass with herb gnocchi

Serves 4

Ingredients

For the gnocchi

125ml (4½fl oz) water

50g (2oz) butter

1 teaspoon Maldon salt

110g (4oz) plain flour, sifted

2 large eggs

1½ teaspoons Dijon mustard

1 teaspoon chopped chervil

1 teaspoon chopped chives

1 teaspoon chopped parsley

1 teaspoon chopped tarragon

60g (2oz) Emmental cheese

For the sea bass

2 tablespoons olive oil

25g (1oz) butter

4 x 175g (6oz) sea bass fillets

salt and freshly ground black pepper

1 shallot, finely chopped

75ml (2½fl oz) white wine

110ml (4fl oz) double cream

150g (5oz) broad beans, podded
and blanched

110g (4oz) char-grilled artichokes
in olive oil

1 tablespoon roughly chopped
flat-leaf parsley

Method

- Place the water, butter and salt in a medium saucepan and bring to a simmer.
- Reduce the heat, add the flour and stir rapidly until the dough pulls away from the sides of the pan and the bottom of the pan is clean, with no dough sticking to it. The dough should be glossy and smooth, but still moist.
- Transfer the dough to a food processor, add the eggs and process until smooth and shiny.
- Transfer to a bowl and stir in the herbs and cheese.
- Place the dough in a piping bag and allow to rest for 30 minutes.
- Bring a large pan of lightly salted water to a simmer.
- Take the bag of dough and hold it above the boiling water. As you squeeze the bag with your right hand, hold a small knife in your left and cut off 2½cm (1in) lengths of dough, allowing them to drop into the water. Cook only twelve at a time.
- The gnocchi will sink. When they float to the top, poach for another 1–2 minutes, then remove with a slotted spoon and drain onto kitchen paper.
- To prepare the sea bass, heat a frying pan and add the oil and half the butter.
- Season the sea bass and place, skin side down, in the pan.
- Fry for 3–4 minutes until crispy and golden, then turn and cook for a further 1–2 minutes.
- Heat another frying pan and add the remaining butter and the shallot.
- Sweat for 3–4 minutes until softened.
- Add the white wine and reduce by half, add the cream and reduce by one third and season to taste.
- Add the beans, artichokes and gnocchi and heat through.
- Add the parsley, spoon onto a plate and top with the sea bass fillet.

Wine expert Olly Smith's choice
Bleasdale Verdelho

food heaven

Ronan Keating

Ronan grew up on traditional Irish cooking and one of his favourite food-related memories is of his mother's bread and butter pudding. However his tastes have broadened over the years: 'I spend a lot of time in Japan, Australia, Europe and South America now, so I have been lucky enough to try a lot of different stuff.' He is particularly keen on Japanese and Thai cuisine.

He admits he is not a very good cook: 'I really enjoy being in the kitchen and cooking basic things like beans on toast for the kids, but my wife is the main cook in our household. In the early Boyzone days, we were all living together in a house in London and I once tried to cook a meal for the lads – I think it was spaghetti. It was a total disaster and I almost burned the house down.

chilli and lemon-roasted salmon with roast plum tomatoes and chilli and fennel salad

Serves 4

Ingredients

For the tomatoes

8 plum tomatoes

1½ tablespoons extra virgin olive oil

sea salt and freshly ground black pepper

3 sprigs of thyme, leaves picked and chopped

For the salmon

4 x 175g (6oz) salmon fillets, skins on

salt and freshly ground black pepper

½ teaspoon chilli flakes

juice of 1 lemon

1 tablespoon olive oil

For the salad

2 heads fennel, thinly sliced

400g (14oz) tinned flageolet beans, drained and rinsed

1 red onion, thinly sliced

2 red chillies, thinly sliced

1 small handful of flat-leaf parsley

2 tablespoons lemon juice

salt and freshly ground black pepper

For the dressing

2 tablespoons soy sauce

1½ tablespoons extra virgin olive oil

1 tablespoon truffle oil

2 tablespoons lemon juice

Method

- Preheat the oven to 175°C/350°F/Gas Mark 4.
- Line a baking tray with baking parchment.
- Cut the tomatoes in half lengthways and place on the tray, cut side up.
- Drizzle with the olive oil, lightly season and bake for about 1½ hours until they colour and shrink a little. If after an hour they start to colour too much, cover with foil.
- Remove the tomatoes and turn the oven up to 200°C/400°F/Gas Mark 6.
- Season the salmon fillets with salt and pepper and the chilli flakes and lemon juice.
- Heat a frying pan and add the olive oil.
- Place the salmon in the pan, skin side down, and fry for 2–3 minutes until the skin is crispy.
- Turn and place in the oven for 5–8 minutes until cooked through.
- To make the salad, place the fennel in iced water to crisp up.
- Mix the beans with the sliced onion, chillies, parsley and lemon juice and lightly season.
- To prepare the dressing, mix together the soy sauce, olive oil, truffle oil and lemon juice.
- Taste and adjust the seasoning if necessary.
- Divide the bean salad between four plates and sit the tomato halves on top.
- Place the salmon on top of the tomatoes.
- Drain the fennel, toss with the dressing, scatter over the salmon and serve.

Wine expert Peter Richards' choice
Peter Lehmann Chenin Blanc

'I like hot, spicy food and love anything with chillies in it.'

food hell

Ronan Keating

'The only food I loathe is mushroom.
I hate the texture and taste.'

baked mushroom rarebit
with apple and tomato chutney

Serves 6

Ingredients

For the chutney

225g (8oz) Demerara sugar

275ml (10fl oz) malt vinegar

110g (4oz) sultanas

10g (½oz) ginger, finely chopped

2 red chillies, finely chopped

1kg (2lb 2oz) ripe tomatoes,
   roughly chopped

500g (1lb 2oz) apples, peeled,
   cored and chopped

200g (7oz) shallots, roughly chopped

1 tablespoon roughly chopped
   rosemary

salt and freshly ground black pepper

For the mushroom rarebit

225g (8oz) Stilton cheese, crumbled

110g (4oz) Cheddar cheese, grated

50ml (2fl oz) milk

25g (1oz) breadcrumbs

25g (1oz) flour

dash of Worcestershire sauce

1 egg

1 egg yolk

½ teaspoon English mustard powder

salt and white pepper

6 large field mushrooms, stalks
   removed

2 tablespoons olive oil

6 slices ciabatta bread, toasted

Method

- To make the chutney, place the sugar, half the vinegar and the sultanas in a saucepan and heat to a sticky caramel.
- Add the rest of the ingredients except the rosemary and bring to the boil.
- Add the rosemary and simmer for 30–40 minutes.
- Allow to cool, then season to taste.
- Meanwhile, preheat the oven to 200°C/400°F/Gas Mark 6.
- Place the cheese and milk in a saucepan and heat until the cheese is melted, stirring occasionally to prevent it from catching.
- Add the breadcrumbs and flour and cook for 2–3 minutes, stirring all the time.
- Allow to cool before adding the Worcestershire sauce, egg, egg yolk and mustard.
- Mix thoroughly and season with salt and white pepper.
- Place the mushrooms on a baking tray, spoon the rarebit mixture into the cavities and drizzle with the olive oil.
- Place in the oven and bake for 10–15 minutes until the mushrooms are soft and the cheese bubbling and brown.
- Serve on toasted slices of ciabatta bread with some of the juices poured over and a spoonful of chutney.

Wine expert Peter Richards' choice
Brown Brothers Orange Muscat and Flora

food heaven

Claire Sweeney

Claire's father was a butcher. 'When I was twelve, my dad brought home some lambs' testicles, skinned and fried them and we had them with chips and beans!'

One of her favourite foods is sushi: 'It gives you loads of energy and is low in fat.' She was not always so adventurous, though: 'I was brought up on quite basic food and didn't try sushi until four years ago. When I was younger, I worked on cruise ships and it was during this time that my eyes were opened to lots of different foods, particularly seafood.'

butternut squash soup

Serves 6–8

Ingredients

1 butternut squash, about 1 kg (2lb 2oz), peeled and cut into 2½cm (1in) cubes

2 tablespoons clear honey

2 tablespoons olive oil

1 onion, diced

2 cloves garlic, roughly chopped

110ml (4fl oz) white wine

500ml (17½fl oz) fresh chicken stock

20g (¾ oz) basil leaves, chopped

20g (¾oz) chervil, chopped

75ml (2½fl oz) extra virgin olive oil

salt and freshly ground black pepper

150ml (5fl oz) double cream

juice and zest of 3 limes

50g (2oz) crème fraîche

25g (1oz) pine nuts, lightly toasted

Method

- Preheat the oven to 200°C/400°F/Gas Mark 6.
- Place the squash on a baking tray and drizzle with the honey and olive oil.
- Place in the oven for 30–40 minutes until tender.
- Heat a frying pan, add the onion and garlic and fry for 1–2 minutes.
- Add the wine and stock and bring to the boil.
- Simmer for about 3–4 minutes, then add the cooked squash.
- Place half the basil and all the chervil in a blender with the extra virgin olive oil, season and blend to a fine purée. Remove from the blender and set aside.
- Place the soup in the blender with the cream, lime juice and zest and blend to a purée.
- Place the soup back in the saucepan and heat through. Season to taste.
- Ladle into bowls, then top with a dollop of crème fraîche and the pine nuts, drizzle with the puréed herb oil and sprinkle with the rest of the basil.

Wine expert Susie Barrie's choice
Yalumba Y Series Viognier 2005

'I love butternut squash and anything else that is savoury but with a sweet flavour. I love most sweet vegetables.'

food hell
Claire Sweeney

'I have never liked dark chocolate, as I find it too bitter. I much prefer the sweetness and creaminess of milk chocolate. In fact, I never order desserts when I eat out.'

black forest gateau with mint shards

Serves 8

Ingredients

For the sponge

6 eggs

150g (5oz) caster sugar

125g (4½oz) self-raising flour, sifted

25g (1oz) cocoa powder, sifted

For the filling and topping

3 x 425g (15oz) tins black cherries

2 tablespoons cornflour

good dash of Kirsch

750 ml (1¼ pints) double cream,
    whipped

50g (2oz) flaked almonds, toasted

For the mint shards

300g (11oz) dark chocolate

½ teaspoon peppermint essence

110g (4oz) Demerara sugar

Method

- Preheat the oven to 175°C/350°F/Gas Mark 4.
- Grease and line a deep, 30cm (12in) in diameter, round cake tin.
- Break the eggs into a mixing bowl, add the sugar and whisk well until very light and fluffy.
- Carefully fold in the sifted flour and cocoa powder.
- Pour the mixture into the prepared tin and place in the oven for about 40–45 minutes until cooked through.
- Turn out onto a wire rack and leave to cool.
- Drain the cherries, reserving the juice.
- Put the juice in a pan and bring to the boil.
- Make a paste by mixing the cornflour with a little water in a bowl.
- When the cherry juice is boiling, pour the paste into it and simmer for 1 minute.
- Strain through a sieve over the cherries, then add the Kirsch and leave to one side to cool.
- Using a sharp knife, cut the sponge into three layers.
- Sandwich the three layers together with the whipped cream and half the cherries and almonds.
- To make the mint shards, melt the chocolate, add the mint essence and sugar, spread on a tray lined with cling film. Place in the fridge to set.
- When the chocolate is set, break it into large shards and stick randomly around the edge of the cake.
- Scatter the remaining cherries and almonds on top and serve.

Wine expert Susie Barrie's choice
Elysium Black Muscat 2004

food heaven

Diarmuid Gavin

'I was brought up with meat and two veg. My mother was not very adventurous with food, but it was healthy, tasty stuff. Being a Paddy, I love potatoes – done any way. To be honest, I don't cook at all, my wife does most of the cooking at home. In fact, I have never cooked for her. I would love to cook and I am interested in it, but I just don't have the time. I rarely even eat out. I generally eat on the go, just buying food wherever I can get it.

It has always been my dream to grow my own produce – fruit and all sorts of vegetables. It is just a matter of finding the time to do it.'

grilled bananas with rosemary, toffee sauce and instant ice cream

Serves 4

Ingredients

For the bananas

4 large bananas

4 sprigs of fresh rosemary

For the toffee sauce

200ml (7fl oz) double cream

150g (5oz) butter

150g (5oz) dark-brown sugar

2 tablespoons black treacle

2 tablespoons golden syrup

For the ice cream

4 bananas, peeled, cut into chunks
and frozen in a freezer bag or on a tray

¼ teaspoon vanilla essence

3-4 tablespoons caster sugar

150ml (5fl oz) buttermilk

Method

- With a sharp knife, make a slit in one end of the bananas and insert the sprigs of fresh rosemary.
- Place the whole bananas, with the skins on, on a hot griddle pan for 3–4 minutes each side until the skin is dark-brown and starting to split.
- To make the toffee sauce, simply put the double cream, butter, sugar, treacle and golden syrup in a pan over a medium heat and bring to the boil.
- To make the ice cream, tip the frozen banana chunks into a food processor and add the vanilla, sugar and half the buttermilk.
- Turn on the processor and let it run for a few moments.
- Then, while it is still running, pour in the remaining buttermilk in a thin, steady stream, letting the machine run until the mixture is smooth and creamy.
- Serve the bananas, cut open with the skins on, with a good spoonful of the toffee sauce and a scoop of ice cream on the top.

Wine expert Susy Atkins' choice
Sainsbury's Muscat de St Jean de Minervois

'I love bananas and eat them regularly
to give me energy.'

food hell

Diarmuid Gavin

'I absolutely hate the idea of fish – any fish.'
For the Irish travel show *No Frontiers*, Diarmuid
had to be filmed eating various types of raw fish:
'It really was my worst nightmare. The worst part
of it was eating octopus. Anchovies are my real food
hell, they are *so* fishy.'

anchoïade with crudités

Serves 4

Ingredients

For the anchoïade

50ml (2fl oz) extra virgin olive oil

4 cloves garlic, roughly chopped

2 shallots, roughly chopped

60g (2oz) white anchovy fillets,
    roughly chopped

110ml (4fl oz) white wine

1 egg yolk

110ml (4fl oz) double cream

freshly ground black pepper

For the crudités

A selection of raw vegetables, such
as celery, carrot sticks, cucumber
sticks, radishes, strips of fennel, strips
of peppers and cherry tomatoes

Method

- Heat a frying pan, add the olive oil, garlic and shallots and cook for 1–2 minutes.
- Add the anchovies and wine cook for a further 1–2 minutes until the wine has reduced by half and the anchovies have softened.
- Place in a blender, add the egg yolk and cream and blend to a purée.
- Season with black pepper and pour into a bowl.
- Serve immediately with the crudités.

Wine expert Susy Atkins' choice
Domaine de Planterieu Vin de Pays des Côtes de Gascogne

food heaven

Duncan James

'When I was about seven, I used to come home from school and my grandmother would always have a fresh bag of cockles waiting for me. Most kids would come home and have a nice bun, but I'd have cockles.

'When I went to Japan with Blue, I wanted to try abalone, which is like a giant slug in a shell. It looks like a snail and I love snails. So the chef puts one on the grill and I eat it and it's lovely. The next day I wake up and I'm covered from head to toe in spots. I'd had an allergic reaction to it. I had to have an injection of antihistamine. And that taught me a lesson – not to be so adventurous. No more sea slugs for me!

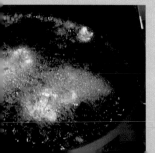

goujons of sole with lemon and tartare sauce

Serves 2–4

Ingredients

For the goujons

125g (4½oz) fresh, fine breadcrumbs

½ teaspoon cayenne pepper

sunflower oil for deep-fat frying

450g (1lb) sole or lemon sole fillets, skinned

50g (2oz) plain flour

3 medium eggs, beaten

salt and freshly ground black pepper

2 lemons, cut into wedges

For the tartare sauce

100g (4oz) mayonnaise

2 tablespoons chopped capers

4 gherkins, chopped

1 tablespoon flat-leaf parsley

For the salad

1 bag mixed salad leaves

1 lemon

4 tablespoons olive oil

Method

- Mix the breadcrumbs with the cayenne pepper and leave to one side.
- Cut each lemon sole or sole fillet into strips on the diagonal, about 1cm (½in) thick.
- Heat the oil in the deep-fat fryer to 190°C/375°F.
- Coat the fish in flour, then the beaten egg and finally the crumbs. Do a few pieces at a time, making sure the fish is fully coated in each of the dips.
- Place a few of the goujons in the fryer at a time and cook for about 1 minute until crisp and golden-brown. Once cooked, remove onto some kitchen paper to soak up the excess oil.
- To make the tartare sauce, mix together all the ingredients and season to taste.
- Pile the goujons in a serving dish or on plates and serve with the wedges of lemon and tartare sauce and a dressed green-leaf salad on the side.

Wine expert Olly Smith's choice
Château de Beranger Picpoul de Pinet

'As I was brought up by the sea, I love all seafood. A nice lemon sole is lovely.'

food hell

Duncan James

'I like most foods, but I'm not a big fan
of rice. It's just a bit white and boring.'

Thai roasted crab risotto

Serves 4

Ingredients

900ml (1½ pints) chicken stock, hot
5 stems lemongrass, crushed
5cm (2in) piece ginger, finely chopped
30g (1oz) butter
2 cloves garlic, finely chopped
2 shallots, finely chopped
275g (10oz) Arborio rice
100ml (4fl oz) white wine
2 green chillies, finely chopped
1½ tablespoons Thai green curry
   paste, or more to taste
450g (1lb) white and dark fresh
   crab meat
juice of 1 lime
1 tablespoon chopped flat-leaf parsley
1 tablespoon chopped coriander
2 tablespoons Mascarpone cheese
100g (4oz) Parmesan cheese, grated
50ml (2fl oz) double cream
salt and freshly ground black pepper

Method

- Place the stock, lemongrass and ginger in a saucepan and bring to a simmer.
- Melt the butter in a deep frying pan, add the garlic and shallots and fry for one minute.
- Add the rice and then the wine.
- Stir in the chopped green chillies and curry paste.
- Add a ladle of the stock to the rice and stir until the rice has absorbed all the liquid. Continue adding the stock, a ladle at a time, until all the stock has been absorbed. This should take about 13–15 minutes.
- Once the rice is cooked remove the lemongrass and add the crab, lime juice and chopped herbs.
- Add the Mascarpone, Parmesan and cream.
- Season well, spoon onto warmed plates and serve with extra Parmesan.

Wine expert Olly Smith's choice
Otra Vida Viognier

food heaven

Carol Thatcher

'My father never cooked; my mother did most of the cooking in our house. I was bought up eating quite traditional food. She never really cooked spicy foods or world cuisine as such. It was only a bit later in life that I became interested in spicy foods. I have always been an extremely keen traveller and I was inspired by different foods on my travels.'

'I admit I rely a lot on the microwave and never really host dinner parties. I am very good at pouring the wine though!'

Carol believes that interest in food and cooking has skyrocketed in the UK: 'English cooking has been transformed.' She likes eating out at the many great restaurants that London has to offer: 'When eating out, I live by something my mother always used to say – "In a restaurant, have something you couldn't, or wouldn't cook at home."'

spinach and Emmental cheese double-baked soufflé

Serves 4

Ingredients

For the soufflés

40g (1½oz) butter

40g (1½oz) plain flour

275ml (10 fl oz) milk

175g (6oz) Emmental cheese, grated

4 eggs, separated

salt and freshly ground black pepper

3 tablespoons lemon juice

2 tablespoons butter

400g (14oz) spinach

For the sauce

400ml (14fl oz) double cream

4 tablespoons Kirsch

salt and freshly ground black pepper

Method

- Preheat the oven to 175°C/350°F/Gas Mark 4.
- Place the butter and flour in a saucepan and heat until the butter is melted.
- Add the milk and stir to form a thick, smooth béchamel sauce.
- Add two-thirds of the Emmental cheese and stir until smooth.
- When cool, add the egg yolks and season.
- Line four ramekins with butter and flour.
- Whisk the egg whites with the lemon juice until firm.
- Stir a quarter of the egg whites into the cheese béchamel, then carefully fold in the remaining egg whites.
- Fill the ramekins two-thirds full and place on a tray in the oven for 8–10 minutes.
- Allow to cool, then remove from the moulds.
- Meanwhile, heat a frying pan, add the butter and spinach and cook for 2 minutes until wilted.
- To make the sauce, place the cream and Kirsch in a saucepan, bring to a simmer and season to taste.
- Place the spinach in a baking dish, put the soufflés on top, spoon over the cream sauce and top with the remaining Emmental.
- Place under a hot grill for 4–5 minutes until bubbling.

Wine expert Peter Richards' choice
Oyster Bay Sauvignon Blanc 2005.

'I love most green vegetables, especially spinach. I was part of the Popeye generation. It is an extremely versatile and yummy vegetable.'

food hell
Carol Thatcher

'I hate rhubarb. It looks disgusting and never tastes of anything. It looked genetically modified before genetically modified food was invented.'

rhubarb and baked ginger parkin with rhubarb, vanilla ice cream and hot, spiced syrup

Serves 8

Ingredients

For the parkin

110g (4oz) self-raising flour

salt

2 tablespoons ground ginger

½ teaspoon ground nutmeg

½ teaspoon mixed spice

75g (3oz) oat flakes

175g (6oz) golden syrup

50g (2oz) black treacle

110g (4oz) unsalted butter

110g (4oz) soft brown sugar

1 free-range egg, beaten

2 teaspoons full-fat milk

For the syrup

200g (7oz) golden syrup

2 teaspoons dry cider

½ teaspoon ground mixed spice

For the rhubarb

250g (9oz) rhubarb, cut into 1cm (½in) chunks

3–4 tablespoons caster sugar

To serve

500g (1lb 2oz) vanilla ice cream

Method

- Pre-heat the oven to 135°C/275°F/Gas Mark 1.
- Grease a 20cm (8in) square cake tin with butter.
- Sieve the flour, a pinch of salt, the ginger, nutmeg and mixed spice together into a large bowl.
- Mix in the oat flakes.
- Warm the tins of syrup and treacle in hot water to make it easier to measure them out accurately.
- Put the syrup, treacle, butter and soft brown sugar in a small saucepan and melt over a gentle heat. Bring up to a simmer, but do not boil.
- Stir into the flour mixture.
- Mix in the beaten egg and milk to create a soft, almost pouring consistency.
- Pour into the buttered tin and bake for 1¼ hours until firm in the centre.
- Remove from the oven and leave in the tin for 5–10 minutes before turning out and cutting into squares.
- To make the hot spiced syrup, simply whisk all the ingredients together in a small pan and warm, without boiling.
- To prepare the rhubarb, put it in a saucepan with a little water and the sugar.
- Bring to a simmer and cook until just tender.
- To serve, place a spoonful of rhubarb in the centre of each plate and top with a ball of ice cream. Place a piece of parkin on the side and drizzle the syrup over.

Wine expert Peter Richards' choice
Stella Bella Pink Muscat 2005

food heaven

Laurie Brett

'A lot of the food that I ate when I was growing up was made from scratch – things like homemade lentil soup, stock made with ham ends, stews and homemade pies. It was not showy fare, but it was good quality. We didn't use many herbs or spices, and this really allowed the flavours of the food to come through. We lived near the sea, so we had lots of fresh fish, which I loved.

'My grandfather grew his own vegetables, so we always had lots of fresh produce.'

Laurie loves to cook: 'I have been very influenced by my family's style of cooking. I love good cuts of meat, well seasoned. I enjoy fancy cooking in restaurants, but like to keep things simple at home.'

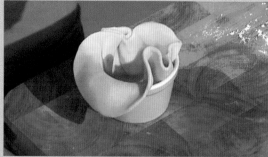

blueberry and blackberry pie with clotted cream

Serves 4

Ingredients

350g (12oz) shortcrust pastry

225g (8oz) blueberries

225g (8oz) blackberries

juice and zest of ½ lemon

½ teaspoon cinnamon

25g (1oz) Demerara sugar

1 egg, beaten

4 tablespoons apricot jam

2 tablespoons water

150g (5oz) clotted cream

Method

· Preheat the oven to 200°C/400°F/Gas Mark 6.

· Grease and flour four dariole moulds.

· Roll out the pastry and cut it out to line each of the moulds.

· Mix the blueberries, blackberries, lemon juice and zest and sugar together and completely fill the moulds.

· Top with the remaining pastry and seal.

· Brush with the beaten egg and put in the oven for 20–30 minutes.

· Once cooked, allow to rest before removing from the mould.

· Place the jam and water in a pan. Bring to the boil and whisk until smooth. Spoon over the pie.

· Serve with the clotted cream.

Wine expert Jonathan Ray's choice
Andrew Quady Essensia

'I like most foods, but my favourites are blueberries and blackberries.'

food hell

Laurie Brett

Laurie hates peas: 'They're no use to man nor beast. You have to chase them round on your plate and I don't like them. Some people try and get them on their fork, others mush them up, I just avoid them completely.'

pan-fried chicken
with lettuce, peas and pancetta

Serves 4

Ingredients

For the peas

25g (1oz) butter

1 small onion, finely chopped

2 cloves garlic, crushed

2 tablespoons horseradish cream

dash of white wine

150ml (5fl oz) double cream

½ butterhead lettuce, finely shredded

350g (12oz) frozen peas

pinch of caster sugar

salt and freshly ground black pepper

For the chicken

4 chicken fillets, boneless

olive oil

salt and freshly ground black pepper

8 slices grilled, crispy pancetta

Method

- To prepare the peas, melt the butter over a low heat, add the onion and garlic and soften without allowing them to colour.
- Add the horseradish and wine, bring to a simmer and add the cream.
- Add the lettuce, peas and sugar, stir, season to taste and simmer for a few minutes.
- Brush the chicken fillets with the olive oil, season and pan-fry or griddle until just cooked.
- Place a portion of the peas and lettuce in their sauce in the centre of the plate and top with the chicken and slices of pancetta.

Wine expert Jonathan Ray's choice
Zonte's Footstep Shiraz Viognier Blend

food heaven

Graeme Le Saux

Graeme was brought up in Jersey and is a huge fan of locally grown produce. He is married to an Argentinian: 'I love Argentinian food and the way that most of the social life in Argentina revolves around mealtimes.'

weeping lamb with boulanger potatoes

Serves 8

Ingredients

For the lamb

2.7kg (6lb) leg of lamb

50g (2oz) butter, softened

3–4 cloves garlic, cut into slivers

3 stems of rosemary

For the potatoes

6 potatoes, peeled and thinly sliced

4 onions, thinly sliced

salt and freshly ground black pepper

450ml (16fl oz) chicken or lamb stock

For the salad

300g (11oz) mixed salad leaves

juice of 1 lemon

50ml (2fl oz) olive oil

Method

- Preheat the oven to 230°C/450°F/Gas Mark 8.
- Rub the meat with the softened butter and place it in a roasting tin.
- Using a small, sharp knife, make a series of small, deep slits, about 4cm (1½in) apart, all over the leg of lamb and insert a sliver of garlic and a small sprig of rosemary in each one.
- Drizzle over some olive oil and place in the oven for about 30 minutes.
- While the meat is cooking, place the potatoes and onions in a bowl, season and toss together.
- After 30 minutes, take the meat from the oven and lift it out of the tin.
- Layer the potatoes and onions in the fat in the tin and pour over the stock.
- Return the roasting tin to the low shelf and place the lamb directly on the shelf immediately above, so that the juices will 'weep' onto the potatoes.
- Roast for about 1 further hour, depending on how well-done you like your meat.
- Dress the salad leaves with the lemon and olive oil and season to taste.
- Carve the lamb and serve with the potatoes and salad.

Wine expert Olly Smith's choice
Casillero del Diablo Cabernet Sauvignon 2005

'I have such fond memories associated with eating lamb. My mum used to cook a roast leg of lamb on Sundays. The following day she would mince up the leftovers and make shepherd's pie.'

food hell

Graeme Le Saux

'Cauliflower is just dull, boring and pointless. I have had bad experiences with cauliflower cheese. My friend's wife once cooked a cauliflower cheese that resembled a soup at a dinner party and it was truly horrendous. It is a standing joke amongst us. We call it her cauliflower surprise.'

cauliflower cheese with salmon

Serves 4

Ingredients

1 large cauliflower, cut into florets
50g (2oz) butter
50g (2oz) flour
450ml (16fl oz) milk
2 egg yolks
1 teaspoon English mustard
splash of Worcestershire sauce
150g (5oz) cooked salmon, flaked
125g (4½oz) Cheddar cheese, grated
75g (3oz) Emmental cheese, grated
1 bag mixed salad
2 tablespoons extra virgin olive oil
juice of ½ lemon
salt and freshly ground black pepper

Method

- Preheat the oven to 200°C/400°F/Gas Mark 6.
- Bring a large pan of salted water to the boil, then add the cauliflower and cook for 2 minutes.
- Drain and place in a buttered ovenproof dish.
- Place the butter and flour in a saucepan and heat to melt the butter.
- Cook for 1–2 minutes until lightly golden.
- Remove from the heat and gradually whisk in the milk to form a smooth sauce.
- Return to the heat and simmer for 2–3 minutes.
- Remove from the heat, beat in the egg yolks, mustard and Worcestershire sauce and season.
- Add the flaked salmon to the sauce, stirring carefully.
- Pour the mixture over the cauliflower and top with the grated cheese.
- Place in the oven for 10–15 minutes until golden-brown.
- Place the leaves in a bowl, toss with a little olive oil and lemon juice and season. Serve with the cauliflower cheese.

Wine expert Olly Smith's choice
Alamos Chardonnay 2004

food heaven

Abi Titmuss

Abi grew up in a village in Lincolnshire and was brought up on healthy local produce: 'My mum would always buy organic food and we used to eat a lot of game, such as pheasant and rabbit. I remember my mum skinning rabbits. They were great biology lessons'.

'Everything was always very healthy. I don't remember my mum ever making chips – not once. Now I look back and realise how lucky I was to be eating good quality, healthy food'.

Abi's foodie highlight was when she won a cooking competition at school: 'Everyone else was making incredible breads and things. I chose to make something out of marzipan so I could avoid cooking and because I love it. I made a huge marzipan model of a dragon in a dinner jacket eating a man in a sandwich and I won! It was a very proud moment.'

coconut tart with passion fruit

Ingredients

For the tart

2 eggs

juice and zest of 2 lemons

200g (7oz) caster sugar

375ml (13fl oz) double cream

300g (11oz) desiccated coconut

1 x 25cm (10in) sweetened shortcrust
    pastry tart shell, blind-baked

For the cream

250g (9oz) Mascarpone cheese

50ml (2fl oz) double cream

2 tablespoons icing sugar

3 passion fruits, pulped

Method

- Preheat the oven to 165°C/325°F/Gas Mark 3.
- Mix the eggs, lemon zest and caster sugar together for 1 minute.
- Gently mix in the cream, then the lemon juice and finally the desiccated coconut.
- Pour into the pastry shell and bake for about 40 minutes until golden all over.
- Remove from the oven and leave for 1 hour to cool and firm up.
- To make the cream, let the Mascarpone warm to room temperature before putting it in a bowl with the double cream and sugar.
- Whip until it begins to thicken, add the passion fruit pulp and beat until firm.
- To serve, simply cut the coconut tart into wedges and place on plates with a spoonful of the passion fruit cream.

Wine expert Tim Atkin's choice
Taste The Difference Sauternes

'I go to the gym five times a week at the moment, the reason being that then you can eat pudding. So my food heaven would be something really fattening with loads of calories in it. And I really love coconut.'

food hell
Abi Titmuss

'I'm not very keen on tripe or offal, but the worst is fennel. I'm not really wild about fennel. It doesn't smell good so why eat it? There is no need to eat it!'

pan-fried pork steak
with aubergine, chorizo and fennel

Serves 2

Ingredients

For the aubergine confit

1 aubergine, thickly sliced

125 ml (4½floz) olive oil

2 shallots, roughly chopped

½ clove garlic, finely sliced

salt and freshly ground black pepper

For the pork steaks

2 tablespoons olive oil

1 tablespoon butter

salt and freshly ground black pepper

2 x 225g (8oz) pork leg steaks

4 baby fennels, trimmed

40g (1½oz) chorizo, sliced

10 black olives

8 cherry tomatoes

½ clove garlic, finely sliced

10g (½oz) basil leaves

10g (½oz) chervil

Method

- Preheat the oven to 175°C/350°F/Gas Mark 4.
- To make the confit, slice the aubergine, put in a roasting tray with the olive oil, shallots and garlic and place in the oven for 30 minutes.
- To prepare the pork steaks, season them on both sides.
- Heat a tablespoon of the olive oil in a non-stick frying pan, then add the butter and cook until it is a nutty-brown colour.
- Add the pork steaks and cook quickly for about 3 minutes on each side until just cooked through.
- Bring a saucepan of salted water to the boil, blanch the fennel for 2–3 minutes until just tender, then drain.
- Heat the remaining olive oil in a pan, add the chorizo, olives and tomatoes and fry for 2–3 minutes.
- Add the garlic and fennel and cook slowly for about 2 minutes.
- Add the basil and season to taste.
- Place a slice of aubergine in the middle of each plate and top with a pork steak and a spoonful of the fennel mixture. Garnish with sprigs of fresh chervil and serve.

Wine expert Tim Atkin's choice
Campo Viejo Rioja Crianza 2003

food heaven

Trudie Goodwin

'My love of food comes from my mum. She was a fantastic cook, but I am terrible. Luckily, my husband can cook, and so can my daughters. We used to go abroad a lot – not because we were rich, but because my father loved travelling. My mum always encouraged us to try everything. Once when we were in a restaurant in Greece, this bowl of black squid ink with bits of squid floating in it appeared. Ugh!'

lobster thermidor with hand-cut chips

Serves 2

Ingredients

sunflower oil for deep-fat frying
2 large baking potatoes
1 x 750g (1½lb) lobster, cooked
25g (1oz) butter
1 shallot, finely chopped
275ml (10fl oz) fish stock
50ml (2fl oz) white wine
110ml (4fl oz) double cream
½ teaspoon English mustard
2 tablespoons roughly chopped flat-
   leaf parsley
juice of ½ lemon
salt and freshly ground black pepper
20g (¾oz) Parmesan cheese, grated

Method

- Heat a deep-fat fryer to 135°C/275°F.
- Slice the potatoes into 1½cm (½in) thick chips.
- Place in the fryer for 5–6 minutes until just tender but without colour.
- Remove from the fryer and turn up the heat to 190°C/375°F.
- Drop the chips back into the fat and cook for 3–4 minutes until golden and cooked through.
- Remove onto kitchen paper to drain and season with salt.
- Meanwhile, cut the lobster in half and remove the meat from the claws and tail and set aside.
- Remove any head matter and set aside.
- Cut the meat up and place back into the shell.
- To make the sauce, put the butter in a pan, add the shallots and cook until softened.
- Add the stock, wine and double cream and bring to the boil.
- Reduce by half.
- Add the mustard, parsley and lemon juice and season to taste.
- Spoon the sauce over the lobster meat and sprinkle with the grated Parmesan.
- Place under a preheated grill for 3–4 minutes until golden-brown.
- Serve with the chips.

Wine Susy Atkins' choice
Knappstein Hand-picked Riesling 2005

'My food heaven is definitely lobster. I love fish and shellfish generally, but lobster is my favourite. I connect it with being in wonderful places – abroad or in a lovely restaurant – because it is expensive and a bit of a luxury.'

food hell

Trudie Goodwin

'I used to like pork, but I had a very bad experience with it. I'm not going to name and shame, because they are still friends of ours now. We went round for dinner and the pork wasn't cooked. It was just awful.'

roast belly of pork with root vegetables

Serves 6–8

Ingredients

For the pork

1.8kg (4lb) pork belly, skin on

4 tablespoons cider vinegar

3 tablespoons pork dripping or butter

8 bay leaves, crushed

8 cloves garlic, minced

2 tablespoons Maldon sea salt

1 tablespoon crushed black
  peppercorns

400ml (14fl oz) red wine gravy

For the root vegetables

4 parsnips, cut into long wedges

400g (14oz) carrots, cut into long
  wedges

6 whole shallots

1 whole head garlic, sliced in half

3 sprigs of fresh thyme

1 tablespoon olive oil

250g (9oz) baby leaf spinach

Method

- The night before, boil a kettle and pour the boiling water over the pork rind. This oriental method helps tighten the rind and gives you better crackling.
- Then baste the raw joint with the cider vinegar, rubbing it all over to ensure the vinegar gets into the rind.
- Place the joint on a plate in the fridge, uncovered, overnight.
- Preheat the oven to 200°C/400°F/Gas Mark 6.
- Spread the pork with the dripping or butter, crushed bay leaves, garlic, salt and pepper and set aside for the flavours to develop.
- Place the pork, skin side up, on a wire rack that fits over an empty roasting tray.
- Roast for 1 hour and then reduce the oven temperature to 175°C/350°F/Gas Mark 4.
- Place the parsnips, carrots, shallots and garlic in a roasting tray and add the thyme, olive oil and a glass of water.
- Remove the empty tray from underneath the pork and pour any fat that has collected over the vegetables.
- Place the tray with the vegetables underneath the pork.
- Roast for 1 further hour, basting the vegetables with the juices from the pork from time to time.
- Remove the pork from the wire rack and allow to rest for 15 minutes in a warm place.
- Toss the spinach leaves with the vegetables in the roasting pan, drain off any excess fat, leaving the cooking juices behind, and keep warm.
- Carve off the crackling in one piece and divide into portions.
- Serve the pork with the roasted root vegetables, crackling and gravy.

Wine expert Susie Atkins' choice
Palacio de la Vega Cabernet Sauvignon/Tempranillo Blend 2000

food heaven

John Savident

During his years playing a butcher on Coronation Street, John learnt little that he did not already know: 'I have always had a huge interest in food, so I already had a good understanding of everything my character talked about. When I was a child, we would go to a local company which sold products such as pigs' trotters, cow heels and so on. The sad thing is that there is nothing like it anymore. I remember Lancashire hotpot would be made with cheap meat, like the best end of neck, and would be cooked for ages. You can't really get cuts of meat like that from the supermarkets. It is a shame.'

caesar chicken salad

Serves 2

Ingredients

For the salad

4 slices speck

2 corn-fed chicken breasts, boneless
and skinless

salt and freshly ground black pepper

1 tablespoon olive oil

1 teaspoon butter

2 thick slices white bread, cubed

2 Little Gem lettuces

For the dressing

2 cloves garlic

75ml (2½fl oz) white wine

2 egg yolks

1 anchovy fillet

75g (3oz) Parmesan cheese, grated

150ml (5fl oz) extra virgin olive oil

2 teaspoons Dijon mustard

salt and freshly ground black pepper

Method

- Preheat the grill to high.
- Place the speck on a baking tray and place under the grill for 3–4 minutes until crispy.
- Remove and drain on kitchen paper.
- Butterfly the chicken breasts so that they form one large, flat piece.
- Season and brush with olive oil.
- Heat a griddle pan and cook the chicken breasts for 2–3 minutes on each side until just cooked through.
- Heat a frying pan and add the butter and cubed bread.
- Fry until golden-brown, then remove from the heat.
- Separate out the lettuce leaves and rip into chunky pieces.
- To make the dressing, bring the garlic and wine to a boil in a medium saucepan and simmer for about 5 minutes until the cloves have softened.
- Leave to cool, then combine with the egg yolks, anchovy and cheese in a mixing bowl.
- Blend with a stick blender or in a liquidizer.
- Drizzle in the oil in a thin, steady stream, taking care not to add it too quickly so that the dressing does not split and curdle.
- Stir in the mustard and season to taste.
- Add the crispy speck, croutons and lettuce to the dressing and toss to combine. Serve straight away with the chicken.

Wine expert Olly Smith's choice
Argento Chardonnay, Mendoza, Argentina

'I can't eat enough garlic. I make a rather lovely Indian garlic chutney. It is damn hard work peeling umpteen hundred cloves of garlic, but the chutney is quite mild, believe it or not.'

food hell

John Savident

'I had a very unfortunate experience many years ago, when I was exploring Sarawak in Malaysia. I was invited to eat with a small group of locals, including a driver with the Malaysian army. In the middle of the shack was a table with a platter heaped high with shredded liver. I had to tuck into it. They were saying, "Eat more, eat more!"'

duck liver and basil pâté

Serves 6–8

Ingredients

500g (1lb 2oz) duck livers, trimmed

3 tablespoons Cognac

1 clove garlic, chopped

1 handful of fresh basil leaves

175g (6oz) unsalted butter, softened

salt and freshly ground black pepper

Method

- Preheat the oven to 200°C/400°F/Gas Mark 6.
- Place the whole livers in a baking tray, pour over the Cognac and toss so both sides of the liver absorb the Cognac.
- Sprinkle over the garlic and basil, retaining a few leaves, and season.
- Place in the oven for 6–8 minutes until just cooked. The livers should still be slightly pink inside.
- Remove from the oven, place in a blender along with 110g (4oz) of the butter and blend until smooth.
- Check the seasoning then spoon into ramekins.
- Place the remaining butter in a saucepan and heat until melted.
- Pour the clear butter over the surface of the pâté.
- Decorate with the remaining basil leaves and place in the fridge to set.
- Serve with Melba toast and some dressed salad leaves.

Wine expert Olly Smith's choice
Pfeiffer Beerenauslese

food heaven

Shaun Williamson

When he was growing up, Shaun's parents cooked very simple, hearty, traditional English food: 'If you give me potatoes and meat I am happy. I love stews. I used to make a lovely venison casserole with potatoes, carrots and cheesy herb dumplings. I live in the middle of the countryside and I love our local pub. Their menu is very seasonal. I persuaded them to serve dumplings. You've got to have dumplings.'

Shaun started cooking for the first time when he was at drama school and his wife was working: 'I would try to cook meals for her for when she arrived home from work. It was a hit and miss affair. I can cook okay. I like to cook simple dishes, nothing too ambitious. Back then my wife and I would put a roast in the oven on a low heat and nip out to the pub for a drink. We would invariably end up arriving home at midnight having forgotten about the roast. By that point it would be charcoal.'

beef wellington with new potatoes and red wine gravy

Serves 4–6

Ingredients

For the pancakes

3 medium eggs

6 tablespoons plain flour

150ml (5fl oz) milk

25g (1oz) butter

For the beef Wellington

500g (1lb 2oz) beef fillet,
   middle section

freshly ground black pepper

1 packet ready-rolled puff pastry

4 slices Parma ham

75g (3oz) smooth pâté

1 egg

1 egg yolk

For the gravy

500ml (17½fl oz) fresh chicken stock

150ml (5fl oz) red wine

dash of balsamic vinegar

3 tablespoons butter

salt and freshly ground black pepper

Method

- Preheat the oven to 200°C/400°F/Gas Mark 6.
- To make the pancakes, place the eggs and flour in a bowl and whisk together.
- Gradually add the milk, whisking until you have a batter that will coat the back of a spoon.
- Heat a frying pan until really hot, then add a knob of butter and a ladle of batter to thinly coat the base of the pan.
- When set, flip over and cook the other side.
- Tip out onto a plate lined with greaseproof paper. Cover with more paper and repeat.
- To prepare the Wellington, heat a frying pan.
- Season the beef fillet with black pepper then place in the frying pan and seal on each side.
- Roll out the pastry until it is 5mm (¼in) thick.
- Take two pancakes and place on the centre of the pastry and top with the Parma ham.
- Spread the pâté on the top of the beef and then place, pâté side down, onto the Parma ham.
- Beat together the egg and egg yolk, brush over the pancakes and pastry and fold up to enclose the beef.
- Turn seam side down onto a baking sheet and brush with the remaining egg wash.
- Place in the fridge for 30 minutes.
- Remove from the fridge and brush with the egg wash once more.
- Place in the oven for 25 minutes until golden. Cook for 30–35 minutes if you do not like your beef rare.
- Allow to rest for 5 minutes while you make the gravy.
- Place the stock and red wine in a saucepan and bring to the boil.
- Reduce by a third, then whisk in the balsamic vinegar and butter.
- Season and serve poured over the sliced Wellington with some cooked new potatoes.

Wine expert Peter Richards' choice
Peter Lehmann 'Clancy's' Shiraz/Cabernet/Merlot 2003

food hell

Shaun Williamson

'I have never understood people who pad out a decent meal with tasteless, uninteresting food such as parsnips, turnips, swedes and so on. I am not a big vegetable fan, as you can probably tell, although I have to be careful around our kids, as obviously I want to be responsible and encourage them to eat healthy food.'

curried roast parsnip soup
with vegetable chips

Serves 6

Ingredients

For the soup

2 tablespoons olive oil

1 onion, roughly chopped

2 cloves garlic, sliced thickly

1kg (2lb 2oz) parsnips, cut into
  chunks

3 sprigs of thyme

3 tablespoons honey

1–2 teaspoons hot curry powder

salt and freshly ground black pepper

1½ litres (2½ pints) chicken stock

450ml (16fl oz) double cream

For the garnish

sunflower oil for deep-fat frying

½ parsnip

½ beetroot

½ turnip

½ carrot

250ml (9fl oz) double cream

juice of ½ lemon

Method

- Preheat the oven to 200°C/400°F/Gas Mark 6.
- Place all the soup ingredients, with the exception of the stock and cream, in a roasting tray, season and toss to combine.
- Place in the oven for 25 minutes until golden and tender.
- Place all but 250ml (9fl oz) of the chicken stock in a saucepan along with the cream and bring to a simmer.
- Add the roasted parsnips and return to a simmer.
- With the remaining stock, deglaze the roasting tray and add to the saucepan.
- Place in a blender and purée, or blend in the saucepan using a stick blender.
- Return to the pan and check the seasoning.
- Meanwhile, to prepare the garnish, heat a deep-fat fryer to 190°C/375°F.
- Using a potato peeler make slices of each of the garnish vegetables.
- Drop them into the fryer and fry until golden.
- Remove and drain on kitchen paper.
- Place the cream in a bowl and lightly whip.
- Add the lemon juice and fold in.
- Serve the soup with a dollop of cream and a pile of vegetable crisps.

Wine expert Peter Richards' choice
Laurent Miquel, Nord Sud Viognier 2005,
Vin de Pays d'Oc

food heaven

Rupert Everett

'My parents lived in Morocco for a while and I loved the French/Moroccan cuisine. However, I have always eaten quite conventionally and love fish fingers and beans on toast.'

Rupert has been a vegetarian for a few years: 'I was walking on holiday in Switzerland and all these cows came over. They were so lovely and curious. A little later on, I was in Brazil and visited an abattoir. The methods of killing were terrible and from then on I decided that I couldn't possibly eat meat any longer. I do eat fish sometimes, but I am appalled by the current plundering of the sea and the problems created by over-fishing.'

courgette and thyme tagliatelle with langoustines

Serves 4

Ingredients

For the langoustines

20 langoustines, cooked

1 tablespoon tomato purée

1 celery stick, roughly chopped

1 carrot, roughly chopped

1 onion, roughly chopped

500ml (17½fl oz) olive oil

For the tagliatelle

1 tablespoon olive oil

12 small courgettes with flowers,
   cut lengthways and in chunks

1 sprig of thyme

2 large courgettes, sliced into ribbons

500g (1lb 2oz) fresh tagliatelle pasta

salt and freshly ground black pepper

freshly grated Parmesan cheese
   to serve

Method

- Preheat the oven to 200°C/400°F/Gas Mark 6.
- Peel the langoustines and set the meat to one side.
- Place all the langoustine shells on a baking tray along with the tomato purée, celery, carrot and onion.
- Toss to combine then place in the oven for 30 minutes until golden.
- Remove and reduce the heat to 165°C/325°F/Gas Mark 3.
- Pour the olive oil over the roasted shells and stir well.
- Return to the oven for a further hour.
- Remove and drain off the oil, passing it through a fine sieve.
- Set aside the oil and discard the shells.
- To prepare the tagliatelle, heat a frying pan, then add the olive oil, small courgettes and thyme.
- Fry until golden-brown and just tender.
- Meanwhile, bring a large saucepan of water to the boil, add the pasta and cook for 2 minutes.
- Add the courgette ribbons and chunks and cook for a further minute until just wilted.
- Drain and place back in the saucepan.
- Add the browned courgettes and season. Pile onto a serving plate.
- Toss the langoustines with olive oil, season and place on top of the pasta.
- Sprinkle with the Parmesan, spoon over a little of the langoustine oil and serve immediately.

Wine expert Susie Barrie's choice
Peter Lehmann Semillon 2004

'I believe the more complicated food is, the worse it becomes. It is all about good quality produce, simply cooked, especially courgettes.'

food hell

Rupert Everett

'I hate the look of capers, the taste of them. Anything they are on, I hate – the sourness. Anything at all with capers I just can't eat!'

skate wings with caper beurre noisette and olive oil mash

Serves 2

Ingredients

For the skate

2 skate wings, boned

50g (2oz) plain flour

25g (1oz) butter

1 tablespoon olive oil

For the buerre noisette

175g (6oz) butter

4 tablespoons lemon juice

3 tablespoons caperberries

3 tablespoons capers

2 tablespoons roughly chopped flat-
leaf parsley

For the olive oil mash

2 large potatoes, peeled and cut
into chunks

110ml (4fl oz) olive oil

salt and freshly ground black pepper

Method

- Dust the skate wings with the flour.
- Heat a large frying pan and add the butter and oil.
- Carefully place the skate in the pan and fry for 3–4 minutes on each side.
- Meanwhile, for the caper beurre noisette place the butter in a small saucepan and heat until nut-brown.
- Add the lemon juice, caperberries, capers and parsley and stir through.
- To make the mash, place the potatoes in a saucepan and cover with water.
- Bring to a simmer and cook for 10–25 minutes until tender.
- Drain and place back in the pan.
- Mash until smooth, then beat in the olive oil and season.
- To serve, place the skate on plates with 2 quenelles each of mash, then spoon over the caper butter.

Wine expert Susie Barrie's choice
Boschendal 1685 Chardonnay 2005

food heaven

Ray Fearon

Ray's parents are from the West Indies and moved to England in the early 50s. 'My mum and dad both loved cooking, although dad only really got into it once he had retired. We used to have things like traditional English breakfasts with a Caribbean twist. This would consist of fried dumpling, plantain, fried eggs and beans. I love to cook; I used to watch Mum cook, so I picked up a lot of tips. I first started cooking for myself when I went to drama school. As I grew up eating healthily, I have always craved vegetables and have never wanted junk food.'

pineapple tarte tatin
with black pepper and rum caramel

Serves 2

Ingredients

For the tarte tatin

100g (4oz) caster sugar

20g (¾oz) butter

2 rings of pineapple, 2½cm (1in) thick

150g (5oz) puff pastry, rolled to
5mm (¼in) thick

For the caramel

100g (4oz) caster sugar

75ml (2½fl oz) double cream

2 tablespoons rum

¼ teaspoon cracked black pepper

coconut ice cream, to serve

Method

· Preheat the oven to 200°C/400°F/Gas Mark 6.

· Divide the sugar and place half in each of two small blini pans.

· Heat gently, without stirring, until the sugar caramelizes, turning golden-brown.

· Remove from the heat, divide the butter in half and stir gently into the sugar in each pan.

· Place a pineapple ring into each pan.

· Cut the pastry into two circles, which are just slightly larger than the circumference of the pans.

· Top both pineapple rings with the pastry circles, pushing the edges down underneath the pineapple.

· Place in the oven for 10–12 minutes until the pastry is golden-brown and cooked through.

· Meanwhile, make the caramel by placing the sugar in a saucepan and heating gently, without stirring, until it caramelizes.

· Remove from the heat and place the base of the pan in a cold pan of water to reduce the heat.

· Add the double cream, rum and black pepper and stir to combine.

· Remove the tarts from the oven and allow to sit for a couple of minutes.

· Turn out onto the centre of plates, spoon the black pepper caramel around the tarts and top with a spoonful of coconut ice cream.

Wine expert Olly Smith's choice
Pfeiffer Beerenauslese 2002

'My Aunt grows pineapples in the Caribbean,
and on my last visit I went picking and filled
up two huge sacks with them.'

food hell

Ray Fearon

'My dad used to grow tons of pumpkins, particularly around Halloween. He would hand them out to everyone and we would have lots of pumpkin soup. In the end I was sick of it. It was too much. I haven't liked pumpkin since.'

spiced pumpkin tart with stem ginger cream

Serves 8

Ingredients

For the pumpkin tart

1 pack dessert pastry, rolled to
   5mm (¼in) thick

500g (1lb 2oz) pumpkin, cut into
   large chunks

2 eggs

100g (4oz) caster sugar

50g (2oz) ground almonds

¼ teaspoon ground cloves

¼ teaspoon ground cinnamon

¼ teaspoon ground ginger

¼ teaspoon grated nutmeg

200ml (7fl oz) single cream

For the stem ginger cream

200ml (7fl oz) double cream

3 tablespoons stem ginger syrup

25g (1oz) stem ginger, finely chopped

Method

- Preheat the oven to 190°C/375°F/Gas Mark 5.
- Line a 23cm (9in) tart tin with the pastry, line with cling film and fill with baking beans or rice.
- Place on a baking sheet and place in the oven for 15 minutes.
- Remove the cling film and baking beans and return to the oven for a further 10 minutes to crisp the base of the case.
- Meanwhile, place the pumpkin in a steamer over the top of a saucepan of boiling water and steam for 15–20 minutes until tender.
- Remove from the steamer and cool.
- Place the cool pumpkin in a food processor and blend to a purée.
- Place the eggs and sugar in a large bowl and whisk to combine.
- Add the ground almonds, spices and cream and whisk until smooth.
- Add the puréed pumpkin and mix once more.
- Pour into the pastry case and place in the oven for 40–45 minutes until set.
- Remove from the oven and cool for at least 1 hour.
- To make the stem ginger cream, place the cream, syrup and ginger in a bowl and whisk until soft peaks are formed.
- To serve, cut a slice of tart and place on a plate with a spoonful of the cream, a dusting of icing sugar and a sprig of mint.

Wine expert Olly Smith's choice
Pfeiffer Beerenauslese 2002

food heaven

Justin Lee Collins

'I can't and don't cook. I am totally useless in the kitchen – I even burn toast. If any cooking is ever done, which is unusual, it is done by my wife. To be honest, most of the time we eat out or get takeaways. We generally have Indian, Thai or Mexican food.'

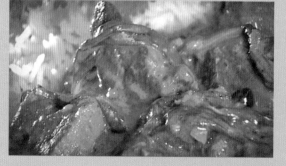

lamb curry with basmati rice

Serves 4

Ingredients

2 tablespoons vegetable oil

900g (2lb) lamb fillet, cut into 3cm
   (1¼in) cubes

2 onions, roughly chopped

3 cloves garlic, peeled and crushed

2 green chillies, finely chopped

1 tablespoon fresh, grated ginger

1 tablespoon ground turmeric

1½ tablespoons garam masala

1½ tablespoons ground cumin

1 tablespoon chilli powder

1 tablespoon plain flour

6 large tomatoes, roughly chopped

400ml (14fl oz) coconut milk

600ml (1 pint) chicken stock

250g (9oz) baby spinach leaves

1 pomegranate, seeded

200g (7oz) natural yoghurt

salt and freshly ground black pepper

steamed basmati rice, to serve

Method

- Heat a large saucepan and add 1 tablespoon of vegetable oil and all the lamb.
- Cook over a high heat for 3–4 minutes until the lamb is browned, then remove and set aside.
- Reduce the heat and add the remaining oil, along with the onions, garlic, chillies and ginger.
- Cook for 2–3 minutes until golden and softened.
- Add the spices and cook for 1 minute, then add the flour and cook for 1 further minute.
- Add the tomatoes and coconut milk and bring to a simmer.
- Add the lamb and enough chicken stock to just cover the lamb.
- Stir well to release any residue at the bottom of the pan, cover and simmer for about 1 hour until the lamb is tender.
- Skim off any excess fat from the surface.
- Stir in the spinach and pomegranate and cook until just wilted.
- Add the yoghurt, season and stir through.
- Serve with steamed basmati rice.

Wine expert Peter Richards' choice
Viña Albali Reserva Tempranillo

'I eat Indian food all the time. I love all the ingredients that go into curries. I have started eating lamb curries and I'm really getting into them. Lamb is one of my favourite meats now. Heaven for me would be a lamb bhuna. If you go to a good restaurant and they cook it properly it is delicious'.

food hell

Justin Lee Collins

'I dislike the beetroot – I find it offensive. It's not the taste, it's the fact that it turns everything else on the plate purple. I've got a little boy called Archie and it's like he's spilt his paints all over my plate.'

pan-roasted chicken with beetroot and cauliflower with horseradish cream

Serves 4

Ingredients

For the chicken

1 tablespoon butter

1 tablespoon olive oil

4 chicken breasts, skin on

salt and freshly ground black pepper

For the beetroot

1 tablespoon olive oil

1 clove garlic, finely chopped

4 shallots, finely chopped

2 tablespoons balsamic vinegar

75ml (2½fl oz) extra virgin olive oil

10g (½oz) chives, roughly chopped

10g (½oz) flat-leaf parsley,
   roughly chopped

10g (½oz) dill, roughly chopped

8 medium beetroots, cooked, peeled
and cut into segments

salt and freshly ground black pepper

For the cauliflower

1 large cauliflower, cut into florets

4 tablespoons horseradish cream

juice of 1 lemon

150ml (5fl oz) double cream,
   lightly whipped

salt and freshly ground black pepper

Method

- Preheat the oven to 175°C/350°F/Gas Mark 4.
- Heat an ovenproof frying pan and add the butter and olive oil.
- Season the chicken, place in the pan, skin side down, and fry for 2–3 minutes until golden.
- Turn over and place in the oven for 8–10 minutes until cooked through.
- Meanwhile, to prepare the beetroot, heat a small pan until warm, add the tablespoon of olive oil, garlic and shallots and sweat for 2–3 minutes until tender but not coloured.
- Add the balsamic vinegar, extra virgin olive oil and herbs and pour over the beetroot.
- Season and toss to combine.
- Next, bring a pan of water to the boil and add the cauliflower.
- Cook for 4–5 minutes until just tender, then drain and refresh in iced water.
- Drain again and set aside.
- Place the horseradish and lemon juice in a bowl and whisk together.
- Fold in the whipped cream and season.
- Fold in the cauliflower.
- Place a spoonful each of the beetroot and cauliflower on plates and top with the chicken breasts.

Wine expert Peter Richards' choice
Boschendal Rosé

food heaven

Darren Gough

Darren was bought up in Yorkshire and was a picky eater as a child: 'I would eat hardly any food. My brother and sister were the same – my parents had no chance. I wouldn't even try tomatoes.

'While playing cricket I was travelling around the world and going to different restaurants. I remember the first time I had lobster – in Cape Town, eleven years ago. I loved it. We spent a lot of time in India and I could eat anything there. Everyone else got Delhi Belly, but I never got ill. I was the only one who put weight on! Most of the lads only ate English dishes, but I always ate the local food. I will try most foods now.'

crunchy chilli chicken, rocket pesto and oven-roasted spuds

Serves 4

Ingredients

For the chicken

2 plum tomatoes

1 red chilli, deseeded and
   roughly chopped

½ teaspoon crushed red chilli

¼ red pepper, roughly chopped

¼ red onion, roughly chopped

1 clove garlic

2 tablespoons olive oil

salt and freshly ground black pepper

110g (4oz) instant polenta

4 x 225g (8oz) chicken breasts,
   boneless and skinless

1 tablespoon olive oil

For the rocket pesto

110g (4oz) rocket leaves

1 clove garlic

1 tablespoon pine nuts, toasted

juice of 1 lime

8 tablespoons olive oil

For the spuds

3 large baking potatoes

4 tablespoons olive oil

1 teaspoon paprika

salt and freshly ground black pepper

Method

- Preheat the oven to 200°C/400°F/Gas Mark 6.
- Place the tomatoes, chilli, crushed chilli, red pepper, red onion and garlic in a food processor and blend to a rough paste.
- Stir in the olive oil and season.
- Put the paste in a bowl along with the polenta and mix well.
- Flatten the chicken breasts slightly and season.
- Heat a frying pan and add the olive oil and chicken breasts.
- Seal on each side then place on a baking tray.
- Top with the polenta mixture and place in the oven for 12–15 minutes until the chicken is cooked through and the topping crunchy. If the topping is still slightly soft, place under the grill for 2–3 minutes.
- To make the pesto, place the rocket, garlic, pine nuts, lime juice and olive oil in a blender and process to form a fine paste.
- Slice the potatoes lengthways into wedges and toss with the olive oil, paprika, salt and pepper.
- Place on a baking tray in the oven for 20–25 minutes until tender but crunchy on the outside.
- Serve the chicken with a dollop of pesto and a few potato wedges.

Wine expert Susie Barrie's choice
**St Hallett Poacher's Blend Semillon/Sauvignon/
Riesling Blanc**

'I love steak once in a while, but I don't really eat much pork, lamb or fish. I am a plain man – I like chicken. Not the legs or any of that, just the breast.'

food hell

Darren Gough

'I hate tinned tuna and really dislike tuna steaks.
I certainly wouldn't choose to eat them.'

spiced seared tuna salad nicoise

Serves 4

Ingredients

For the salad

400g (14oz) fresh tuna, cut into 5cm (2in) cubes

4 tablespoons apricot jam

2 teaspoons ground cumin

2 teaspoons ground coriander

8 quail eggs

110g (4oz) French beans

10 cherry tomatoes

8 new potatoes, cooked

10 black olives

1 small baguette, thinly sliced and toasted

1 clove garlic

For the dressing

½ clove garlic

2 tinned anchovy fillets

1 egg yolk

Juice of ½ lemon

110ml (4fl oz) olive oil

1 teaspoon Dijon mustard

salt and freshly ground black pepper

Method

- Preheat the oven to 220°C/425°F/Gas Mark 7.
- Spread the apricot jam over the tuna.
- Place the ground cumin and coriander in a bowl and mix to combine.
- Roll the tuna in the spices then leave to marinate for 20 minutes.
- Heat a frying pan and sear the tuna for 15 seconds on each side.
- Place in the oven for 3–4 minutes until just cooked, but still pink in the centre.
- Meanwhile, make the dressing by placing the garlic, anchovy and egg yolk in a pestle and mortar and mixing to a paste.
- Add the lemon juice and drizzle in the olive oil while mixing well.
- Add the mustard, season to taste and set aside.
- Bring a small pan of water to the boil and drop in the quail eggs.
- Boil for 2½ minutes, then drain, run under cold water to stop them cooking further and peel.
- Bring another pan of water to the boil, add salt and the French beans and cook for 3–4 minutes until just tender.
- Drain and refresh, then peel lengthways into two halves.
- Place the tomatoes on a roasting tray and drizzle with a little olive oil.
- Place in the oven for 3–4 minutes until just softened.
- To assemble the salad, place the beans, potatoes, olives and eggs in a bowl and toss with the dressing.
- Place on a serving plate, cut the tuna cubes in half and place on top.
- Rub the croutons with the garlic clove, top with the tomatoes, place around the edge of the salad and serve.

Wine expert Susie Barrie's choice
Torres San Medin Cabernet Sauvignon Rosé

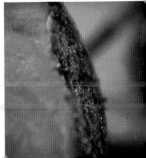

Index

Acknowledgements

Amanda Ross, Executive Producer of Saturday Kitchen who devised and co-edited this book would like to thank the following for their considerable efforts:

Series Producer James Winter and the production team Dave Mynard, Elissa Standen and James Cook.
Simon Ross, Ben Rigden and Chris Worthington for development of the show.
Will Learmonth for the screen grabs and original graphics.
Janet Brinkworth and Helen Alexander-Gillen for food preparation.
Anna Ratcliffe for her endless eating, and Leo Holden and Fiona Jones for their endless washing up.
All our celebrity guests and the celebrity booking team Sinead Oldnall, Charlotte Johnstone and Jonathan Perry.
The BBC Executives for all their support – Jay Hunt, Alison Kirkham, Jacqueline Hewer, Karen Brown and Carla-Maria Lawson.
Thank you to Eleanor and Fiona at BBC Books for their patience.

And of course most of all James Martin, and all the amazing chefs and wonderful wine experts – it's a privilege and a pleasure working with you all!

Credits
Project editor: Eleanor Maxfield
Copy editor: Juliana Foster
Production controller: Ken McKay

Design by Grade Design Limited
Photography by Will Heap

Elements
of
Cartography

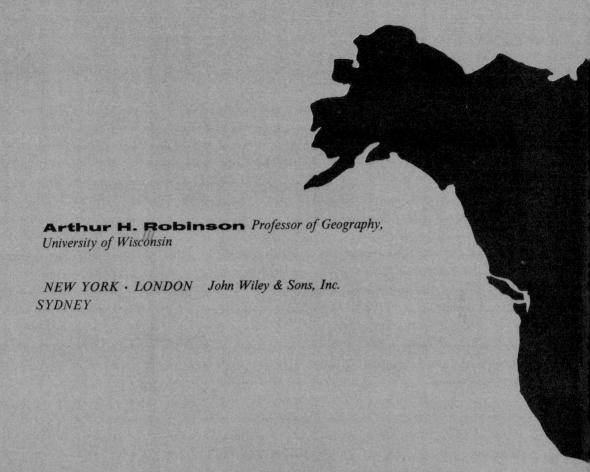

Arthur H. Robinson *Professor of Geography,*
University of Wisconsin

NEW YORK · LONDON   *John Wiley & Sons, Inc.*
SYDNEY

2nd edition

Elements
of
Cartography

Original Illustrations Drawn by
James J. Flannery
Assistant Professor of Geography
Wharton School
University of Pennsylvania

SECOND EDITION
FOURTH PRINTING, NOVEMBER, 1964

LIBRARY OF CONGRESS CATALOG CARD NUMBER: 60–5604
PRINTED IN THE UNITED STATES OF AMERICA

Preface

Since the preparation of the manuscript for the first edition, about seven years ago, many changes have occurred which affect the art and science of cartography. Perhaps the most significant has been a continuation of the recent expansion of interest in cartography and in area analysis in all fields. The persistent growth of population pressures and the strengthening of regional ties throughout the world have multiplied many times over the need for both the smaller-scale map and the topographic map. Cartography has therefore continued to develop rapidly, both as a research technique as well as a tool of presentation. In the past not many disciplines were greatly concerned with relationships over area, and geographers, naturally, and some other earth scientists were the major producers and consumers of these maps. Recently, however, the importance of perceiving, describing, and understanding areal distributions and the significance of their interrelationships has spread to other disciplines, and they too are finding the map a most useful analytical and descriptive tool. This second edition has been prepared with this in mind.

Two other recent major developments in cartography are (1) the rapid growth of techniques for the gathering and processing of areal data ranging from the electronic to the statistical, and (2) the considerable advance in the technology concerning the preparation of material for reproduction. Both these sets of developments, being of undoubted significance as well as technically fascinating, have tended somewhat to steal the current spotlight from the primary process of cartography, viz., the conceptual planning and designing of the map as a medium for communication or research. The latter remains, however, the fundamental aim of this edition.

A great many changes and additions have been made. Most of the text has been rewritten and over seventy new illustrations have been added; a few have been deleted. New material has been incorporated in major proportion in several places. The most inadequate section of the first edition turned out to be that dealing with the symbolization and representation of the mapped data. Accordingly, this has been expanded from one to three chapters, completely reorganized and some of the elementary statistical concepts appropriate to the cartographic process have been included. Experience with the preceding edition also showed that the subject of map projection, so fundamental to cartography, needed fuller treatment. This section has been reorganized, incorporating a new introductory chapter treating the basic concepts involved in the projectional transformation of the spherical sur-

v

face to a plane. It has been kept essentially nonmathematical. I have also attempted to include the major developments in technology which affect the planning and execution of smaller-scale "geographic maps," without going into great detail concerning mechanical aspects. Among considerable new material included in the Appendixes is a table of common logarithms. This will make much easier the students' completion of exercise material that may be assigned from the text.

As is always the case in an undertaking like this a feeling of frustration arises when one contemplates providing adequate acknowledgment. Numerous active professionals in the field have contributed many ideas and developments, both in the literature and at professional meetings; yet, it is obviously impossible to identify them all. I have tried to make suitable acknowledgment in the book where specific references are appropriate; but this cannot include everyone, and any oversight in this respect is just that. In addition, no textbook of this kind could be prepared without the continuing informal assistance of many to whom individual recognition cannot be given. Especially helpful have been my former and present students, who have been both a source of excellent suggestions and criticisms, as well as a more or less willing testing group. To them I owe a great deal. My colleague, Mr. Randall D. Sale, has been especially helpful in more ways than I can say. His work with students in laboratory sections and his experiences in the University Cartographic Laboratory at the University of Wisconsin have produced many ideas for improvement in textual and illustrative presentation. Professor John C. Sherman of the University of Washington read the entire manuscript and made many useful comments and suggestions.

The illustrating of this edition was as pleasant an experience as illustrating the first. Professor James J. Flannery of the University of Pennsylvania continued to be most helpful and skillful. In all cases permissions for reproducing published material were graciously given.

The very considerable direct and indirect assistance of typists, the editor, and especially one's wife, in connection with the production of a book is, unfortunately, usually taken for granted, because in one way or another "it's their job." Without their help, however, writing a book would be really hard work.

ARTHUR H. ROBINSON

June 1959

Contents

Appendix

The Art and Science of Cartography

1.1 MAPS, INDISPENSABLE TOOLS

Man is so small and he is tied so closely to his earth habitat that he must employ, among other techniques, that of cartography in order to see the broader spatial relationships that exist in his complex world. The cartographic technique enables him to rise, so to speak, above his immediate range of vision and contemplate the salient features of larger areas. A large-scale map of a small region, depicting its land forms, drainage, settlement patterns, roads, geology, or a host of other geographic and economic distributions, provides him with the knowledge of the relationships necessary to carry on his works intelligently. The building of a road, a house, a flood-control system, or almost any other constructive endeavor requires prior mapping. At a smaller scale, maps of soil erosion, land use, population character, climates, income, and so on, are indispensable to understanding the problems and potentialities of an area. At the smallest scale, maps of the whole earth indicate generalizations and relationships of broad earth patterns with which we may intelligently consider the course of events past, present, and future.

The increasing complexity of modern life with its attendant pressures and contentions for available resources has made necessary increasingly detailed studies of land utilization, soil characteristics, disease migrations, population and settlement distributions, and numberless other social and economic factors. The geographer, preeminently, as well as the historian, economist, agriculturalist, and others of the social and applied physical science fields, has found the map a useful and often indispensable aid to his research and its presentation.

The map is a promotor of business, and it is seen in increasing numbers in advertising; and the demand for market and resource information encourages distribution mapping for commercial purposes. The familiar and excellent road map, standard equipment of any driver in the United States, is prepared and distributed free in such quantities that every year each adult in this country could have his own personal copy.

To attempt to catalog with precision the infinite number of kinds and uses of maps is an impossible task. Anything that man can observe, tangible or otherwise, can be mapped in its two- or three-dimensional distribution on the earth. The uses of maps may vary from that of the historian plotting and analyzing the routes of Marco Polo or Alexander in order to evaluate their cultural influences to the engineer analyzing the

drainage characteristics of a portion of a city to determine the run-off potential in order to supply adequate storm sewers. The scales may vary from a page-size map of the world presenting airline routes focusing on Chicago to a foot-square insurance map of a city block including the building in which the airlines map was made. The most meaningful listing of varieties of maps is one based on utility, and many such catalogs have been attempted. They include the standard divisions such as topographic maps, nautical charts, economic maps, historical maps, and other broad use categories. However, they all fail to impress on the reader that all maps are related, being of the earth, and that uses, scales, varieties, and sizes all shade, imperceptibly, one into another.

Truly, as far as modern maps of the earth are concerned, the "sky is the limit."

1.2   THE BACKGROUND OF MODERN CARTOGRAPHY

In ancient times the limits of cartography were apparently very narrow. Islanders of the South Seas are said to have constructed at an early date charts of reeds and sticks to record the relative positions of islands. Perhaps the oldest authentic map which survives is a record of some land holdings in Babylon. Certainly, the valley of the Nile was carefully mapped in order to record property lines. Aside from the islanders' maps and others like them, it is probable that the earliest maps were records of land ownership. This same kind of map still survives as one important use-category of cartography. Today they are called cadastral maps, and they record land holdings the same way they did several thousand years ago (see Fig. 1.1). One of the principal uses of cadastral maps is to assess taxes, which may account for the fact that they have always been with us.

Concern with areas larger than the local scene developed long before the time of Christ. The spherical shape of the earth was early inferred from the difference in the altitudes of stars at different places, from the fact that shorelines and ships seemed to "come over" the horizon as one moved across the sea, and even from the assumption that the sphere was the most perfect form. The development of civilization allowed more frequent travel, and a greater interest in faraway places was accompanied by increased thought about ways of presenting the relationships of areas on maps. Estimates of the size of the earth were made by ancient scholars such as Eratosthenes and Posidonius from angular observations on the sun and stars in the eastern Mediterranean area. The methods used were correct, but the precision of their observations was not very great because of less-than-perfect instruments. Nevertheless, although we cannot be sure of their results in terms of modern units of measure, the estimates were possibly not far off. From the few manuscripts that have survived there is evidence that many maps were made during the time of the classical Greeks, but none of the original drawings appears to have survived. Fortunately for our understanding of the cartography of the ancient period there is, however, a record which apparently clearly reflects the stage to which cartography had developed by the end of the Greek period. These are the writings of Claudius Ptolemy.

In Alexandria, Egypt, which had become the intellectual center of the western world, there had been established a great library and a cultural climate where a scholar could study and write. Claudius Ptolemy, who lived during the first and second centuries A.D., brought together all that was available concerning the known areas of the earth and wrote a long manuscript which included, among other things, a treatise on cartography. He described how maps should be made; he gave directions for dealing with

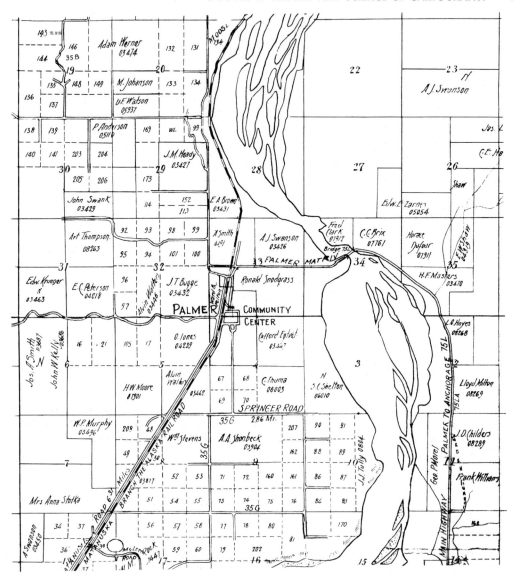

FIGURE 1.1. Portion of a cadastral map showing property lines.

the problem of presenting the spherical surface of the earth on a flat piece of paper; he recognized the inevitability of deformation in the process; and in many other ways he described what was known about cartography at that time. Ptolemy also made a list of numerous places in the world he had obtained from other writings and from travelers, and gave his best estimate of their positions in latitude and longitude terms. To illustrate this it is thought that he had made a series of maps of local and larger areas (see Fig. 1.2). This is not certain, however, for if he did they have since been lost. He did, however, give a detailed account of how they were made. Ptolemy's writings were lost to the western world for more than a thousand years, but fortunately

FIGURE 1.2. One of "Ptolemy's" maps. His written works were "rediscovered" during the fifteenth century, but his maps had to be reconstructed from his directions. His world map was better than any other, even in the fifteenth century, a thousand years after its original construction. (From the Library of Congress collection.)

they were preserved and came to light via the Arab world. From these descriptions the maps were reconstructed, and they had a profound influence upon European geographical and cartographical thinking during the Renaissance. Ptolemy was probably the earliest real counterpart of the modern-day cartographer. Rather than surveying in the field he gathered his materials from divers sources and leaned heavily on the excellent library facilities of Alexandria. In general, he did what most modern cartographers do. Ptolemy was a *compiler* of small-scale maps of large areas, and he left to the *surveyor* the job of gathering the data for large-scale maps of small areas.

After the enlightened period which cul-

minated with the writings of Ptolemy, cartography, along with other scientific and intellectual matters, entered the period called the Dark Ages and suffered a steady decline. For a time the practicality of the Romans showed in administrative types of maps; but concern with the theory and practice of cartography all but died out. Objective thinking about faraway places was replaced by fancy and whimsey. Maps of the world were produced; but, whereas during the Greek period these had been based upon observation and reason, they now came to be but media for preserving the results of fanciful speculation, such as the writings of Solinus, and literal interpretations of Biblical references. Rectangular maps of the

world were made, probably based upon the "four corners of the earth"; but even more common were circular maps (also probably because of a Biblical reference) with Jerusalem at the center. These maps reflected the threefold division of the earth among Shem, Ham, and Japheth, the sons of Noah. They are called *T in O* maps, for they were designed with the Mediterranean the upright part of the *T,* the Don and Nile rivers the crosspieces, and the whole inside a circular ocean (see Fig. 1.3). The area least known was the Far East. This area, the most distant, was placed in the upper portion so that the map had the orient at the top. On these maps were placed mythical places, beasts, and dangers such as the kingdom of the legendary Gog and Magog, who were nonbelieving menaces to the Christian world. This kind of cartography hung on for a long time, and some of the later maps which follow this general pattern are very detailed and ornate. One of them is the map from the Hereford cathedral in England (see Fig. 1.4).

There was, however, one bright cartographic light in the comparative darkness of the period, viz., the sailing charts prepared to accompany the sailing directions, or *peripli,* which apparently existed in considerable numbers. These charts, called *portolani,* or harborfinding charts, were the products of the experience of a large amount of navigation and coastwise sailing in the Mediterranean and adjacent areas (see Fig. 1.5). They were remarkably accurate in their outlines and shapes of the bounding coasts of the seas, but unfortunately their accuracy did not seem to penetrate to maps of the land until toward the end of the Dark Ages. Although many of them must have been made, none earlier than the fourteenth century has survived. Undoubtedly they were jealously guarded by their owners, which may account for their rarity.

The first few centuries of the second millenium A.D. saw a change taking place in intellectual standards which was, of course, reflected in the cartography. The transformation began slowly; but the Crusades, the travels of merchants like the Polos, and the generally increased movement of peoples and goods began to push aside the fancy and superstition of the Dark Ages.

With the discovery and distribution of Ptolemy's writings and maps in the fifteenth century, after lying dormant for a thousand years, a new interest in cartography developed and the Dark Ages came to an end.

The Age of Discovery, the monumental achievements of Columbus, Magellan, and others, kindled such an interest in the rapidly expanding world that map publishing soon became a lucrative calling, and by the sixteenth century the profession was generally in good standing and well supported, albeit its products were still far from being first-class examples of objective scientific thought. One of the circumstances that contributed greatly to the rapid advance of cartography was the invention in Europe of printing and engraving, which made possible the reproduction of maps in numerous copies. Pre-

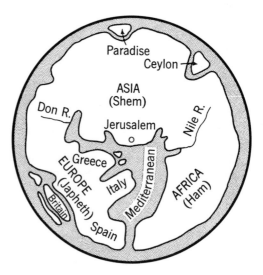

FIGURE 1.3. The layout of the *T in O* maps. Jerusalem was usually located at the center and Paradise in the top central section.

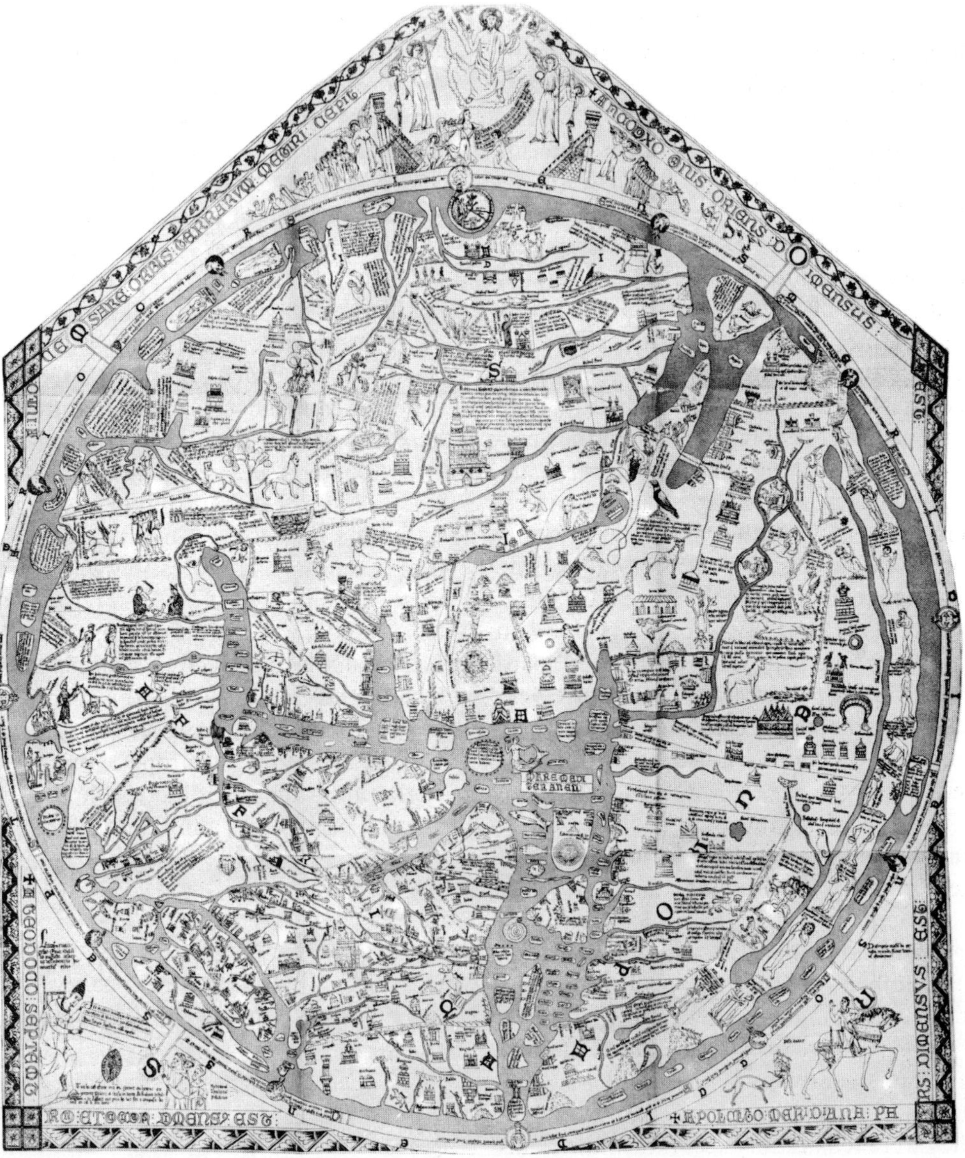

FIGURE 1.4. The Hereford world map. This map made in the thirteenth century illustrates the degree to which cartography had degenerated from the time of Ptolemy, a thousand years earlier. The map is oriented with east at the top and Jerusalem at the center. (From the Library of Congress collection.)

viously, each map had had to be laboriously hand drawn. Great map-publishing houses such as Mercator, Blaeu, Hondius, and others in Holland and France rose and flourished.

Their maps were still little more than reference maps containing hardly anything other than coastlines, rivers, cities, and occasional crude indications of mountains. Fancy and intricate craftsmanship was pop-

ular, and the maps were richly embellished with scrolls, compass roses, and drawings of men, animals, and ships. Except for religious and some navigational data, the mapping of any geographic information beyond what we call today base data was unknown. Accurate positioning of places and the mapping of other kinds of distributions had to wait for more accurate methods of survey and the internal surveys based upon them, especially for the inquiring minds who would want such maps.

1.3   THE EARLY MODERN PERIOD OF CARTOGRAPHY

The dawning of the seventeenth century saw the beginnings of a new and fresh atti-

tude among all thinkers and investigators, including the cartographers. For the first time since the ending of the Greek era, accuracy and the scientific method became fashionable. This attitude, replacing the dogmatic and unscientific outlook which was more or less dominant during the long Dark Ages, made itself evident in a number of ways in cartography.

In the second half of the seventeenth century the French Academy was founded and it included the growing science of cartography among its important functions. Precise navigation was becoming a serious problem and its solution depended upon an accurate determination of the size and shape of the earth and upon the development of a method for determining the

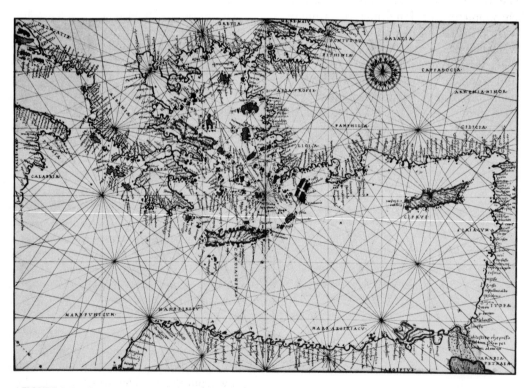

FIGURE 1.5. One of the later harbor-finding charts or *portolani.* **Note the detail and relative accuracy of the delineation of the coasts. From Plate 12 of the manuscript atlas prepared by Battista Agnese of Venice about 1543, now in the Library of Congress. The maps are drawn on vellum and are decorated in colors and gold. (From the Library of Congress collection.)**

longitude. The necessity for increased mobility in military actions also made desirable the development of land survey methods.

The French Academy set to work and measured the arc along a meridian, and, by triangulation, it began to position accurately the outlines of France (see Fig. 1.6). Because of differences noted in the lengths of degrees along the meridian the question arose as to the precise shape of the earth, and during the first half of the eighteenth century expeditions were sent to Peru and Lapland to measure other arcs along meridians. Their determinations settled once and for all that the polar radius was shorter than an equatorial radius. The French initiated a detailed topographic survey of their country at a scale approximately 1¼ miles to the inch and almost completed it prior to the end of the eighteenth century. Harrison's chronometer for longitude determination was perfected in England in 1765; and there were many other evidences of curiosity about the earth. But perhaps the most notable and significant cartographic trend was the realization by many that their fund of knowledge about the land behind the coastlines was quite erroneous. Even the administrators and rulers of countries, particularly in Europe, became aware that it was impossible to govern (or fight wars) without adequate maps of the land.

This led to the establishment of the other great national topographic surveys of Europe, such as that of England in 1791, and the relatively rapid production thereafter for the first time of the topographic kind of map. The problem of representing landforms arose, and almost as quickly devices like the hachure and contour were developed. By the last half of the nineteenth century a large portion of Europe had been covered by topographic maps. These maps were expensive to make, however, and did not have a wide distribution. But they were the foundation upon which all future cartography of the land was to be based.

Of unusual significance to cartography was the establishment of the metric system at the beginning of the nineteenth century. Before that time the scale, or relation of map distance to earth distance, was always expressed in local units of measure such as English yards or miles, Russian versts, or French toises. The relationship of one national unit to another was not precisely known and it was therefore difficult to convert one map to the scale of another. With the definition of the meter as one ten-millionth part of the arc distance from the equator to the pole, as then calculated, an international unit of measure was available. Since then scales of maps have been expressed as fractions or proportions; thus conversions are easy to make since such a proportion is independent of any one kind of unit.

One would expect that as topographic maps became available compilations of smaller-scale maps of many kinds would grow from them. This was the case. Several factors influenced the growth of the compiled map during the nineteenth century. In addition to those mentioned, a new reproduction process, lithography, was developed.

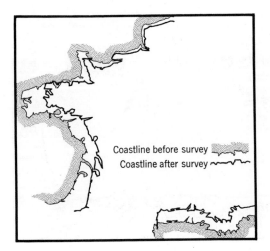

Coastline before survey

Coastline after survey

FIGURE 1.6. The outlines of France before and after the first accurate triangulation (essentially completed by 1740). Similar corrections of other areas could be made after they were accurately triangulated.

It made possible for the first time the relatively easy and inexpensive duplication of drawings. Far more important, generally, than any single technical advance, however, was the branching out of science into a number of separate fields, in contrast to its previous state which was a kind of all-inclusive complex of physical science, philosophy, and general geography. To be sure, the more exact studies such as physics, chemistry, mathematics, and astronomy had progressed far; but earth and life scientists who were concerned with certain classes of earth distributions, as the geologist, meteorologist, and biologist, as well as the host of investigators whom we now call by the general term "social scientist," were just getting under way. The taking of censuses was generally initiated during the early part of the nineteenth century, and this too had a significant effect upon small-scale mapping. Most of the rapidly growing earth, life, and behavioral scientists needed maps; and in general their needs were for the smaller-scale maps, the compiled maps, of the land areas.

By the beginning of the twentieth century this search for knowledge about the earth had led to remarkable strides in cartography. Many investigations had been made into projection problems; the colored lithographic map was fairly common; a serious proposal to map the earth at the comparatively large scale of 1:1,000,000 had been made, and, of particular importance, some great map-publishing houses such as Bartholomew in Great Britain and Justus Perthes in Germany had come into being. The discipline most concerned with the description and analysis of spatial distributions, geography, was beginning to grow rapidly. The way was open for the small-scale, compiled map for use as an investigative and teaching tool.

1.4   TWENTIETH CENTURY CARTOGRAPHY

During the past fifty years or so, cartography and maps have advanced more technically and have become more widely used than at any other period. It is probably correct to say that the number of maps made in the last half century is greater than the production during all previous time, even if we do not count the millions made for military purposes. Almost everyone in the United States has handled numerous maps; maps are frequently in the newspapers; atlases have enjoyed a wide sale; and a comforting proportion of the population now knows the meaning of the words "cartography" and "cartographic." The profession is again attaining a position comparable to that which it held during the period of Flemish and French dominance in the sixteenth and seventeenth centuries. Its position is on somewhat sounder ground now for it has a more universal appeal.

Several factors have combined to promote this phenomenal growth. One of the most important is the fact that two world wars have occurred. Both wars have required vast numbers of maps for military purposes. Particularly, the Second World War with its requirements of rapid movement and air activity made necessary literally millions of maps. Wartime travels and military activities all over the globe created a demand for information from the general public which was supplied by a flood of small atlases, separate maps, and newspaper and magazine maps. War clearly has been a great influence in the course of cartographic history, and the Second World War was probably the most influential. Since 1940 several maps of the entire world have been made at a scale of 16 miles to 1 inch. The far-flung theaters of activity, new routes, new relationships, and the necessity for world-wide understanding created feverish activity in all phases of cartography.

That so much mapping activity was actually possible was the result of a number of factors that entered the cartographic scene early in the present century or late in the last.

Although lithography was much cheaper and easier than engraving as a process for reproducing maps, it was still highly tech-

nical and required considerable skill. Consequently, the invention of photography and its union with the lithographic process late in the nineteenth century provided at last an easy and relatively inexpensive means of reproducing an original drawing on almost any substance. From then on advances in the photolithographic and photoengraving fields have been rapid and continuous. Today, although costs are considerable, the high-speed, multicolor presses are capable of handling almost any kind of cartographic problem. Consequently, reproduction is no longer the fundamental problem to the cartographer that it once was.

Of equal significance to modern cartography is the development of the airplane. It has operated as a catalyst in bringing about the demand for more mapping, and at the same time the airplane has made it possible. The need for smaller-scale coverage of larger areas, such as the aeronautical chart, promoted larger-scale mapping of the unknown areas. Furthermore the earth seen from the vantage point of an airplane in flight is somewhat like a map, and those who fly above the earth develop an interest in maps.

The quantity of maps and mapping and the diversity of cartographic subject matter are indeed staggering. As society becomes even more complicated, we can expect that the demand in future years will increase. Certainly, there are numerous subjects and areas of which we do not have adequate or, in many cases, any maps. The new processes and techniques of making maps, together with the wealth of compilation material from air photography, census activity, and other outgrowths of modern organized society, make the field of cartography a broad and always interesting endeavor.

1.5 PRESENT DIVISIONS OF CARTOGRAPHY

As must be apparent from the preceding, cartography has in recent years developed rapidly and has branched out, as it were,

into a number of somewhat separate kinds of activity. It is a perfectly natural indication of growth, for as each science or art has developed it has separated into various specialized divisions.

The entire field of map making is usually thought of as consisting of two distinct phases. The first is concerned with the detailed large-scale topographic mapping of the land or charting of the sea. The remaining large proportion of cartographic activity is less clearly defined, being usually thought of merely as smaller-scale, special cartography, or simply as *not* the first mentioned. Within each of these two broad categories there is also considerable specialization such as may occur among the survey, drafting, and reproduction phases of making a topographic map. All divisions and activities shade one into another, and it is to be expected that sharp compartmentalization rarely occurs.

Notwithstanding the obvious overlapping there is no doubt that large numbers of cartographers are concerned with smaller-scale map making and are generally quite separate from those who do survey, topographic mapping, and nautical charting. Although not strictly exclusive, the one group makes maps from field or air survey and is concerned with such things as the shape of the earth, height of sea level, land elevations, and exact and detailed locational information. Generally speaking, this group, which includes the great national survey organizations, national land offices, and most military mapping organizations, makes the basic maps from which the other group starts.

The second category of cartographers does not usually make maps from surveys but, using the detailed maps, compiles from them the basic data required and then proceeds to add relationships, generalizations, and a host of other kinds of material. To this group belong the geographers, historians, economists, and many others of the social and physical sciences who are seeking to understand and interpret the social and

physical complex on the earth's surface. The subject matter and the base material are unlimited. The climatic map, the synoptic chart, the agricultural map, the traffic-flow map, the political map, and many others are all products that belong to this second group.

It should not be inferred that the practical considerations that usually separate the cartographers concerned with survey from those concerned with compilation necessarily create a well-defined void between the two groups. Quite the contrary is the case. For example, the fundamental problems of each group are conceptually similar. The basic concepts upon which the delineation of landforms by contours depends are the same as those upon which the delineation of an abstract statistical surface by isopleths depends. A great many of the principles upon which cartographic techniques are based are equally applicable in either division of the field. Rather the major distinction is based upon the methods of acquiring the data to be mapped; these are commonly different. On the other hand, the *cartography*, that is, the conception, the designing, and the execution of the map, as distinct from the gathering of the data, is fundamentally the same in both divisions.

1.6 THE MAP DATA

As has been suggested, almost any kind of information is mappable. From this array of possibilities it may be questioned whether any valid generalization can be made concerning the kinds of information with which a cartographer deals. Although there are no limits to the possibilities, in practice the map maker finds that the entire gamut is rarely approached and that most of his concern is with recurring kinds of information.

By its very nature any map is the presentation of spatial relationships. Therefore the cartographer's first problem is to transform the surface of the sphere which curves away in every direction from every point (called the allside curved surface) into a surface that does not curve in any direction at any point (a plane). Such a radical transformation introduces some unavoidable changes in the directions, distances, areas, and shapes from the way they appear on the spherical surface. A system of transformation from the spherical to the plane surface is called a projection, and the choice, utilization, and construction of map projections is of perennial concern to the cartographer. Properly approached, the study of projections becomes a fascinating endeavor, for it involves in a sense the weighing and balancing of the assets and liabilities of a surprisingly large number of possibilities. The theoretical and actual derivation of many systems of projection are undertakings that require considerable mathematical competence, as would be expected. Their utilization and very often their construction require, however, little more than arithmetic, some very elementary geometry, and, most necessary, some clear thinking.

Of equally universal concern is what is usually called "base data." This ordinarily consists of coastlines, rivers, boundaries, and occasionally settlements, roads, or other outstanding features. On this base are plotted the materials that prompted the making of the map. Of course, some small-scale maps such as general atlas maps are primarily detailed base or reference maps only and consequently they seldom emphasize or portray any special information. The base data serve the very important function of providing orientation and background for the other information being presented. It is useless to provide considerable detail in the mapping of a distribution, such as vegetation, if the reader has no base data with which to correlate it visually. The base information, of course, varies from one map to the next and must be selected especially for the purpose at hand. This selection, together with the compilation and representation of the particular base infor-

mation desired, constitutes the second major portion of the cartographer's concern with map data.

The third kind of map material with which the cartographer works is that which prompted the making of the map. As noted earlier, it can consist of almost anything from election returns to soil constituents. Upon a clear understanding of its significance and of the possible inferences that may be derived from the readers' viewing it depend the selection and employment of the base materials and the projection. Usually, substantive material may be modified or presented in numerous ways. Only the cartographer who is familiar with his subject matter, and who at the same time allows his imagination to roam widely, will be able to determine the most desirable form and manner by which to serve this, the main, course.

1.7 THE TECHNIQUES OF CARTOGRAPHY

The means whereby the map data are graphically portrayed, or, in other words, the techniques and media of representation, make a considerable list. In the early days of cartography there was little choice of ways and means of presenting data or of the media with which to work. The methods of producing inks and colors and the techniques of draftsmanship and map printing were known only to a few, and they were sufficiently difficult so that great skill was necessary to produce an acceptable map. Today the cartographer is fortunate indeed, for, as in most other mechanical and technical fields, great advances have been made toward the perfection of devices, drawing media, and other aids to map making. In addition drafting has become a kind of standard technique in a number of activities, and manual skill in drawing is widespread.

The actual drawing is only a portion of the technical effort that goes into the making of a map. That part of the effort might be referred to as the mechanical phase of the technique. Considerably more important is the skill with which the cartographer (1) plans the entire map-making process from the beginning through reproduction (see Article 14.2), (2) devises ways and means of organizing the data and of fitting the data to the media, and (3) the general manipulation of the various substantive elements of the map in order to have the final result equal the expectations. Unfortunately, these two aspects are often confused to the end that we mistakenly assume that a "nicely drawn" map is a good map. Likewise, a skillfully planned map may be depreciated because of poor drafting. Both good planning and good execution are, of course, indispensable to excellent cartography, but they are quite different in regard to the training and skills required.

Drafting is an honorable calling, and a good, versatile cartographic draftsman is rare enough to command great respect. He is fully familiar with all the tools and with the use of the various media such as lettering, screens, and different kinds of papers. He is a good freehand letterer and is capable of using all the various pens, brushes, inks, and paints. There is no other trade quite comparable to that of cartographic drafting. The judgment and skills required make it always interesting, and there is considerable creative pleasure in completing a well-drawn map. On the other hand, the act of drafting a map is no more cartography than typing is authorship. The analogy is not strictly correct, for the draftsman, if good, is usually given some latitude in the execution of the cartographer's desires.

It is important to understand the above relation between drafting and cartography. There has been and still is a tendency to think of the two as synonymous. Many draftsmen think of themselves as cartographers, and many cartographers, who are themselves good draftsmen, feel that drafting ability is indispensable to the cartographer. There is no question that drafting is a desirable and useful ability, but it is by

no means indispensable. A lack of manual skill need deter no one from entering the field of cartography, and particularly it should not deter the geographer and other physical and social scientists from learning the principles of graphic expression. Since learning by doing is one of the better ways of gaining a well-founded understanding of any endeavor it is to be expected that one who would learn cartography should also learn the elements of drafting. If he finds that he is deficient in the manual skills he should in no way be discouraged. Trying the techniques and studying their difficulties and possibilities will better prepare him to direct a more skillful draftsman.

There are some drafting procedures that are better done by the cartographer if he is to work with certain kinds of maps. For example, the drawing of terrain as in a physiographic diagram must, except in unusual cases, be done by the cartographer who is planning and executing as he proceeds. The dotting of a dot map, which requires relatively little drafting skill but considerable geographic understanding, cannot be done by directing a draftsman, except in extraordinary circumstances. Similarly, the brushing on of colors in gradation with a wet brush or an airbrush must be done by the cartographer in most circumstances, not by the draftsman.

Probably as valid a reason as any for the would-be cartographer to learn at least the elements of drafting is that, in many cases, the research investigator must lay out preliminary plans for maps, and his job is much easier if he knows the limitations and possibilities of the drafting technique. Also, frequently the teacher or researcher must do his own elementary map drawing for slides and professional papers because a competent draftsman is either unavailable or too expensive. In any case, the manual skills required for simple drafting are capable of attainment by almost everyone. The rare person who cannot learn to use the ruling pen, triangle, and T-square need not be dis-

couraged, for the art and science of cartography are based primarily on intellectual and visual skills, not on manual skills.

1.8 THE SCIENCE OF CARTOGRAPHY

The skills or techniques of the cartographer are based upon the findings of many scientists. These skills generally fall into two categories, intellectual or visual, depending upon whether their main function is to stimulate the reason or the visual sense of the map reader.

In the first category we find such cartographic activities as generalization or small-scale simplification. This is one of the most difficult of the cartographer's tasks, for, as was pointed out by one of the great German cartographers, "only a master of the subject can generalize well." It is one of the ways wherein cartography differs from drafting. If we are to draw a small-scale coastline we must know the characteristics of that coastline or at least the characteristics of that type of coastline. Similarly, if we are to generalize a river we must know whether it is a dry-land or a humid-land stream, something of its meanderings, its volume, and other important factors which might make it distinctive from or in character with others of its nature. The selection of the important and the subordination or elimination of the nonessential factors of the map data require that the map maker be well trained in each of the fields in which he essays to prepare maps. He must apply logic in his approach to projections, generalizations, line characterizations, and so on, and in this respect he is a kind of practical scientist much like an engineer. He must study the characteristics of his building materials and know the ways and means of fitting them together so that the end product will convey the correct intellectual meaning to the reader.

Of equal, and sometimes greater, importance are the visual relationships inherent in this form of expression. People, or map readers, think and react in certain ways to

visual stimuli. With knowledge of the laws governing these reactions the cartographer can design his product to fit these habits. A great many principles of visual design have been established in recent years, and the cartographer cannot afford to ignore these findings. The selection of dot size for representing statistics and the colors and tones to be used in representing gradations of amount are examples of questions to be answered by reference to the principles of visibility as applied to symbols. They constitute problems of visual logic.

The cartographer is scientific in other ways. One of the largest categories of information with which he works is that contained in other maps, and since he can hardly have first-hand familiarity with all places in the world he must be able to evaluate his source materials. This means that he must be familiar with the state of topographic mapping and its geodetic foundations. To supplement his map information he needs to be able to evaluate and rectify census data, air photographs, documentary materials, and a host of other kinds of sources.

Cartography is neither an experimental science in the sense that chemistry or physics is nor is it searching for truth in the manner of the social sciences. Nevertheless, it employs the scientific method in the form of reason and logic in constructing its products. Its principles are derived through the analysis of scientific data. It has its foundations in the sciences of geodesy, geography, and psychology. In the sense that it is based on sound principles and seeks to accomplish its ends by way of intellectual and visual logic it is scientific in nature.

1.9 THE PRINCIPLES OF CARTOGRAPHY

Any scientific activity must be founded on principles of procedure derived from fundamental concepts and laws. These laws may be either more precisely demonstrable, as in physics, or less precisely based on empir-

ical data and inductive reasoning. The principles of cartography are built from both kinds of concepts.

On the one hand there have been many investigations by psychologists and others in the field of optics. We know, for example, what colors are seen first, how many shades of gray can be easily detected, what sizes of lettering are legible, and many other precise reactions of the eye to visual stimuli. Since a map is, quite obviously, a visual stimulus intended to portray an intellectual thought it is, of course, necessary to base the selection and utilization of the lines, colors, letters, and other map parts on principles derived from these precise determinations.

On the other hand, investigators of the intellectual responses to visual stimuli provide us with a more or less precise understanding of how peoples' minds react to visual stimuli. Through experiment, study of fundamental design, and recording of reactions to such ubiquitous present-day phenomena as advertising, these researchers have been able to compile a number of principles of design. For example, it is known what kind of rectangle is best, what kinds of layout or lettering can be employed (or avoided) in order to suggest (or not to suggest) such intangibles as stability, power, movement, and so on. There are widespread preferences as to colors, shapes, and designs that must be utilized to make a more effective presentation. The number of cartographic principles based on research and analysis in optics and psychology is surprising.

In addition to the well-founded physical and intellectual principles there are a great many conventions and traditions in cartography which have almost the stature of principles. Cartography is an ancient art and science, and it is to be expected that over the centuries these traditional procedures would become almost standard practice. Many of them have been changed and modified by long-continued use until they have, through the process of trial and error,

become "good practice." Many forms of symbolism such as that for political boundaries and cities, or such practices as north orientation, carry as much authority, in many circumstances, as do more objectively based principles. However, one would expect in such a conventionalized profession as cartography that many conventions, especially those of recent vintage, are hardly of sound foundation. These must be carefully analyzed before being used in the light of known principles in order that the purposes of presentation will not be violated by the methods employed. A good example of this kind of "new" convention is the use of the color progression of the spectrum for altitude tints on colored relief maps. Originally, some fifty or seventy-five years ago it was thought logical to parallel increasing altitude above sea level with increasing wave length of light. But more recent researches have shown that elements other than wavelength are of more significance in vision. Consequently, the convention does not fit the known principles. There are other examples of modern or new conventions that have developed in the recent history of cartography but which have not had the benefit of the judgment of time.

In general, however, the basic principles of optics and vision as applied to cartography are known, and the cartographer, with these guides, may proceed without much doubt.

1.10 ART IN CARTOGRAPHY

The question is frequently raised as to whether cartography is a legitimate branch of art and what function an artistic talent plays in the making of a map. Before the last century the question never arose, for cartography was very definitely an art. This is evident when one views the products of the earlier cartographers who embellished their maps with all sorts of imaginative things, together with fancy scroll work, or-nate lettering, and intricate compass roses. Special coloring methods and ingredients were carefully guarded secrets. Even as late as a hundred years ago the coloring of maps in one of Germany's greatest map houses was done by the society ladies of the town. Throughout the history of cartography, great emphasis has been laid on fine pen and brush skill, and the aim has been to make something good to look at and perhaps even to hang on a wall as a decoration.

Today a great many people still think of cartography as being an artistic calling, and it is likely that a considerable number of otherwise intelligent students shy away from it for fear they are "not artistic." Good judgment based on principles is the major requirement of design in cartography; and such judgment may be easily acquired by training.

Most maps are functional in that they are designed, like a bridge or a house, for a purpose. Their primary purpose is to "get across" a concept or relationship; it is not to serve as adornment for an office wall. As a matter of fact, if a map is made too much of a work of art, it is very likely that the viewer will be stimulated first by its beauty and will fail to see the concept. Probably one of the cartographer's major concerns is to refrain from making the map ugly, and in this respect he is definitely an artist, albeit in a somewhat negative sense.

Although the question of whether cartography is an art will always be debated with vigor, there is no question that it is a creative kind of endeavor which repays the effort by the satisfaction that comes from producing something that has never been done before. Every map is a different problem requiring a new solution in the field of design. It requires a good command of the principles of presentation to build a map anew each time. In this it is like creative writing that requires new combinations of technique and media. In this respect cartography is certainly a creative art.

The Earth and the System of Coordinates

2.1 THE SHAPE OF THE EARTH

The earth is a complex geometric figure. The shape of this massive, plastic planet, spinning on its axis through space, is the result of the interaction of several internal and external forces, such as gravity, the centrifugal force of rotation, and variations in the density of its rock constituents. The interaction of tectonic and gradational forces has produced other irregularities such as mountains, plains, and ocean basins. This class of irregularities, noticeable to the human eye, is relatively so small, however, that they are significant only to the cartographic problem of the delineation of the terrain. For example, on a globe with a diameter of 1 foot, mountains and ocean basins would scarcely be noticeable; the maximum deviations from sea level would be less than $\frac{1}{100}$ of an inch.

Because most maps are representations of the earth on a plane, it is necessary to transfer systematically the geometric relations from the one shape to the other. If this is to be done accurately it is apparent that the characteristics of both shapes must be known. Furthermore, in order for the transformation to be done in a relatively systematic fashion it is convenient to assume the earth shape as a simple solid form. The procedures followed then are: (1) the de-termination of the regular geometric shape which most closely approximates the actual form of the earth, (2) the transfer of the earth positions to that form, and (3) the transformation of that shape to a plane. The determination of the precise figure of the earth is part of the responsibility of the science of geodesy.

Man's first ideas of the earth around him included little beyond that which he could see, since his view was limited to the horizon; consequently the surface appeared flat. The earliest world maps apparently represented it so, and the idea of sphericity was not generated until the philosophers of the pre-Christian, Greek era applied reason to the problem. Well before the time of Claudius Ptolemy (second century A.D.) the earth was recognized as being a sphere. Although the idea of sphericity did not altogether die out during the Dark Ages, it languished, to say the least, and the notion of a flat surface again prevailed. With the reissuance of Ptolemy's *Geographia* and the subsequent Age of Discovery following the fifteenth century the representation of the earth reverted to the sphere. In the late seventeenth century the idea of oblateness because of rotation was advanced by Newton and eagerly pursued. During the last century or so several determinations of the amount of bulging and flattening have been

made, and there are several oblate spheroids recognized.

The oblateness, the largest of the earth's deformations from a true sphere, must occasionally be acknowledged, even in small-scale mapping. On account of its spinning on an axis the earth ball is bulged somewhat in the area midway between the poles and consequently flattened a bit in the polar regions. The actual amount of flattening is of the order of some 13.5 miles difference between the polar and equatorial radii, the equatorial, of course, being the larger.

Because of the bulging and flattening, a line extending around the earth that passes through the poles will not be a circle but will be slightly oval in shape. The flatter portion is in the polar regions and the more rapid curvature is in the equatorial areas. Since a considerable amount of navigation is based upon observations aimed at finding the angle between some celestial body and the horizon plane (or a perpendicular to it—the vertical) at a point, it is apparent that complications result from this departure from a true sphere. Consequently, whenever maps are being prepared for navigation or for plotting exact courses and distances from one place to another, it is necessary to take the oblateness into account. In most cases of very small-scale mapping it may safely be ignored.

As a result of ground measurements made for topographic mapping and a comparison of these with measurements resulting from astronomic observations, it is clear that the generally oblate spheroidal form is locally deformed because of variations in the character of the materials of which the earth is composed. The accumulation of data which will finally reveal the world-wide nature of these irregularities of the spheroid is underway, and in the forseeable future the precise shape of the earth, called the *geoid*, will be known. When this information is available, then the size and shape of the simple spheroid which most closely approximates it will be known.

2.2   THE SIZE OF THE EARTH

Since ancient times man has been attempting to arrive at exact measurements of the planet on which he lives. Well before the beginning of the Christian era several calculations of the size of the earth were made that apparently came quite close to the figures we now accept, but their closeness was partly the result of fortunate compensation of errors rather than precision. These early estimates were reported by others and recorded by Ptolemy, who, recognizing the observational errors, accepted "corrected" values which reduced the earth's circumference by nearly a fourth. Unfortunately, or fortunately, depending upon one's viewpoint, Ptolemy's convictions were generally accepted. If Columbus had known the true size of the earth he probably would not have dared set sail to find the orient by going west. At any rate, there was apparently no thought that there was a land mass intervening between western Europe and Asia. Consequently one may say that because of Ptolemy's acceptance in the second century A.D. of the reduced value, the native of America is called an Indian instead of an American, as he should be!

In recent times the dimensions of the earth have been calculated with relatively great precision. International standardization has been proposed but is not completely accepted as yet. The values below in Table 2.1 are those generally used in the United States and are those of the Clarke spheroid of 1866:

TABLE 2.1
DIMENSIONS OF THE EARTH

Equatorial radius	6 378 206.4 meters	3 963.0 statute miles
Polar semi-axis	6 356 583.8 meters	3 949.5 statute miles
Radius of sphere of equal area	6 370 997.2 meters	3 958.5 statute miles
Area of earth (approx.)	510 900 000 sq km	197 260 000 sq miles
Equatorial circumference	40 075 km	24 899 miles

2.3   THE NECESSITY FOR A COORDINATE SYSTEM

In order to locate points on any surface it is necessary to have concepts and definitions of direction and distance. Primitive man probably developed these concepts in relation to the directions of the rising and setting sun and the time required for travel. All spatial locations are relative, and they must, therefore, be established in relation to some reference or starting point. If such a point is designated, then the location of every other point on the surface can be stated in terms of a defined direction and distance from it.

On a limitless plane surface or on a motionless spherical surface, there is no natural reference point; that is, every point is the same as every other point except for relative location. In mathematics an arbitrary system of location on a plane surface is developed by establishing a "point of origin" at the intersection of two conveniently located perpendicular axes. The plane is then divided into a rectangular grid by adding equally spaced lines parallel to the two axes. Position of any point on the plane with reference to the point of origin is then stated by indicating the perpendicular distance from each axis to the point. In the familiar cartesian system, for example, cross-section paper, the "horizontal" distance is called the *X* value or *abscissa,* and the distance perpendicular to it is called the *Y* value or the *ordinate* (see Fig. 2.1). In order to designate relative position on the surface of the earth a similar, but much older, coordinate system is used; but the earth's surface is an "allside" curved one (that is, it curves away in every direction from every point), and the use of parallel straight lines is impossible. Nevertheless, the two kinds of coordinate grids have much in common. In the earth's spherical coordinate system the grid lines are perpendicular to one another, but in only one set are the lines parallel to one another.

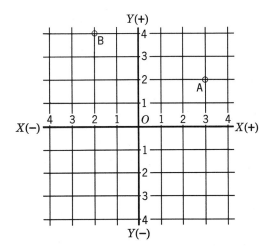

FIGURE 2.1. The cartesian plane coordinate system. The origin is O. *XOX* constitutes the abscissa values and *YOY,* the ordinate values. The position of point A is 3, 2; the position of point B is −2, 4. In the earth's coordinate system Y values are latitude north and south and X values are longitude east and west of the origin (0° latitude and 0° longitude). In designating position on a plane coordinate system the X value is always given first; on the earth's coordinate system latitude is usually given first.

On the earth, however, fortunately two convenient reference points are established by nature; these are the poles or points where the axis of rotation intersects the spherical surface.

In the earth's coordinate system the distances corresponding to the *Y* values in the cartesian system are called latitude and the *X* values, longitude. The arrangement of these two sets of coordinate lines establishes the cardinal directions. Furthermore, on the surface of the sphere one can conveniently measure distance in degrees of arc.

2.4   LATITUDE

As long ago as Greek times a system of locating oneself between the two poles was devised. A line joining the poles on the earth's surface is a half-circle containing

180°. When one stands anywhere on this line, his horizon seems to him to bound a flat (or nearly flat) circular plane. If one can imagine oneself being out in space and looking at this little horizon plane, he will see that the plane is tangent to the circle, and that if he were to slide it north or south along the line it would always be tangent. If the star Polaris is assumed to lie on an extension of the earth's axis, then an observer at the north pole would see Polaris at a 90° angle with his horizon plane. If it were possible for him to see Polaris through the great thickness of the hazy atmosphere were he at the equator, he would find the direction to Polaris to be tangent to his horizon plane, that is, at an angle of 0°. Movement directly toward a pole is accompanied by a change in the angular elevation of celestial bodies in relation to a horizon plane on the earth in a one-to-one relationship; that is, for each degree of arc distance traveled, the elevation above the horizon of a celestial body will change by 1°. Any star or the sun can be observed and the result will be the same.

The foregoing simplifies the problem somewhat, for the earth rotates on its axis and most of the celestial bodies therefore seem also to move while the observer is moving from one place to another. The essential information to correct for apparent celestial motion is, however, readily available. The fundamental fact remains that position north-south can be determined by measuring the angle between the horizon and a celestial body.

To utilize this relationship in a spherical coordinate system was natural, even for the ancients. They imagined a series of circles around the earth parallel to one another (see Fig. 2.2). The one dividing the earth in half, equidistant between the poles, was named, as might be expected, the equator. The series north of the equator was called north latitude. Similarly, the series south from the equator was called south latitude. To determine which circle one was on, and

hence his distance north or south of the equator, required only the observation of the angle between the horizon and some known celestial body such as the sun, Polaris, or some other star.

No change has been made in the system since it was first devised nearly twenty-two hundred years ago.

2.5   THE LENGTH OF A DEGREE OF LATITUDE

In the generally accepted system of measuring angles, a circle contains 360°; a half-circle, 180°. Consequently, there are 180° of latitude from pole to pole. The quadrant of the circle from the equator to each pole is divided into 90°, and the numbering starts from 0° at the equator and goes to 90° at each pole. Latitude is always designated as north or south.

On a perfect sphere each Y value, or degree of latitude, would be the same length, but the earth is not a perfect sphere. Rather, as previously observed, it is slightly bulged at the equator and flattened near the poles. Since, because of the bulging, the surface has more curvature near the equator, one does

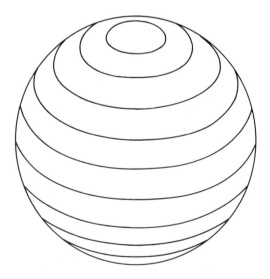

FIGURE 2.2. Parallels on the earth.

not need to travel so far there in order to observe a change of 1° between the horizon and a celestial body. Conversely, one must travel farther near the poles where there is not so much surface curvature. Consequently, degrees of north-south arc on the earth are not quite the same lengths in units of uniform surface distance but vary from a little less than 69 statute miles (68.7) near the equator to a little more than 69 (69.4) near the poles. It is apparent that this difference of less than 1 mile in 69 is of little significance in small-scale maps, but it is important on large maps of small areas. Table 2.2 provides in abbreviated form the lengths of the degrees of the meridian. A more complete table is included in Appendix D.

TABLE 2.2
LENGTHS OF DEGREES OF THE MERIDIAN

Latitude	Statute miles	Kilometers
0–1°	68.703	110.567
9–10°	68.722	110.598
19–20°	68.781	110.692
29–30°	68.873	110.840
39–40°	68.986	111.023
49–50°	69.108	111.220
59–60°	69.224	111.406
69–70°	69.320	111.560
79–80°	69.383	111.661
89–90°	69.407	111.699

For ordinary map use it is well to keep in mind the fundamental fact that the parallels (as the latitude lines are called) are very nearly the same distance apart from pole to pole.

2.6   LONGITUDE

The latitude component of the coordinate system establishes position north or south of the equator, but it cannot, of course, do more than that. If one is, for example, on the 45th parallel north he may in fact be anywhere on that parallel, which is a small circle ex-

tending all the way around the earth halfway between the equator and the north pole. In a sense, the ordinate of the coordinate system is established, but an abscissa is also necessary to establish position along the parallel. This is accomplished by another set of lines, called meridians, arranged at right angles to the parallels (see Fig. 2.3).

All parallels, including the equator, are east-west circles; and since each circle is divided in 360° it is possible to arrange a series of lines through the corresponding divisions of each parallel. Each of these lines (meridians) will then extend due north-south and they will be equally spaced east-west on each parallel. They will intersect the parallels with right angles and thus provide a coordinate system which is like the cartesian system, except that in this case the graticule lies on a spherical surface rather than on a plane surface (see Fig. 2.4).

If one chooses a meridian from which to start numbering he may then establish his position as so many degrees east or west of that line. If he were 180° from it he would be halfway around the earth from the starting line. It has already been observed that it was not difficult for the ancients to deter-

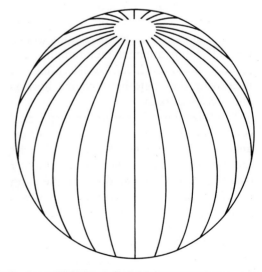

FIGURE 2.3. Meridians on the earth.

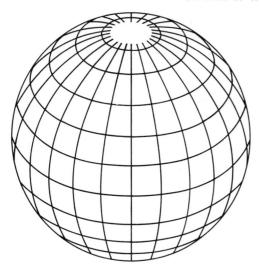

FIGURE 2.4. The earth's spherical coordinate system.

mine latitude. Although longitude is conceptually a simpler part of the coordinate system, the ancients were unable to determine it with any precision. This led to considerable error in east-west location, and it was one of the contributing factors to the glorious error of the fifteenth century that the distance separating Europe from Asia was less than half its actual value.

Angular distance north-south can be determined by observing the difference in the angle of a celestial body with the horizon. Since the earth is a sphere, differences in these angles will also show longitude differences, but only if the observations are taken at the same instant at the two locations. Since the ancients had no way of coordinating such observations, they instead had to calculate east-west distance by converting actual land distance to arc distance. Estimates of land distance were subject to considerable error and were usually overestimated by travelers. The error involved within the small limits of the ancient world was not significant. Later, toward the end of the Dark Ages when the great land distances to the orient were added to what was

previously known and the whole converted to arc distance using a too-small degree (because of the error in the size of the earth assumed and reported by Ptolemy), the arc distance westward remaining between Europe and Asia was far too small.

When the determination of longitude became critical for navigation, all sorts of suggestions were put forward to solve the problem, from the observations of the declination of the compass needle to coordinating observations by a celestial timepiece such as the behavior of the satellites of Jupiter. When the chronometer (a very accurate clock) was developed by Harrison and others in the middle of the eighteenth century, the problem was solved. Because all parallels are concentric circles they all rotate at the same angular speed—360° per day or 15° per hour. By carrying a clock showing the accurate time somewhere else the difference between that time and local suntime in hours, minutes, and seconds can be converted to longitude difference merely by arithmetic. Today this is accomplished not only by using chronometers but also by radio time signals broadcast at regular intervals.

2.7 THE LENGTH OF A DEGREE OF LONGITUDE

The length of the equator is very nearly the same as the length of a meridian circle, but as one goes toward the poles all other parallels become smaller and smaller circles; yet each is divided into 360°. Therefore each east-west degree of longitude becomes shorter with increasing latitude and is finally reduced to nil at the poles. The relationship between the length of a parallel (the circumference of a small circle) and the circumference of the earth (the equator or a meridian circle) is the circumference of the earth multiplied by the cosine of the latitude; or stated another way, the length of a degree of longitude = cosine of the latitude × length of a degree of latitude.

A table of cosines (see Appendix B) will show that

$$\cos 0° = 1.00$$
$$\cos 60° = 0.50$$
$$\cos 90° = 0.00$$

Thus at 60° north and south latitude the distance between the meridians is half the distance between the parallels. This relationship is helpful in judging the quality of representation of the earth grid on maps, as we shall see later. Table 2.3 is included here as an illustration of the decreasing length of a degree of longitude from the equator toward the pole. A more complete table is included in Appendix D.

TABLE 2.3
LENGTHS OF DEGREES OF THE PARALLEL

Latitude	Statute miles	Kilometers
0°	69.172	111.321
5°	68.911	110.900
10°	68.129	109.641
15°	66.830	107.553
20°	65.026	104.649
25°	62.729	100.952
30°	59.956	96.448
35°	56.725	91.290
40°	53.063	85.396
45°	48.995	78.849
50°	44.552	71.698
55°	39.766	63.996
60°	34.674	55.802
65°	29.315	47.177
70°	23.729	38.188
75°	17.960	28.903
80°	12.051	19.394
85°	6.049	9.735
90°	0	0

2.8   THE PRIME MERIDIAN

Unlike the parallels, which have different lengths and bear different relationships to the celestial bodies, the meridians are all alike. Consequently, the choice of the one from which to start the numbering has been, as might be expected, a problem of international consequence. Each country, with characteristic national ambition, wished to have 0° longitude within its borders or as the meridian of its capital. For many years each nation published its own maps and charts with longitude reckoned from its own meridian of origin. This, of course, made for much confusion when referring to coordinate positions while using maps of different countries.

During the last century many nations began to accept the meridian of the observatory at Greenwich near London, England, as 0°, and in 1884 it was agreed upon at an international conference. Today this is almost universally accepted as the prime meridian. Since longitude is reckoned as either east or west from Greenwich (to 180°), the prime meridian is somewhat troublesome because it divides both Europe and Africa into east and west longitude. The choice of the meridian of Greenwich as the prime meridian establishes the "point of origin" of the earth's coordinate system in the Gulf of Guinea. The opposite of the prime meridian, the 180° meridian, is more fortunately located, for its position in the Pacific provides a convenient international date line, requiring only a few departures.

2.9   THE GREAT CIRCLE

The shortest distance between two points is a straight line; however, on the earth it is obviously impractical to follow this straight line through the solid portion of the planet. The shortest distance between two points on a sphere is the arc along the surface directly above the straight line. This arc is formed by the intersection of the spherical surface with the plane passing through the two points and the center of the earth. The circle established by the intersection of this plane with the surface, if extended, divides the earth equally into hemispheres and is termed a *great circle*. Each meridian is an

arc of a great circle, and if joined with its opposite (e.g., 0°–180°, 90°E–90°W) it constitutes a great circle. The equator is a great circle, but all other parallels are "small circles" since they do not bisect the earth.

Great circles bear a number of geometrical relationships with the spherical earth that are of considerable significance in cartography and map use:

(1) Any great circle always bisects any other great circle.

(2) An arc of a great circle is the shortest distance between two points on the spherical earth.

(3) The plane in which any great circle lies always bisects the earth and hence always includes the center of the earth.

Because a great circle is the shortest distance between two points on a spherical surface, air and sea travel, insofar as is possible or desirable, moves along such routes. Radio waves and certain other electronic impulses tend to travel along great circles. For this reason many maps must be made on which great circles are shown to best advantage.

2.10 DISTANCE MEASUREMENT

Distances on the earth's surface are always reckoned along arcs of great circles unless otherwise qualified. Because no map, except one on a globe, can represent the distances between all points correctly it is frequently necessary to refer to a globe, to a table of distances, or to calculate the length of the great-circle arc between two places. A piece of string or the edge of a piece of paper can be employed to establish the great circle on a globe. If the scale of the globe is not readily available, the string or paper may be transferred to a meridian and its length in degrees of latitude ascertained. Since all degrees of latitude are nearly equal and approximately 69 miles, the length of the arc in miles can be determined.

The arc distance on the sphere between two points, A and B, the positions of which are known, can be calculated by means of the formula

$$\cos d = (\sin a \sin b) + (\cos a \cos b \cos P)$$

in which

$d =$ arc distance between A and B
$a =$ latitude of A
$b =$ latitude of B
$P =$ degrees of longitude between A and B

Note: If A and B are on opposite sides of the equator, then the product of the sines will be negative. If P is greater than 90°, the product of the cosines will be negative. Solve algebraically.

When d is determined in arc distance, it may be converted to any other convenient unit of measure.

There are, of course, many units of distance measurement used in cartography. For foreign maps not using the English or the metric system it is necessary to refer to glossaries or some other source having the information needed for conversion. The common English and metric units are given here together with some other units occasionally used in cartography.

	Feet	Meters
Statute mile	5 280	1 609.35
Nautical mile (Int.)	6 076.10	1 852.00
Kilometer	3 280.83	1 000.00
Foot	—	0.3048
Meter	3.2808	—

2.11 THE COMPASS ROSE

The points of the compass, collectively called the compass rose, were formerly standard items on most maps, and they were usually embellished and made quite ornate. Today the compass points appear less frequently except that, of course, they are included on all charts for navigational purposes. Nevertheless, the compass points and their relation to the earth grid and to

earth directions are important concepts in cartography.

The familiar compass is well known to everyone. Its cardinal directions at 90° to one another are the result of the geometric relations of the earth grid. Parallels and meridians are perpendicular to one another everywhere on the earth. Meridians establish the north-south direction, and parallels, the east-west; but the meridians converge to a point at each pole, whereas the parallels in each hemisphere simply become smaller and smaller circles until the 90° "parallel" is one point, the pole. Consequently, north, east, south, and west are never the same actual directions at any two points. This does not appear to create much of a problem when we look at a globe map, but if we transfer the parallels and meridians to a plane surface we find that, just as it is impossible for any map to show all the distances correctly, so also is it impossible to duplicate everywhere the orientation of the compass rose as it appears on the globe.

2.12 THE AZIMUTH

As we have seen, the directions on the earth, established by the earth grid, constantly change if one moves across the face of the sphere. Only on a meridian or on the equator does direction remain constant along a great circle; but since arcs of a great circle represent the shortest distances between any two points on that great circle, it is convenient to be able to designate the "direction" the great circle has at any starting point toward a destination. This direction is reckoned by observing the angle the great circle makes with the meridian of the starting point. The angle is described by the number of degrees (0° to 360°), reading clockwise from either north or south.

In these days of radio waves and air transport the direction and route of travel along great circles are of major importance. Hence many maps are constructed so that directional relations are maintained as far as possible.

2.13 THE LOXODROME

A great circle, being the shortest route between points on the sphere, is the most economical route to follow when traveling on the earth. But it is practically impossible to do this, except when travel is along a meridian or the equator. The difficulty arises from the fact that, except for those particular great circles, directions constantly change along all other great-circle routes. This is illustrated in Fig. 2.5. Because a course of travel must be directed in some manner, such as by the compass, it is not only inconvenient but impracticable to try to change course at, so to speak, each step.

The line of constant compass direction is called a loxodrome or rhumb line. Meridians and the equator are loxodromes as well as great circles, but all other lines of constant compass direction are not great circles. As a matter of fact, loxodromes are complicated curves, and if one were to continue along a loxodrome (other than the meridians or the equator), he would spiral toward the pole but in theory never reach it.

In order for ships and aircraft to approximate as closely as possible the route between two points, great-circle movement is directed along a line of constant compass direction, which begins on the great circle and shortly returns to it, then departs and returns as shown in Fig. 2.6. This procedure is similar to following the inside of the circumference of a circle by a series of short straight-line chords. It is not the same, of course, since the great circle is the straight line, if viewed from above as it should be, and the short (rhumb) lines of constant compass direction are curved lines and are actually longer routes.

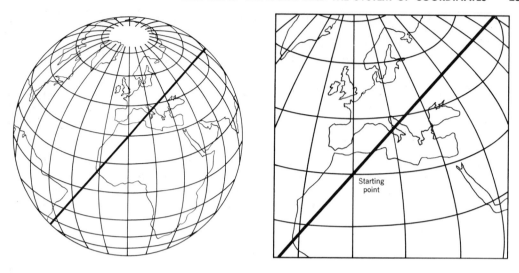

FIGURE 2.5. How azimuth (direction) is read. The drawings show a great circle on the earth grid. The drawing on the right is an enlarged view of the center section of the drawing on the left. The azimuth, from the starting point, of any place along the great circle to the northeast is the angle between the meridian and the great circle, reckoned clockwise from the meridian. Note that the great circle intersects each meridian at a different angle.

2.14   DIRECTION AND ORIENTATION

As may be seen from the preceding, the representation of directions on maps is no simple matter. Consequently, the determination of directions from maps should be done with caution, even from those maps that have been constructed especially for the purpose.

Many conventions exist in cartography, and one of the stronger is that of orientation or the way the directions on the mapped earth segment are arranged on the sheet. Naturally, on a spherical surface there is no up or down along the surface. But a sheet when looked at or held in the hand has a top and a bottom. The top seems to be the direction in which the reader is looking. Originally, when maps were made of the as yet unknown earth it was common for the medieval European cartographer to place the "more important" area at the top or in the center. Because of the significance that paradise and the place of origin of Christianity had in men's minds during that period, it was the practice to place the east or the orient (Paradise) at the top and Jerusalem at the center. Hence the term "orientation." Other orientations were common in other areas.

Several centuries ago the convention of placing north at the top became the practice and has become so strongly established that we think of "up north" and "down south"; upper Michigan and lower California are examples of the unconscious adjustment to this convention. Needless to say, save for the convention, there is no reason why a map cannot be oriented any way the cartographer pleases. Since we think of the top of a sheet as "away" from us it is apparent that orienting the maps in the direction of interest or movement, if any, may well promote the purpose of the map.

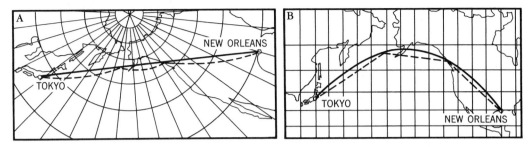

FIGURE 2.6. Two maps showing the same great circles and rhumb lines. Map A is constructed so that the great circle appears as a straight line and the loxodromes as somewhat longer "loops." In reality this is more correct. In map B the representation has been reversed by constructing the map in such a way as to straighten out the loxodromes, which deforms the great circle into a curve.

2.15   AREAS ON THE EARTH

As the spherical earth complicates the determination and representation of distances and directions, the allside curved surface likewise makes difficult the reckoning and representing of areas. To arrive at the area of a segment of the surface of a sphere is relatively easy, but the earth is not a sphere, and for various other reasons that were suggested earlier, the establishment of exact position is difficult. If positions are doubtful, then the shape of the spherical segment is in doubt and thus the area of it is open to question. Besides, most of the areas in which one would be interested, aside from some small land holdings, are extremely irregular, for instance, continents or countries with complex boundaries or coastlines. Consequently, the only way to measure these areas is to map them first and then calculate in some manner the area enclosed. Of course, such a map must be one in which the transformation from the spherical surface to the plane surface has been made so that areas are uniformly represented as to size anywhere within the map.

2.16   THE MAP SCALE

Since maps must necessarily be smaller than the areas mapped, their use requires that the ratio or proportion between comparable measurements be expressed on the map. This is called the map scale and should be the first thing the map user reads. The scale is commonly expressed as a *distance on the map to distance on the earth ratio* with the distance on the map always expressed as unity. The map scale may be expressed in the following ways:

(1) As a simple fraction or ratio. This may be shown either as 1:1,000,000 or $\frac{1}{1,000,000}$. The former is preferred. This means that 1 inch or 1 foot or 1 centimeter on the map represents 1,000,000 inches, feet, or centimeters on the earth's surface. It is usually referred to as the representative fraction, or "RF" for short. The unit of distance on both sides of the ratio must be in the same units.

(2) As a statement of map distance in relation to earth distance. For example, the ratio 1:1,000,000 works out to be approximately 1 inch to about 16 miles. Many map series are commonly referred to by this type of scale, for example, 1-inch or 6-inch maps of the British Ordnance Survey (1 inch to 1 mile, 6 inches to 1 mile).

(3) As a graphic representation or bar scale. This is simply a line on the map which is subdivided to show the length of a unit of earth distance. One end of the bar scale is usually subdivided further in order

that the map reader may measure distances more precisely.

(4) As an area scale instead of a distance scale. When the transformation from the sphere to the plane has been made so that all area proportions on the earth are correctly represented, the stated scale is one in which 1 unit of area (square inches, square centimeters) is proportional to a particular number of the same square units on the earth. This may be expressed, for example, either as $1:1,000,000^2$ or as 1 to the square of 1,000,000. Usually, however, the fact that the number is squared is assumed and not shown.

2.17   DETERMINING THE SCALE OF A MAP

Sometimes maps are made that do not include a scale. This is poor practice, to say the least, but nevertheless it occurs. More often it is necessary to determine the scale for a particular part of the map, for, as was observed previously, the distance scale can never be the same all over a flat map. Determination of the map scale may be accomplished by measuring the map distance between two points that are a known earth distance apart and then computing the scale or making a bar scale. Certain known distances of the earth grid are easy to use, such as the distance between parallels (average of 69 miles) or the distance between meridians (see Table D.1, Appendix D). Care should be exercised that the measurement is taken in the direction the scale is to be used, for frequently the distance scale of the map will not be the same in all directions from a point.

If the area scale is desired, a known area

on the earth (see Table D.3, Appendix D) may be measured on the map with a planimeter and the proportion thus determined. It should be remembered that area scales are conventionally expressed as the square root of the number of units on the right of the ratio. Thus if the measurement shows that 1 square unit on the map represents 25,000,000,000,000 of the same units on the earth it would not be recorded that way, but as $1:5,000,000^2$ or merely by the square root, $1:5,000,000$, which approximates the linear scale.

2.18   TRANSFORMING THE MAP SCALE

Frequently the cartographer is called upon to change the size of a map, that is, to reduce or enlarge it. The mechanical means of accomplishing this are dealt with in a later chapter, but the problem of determining how to change it in terms of scale is similar to the problem of transforming one type of scale to another. If the cartographer can develop a facility with scale transformation, he will experience no difficulty in enlarging or reducing maps.

The essential information necessary for transforming linear scales is that 1 mile (statute) = 63,360 inches. With this information one can change each of the linear scales (RF, graphic, inch to mile) previously described to the others. Examples follow.

If the RF of the map is shown as $1:75,000$

Example 1.   The inch/mile scale will be

(1) 1 inch (map) represents 75,000 inches (earth), and

(2) $\dfrac{75,000}{63,360} = 1.183$; therefore

(3) 1 inch represents 1.183 miles.

Example 2.   To construct the graphic scale a proportion is established as

(1) 1.183 miles/1 inch = 10 miles/x inches; since

(2) $1.183x = 10$, then

(3) $x = 8.45$, and

FIGURE 2.7.   **A graphic or bar scale. They may be made in simple fashion, as above, or they may be made in more complex form such as those shown in Fig. 12.18.**

(4) 8.45 inches represents 10 miles, which may be easily plotted and subdivided.

If the graphic scale shows by measurement that 1 inch represents 35 miles

Example 3. The RF may be determined

(1) 1 inch represents 35 × 63,360 inches, or

(2) 1 inch to 2,217,600 inches, and therefore

(3) RF = 1:2,217,600.

The number of miles to the inch may be read directly from the graphic scale.

If the inch/mile scale is stated as 1 inch to 26 miles the graphic scale may be constructed as in Example 2. The RF can be determined as in Example 3.

The changing of the scale of a map which has an area scale is accomplished by converting the known area scale and the desired area scale to a linear proportion.

Maps have been made at a great variety of scales. The experienced map user learns automatically to translate the representative fraction into common units of measure. Table 2.4 below contains a listing of some of the more common scales:

TABLE 2.4
COMMON MAP SCALES AND THEIR EQUIVALENTS

Map scale	One inch represents	One centimeter represents	One mile is represented by	One kilometer is represented by
1:2,000	56 yards	20 meters	31.68 inches	50 cm
1:5,000	139 yards	50 meters	12.67 inches	20 cm
1:10,000	0.158 mile	0.1 km	6.34 inches	10 cm
1:20,000	0.316 mile	0.2 km	3.17 inches	5 cm
1:24,000	0.379 mile	0.24 km	2.64 inches	4.17 cm
1:25,000	0.395 mile	0.25 km	2.53 inches	4.0 cm
1:31,680	0.500 mile	0.317 km	2.00 inches	3.16 cm
1:50,000	0.789 mile	0.5 km	1.27 inches	2.0 cm
1:62,500	0.986 mile	0.625 km	1.014 inches	1.6 cm
1:63,360	1.00 mile	0.634 km	1.00 inch	1.58 cm
1:75,000	1.18 miles	0.75 km	0.845 inch	1.33 cm
1:80,000	1.26 miles	0.80 km	0.792 inch	1.25 cm
1:100,000	1.58 miles	1.0 km	0.634 inch	1.0 cm
1:125,000	1.97 miles	1.25 km	0.507 inch	8.0 mm
1:250,000	3.95 miles	2.5 km	0.253 inch	4.0 mm
1:500,000	7.89 miles	5.0 km	0.127 inch	2.0 mm
1:1,000,000	15.78 miles	10.0 km	0.063 inch	1.0 mm

Cartographic Drawing and Measuring Techniques

3.1 DRAWING AND MEASURING IN CARTOGRAPHY

A great many individuals work with maps and use them in various ways. Only those who are involved in their preparation are properly called cartographers. This includes several categories: the scientist who in the course of his research finds it necessary to prepare maps as research tools from an analysis of which he derives new knowledge; the writer who employs maps as substitutes for, or as aids to, the presentation of the written word whether it is for textbook, article, atlas, or research findings; the topographic mapper who presents the results of field and photogrammetric surveys; and the cartographic draftsman who more or less independently draws maps for someone else. All these are cartographers in one sense or another and each finds it useful to be familiar with the basic techniques employed in cartography.

It was pointed out previously that practically all the presentational operations involved in map making were together classifiable as cartographic technique. One important portion of that class is composed of the essentially mechanical methods whereby the lines, symbols, letters, and other marks are placed on the drawing surface, that is, the drafting techniques. Essential also are the methods, attendant to the drafting, of deriving many kinds of dimensional elements, such as the ways of determining how large or small to draw something to scale, the methods of subdividing lines into equal segments, or the determination of appropriate lengths along arcs. Some of these methods involve arithmetic, some are accomplished with the aid of simple tools, and some require various kinds of graphic construction. Even the beginning cartographer finds himself confronted early by these kinds of problems.

It was also observed in the introductory chapter that the varieties of types and uses of maps make a long list. Thus, the number of different kinds of technical drawing and measuring operations the cartographer or the cartographic draftsman may ultimately be called upon to perform range from such simple things as drawing straight lines, through somewhat more complicated procedures, such as measuring the area enclosed by an irregular line, to the more advanced techniques, such as applying shading or coloring to a manuscript map for printing by some special process. To encompass all the possible techniques the map maker and user might possibly encounter would require several books of this size; nevertheless, the one who makes maps

FIGURE 3.1. Tools and equipment frequently used by the cartographer and draftsman. (Courtesy of Rand McNally and Company.)

for his own research work, or who draws medium-scale and small-scale maps to present information geographically, or who directs the work of a draftsman, will fre-quently find it useful to be familiar with many of the not-so-specialized techniques. Even these make a long list.

Many map-making establishments sepa-

rate the compilation of maps from the drafting, leaving the latter operation to skillful specialists. In recent years the degree of specialization has increased tremendously. The introduction of plastics and the rapid development of various kinds of drawing, photographic, and printing combination techniques have served to separate the processes of compiling and planning a map from the methods used to produce the lines, letters, colors, shadings, etc., for the final product. This is especially true of large governmental agencies and commercial map houses. The techniques now employed in these places would literally astound a cartographer of even thirty years ago.* Many of these production techniques are only partially applicable to smaller operations where assembly line methods are perhaps not quite so appropriate. The student or earth scientist, who compiles and draws manuscript maps for his own use or for occasional special or scholarly publication, should be familiar with the manual techniques and fundamental methods involved in compilation as well as the basic procedures of map drafting and measurement so that his own compilations will measure up to a reasonable standard. In addition, if he is ever to direct the work of a more skillful draftsman, it is necessary for him to be acquainted with the tools, the media, and their capabilities.

The tools and media with which the draftsman ordinarily works are relatively simple, and they have been designed primarily for the purpose of making it easy to obtain neatness and precision. Very little instruction and skill are necessary to employ them adequately. As is so often the case in matters involving design and execution, the ultimate appearance of a map depends more upon its design than upon its drafting excellence.

* The more ''advanced'' drawing techniques, such as scribing, which are closely allied to, and often are an integral part of, modern map reproduction methods are briefly discussed in Chapter 14.

Like any other operation requiring the coordination of the hand, eye, and brain, the skills of drafting require some practice and patience. The student who approaches drafting with the negative attitude that he "couldn't possibly do that sort of thing" is admonished that he can, presumably, write, walk, eat, throw, button buttons, or perform any number of other operations requiring the same kinds of, and sometimes considerably more, muscular coordination.

Only those who are truly physically handicapped cannot learn to draft.

3.2   DRAWING MATERIALS

The variety of materials, equipment, and instruments the cartographer would sometimes find useful if he had all of them would make a very long list. On the other hand, the vast majority of the drawing operations require only a small number of instruments and a minimum of equipment (See Fig. 3.1). Any student who has any notion of ever finding it useful to prepare even rough maps, charts, or diagrams is well advised to acquire the basic equipment. The capital outlay required for the nonexpendable classes of materials is relatively small because good quality instruments and equipment are available in a wide range of prices. The expendable class of materials such as papers, plastics, inks, pencils, etc., can be purchased as needed.

There are several makers and distributors of drafting equipment, and almost any drafting supply house has a large selection from which to choose. Since first-quality instruments are relatively expensive, the beginner is advised to start with inexpensive tools and make replacements as he becomes acquainted with the desirable qualities.

Drawing instruments and equipment are precision tools made of high-quality materials and it will repay the owner many times over to keep them clean and dry. If instruments are kept loose in a box it is easy for the needle points and sharp edges to be-

come damaged. Ruling pens may be kept sharpened with the aid of a thin triangular whetstone, but broken needle points are difficult to renovate. Clean instruments in good operating order will not make the user a good draftsman, but no draftsman can do a good job with dirty or rusty instruments that are out of adjustment.

3.3   DRAWING EQUIPMENT

Maps and diagrams are usually drawn on drawing boards manufactured especially for the drafting process. They are carefully made of soft wood in such a way that they preserve a flat surface. They are obtainable in a wide range of sizes, but the smallest practicable for general work is 18 × 24 inches. Larger drawing boards are used to form the top of a table which is adjustable for both height and tilt. If one is not able to employ a drawing table of this sort, an acceptable substitute may be improvised by placing a book under the far edge of a smaller drawing board.

Cartographers work with translucent paper or plastics a considerable proportion of the time, and less eyestrain will result if the wood drawing board has a light-colored covering over it so that the contrast is heightened between the board beneath and that which is being drawn on a translucent surface.* The drawing may be affixed to the board with either tape or thumbtacks, but tape is, in general, more satisfactory. Special drafting tape that does not adhere so tightly as cellophane is preferred, for it is not so likely to injure drawing media when it is removed. Thumbtacks leave holes in the board which are occasionally bothersome, and the tack heads prevent the free movement of flat drawing tools. Many of

the drafting operations may be better and more easily performed if the drawing is not fixed to the table but kept loose so that it may be moved about, making it easier to reach the various parts. This is particularly true for the lettering process.

A special kind of table called a tracing or light-table (see Fig. 3.2) is used when tracing is required on a relatively opaque surface such as drawing paper. The same kind of table is used in the printing business and is there called an opaquing table. A light-table has one surface of ground glass illuminated from beneath. They are available from drafting supply houses, or one can be improvised—even a window will do in a pinch.

Adequate lighting of the drawing surface is indispensable to both drafting operations and the maintenance of the vision of the draftsman. Two-bulb fluorescent lamps are preferable to incandescent lights, but more important than the light source is a lamp construction enabling the light to be moved about easily. This makes possible the pre-

FIGURE 3.2. A tracing table with fluorescent illumination. Cool fluorescent illumination is better than incandescent. (Courtesy Hamilton Manufacturing Company.)

---

* Drawing board covers are commercially available which provide a smooth, high-contrast surface, for example, Laminene by Keuffel and Esser Co. Some also have a grid printed on the cover which facilitates layout work.

vention of the shadows of instrument edges in any position from appearing on the drawing surface, a real necessity when plotting positions or drawing precise lines.

A T-square and a variety of triangles and curves are used on the drawing surface. A plain T-square with a fixed head is adequate for all the requirements of most cartographers, although a T-square with an adjustable head would occasionally be helpful. T-squares are made of metal or solid wood with or without a plastic transparent edge. A transparent edge is desirable, however, for it enables the cartographer to see a bit of the drawing beneath the T-square and helps him to start and stop his lines at the correct places. The T-square is moved up or down one side of the drawing board. If perpendiculars to a line drawn along the T-square are required, they should be drawn with the triangle resting against the T-square

rather than by hooking the T-square over the top edge of the drawing board, for the two sides are not usually square.

The curves provide edges against which to rest a pen or pencil when drawing smooth bending lines that are not arcs of circles. Many varieties are available that are based upon curves of differing characteristics such as sines or ellipses. For larger curves, the defining points of which are far apart, a flexible curve or a spline with weights is more satisfactory (see Fig. 3.3).

A useful addition to the drawing edges of the cartographer is a heavy steel straightedge with one beveled edge. As is the case with the spline for curves, the steel straightedge holds its place more readily, and the cartographer has more freedom in drawing long straight lines with it than he has when using the T-square.

There are many other kinds of drawing

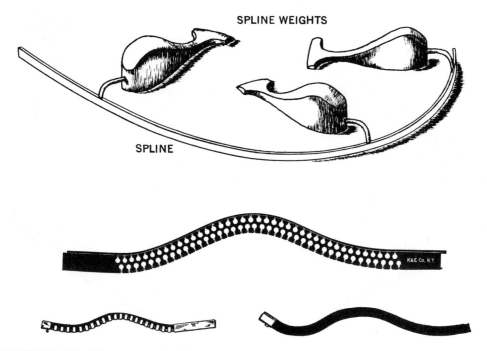

FIGURE 3.3. Flexible curves and a spline with weights. For large curves the spline is most satisfactory because it can be held rigidly in place by the weights, whereas flexible curves have a tendency to creep and must be held in place with one hand. (Courtesy Keuffel and Esser Company.)

equipment that are standard items in drafting rooms, but the student rarely has access to their regular use. For example, one of the most useful is what is called a drafting machine (see Fig. 3.4). This device, which is fixed to the drafting table and swings freely on an arm, is geared to maintain parallel position wherever it may be placed. The head may be rotated according to fixed amounts in degrees, and there are interchangeable drawing edges and scales that may be inserted in the head.

Also of considerable utility, if one is called upon frequently to draft symbols, are punched templates of plastic available at most drafting supply outlets. These have been devised to make available a large number of graded circles, squares, triangles, etc.

All that is necessary is to place a pen of the proper design inside the hole and trace around the edge.

A magnifying glass to assist in detailed work and a reducing glass to help plan for reduction are regularly used.

3.4 DRAWING INSTRUMENTS

Drawing instruments may be obtained either separately or in sets. A drawing set is desirable because it provides a convenient place to keep the instruments in proper storage and is thus an aid toward good care, but a complete set is by no means necessary. One may easily start with the basic instruments and build up his own set. The instruments required by the cartographer fall

FIGURE 3.4. A "Paragon" drafting machine. (Courtesy Keuffel and Esser Company.)

into three classes: ruling pens, compasses, and dividers.

The ruling pen (see Fig. 3.5) is perhaps the most used of the drawing instruments, and the cartographer would be well advised to have a good one and especially to keep it clean and in good order. The closeness of the blades of the ruling pen is adjustable with the small screw on the side so that lines of different thickness may be made with the same pen. The pen is filled by placing ink with a dropper between the adjustable blades. It should be frequently cleaned with a cloth. If ink is kept in the pen too long it will dry a bit, and the same amount will not flow out between the blades; then, uniformity of lines cannot be obtained. Ink is cheap compared to the time required to produce good drawings.

Cleaning the insides of the blades of a ruling pen (or the same kind of pen on an ink compass) is most easily accomplished by covering the thumbnail with the cloth, inserting the nail between the upper position of the blades, and then sliding the blades off the thumbnail. Drawing ink adds nothing to the appearance of a thumbnail, but it does act as a reminder not to overload the ruling pen. Excess ink in the pen can, before cleaning, be allowed to soak into a blotter. Some ruling pens are constructed with a snap assembly which allows the blades to be separated for cleaning and they then can be snapped back in place for further drawing with fresh ink without losing their original adjustment.

A ruling pen with the blade assembly on a swivel (see Fig. 3.5) is useful for drawing smooth curves such as contours. A double-headed swivel called a railroad or road pen is useful for drawing uniform parallel lines. The single- and double-headed swivel pens are handled in the same fashion as the plain ruling pen except that they are ordinarily used freehand, that is, without a drawing edge to guide them.

Dividers, as the name indicates, are used for dividing lines in equal parts and for transferring dimensions from a rule to the drawing paper (see Fig. 3.6). They are adjustable with a needle point on each leg. Proportional dividers (at the right in Fig. 3.6) have two sets of needle points, one at each end. The position of the swivel between them can be adjusted so that whatever the opening between one pair of points, the space between the other pair of points will still remain in a constant ratio with it. They are particularly useful for enlarging or reducing irregular figures with precision.

Compasses are, of course, used for drawing arcs and circles (see Fig. 3.7). There are several kinds for different sizes of circles, but usually only the small and large

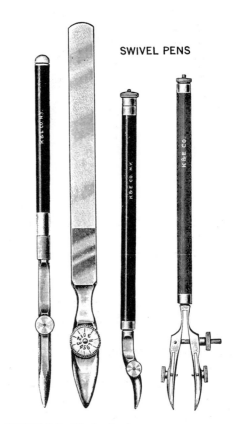

SWIVEL PENS

FIGURE 3.5. Kinds of ruling pens. The plain pen on the left is most frequently used. (Courtesy Keuffel and Esser Company.)

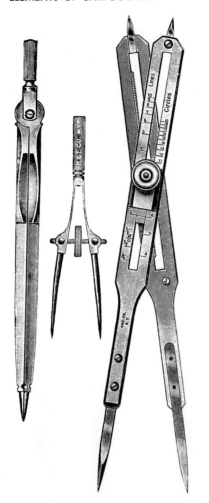

FIGURE 3.6. Kinds of dividers. The one on the right is called a "proportional divider." (Courtesy Keuffel and Esser Company.)

the pen is dropped and twirled, all with one hand. The beam compass is used for drawing large arcs.

3.5   PENCILS AND PENS

A large variety of pencils and pens are available for drafting different kinds of lines on different kinds of surfaces. Some are versatile and can be used for many operations, and some are useful for only a limited range of drawing.

Pencils with which to draw black (actually, usually gray) lines are available in the standard variety of a piece of "lead" with a wood covering. They range from "soft" to "hard" in composition of the lead. For most average cartographic work a hardness of at least 4 or 5H is about the softest practicable. Any softer lead will not hold a point and the oil in the lead makes it easy to smudge the drawing. An excessively hard lead will require too great a pressure on the paper to produce a visible line which causes an indentation or groove in the paper. Attempts to erase such a line are not very successful, and even if the blackness can be removed the groove is likely to remain. Semi-mechanical pencils are available in which leads of varying hardness can be inserted and which are then held by a clamp assembly. These are easy to use and make unnecessary the frequent sharpening of the wood cover on ordinary pencils.

Colored pencils also exist in great variety, and are very useful in cartographic work when compiling the worksheet (see Article 12.12) for a map. The use of different colors for different categories of information helps to prevent mistakes in final drafting. For coloring areas on drawings some colored pencils are compounded so that benzene or some other solvent may be painted over the lightly colored surface to produce an even tint. Some colored pencils are made so that a lightly penciled area may be rubbed over with a stump of card-

standard compass are included in a set of drawing instruments. Some makes have an interchangeable pencil and ruling pen; others are made only for pencil or for pen. In either case their use is the same. The large compass in a set usually has an extension arm which may be fitted into a socket to make even larger circles possible. The drop compass is useful for making small circles. The pen is loose on the pointed shaft, and when the center has been located

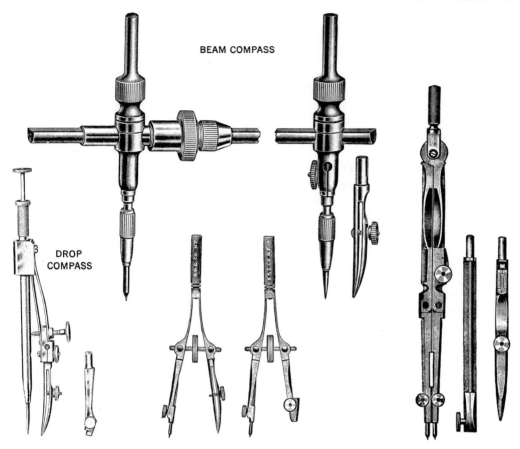

BEAM COMPASS

DROP COMPASS

FIGURE 3.7. Kinds of compasses. The beam of the beam compass may be several feet long. (Courtesy Keuffel and Esser Company.)

board to produce an even tint. Light blue pencils are used to draw preliminary line work, guide lines, etc., on drawings which are to be photographed for reproduction. The orthochromatic emulsion used for such negatives reacts to the blue as white. There are many other types of pencils for special purposes, such as chalk pencils for delicate pastel shaded effects or carbon pencils used for drawing and shading which is to be photographed.

Pencils should be kept sharp if they are to be used for drawing precise lines. This is most easily done with a piece of fine sandpaper. "Paddles" made of many layers

of this sandpaper are available commercially.

Just as there are many kinds of pencils so are there many kinds of pens with which to apply inks to a drawing. Whatever the pen, however, it is important that it is kept clean. Time spent on regular cleaning of pens is in the long run time gained.

Quill-type pens made of metal are among the most used instruments. A large variety is obtainable, and it is helpful to have a good selection on hand. Some are hard and stiff and make uniform lines; others are very flexible and are used for lines, such as rivers, that require a changing width on the

drawing. A favorite is the one called the "crow quill," a relatively stiff pen, which requires a special holder. Quill pens of any type may be dipped in the ink bottle, but a better practice is to use the ink dropper to apply a drop to the underside of the pen. This procedure helps to produce a finer line and allows frequent cleaning without excessive waste of ink.

The stub pen is like a quill except that the tip ends in a flat section instead of tapering to a point. With such a nib a line may be made of varying width, depending upon whether the pen is moved vertically or horizontally on the paper. It is thus a good pen for distinctive freehand lettering.

The Leroy pen (see Fig. 3.8) was originally designed for use with a lettering device (see Article 13.10) but has been found to be a most useful pen for many other purposes. It has a cylinder for a "point," and ink is fed through a small hole in the cylinder. When used freehand in its special holder, it is useful for those lines that should maintain a constant width no matter which direction they may follow. Varying pressure makes little difference in the width of the line.

The Barch-Payzant pen (see Fig. 3.9) was also designed for lettering, but geographers find it a useful pen for making uniform lines or dots. It operates on a different principle from the Leroy, but the result is about the same. The flow of ink is adjustable with a Barch-Payzant, which makes it useful for drafting uniform dots.

Another versatile pen for cartographic use is the Speedball (see Fig. 3.10). Several varieties are obtainable, and the shape of the nib provides different kinds of lines. The Speedball has an ink reservoir, and is filled better with an ink dropper than by dipping.

Several types of pens are made in the manner of fountain pens, that is, they have a large ink reservoir which makes unnecessary the frequent refilling of the pen. Some of these have interchangeable nibs. This changing is a bit messy sometimes, but when one has learned to use such pens and is able to design his drawing so as to require only the line widths available, they make

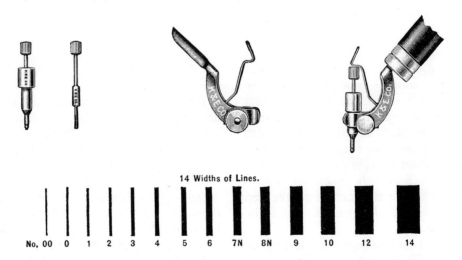

14 Widths of Lines.

No. 00   0   1   2   3   4   5   6   7N   8N   9   10   12   14

FIGURE 3.8. Leroy pens and penholder, and widths of lines made by various sizes of pens. A table showing the widths of the lines in inches appears in Article 9.3. (Courtesy Keuffel and Esser Company.)

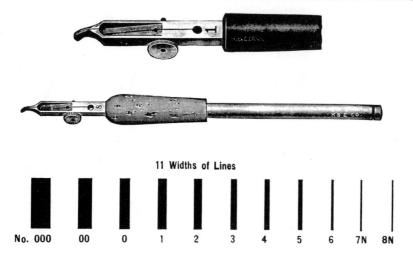

11 Widths of Lines

| No. 000 | 00 | 0 | 1 | 2 | 3 | 4 | 5 | 6 | 7N | 8N |

FIGURE 3.9. Barch-Payzant pens and widths of lines made by various sizes of pens. A table showing the widths of the lines in inches appears in Article 9.3. (Courtesy Keuffel and Esser Company.)

drafting a much faster operation. The largest selection of nibs of various styles and line widths is provided by the Pelican-Graphos set (see Fig. 3.11).

3.6 DRAWING PAPERS, BOARDS, AND PLASTICS

A most impressive variety of drafting surfaces ranging from cloth to plastic may be used for maps, and the neophyte is hard pressed to choose the right one for the purpose at hand. Each use to which a paper or surface is to be put makes distinct demands on the surface. The following brief listing includes the more important qualities of surfaces for cartographic use.

1. Dimensional Stability. This refers to the ability of the material to withstand changes in temperature and humidity without shrinking or expanding. This is particularly important in two instances: (1) when the map must maintain an absolute scale, such as in detailed charting or mapping, and (2) when the drawing must "fit" or register with another drawing. This is necessary whenever drafting is done to

be reproduced in more than one color, or even when two separate drawings are to be combined in the end product. Because so much of modern map production requires several drawings to produce one map this quality has assumed extreme importance in recent years, and a great amount of experimentation and research has been devoted to producing dimensionally stable drawing surfaces.

2. Ink Adherence. This refers to the ability of the surface to "hold on to" the ink. Some surfaces are rather porous, so that the ink sinks in a bit and is held by the fibers when it dries. Other surfaces are so compact that the ink simply dries on the surface, and consequently, it may be easily chipped or rubbed off.

3. Translucence. This refers to the ease with which it is possible to see through the material. It is of special concern in cartographic drafting, not only because a considerable amount of tracing is usually done but also because much drafting for reproduction is done on separate overlays. Although there are ways to insure correct fit or registry of overlays other than by "seeing

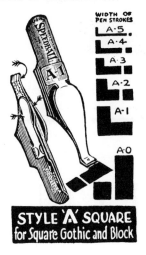

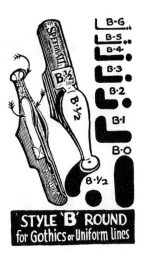

FIGURE 3.10. Speedball pens and widths of lines made by various sizes and styles of pens. Note that various widths of lines can be produced by the manner in which the pen is moved. (Courtesy Hunt Pen Company.)

through" drawings (see Article 14.16), it is usually cheaper and quicker to use a translucent medium.

4. Surface Quality. This refers to the smoothness or roughness of the surface. The quality of the surface has much to do with the "cleanness" of the line that may be drawn on it. Roughness can, however, be a definite asset, as, for example, when "continuous-tone" shading for line reproduction is desired (see Article 14.14).

5. Erasing Quality. Some kinds of map work require frequent erasing of pencil lines, as, for example, in terrain drawing, and final inking must be done on the same sheet. Toughness is obviously required.

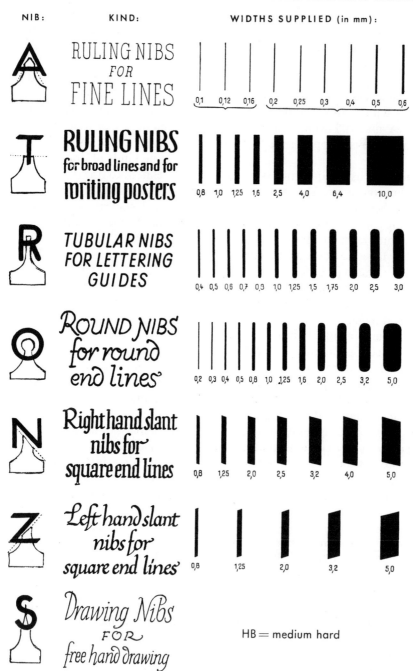

FIGURE 3.11. Illustration of the types of nibs and widths of lines that may be made by Pelican-Graphos nibs. All lines are made by individual nibs which can be inserted in a single fountain type pen. Special inserts are also available to provide the proper rate of flow from the reservoir depending upon the ink requirements of the nib. (Courtesy John Henschel and Company, New York.)

6. Strength. Some drawings must withstand repeated rolling and unrolling or may be made with the idea of frequent revision. For such drawings a strong material is required.

7. Reaction to Wetting. Many maps call for painting with various kinds of paints and inks. A material which curls excessively when wetted is inappropriate for such a purpose.

The preceding list of qualities is not all inclusive, but these are the major ones. The cartographer would do well to approach every drafting job with the question "How will the medium react to what I plan to do to it?" The classic cartographic media are tracing paper, tracing cloth, and drawing paper. During the last decade plastics and glass cloth have become widely used for cartographic drawing.

Tracing paper is available in two forms: the natural tracing paper and the prepared tracing paper. Natural tracing paper is translucent because the paper is made thin. It is relatively weak and is not recommended for most map work. Prepared tracing paper is made of tougher materials and is made translucent by chemical means. It is much more satisfactory for map work. Tracing cloth or linen is a sized, good quality cloth. It is tougher than paper and is desirable if unusual handling of the drawing is required. The sizing frequently clogs a pen. None of the tracing papers or cloths can be wetted much without curling.

Drawing paper is a fine grade rag paper available in a variety of qualities, thicknesses, and surfaces. It is relatively opaque, but if translucence is not required it provides an excellent drawing surface. An illustration board is a heavy cardboard surfaced with drawing paper. It may be wetted, as may some drawing papers, and is especially useful as a base upon which to mount drawings done on translucent paper.

Many types of drawing surfaces made of plastics are now available. Acetate (cellulose acetate) is not so dimensionally stable as either *Vinylite* or type "D" *Mylar** from which a variety of forms of plastic sheeting suitable for ink drafting and scribing (see Article 14.13) has been made. Plastic surfaces range from smooth to matte and any desired degree of translucence or thickness can be had. Plastics have many advantages for some kinds of drafting, some of which are related to the production of multi-colored maps mentioned previously. In addition, plastics are tougher than paper and can stand repeated correction. They last longer, do not absorb water from the atmosphere, and, being practically dimensionally stable, they are particularly useful for those drafting operations involving preprinted symbols and lettering on thin plastic which is made adhesive and then applied to the map (see Article 13.11). If such materials are put on very thin drawing paper, absorption of moisture by the paper over a long period of time may cause the map to wrinkle and become so distorted that it is unusable thereafter.

Some plastics have disadvantages as well as advantages. Some are extremely hard and drawing instruments tend to wear quickly. Of more importance is the fact that ordinary drawing inks may not adhere very well. Consequently, the ink work may be marred by careless rubbing. Mistakes in drafting on plastic are easily corrected, for the ink can merely be scraped off.

There is a variety of other special papers and surfaces that is occasionally useful to the cartographer. For example, large wall maps can be made on sign cloth; transparent overlays can be made on clear plastic; and metal-mounted paper has been used for fine, scale-perfect drawings. The spe-

---

* Vinylite is the trade name for polyvinyl plastic manufactured by the Bakelite Corporation; Mylar is the trade name for polyester plastic manufactured by E. I. DuPont de Nemours Co.

cial or unusual map frequently requires some experimentation.

One type of material that is very useful is Coquille or Ross board. This material is prepared in a variety of rough surfaces so that when a carbon pencil or crayon is rubbed over it the color comes off on only the tops of the small bumps (see Fig. 3.12). For this reason varying shades of gray can be prepared with this material and can be reproduced without the necessity of being halftoned (see Article 14.14), which reduces the reproduction expense to about half.

3.7 DRAWING INKS

The standard black ink for drafting purposes is usually called India ink, and is available in a number of brands. It takes its name from the older product sold in stick form which originally came from India. Modern India or drawing ink is a permanent suspension of fine carbon in a liquid me-

dium. It dries a dense black, which is very important for reproduction. Most brands are waterproof; that is, they will not run if wetted after they have once dried. Drawing ink is also available in transparent colors which can be mixed.

Special inks made for use on some special plastics are available in black and colors. They are compounded so that they become a part of the surface, and consequently they are hard to remove if a correction is necessary. They are thicker than ordinary water-based drawing inks and thus cannot be used in some kinds of pens. Their solvent action on plastic precludes their use in ink-reservoir types of pens such as the Pelican-Graphos, and they will corrode drawing instruments.

Tracing cloths, drawing papers, and plastics commonly pick up oil from the hands, or are oily or slick because of the method of preparation. Drawing ink will either not adhere or "skip" if the surface is oily, and this will result in both poor appearance and

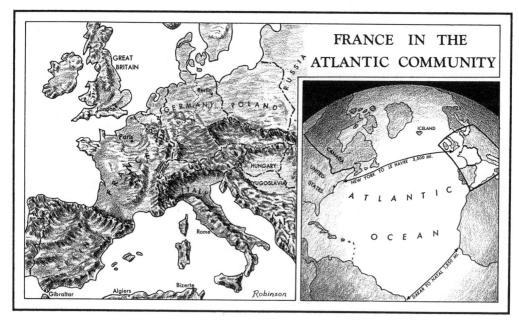

FIGURE 3.12. A map drawn on Coquille board. The reproduction is by ordinary line cut. (Reprinted by permission of the publishers from Donald C. McKay, *The United States and France,* Harvard University Press, Cambridge, Mass.; copyright, 1951, by the President and Fellows of Harvard College.)

reproduction. Consequently, it is necessary to remove any such film before inking begins. On prepared tracing papers and cloths this is most easily done by a commercially prepared powder for this specific purpose. A solution of one ounce of 28% concentrate of ammonia in one quart of water; or carbon tetrachloride; or plain soap and water may be used to clean the surface of many plastics. For photography all ink work should be absolutely opaque black. The draftsman should first clean the drawing surface and then keep it clean by having a piece of soft paper under his drawing hand at all times. Fingers should not touch the paper. A blunt stick or a needle point in a holder are handy substitutes for fingers when the paper needs to be kept tight against the board.

For drawings that are to be photographed the best way to "sharpen" lines and make corrections is to use a white, opaque paint to cover the ink lines not wanted. Showcard or tempera-type paints, although usable, have a tendency to flake off if the drawing is much handled.

3.8 TINTS AND PATTERNS

An indispensable part of many maps is the pattern or shading that must be applied to differentiate one area from another. This can be accomplished either by drafting them laboriously, as in the case of parallel lines or dotted "stippling," or by applying a commercially prepared pattern. Shades of gray as might be prepared by shading with a pencil cannot ordinarily be used, for then reproduction requires halftoning. An appearance of shading can be created with Coquille or Ross board, but other line work is relatively difficult on these surfaces.

Preprinted materials, such as lines and dots printed on transparent film with an adhesive backing, are easy to use and save much of the time which was formerly necessary (see Fig. 3.13). There is a considerable variety commercially available from most graphic arts supply houses. Catalogs may be obtained from the local outlet or from the manufacturer.* Several hundred patterns are available in black, white, and colors. The colors (except red) are not frequently used in cartography. The patterns are available on thin transparent film coated with an adhesive, commonly wax, protected by a translucent backing sheet. The material is placed over the area desired and is cut with a sharp needle or blade to fit. If cut without the backing sheet the excess is stripped away, and the pattern is burnished to the drawing. Extreme care must be exercised when cutting an adhesive pattern without the backing sheet over inked lines on a drawing. The stripping away of the excess will occasionally pull ink off the drawing.

For maps to be photographed for reproduction, patterns printed in translucent red are useful when the pattern to be used is dense, and it would be impossible to see through it (to know where to cut it) if it were black. Red, like black, does not affect the ordinary film used in map reproduction. Large areas to appear ultimately as solid black may be easily constructed by using a solid red "pattern," especially on a paper that cannot be wetted. White patterns are useful for breaking up black areas or other patterns.

Knowledge of the relation of patterns to reduction and the preparation of a graded series of values (darkness) require considerable experimentation by the cartographer.

* Para-Tone, Inc., 512 W. Burlington Avenue, La Grange, Illinois, manufactures *Zip-A-Tone;* Craftint Mfg. Co., 1615 Collamer Avenue, Cleveland 10, Ohio, manufactures *Craftone;* Chart-Pak, Inc., Leeds, Massachusetts, manufactures *Contak* as well as an adhesive tape useful as a substitute for drafted lines; Artype, Inc., 127 S. Northwest Highway, Barrington, Illinois, manufactures dot and line screens with a regular progression of tonal values.

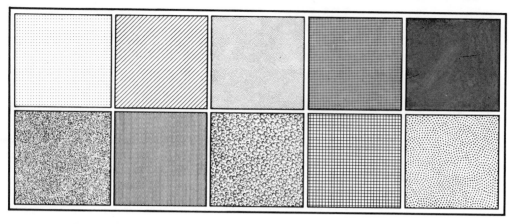

FIGURE 3.13. Examples of preprinted symbols, in this case Zip-A-Tone. Many of the maps and diagrams in this book have been prepared with the aid of these kinds of symbols.

3.9   OTHER TECHNIQUES AND MEDIA OF THE GRAPHIC ARTS

The foregoing brief résumé of the more important materials and media for average black and white cartographic drafting is far from exhaustive. Many other techniques are used in certain kinds of cartography, such as airbrush, intermediate photography, other kinds of media, and painting with various types of colors, that would require a treatment too exhaustive for a book of this kind. There are several manuals on the graphic arts techniques that will answer the majority of the special questions the student might have.

3.10   DRAWING REGULAR LINES

Many of the lines the cartographer draws are regular, that is, smooth (straight or curved) lines in contrast to those lines drawn for most rivers, coasts, etc., which are irregular in shape. In some cases a category of lines will always be regular such as map borders or parallels and meridians; sometimes, whether it will be more or less irregular depends upon the scale of the map and the character of the shape defined by the line. For example, a coast may in detail be irregular (at large scale) but in reduction and generalization it may become relatively smooth. Any absolutely regular line should be drawn with the pen held against a drawing edge such as a T-square or curve; conversely, most irregular lines should be drawn freehand, that is, without the aid of an edge. The eye is quick to notice the visual anomalies that result when this rule is not followed.

The pencil or pen should be held against the drawing edge so that a line along the pen lies in a plane perpendicular to the plane of the drawing (see Fig. 3.14). The pen or pencil may be tilted sideways to make it easier to see just where the line "is going," but it should still lie in the perpendicular plane. A pencil or pen held this way will have the tip removed a bit from the bottom edge of the square or curve along which it is being moved, as shown in Fig. 3.14. This space is important, for it not only keeps ink from running under the edge of the guide or the pencil from marking it, but it also enables the person doing the drawing to see what he is doing, and allows him to make any slight deviations necessary to follow the exact path required. The latter is particularly impor-

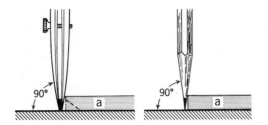

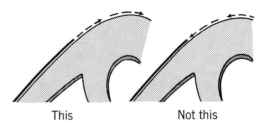

FIGURE 3.14. The pen or pencil should be held always at an angle of 90° from the drawing surface. The drawing edge is indicated by a. The edge may be either straight as shown or beveled; if beveled the sloping edge should be down when inking.

FIGURE 3.16. Draw segments along curves (shaded in drawing) away from previously drawn sections.

tant when drawing curves that are not true arcs.

Drawing an ink line across another already inked line or area calls for special precautions since ink has a tendency to creep along such previously saturated areas. This is particularly true if the ink is slow-drying or wide lines are being drawn that put a heavy load of ink on the line. In these cases the drawing edge should be raised off the drawing surface or a beveled edge can be used. Some curves and triangles are made so that they do not lie flat, but most are not. Several layers of drafting tape or a blotter can be placed beneath and away from the edge as shown in Fig. 3.15.

When one is drawing smooth curves by connecting points with the aid of a curved edge, the line should always be drawn away

from a previously drawn segment (see Fig. 3.16). It is very difficult to meet exactly a previously drawn regular line. In order always to draw away from lines it is desirable to have the paper loose on the drawing board so that it can be turned in any desirable direction. If a tracing is being made, the two sheets may be taped together so that they move together.

An arc of a circle may be drawn with a compass, or a spline and spline weights, or, if enough points along the arc are known, it may be constructed in segments with a curve. Since the radius of curvature of a true arc does not change, any three points define it; consequently, other points may be located in the manner shown in Fig. 3.17. Smooth or regular but undefined curves, too "wiggly" to be drawn with the aid of a curve, may be drawn freehand with a round,

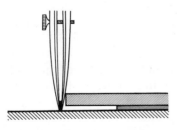

FIGURE 3.15. Placing tape or a blotter beneath and away from the drawing edge prevents ink from creeping under the edge.

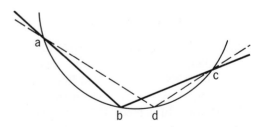

FIGURE 3.17. Points a, b, c lie on an arc. Point d may be located by moving angle abc along the arc so that the legs are kept in contact with a and c. If the angle adc = angle abc, then d lies on the arc. A template may be made of paper or cardboard.

pointed pen, a swivel ruling (contour) pen, or applied with adhesive tape (see footnote, page 44).

3.11   SUBDIVIDING LINES

The cartographer is frequently required to draw angles and lines or arcs of some unknown value and then subdivide them into a number of equal parts. In many cases, elementary geometry and arithmetic provide the means of checking for accuracy, but a number of short cuts and graphic procedures are available.

Most maps are constructed within a rectangle and this is usually the first operation in planning a map. To prevent subsequent bother it is wise to check for squareness as soon as the initial outline has been constructed. The procedure is shown in Fig. 3.18.

A line or an arc of any length may be divided into segments of equal length by merely setting dividers to "about-the-right" spacing and then "walking" the dividers along the line the required number of times. The error of the initial and subsequent estimates may be corrected until the results are perfect. The space between the points of the divider is then exactly the desired subdivision of the given line whatever its total

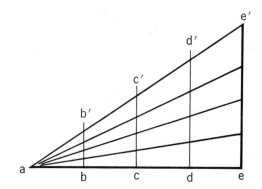

FIGURE 3.19. Lines *bb'*, *cc'*, *dd'*, and *ee'* are parallel and *ab*, *bc*, *cd*, and *de* are equal. Any other line drawn from *a* to line *ee'* is also divided in four equal parts.

length may be. It is well to alternate the swinging back and forth of the dividers so that holding them between the fingers does not become awkward. It is also helpful occasionally to remember the geometric theorem that if parallels intercept equal segments on a transversal they intercept equal segments on any transversal, as illustrated in Fig. 3.19. This is useful when drawing or converting graphic scales.

Sometimes the cartographer is called upon to plot the true length (to scale) of a segment along an arc, e.g., the spacing of meridians on a parallel on a projection. This may be done with dividers as previously indicated, or if the arc has a true length, by calculating the length of a chord of a given angular interval. The general formula for the chord of an arc is

$$\text{chord} = 2r \sin \frac{\lambda}{2}$$

where r is the actual radius of the arc and λ is the actual central angle in degrees subtended by the chord.

3.12   MEASURING DISTANCES AND AREAS

For many purposes connected with cartography it is necessary to make measure-

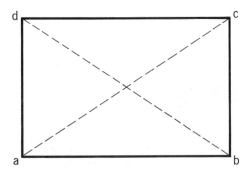

FIGURE 3.18. In any true rectangle the lengths of *ac* and *bd* are equal. They need not be measured; merely compare the lengths by marking the points on the edge of a sheet of paper.

ments on maps. Ordinary linear measure is not difficult, since all that is necessary is a scale. Measuring the length of irregular lines or areas is more likely to result in error unless instrumental aids are employed.

To determine the length of an irregular line a device called a map measure may be used. This consists of a small wheel the revolutions of which are recorded on a larger dial. The small wheel is rolled along the line on the map, and the length traversed and shown on the dial is then converted to linear earth distance according to the scale of the map. Table 2.4 is useful for conversions. Some map measures have several sets of scales on the dial so that a length may be read for more than one map scale.

The area of an irregular shape can be determined in several ways. One simple, but not particularly precise, manner is to lay cross-section paper over the region and count the number of squares and part-squares enclosed by the boundary. The other and more precise manner is to employ a polar planimeter (see Fig. 3.20). This instrument requires merely tracing the outline of the area with a pointer, with the result being read directly in square units from a dial and graduated drum commonly equipped with a vernier (see Fig. 3.21). Some planimeters record only in square inches or centimeters, whereas others are capable of adjustment so that the values read from the instrument are in whatever units the operator may wish.

Occasionally it is necessary to determine the area of a region from a map that does not have a proper scale, or, more often, the result is desired in some unit requiring a knowledge of square values from the map. Although this can usually be computed from the scale (if the scale is expressed properly), it is frequently desirable to determine the relationship with the planimeter by measuring a known area on the map. This has the advantages of rectifying the usual paper distortion of the map (which would make the scale erroneous) and of making certain the relation between the measured units on the map and areas on the earth. Table D.3, Appendix D shows the areas of quadrilaterals bounded by 1° longitude and 1° latitude for latitudes from the equator to the pole.

3.13   SCALES AND COMPUTING AIDS

The cartographer needs several scales with which to measure distances. The most commonly used scales are triangular and are made of wood. They should be either in the metric system or in the English system, decimally divided. Scales are not meant to be used as straightedges, and pens or pencils should never be run along the edge of a scale. This practice may dirty the scales, and any marks on them will make the chance of an error in reading values more likely.

If the cartographer does any maps for books, he will find it also useful to have a

FIGURE 3.20. A polar planimeter. (Courtesy of Keuffel and Esser Company.)

FIGURE 3.21. A vernier is a device with which to read to the third significant figure. For example, in the above drawing the first digit of the reading opposite 0 is 4, the second is 2, and the third is obtained by finding on the top scale (the vernier) the tenth that most closely "lines up" with a graduation mark on the bottom scale, in this case 3. The vernier consists of nine of the units of the main (bottom) scale graduated in ten parts.

scale that shows picas. The pica (about ⅙ inch) is a unit of typographic measure, and most book type and format dimensions are given in picas.

Every cartographer should have available a slide rule. The use of the slide rule for simple multiplication and division may be self-taught in a short time, and many calculations are enormously simplified by its use. Calculations of percentages, proportions, and many other standard cartographic procedures are a matter of minutes with a slide rule.

The easiest way to compute most scale problems and the data needed for projections with the required accuracy is by using logarithms. Their use, like that of the slide rule based upon them, is easily learned, and, as a convenience to the student, a table of logarithms has been included in Appendix A.

The Nature
of Map Projections

4.1 FROM THE SPHERE TO THE PLANE

The study of many of the smaller components of the earth requires that the scientist enlarge them with a microscope in order to bring them into the range of his vision. Conversely, the scientist studying the larger distributions on the earth must reduce their spatial arrangements to bring them into convenient view. In other words, the scale of the earth is so large relative to man that only with the reduced scale of a map can he easily comprehend the relationships among the earth features. One way of accomplishing this is merely to reduce the scale and thereby make a globe. When this is done, all that has been changed is the size of the earth; all other relationships (relative distance, angles, relative areas, azimuths, loxodromes, great circles, and similar geometric relationships) are retained without change. A globe is, therefore, a "naturally accurate" map. A globe map, being on a spherical surface, has, on the other hand, a considerable number of practical disadvantages, one of them being the very fact that it is a three-dimensional round body and only less than half of it can be observed at any time. In addition, it is cumbersome to handle, difficult to store, expensive to make and reproduce, and it is not easy to measure on its three-dimensional surface. Consequently, for most of the purposes for which one uses a map, the globe map is less desirable than one which has included in its preparation a transformation of the spherical surface. Most of the disadvantages inherent in using the spherical form for the map are eliminated by transforming the surface to a plane; a substance in the form of a plane is easy to handle, all of it can be observed at once, it is cheap to prepare and reproduce, and is easy to measure and draw on it with ordinary instruments. Thus the flat map is generally much more useful.

Ever since the Greek philosophers reasoned that the earth must be a sphere, the problem of how to transform the earth's spherical surface to the plane surface of a flat map has been of paramount interest in cartography. The problem arises from the indisputable geometric fact that it is impossible to make the transformation without modifying the geometric relationships in some manner. But it is also a fact that there are innumerable possibilities of systematic transformation that can retain, on the plane, one or several of the spherical relationships. In addition, and of great significance, is the fact that certain systems of transformation can be employed that produce desirable geometric conditions which

do not obtain on a spherical surface. For example, loxodromes, which are different kinds of lines on the sphere, can be changed in one system so that they all appear as straight lines on a plane. In quite a different class, but nevertheless of great utility, is the possibility of the selective but systematic enlargement or reduction of a portion of the map area, or even the changing of its shape, in order to fit the specific needs of a presentation problem. Because a great number of systems have been devised, the cartographer does not lack for possibilities from which to choose. The essential problem of the cartographer, then, is the analysis of the geometrical requirements of the proposed map and the *selection* of the system of transformation which will best or most nearly meet these needs.

The actual process of transformation is called projection, and the term "projection" stems from the fact that many means of transformation can be accomplished by geometrically "projecting," with lines or shadows, the homologous points from the sphere to a plane surface. It is similar to the manner in which an architectural draftsman can construct a scale drawing of a building as seen from a particular point of view. As a matter of fact, there is considerable similarity between architectural projection and some kinds of map projection. Properly done, an architectural drawing of a building is systematically done in perspective so that every aspect of the building appears correct from a given viewpoint. If one attempted to measure one of the foreshortened sides without knowing the system of projection, the result would probably be erroneous. Similarly, the cartographer "projects" the spherical surface to a plane surface in a systematic manner. Consequently, familiarity with systems of projection is as important to the map user as it is to the cartographer.

Actual geometric projection from the sphere to the plane includes only a few of the possibilities. There are a larger number

of possibilities for the retention of significant earth relationships that can be worked out mathematically. These are also called projections, and no purpose would be served by attempting to distinguish between geometric and mathematical projections.

They are all systematic representations of the earth grid on a plane surface, and each has specific qualities which make it more or less useful for specific purposes.

4.2   THE HISTORY OF MAP PROJECTIONS

The earliest thought of projections of the spherical earth on a plane surface probably occurred no earlier than several centuries B.C.; but in the few hundred years following the realization that the earth is a sphere, several solutions to the projection problem were presented. Probably one of the first projections was a simple representation of the spherical quadrilaterals formed by the parallels and meridians as a series of plane rectangles, and today the same kind of projection is still occasionally used. By the end of the Greek era enough had become known about the earth, and the problem of projection was so well understood, that the great Claudius Ptolemy in his monumental work on geography was able to include a section on map projections and to devise and give directions for their construction. After Ptolemy, the western world lapsed into the Dark Ages and the knowledge of projection was one of the casualties.

Elsewhere however, notably in the Arabic world, mathematics, geography, and cartography were kept alive. When, in the fifteenth century, Ptolemy was "rediscovered," the western world again made great strides in cartography and discovery. This period was as much a Renaissance in cartography as it was in anything else, and probably the greatest and most influential map projection ever devised, the Mercator projection, was developed during this period.

The Mercator projection is an excellent

example of the relation between the requirements of a map and the manner in which the necessary transformation may be made in order to meet the needs. The sixteenth century was a time of exploration and sea travel. Columbus had discovered the Americas; Magellan's ships had succeeded in circumnavigating the globe; the earth's land areas were beginning to take shape on the world map; and ships were setting out "to all points of the compass." One of the major trials of an early navigator was that, although he had a rough idea of where lands were and had the compass to help him, he had no way of determining the compass bearing of a course which, with any degree of certainty, would take him to his destination. It was pointed out earlier that the problem of the navigator is that he must sail along a loxodrome, a line of constant compass direction, because he cannot readily travel any other course. The solution was to project (mathematically—not geometrically) the earth's surface in such a way that a straight line on the resulting plane, *anywhere in any direction,* was a loxodrome. Thus, if a mariner knew from where he was starting, he need but draw a straight line (or a series of straight lines) to his destination, and, if he made appropriate allowances for drift, winds, and compass declinations, he had a reasonably good chance of arriving somewhere near his destination. The projection suited perfectly the purpose of the map. It still does.

In the less than four hundred years since Mercator introduced the projection which bears his name the world of man has changed tremendously. Distances have been reduced a thousandfold; man has investigated and mapped an untold number of subjects; and all branches of science, including cartography, have progressed immensely. The development of map projections kept pace with the developments in other fields, and as the needs arose for ways of presenting particular geographic relations, a means of projecting the grid to accomplish the purpose usually became available.

Not all projections by any means were developed in answer to specific needs as was the Mercator. The transformation of a spherical surface to a plane in such a manner as to maintain on the plane certain of the numerous spherical relationships is a most intriguing mathematical problem. Consequently, a number of projections have been devised simply as solutions to interesting problems rather than with a specific utility in mind. Also it should be remembered that some of our common projections were originally contemplated and worked out by the ancients and were only resurrected a thousand years or more later when their utility was appreciated. Such was the case with the gnomonic, orthographic, and stereographic projections, all of which were imagined or devised before the time of Christ, but were not employed thereafter until more than fifteen hundred years later.

The correlation between the purpose of the map and the projection used is strikingly revealed by the tremendous advances made during the last century or so. As transportation capacities have increased and social consciousness has developed, the need for maps for air navigation and other nonoceanic travel (as well as for the display of population, land use, and other geographic factors) has likewise increased. Many new projections have been devised and ways of adapting many old ones worked out; thus today there is literally an unlimited number of projections from which to choose.

It may reasonably be asserted that at present cartographers need to devote little time to devising new projections but rather would do better to become more proficient in selecting from the ones available. On the other hand, if a new and particular use of maps requires a special type of projection, undeveloped as yet, such a projection might well be worth the time and effort spent in devising it.

The foregoing brief survey of the history of map projection would not be complete without the observation that a great many projections have been devised without their inventors being fully aware of exactly what was involved in their transformation of the spherical system to a plane surface. That is, a given requirement such as parallel parallels or the earth within a circle of a certain size may be accomplished through arranging the earth's coordinate system by trial and error methods, without a very clear (or any) knowledge of the mathematical transformational processes involved. As a matter of fact, it has been suggested that even Mercator may not have known exactly the fundamentals behind his famous projection, even though the tremendously important desired result was clearly obtained. Obviously, a book of this sort cannot begin to go into all the theory and proof involved in a subject as mathematically complex as is the subject of map projections. Nevertheless, in order that the student of cartography and the user of maps may have an understanding of the basic propositions and laws involved in the transformation, a relatively nonmathematical description of the more basic elements follows.

4.3 SCALE VARIATIONS RESULTING FROM PROJECTION

The appreciation of map projections cannot clearly be developed unless one becomes fully familiar with the concept of scale variations which result from the system of projection. Since maps are reductions of reality, it follows that representations of reality must be done to scale; this offers no particular problem when the reduction is merely one of size, that is, when a globe is prepared. But when the reduction in size is accompanied by a transformation of the spherical surface to a plane, then complexities enter the picture. Fundamentally, these result from the fact that, whereas reduction to a

globe can be accomplished with no variation of scale from one part of the surface to another, this is not possible when transformation to a plane is involved. Consequently, the distribution of scale variation on the different projections is the key to their understanding and use.

To appreciate the problem involved in representing one surface upon another it is necessary to imagine the establishment of a pattern of infinitely closely spaced points on the one surface, and then to establish the positions of corresponding or homologous points on the other. The system employed to specify the positions of the points on the second surface constitutes the method of projection of the first surface. If the two surfaces are applicable, that is, if the one may be produced by bending the other without tearing or stretching, then the geometric relationships of angles, areas, distances, and directions on the one surface may be retained on the other. If the two surfaces are not applicable, and tearing is disallowed, then the distance relationships among homologous points on the two surfaces must vary, that is, stretching or compression must take place. Since angular and areal relationships are functions of relative distances, then some sorts of deformation of these relationships are bound to occur. Consequently it is impossible to devise a system of projection for two nonapplicable surfaces such that any figure drawn upon the first will appear exactly similar upon the second.

A spherical surface and a plane surface are not applicable; consequently, any method of map projection must include the relative enlargement or reduction of portions of the spherical surface in some fashion in order to represent it on a plane surface. As a result, distances between uniformly spaced points on a spherical surface cannot be represented uniformly on a plane surface. Nevertheless, it is possible by properly arranging the enlargement and reduction involved to (1) retain some kinds of compara-

ble angular relationships, *or* (2) to retain comparable areas of like figures from the one surface to the other. If these particular qualities are not wanted in a projection but some other geometric attribute of the spherical surface is desired, then all angular relationships will usually be changed (except perhaps at particular points), and areas on the two surfaces will not have a constant ratio to each other.

In order to understand and apply these stated facts as they apply to the problem of the projection of the spherical surface of the earth to the plane surface of a map, it is necessary to realize that scale

(1) Exists at a point, and
(2) The scale may be different in different directions at a point.

To demonstrate the first of these propositions imagine an arc of 90°, as in Fig. 4.1, projected orthographically to a straight line tangent at *a*. If *a, b, c, . . . j* are the positions of 10° divisions of the arc, their respective positions after projection to the line tangent at *a* are indicated by *a, b', c', . . . j'*. Line *aj'* therefore represents line *aj*. Whereas the intervals between successive points on

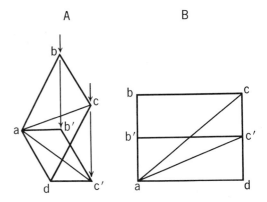

FIGURE 4.2. Projection of a rectangle to another rectangle with one side held constant. The reduced, perspective drawing on the left shows the geometric relation of the two rectangles and the drawing on the right shows the relation of the two rectangles when they are each viewed orthogonally.

the arc are equal lengths, the method of projection has not retained this characteristic. It may be seen from the drawing that the intervals on the straight line, starting at the point of tangency (*a*), become progressively smaller as *j'* is approached. If the scale along the arc is expressed as unity (1), it of course exists as unity anywhere along the arc, but on the projection of the arc, it is gradually reduced from unity at *a* to zero at *j'*. The rate of change is graphically indicated by the increasing diminution of the spaces between the points. Since a line may theoretically be considered as consisting of infinitely close, but uniformly spaced, points, every point on *aj* has its counterpart on *aj'*. But there has been a *continuous change* of scale from unity to zero along *aj'*. Since it is a continuous change, it is evident that every *point* on *aj'* must have a different scale.

In order to demonstrate that the scale at a point may also be different in different directions, imagine a rectangle, *a, b, c, d*, as in Fig. 4.2, an orthogonal projection of which has resulted from rotating it around the axis *ad* so that side *ad* coincides in *abcd* and

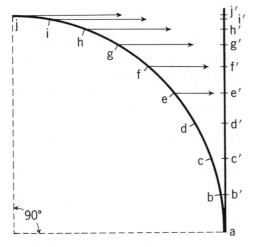

FIGURE 4.1. Orthographic projection of an arc to a straight line tangent.

its projection *ab'c'd*. The perspective drawing on the left in Fig. 4.2 shows how this may be done. If the scale of *abcd* is assumed to be unity, then since the length *ad* is the same in each rectangle there has been no change in scale in that direction. Since the length *ab'* is half the length *ab*, and since it is evident from the method of projection that the change has been made in a uniform fashion, then the scale along *ab'* must be 1:2 or half the scale which obtains along *ad*. By projection line *ac* has become line *ac'*. The ratio of lengths *ac'* to *ac* constitutes the scale along *ac'* and it is evident that it is neither the 1:1 ratio along *ad* or the 1:2 scale ratio along *ab'*; it is somewhere between. Any other diagonal from *a* to a position on the side *bc* would have its corresponding place of intersection on *b'c'*. The ratio of lengths of similar diagonals on the two rectangles would be different for each such line. Hence the scale at point *a* in rectangle *ab'c'd* is different in every direction.

The knowledge of the characteristics of scale in different directions at each point and the change in scale characteristics from point to point on a projection provide the bases for analyzing, to a considerable degree, what the system of projection has accomplished for, or done to, the geometric realities of distances and directions, and their functions, angles, areas, etc., on the sphere.

It may be demonstrated geometrically (see Appendix I) that in every system of representation (of one surface upon another) there is upon the one surface, for example, the sphere, a system of two series of lines intersecting at right angles whose projection on the second surface, for example, a plane, also intersect at right angles. The two surfaces are thus divided into *infinitesimal rectangles* which correspond to one another. Each infinitesimal rectangle on the sphere will have its counterpart on the plane, but the corresponding rectangle on the plane will usually be projected with a scale ratio different from that on the sphere except at

particular points. The explanation and analysis of the effects of scale change upon angles, areas, etc., in the following articles will be facilitated by employing these infinitely small rectangles to illustrate the changes. To make the concepts clear it will be necessary to illustrate the scale ratios that exist at a point, for example, as in Fig. 4.1, with finite dimensions. This does not violate the concepts involved as long as the diagramed dimensions in various directions bear the same ratios of length to one another as do the scale ratios that exist in different directions at a point on the sphere or on the particular system of projection.

4.4 DEFORMATION IN MAP PROJECTIONS

No matter how the spherical surface may be transformed to the plane surface the relationships on the spherical surface cannot be entirely duplicated on the plane. Because of the necessary scale alterations, a number of kinds of deformation involving angles, areas, distances, and directions must or may take place; any system of projection will involve some or all of the following deformations:

(1) Similar angles at different points on the earth *may or may not* be shown as similar on the map.

(2) The area of one section *may or may not* be enlarged or reduced in proportion to that of another region.

(3) Distance relationships among all points on the earth *cannot* be shown without distortion on the map.

(4) Directions among divergent points *cannot* be shown without distortion on the map.

There are many other specific spatial conditions which may or may not be duplicated in map projections, such as parallel parallels, converging meridians, perpendicular intersection of parallels and meridians, the poles being represented as points, and so on,

which may assume great significance for certain maps; however, the major alterations which may or must occur are those listed. In order to provide the student with an understanding of the basic problems resulting from these alterations a brief résumé of their characteristics follows.

4.5   ANGULAR ALTERATION

The compass rose, except at the poles, appears everywhere the same on the globe surface; that is, the cardinal directions are always 90° apart and each of the intervening directions is everywhere at the same angle with the cardinal directions. This is the case because all parallels and meridians cross one another at 90° and man's arbitrary directional concepts are defined with respect to this arrangement.

It is possible to retain this property of angular relations to some extent in a map projection. When it is retained, the projection is termed *conformal* or *orthomorphic*, and the meanings of both words imply "correct form" or "shape." It is important to understand that these terms apply to the directions or angles that obtain at infinitely small points. The property of conformality is not meant to apply to areas of any significant dimension, for no projection can provide correct shape to areas of any extent.

On the sphere, or on a globe, the scale is the same in every direction at any point and, furthermore, the scale is the same at every point. It is evident, since the sphere and the plane are not applicable surfaces, that stretching and compression must take place. Consequently, the scale may never be the same everywhere on the projection, but it is possible to arrange the stretching and compression so that *at each point* on a conformal projection the scale is the same in all directions, although it necessarily must vary from point to point. Thus, on all conformal projections the scale will vary from one point to another. If the condition

of uniform scale in all directions at each point is maintained, then it is apparent that cardinal directions must always be presented correctly on such a projection. Consequently, parallels and meridians will always intersect at 90° on conformal projections; but it is important to realize that just because a projection shows the parallels and meridians as crossing one another with right angles, it does not necessarily mean it has the property of conformality. The reason for this is demonstrated as follows.

In Fig. 4.3 the left-hand drawing, *A*, represents a point *o* on the sphere or on a globe of suitable scale. Points *a* and *b* are defined as infinitely close to *o*. Since the scale on a globe is the same everywhere in every direction, the drawing represents *oa* and *ob* as similar lengths. Line *oc* represents a diagonal. If the rectangle *oacb* is projected to rectangle *oa'b'c'* in such a fashion as to retain the relative lengths of *oa* and *ob* in the projected rectangle, then angles *coa* and *cob* will correspond to angles *c'oa'* and *c'ob'*. If, however, as in *B* in Fig. 4.3, the relative lengths of *oa* and *ob* are not retained, then angles *coa* and *boc* will not be similar to angles *c'oa'* and *boc'*. But it may be seen that angles *boa* and *boa'* are the same. Therefore, just because one pair of directions on

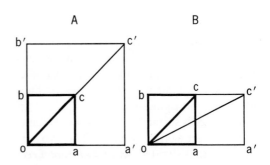

FIGURE 4.3. In A, rectangle oacb has been projected to rectangle oa'c'b' so that the ratio of lengths oa' and ob' corresponds to the ratio of lengths oa and ob. In B this ratio has not been preserved. In A all angles are preserved at o; in B they are not.

the sphere, for example, the cardinal directions, are retained on a projection, it does not necessarily follow that all other directions will be correctly represented.

The amount of angular change that has occurred in the representation of the diagonals from *o*, for example, angle *c'oa'* in Fig. 4.3, can be calculated from the scale ratios along the sides *oa'* and *ob*, the relative orientation of which was not changed in the projection. How this can be done and its use in evaluating the relative amount of angular deformation on one projection as compared to another are considered in Article 4.9.

4.6 AREA ALTERATION

Just as any distance on the earth is "correct" so also is any area in "proper" size proportion; that is, areas constitute one element of reality. That statement is so obvious that it seems ridiculous even to suggest that it has any importance. Yet these two conditions, correct angles and areas, existing on the spherical earth, assume considerable significance when one examines their mutual relationship on a flat projection surface. It has already been pointed out that it is impossible to duplicate all distance relationships on a flat surface, that is, the map distances between all points cannot be retained in a projection. Consequently, it might be concluded that, since area is a function of dimension, it is likewise impossible to duplicate the areas in proper proportion to one another; however, it is possible.

In Fig. 4.4 the left-hand drawing, *A*, represents a point *o* on the globe. Points *a*, *á*, *b*, and *b'* are infinitely close to *o* and lie in directions 90° from one another at *o*. Since on the globe the scale is the same in every direction *aa'* and *bb'* are represented as similar lengths. Length *aa'* will be designated as *a*, and *bb'* as *b*. They constitute the bisectors of a rhombus, in this case a square.

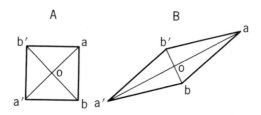

FIGURE 4.4. Rhombus *aba'b'* in A has been projected to rhombus *aba'b'* in B. The products of the bisectors in A is the same as the product of the bisectors in B, hence the areas of the two figures are the same.

The area scale at *o* is considered unity.* The right-hand drawing, *B*, in Fig. 4.4 shows a projection of point *o* in which the directions toward *a* and *b* from *o* are the same as on the sphere, but the scale in the direction *a* has been doubled and the scale in direction *b* has been halved. It is evident from the conditions that the area of the rhombus in *B* remains equal to unity.† It is also clear, merely by inspection, that angular relationships from *o* to points other than *a*, *a'*, *b*, or *b'* in *A* would be markedly changed in the projection *B*. That this must be so was demonstrated in Fig. 4.3.

To state the proposition in general terms: if a system of projection is employed such that the *product* of the scales along the spherical perpendiculars that are retained as perpendiculars on the projection is equal at every point, then all areas of figures on the projection will be represented in correct relative size. A map projection that retains the area relationships in this way is called an *equivalent* or *equal-area* projection. Such a projection can have the scale the same in *all* directions at only one or (at the most) two points or along one or two lines, these

* The area of the rhombus is *ab*/2. If lengths *a* and *b* in the drawing are made equal to $\sqrt{2}$ then the area of the rhombus = 1.

† $\dfrac{2\sqrt{2} \times \frac{1}{2}\sqrt{2}}{2} = 1$

being construction lines or points around which the rest of the projection is developed. At all other places the scale will be different in different directions from each point. Hence, angles around all such points will be deformed.

Since the scale requirements for conformality and for equivalence in a map projection are essentially opposite, it is apparent that no projection can be both conformal and equivalent. Thus all conformal projections will present similar earth areas with unequal sizes and all equivalent projections will deform most earth angles.

The alterations of areas and angles which occur when the spherical surface is represented on a plane are the most important for the majority of cartographic representations. Two other alterations need to be considered, however, in order that the student may have a sound understanding of what must happen when the one surface is projected to another. One of these concerns the problem of the alteration of distances.

4.7   DISTANCE ALTERATION

It must be thoroughly understood that it is quite impossible to represent at a consistent scale *all* distances of the sphere on a plane. It is possible, on the other hand, to maintain some elements of distance, and on certain types of maps this may assume an importance above even conformality or equivalence. If, for example, one is mapping certain aspects of temperatures on the earth it may be that these are so intimately related to distances north or south from the equator that it might be necessary to retain on the map the appearance of the parallels at their correct spacing. This is possible, but only at the expense of considerable angular alteration or other distortion.

Distance representation is a matter of retaining consistency of scale; that is, for finite distances to be represented "correctly" the scale must be uniform along the ap-

propriate line joining the points being scaled, and must be the same as the scale on the globe from which the projection was made. The following are possible:

(1) Scale may be maintained in one direction, for example, north-south or east-west, but only in one direction. When this is done the parallels or meridians that are the correct scale are called *standard* (see Article 5.3).

(2) Scale may be maintained in all directions from *one* or *two* points, but only from those points. Such projections are called *equidistant*.

Any other scale relationship must be a compromise in order to gain better distance relationships in some or all directions in one part of the map at the expense of the representation in some other part.

4.8   DIRECTION ALTERATION

Just as it is impossible to represent all earth distances with a consistent scale on the flat projection, so also is it impossible to represent all earth directions correctly with straight lines on the map. It is true that conformal projections, for example, the Mercator, represent angular relationships around each point correctly, and it is also true that the conventional Mercator projection provides "straightened" loxodromes. Consequently, if one were to follow on the earth the course shown by a straight line on the map with a constant compass bearing one would actually pass through the points along the line. But the oftstated assertion that the Mercator projection "shows true direction" is erroneous in the sense that *true direction* on the sphere is along a great circle, not along a loxodrome except when the two coincide.

All loxodromes, except for the meridians and the equator, are curved small circles or spiraling lines of constant compass direction. As a matter of fact, if one were to

point to Russia from central United States he would point in a northerly direction, for that is the direction of the great circle joining the two areas. On the Mercator chart western Siberia is shown in a more easterly direction from central United States (see Fig. 4.5).

When directions are defined properly as great circle bearings, and if one thinks of a correct direction as being that shown by a great circle as a straight line on the map having the proper azimuth reading with the local meridian, then certain representations are possible:

(1) The course of great circle arcs between all points may be shown as straight lines for a limited area although the intersections of all the great circles with the meridians (azimuths) will not be shown correctly. To do this causes such a strain, so to speak, on the transformation process that it is not possible to extend it to even an entire hemisphere.

(2) Straight great circles with correct azimuths may be shown for all directions from *one* or, at the most, *two* points. Such projections are called *azimuthal.*

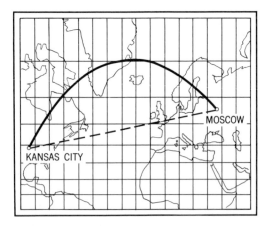

FIGURE 4.5. The great circle and the loxodrome from a point in the United States to a point in Russia. The great circle shown as a solid line is the "true direction" from the one point to the other, not the loxodrome.

Any other direction relationship must be a compromise, just as is the case with distance relationships.

4.9 THE ANALYSIS OF THE AMOUNT OF DEFORMATION

In order to compare one projection with another in terms of the efficiency with which each portrays earth relationships, it is necessary to determine the amount of deformation that occurs from place to place on the projections. Some kinds of deformation, such as directional relationship among widely divergent points, are not capable of being measured. Instead the qualitative judgment of the cartographer must be employed. On the other hand, specific values of some of the usually more important kinds of deformation, such as angular deformation or relative area exaggeration or reduction, can be determined for points or projections. To do this Tissot's indicatrix is employed.

In Article 4.3 the geometric proposition was stated that the surfaces of each of two nonapplicable shapes can be divided into a series of infinitesimal rectangles, each of which on the one surface has its counterpart on the other at a suitable scale. These infinitesimal rectangles are formed as a result of the intersection of a series of orthogonal (meeting at right angles) curves on the one surface whose projection on the second surface are also orthogonal. If the two surfaces are a sphere and a plane, then the system of orthogonal lines on the sphere is transformed on the plane to a system of perpendicular tangents, the relative direction of which has not been changed. The scales in the directions of the tangents on the plane, however, must necessarily have been changed. If angles have been preserved in the projection (conformality), there will be an infinite number of pairs of perpendicular tangents at each point in the directions of which the scale is the same.

If conformality has not been preserved, there will be at each point only one pair of perpendicular tangents preserved on the plane (except at particular points), and the scale at each point in the directions of these tangents will be unequal. The law of deformation states that, whatever the system of representation, *there are at each point of the spherical surface at least two tangents perpendicular to each other which will reappear at right angles to each other on the projection,* although all the other angles at that point may be altered from their original position.

An *infinitely small* circle, the center of which is the intersecting point of the tangents on the spherical surface, will appear on the projection either as a smaller or larger circle, if angles are preserved, or as an ellipse, if angles have not been preserved.* The two perpendicular diameters of the infinitely small circle on the sphere which are retained as perpendicular on the plane constitute the major and minor axes of the ellipse. By an analysis of the geometric changes that have resulted from the transformation of the original circle to an ellipse, one can determine the amount of angular and areal deformation that has occurred at that point. To demonstrate how this may be done an illustration is provided here without the mathematics involved in the computations or their proofs. A more complete development, with the formulas involved, is presented in Appendix I for the interested student.

Figure 4.6 represents a point on the sphere at O. The scale ratio in every direction at O is considered unity so that the point O can be represented by a circle with $OM = 1 =$ the radius r. In the system of projection directions OB and OA are the directions of

---

* If a circle is considered as a special form of an ellipse in which the major and minor axes are equal, then it can be stated that the infinitely small circle on the sphere is always transformed to an infinitely small ellipse. This will simplify subsequent wording.

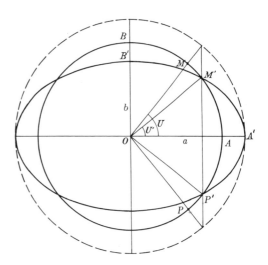

FIGURE 4.6. The indicatrix in the above illustration has been constructed as an equal-area representation of the circle to which the following indices apply: $OM = OB = OA = r = 1$; $OA' = 1.25$; $OB' = 0.80$; $MOA = U = 51°21'40''$; $M'OA' = U' = 38°39'35''$; $U-U' = \omega = 12°42'05''$; $2\omega = 25°24'10''$. (Modified from Marschner.)

the perpendicular tangents on the sphere that are retained as perpendicular in the projection. The scale ratio in the direction OA will be designated as a and that in the direction OB as b. Since $OB = OA = OM$ then a and b in the original circle $= 1$. If the system of projection is equivalent, the original circle will be transformed to an ellipse in which OA' is the semi-major axis and OB' is the semi-minor axis. Since, as was demonstrated in Article 4.6, the product of the scale ratios must be equal in an equivalent projection, then in the projection (the ellipse) $a = 1.25$ and $b = 0.80$. These are the directions of maximum changes in scale, and the values for a and b are all that is necessary to determine for any point on any projection the amount of angular or areal alteration that has occurred at that point.

To analyze first the angular deformation that has taken place at O it is necessary to understand that all points on the circum-

ference of the circle will have their counterparts on the periphery of the ellipse. Point B has been shifted to point B', and A to A' on the ellipse. It is evident that no angular change in these directions has taken place since angle BOA = angle $B'OA'$. All other points on the arc between B and A will, when projected to the ellipse, be shifted a greater or lesser amount in their direction from O. The point subjected to the greatest deflection is identified in the circumference of the circle with M, and has its counterpart in the periphery of the ellipse in point M'. The angle MOA on the sphere thus becomes $M'OA'$ in the projection. If angle MOA = U and angle $M'OA'$ = U', then $U - U'$ denotes the maximum angular deformation within one quadrant. The value of $U - U'$ is designated as *omega* (ω). If an angle such as MOP were to have its sides located in two quadrants and if they were to occupy the position of maximum change in both directions, then the angle in question would be changed to $M'OP'$ and would thus incur the maximum deflection for one quadrant on both sides. Consequently the value 2ω denotes the possible *maximum angular* change that may occur at a point. All other angular deformations at O would be less than 2ω. Since the values of ω will range from $0°$ in the directions of the axes to a maximum somewhere between the axes, it is not possible to state an average angular deformation.

Changes in the representation of areas may or may not be a corollary to the transformation of the circle into an ellipse by the projection system. If there has been a change in the surface area its magnitude can be readily established by comparing the areal contents of the original circle with that of the ellipse. The area of a circle is $r^2\pi$, whereas the area of an ellipse is $ab\pi$, where a and b represent the semimajor and the semiminor axes respectively. Therefore, since the axes of the ellipse are based upon the original circle whose radius was unity and since π is constant, the product of ab

compared to unity expresses how much the areas have been changed. The product of ab is designated as S.

For the purpose of comparing projections only the values of 2ω and S are needed. On conformal projections the scale, by definition, is the same in every direction at a point. The scale differs, however, from point to point. It will be equal to unity at some points; but it will always be the same in every direction around a point. Therefore, on all conformal projections $a = b$ everywhere on the projection. When $a = b$ the value of 2ω is $0°$. Hence there is no angular deformation at points on a conformal projection. But because the values of a and b vary from place to place the product of ab, that is, S, will vary from place to place. Consequently, all conformal projections exaggerate or reduce relative areas, and S at various points provides an index of the degree of areal change.

On equivalent projections the scale relationships at each point are such that the product of ab always equals 1. Except when a and b are equal to unity any difference in the value of a and b will produce a value of 2ω that is greater than $0°$. Consequently, all equivalent projections deform angles and the value of 2ω at various points provides an index of the degree of angular deformation.

On all projections that are neither conformal nor equivalent a will neither equal b nor will the product of $ab = 1$. Therefore, on such projections both the values of S and of 2ω will vary from place to place. Their relative magnitudes will provide an index of the degree of areal change and of the angular deformation.

The values of S and 2ω which occur at various points may be plotted on a projection. The distribution of intermediate values may be shown by drawing lines of equal values. In this manner a diagram showing the pattern of the distribution of angular deformation and areal change over the en-

tire projection may be prepared. Many of the projections illustrated in the following chapters have such distributions shown on them. For some the data have not been determined. It is also possible from such a diagram of the angular or areal deformation on a projection to derive the value of the mean deformation for either the entire projection or for only a portion, such as the land area shown. A comparison of mean values for several similar projections is also helpful in evaluating the relative qualities of different systems of projection.

4.10 OTHER METHODS OF DEPICTING AND RECOGNIZING DEFORMATION

Tissot's indicatrix is limited in its analytical function to values at a point, and when these values are plotted over a projection, one may see the change of deformation from point to point. It does not, however, provide much help in depicting another kind of deformation which exists in all projections, that of changes in the distance and angular relation between widely spaced points or areas such as continents. To date this kind of deformation has not been found to be commensurable, and consequently, graphic means have been employed to help show the change which takes place with respect to the larger spatial relations.

Various devices have been employed to this end, such as a man's head plotted on different projections to illustrate elongation, compression, and shearing of larger areas. Another device has been the covering of the globe with equilateral triangles and then reproducing the same triangles on the different projections. This device appears to be particularly helpful, and the reader is referred to the book by Fisher and Miller, *World Maps and Globes,* Essential Books, New York, 1944, for excellent illustrations of this use of triangles.

One who uses maps frequently is often confronted by a map on a projection which has not been identified (a bad practice) or on an unfamiliar projection. A visual method of recognizing to some extent the kinds and distribution of the deformation may be employed. This involves becoming familiar with certain of the geometric characteristics of the earth's coordinate system, since this supplies a kind of index of the spacing and location of points, and then comparing these same characteristics as they are portrayed by the earth grid on the projection.

The visual characteristics of the earth grid, some of which have been discussed previously, are given in the following list.*

(1) Parallels are parallel.

(2) Parallels are spaced equally on meridians.

(3) Meridians and other great circle arcs are straight lines (if looked at perpendicular to the earth's surface as is true on a map).

(4) Meridians converge toward the poles or diverge toward the equator.

(5) Meridians are equally spaced on the parallels, but their distance apart decreases from the equator to the pole.

(6) Meridians at the equator are spaced the same as parallels.

(7) Meridians at 60° are half as far apart as parallels.

(8) Parallels and meridians cross one another at right angles. (Therefore, with 10 below, the compass rose is the same anywhere.)

(9) The area of the surface bounded by any two parallels and two meridians (a given distance apart) is the same anywhere between the same two parallels.

(10) The scale at each point is the same in any direction.

* In this list several slight variations have been approximated in order that the principles may be more clearly grasped. In (2), parallels actually vary in their spacing by about 0.7 mile; in (6), the discrepancy is negligible; and in (7), there is a difference of about 0.1 mile. None of these approximations would be of significance in a general-use map with a scale smaller than 1:2,000,000.

To illustrate the mental processes the cartographer should employ when analyzing a projection, Figs. 4.7 and 4.8 together with their analyses are given. The numbers of the visual characteristics in the foregoing list, referred to in the legends, are placed in parentheses.

4.11   THE COORDINATE SYSTEM AND
MAP PROJECTION

Repeated operations over a long period of time usually result in the establishment of conventions. These are generally the consequence of the realization that one way of doing something is more convenient or efficient than another way. Map projections have not escaped this process.

Since the earth's surface is that of a sphere it is the same everywhere insofar as its ge-

ometry is concerned. At any point on the earth the surface curves away in all directions at the same rate. One segment is just like any other segment. In order to have something to provide positive identification of location on such a limitless, unchanging surface, man devised the earth's coordinate system. It is so useful that one cannot think of the earth's surface without automatically including it. Consequently, one tends to think of a map of the earth's surface as a map of its coordinate system. Furthermore, because the concept of cardinal directions is so important to man in his thinking about the earth, it has become conventional to represent the surface in such a way as to present these directions to good advantage. This is commonly done by making significant directions appear as straight lines, such as east-west parallels or north-south meridi-

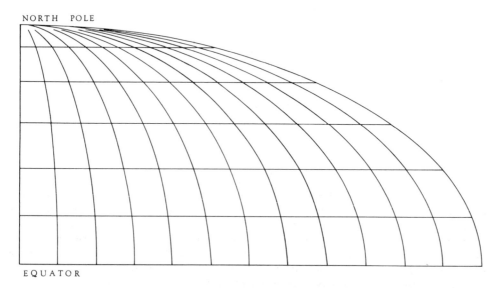

NORTH POLE

EQUATOR

FIGURE 4.7. One quadrant of the Mollweide projection. Since the scale is not the same in every direction (10), as shown by the disproportionate length of the meridian sections at the equator (6), and the compass rose is not the same because parallels and meridians do not cross one another at right angles (8), the projection obviously is not conformal. Because numbers nine (9), and five (5) appear to be satisfied, it is likely that the projection approaches equal-area. Because the parallels are not equally spaced (2) and because they do not always cross meridians at right angles (8), it is evident that angular relations are greatly distorted. (Courtesy *Annals of the Association of American Geographers.*)

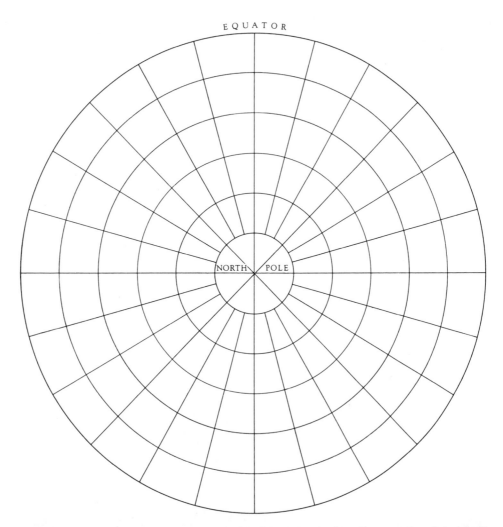

FIGURE 4.8. One hemisphere of the azimuthal equidistant projection. Since a series of straight-line meridians (3), which are, of course, arcs of great circles, converge to a point and are properly arranged around the point as shown by their equal spacing on each parallel (5), the projection must be azimuthal from the point of convergence.   The foregoing plus the fact that the parallels are equally spaced on the meridians (2) make it evident that there is no scale change along the meridians; hence the projection must be equidistant from the point of convergence. Because, however, on the projection the meridians at the equator are not spaced the same as parallels (6) the scale cannot be equal in every direction from each point. Hence the projection cannot be conformal. Also, since the scale along the meridians has been shown to be correct by the spacing of the parallels (2) and because of the fact that azimuths from the pole are correct, it is likely that the central (polar) area is close to truth. If that is true, then the equatorial areas are disproportionately large because of the excessive distances between the meridians (6). Therefore, the projection cannot be equivalent. (Courtesy *Annals of the Association of American Geographers.*)

ans. This necessitates organizing the chosen system of projection in a particular or conventional way.

It is important for the student to realize that, however the system of projection may be arranged or oriented with respect to the earth grid, any system of projection is merely one of transforming a sphere to a plane. The grid theoretically has nothing to do with it. For example, a projection which shows the meridians and parallels as straight lines intersecting at 90° is in reality merely showing one set of great circles which intersect at two points and a series of small circles concentric to those points as parallel orthogonal straight lines. There are an infinite number of such arrangements of great and small circles on a sphere, and whichever set the system of projection displayed, its representation would still be the same. The pattern of deformation and the amounts of deformation would not change.

On the other hand, in working with a spherical surface one must have reference points. The coordinate system provides these. Therefore, since the earth grid is use-ful to establish convenient reference points, because it is well known and because the cardinal directions are important, it is common for a projection system to be applied to the sphere in such a way that the grid is displayed in a regular fashion. This may be accomplished by arranging the system so that deformation is symmetrical around well-known lines such as a meridian or one or two parallels. Such lines, when the scale is held constant along them and is made equal to that on a globe of the same scale, are the standard lines. They constitute reference lines which define the scale employed and from which the scale departs in other parts of the map.

The concept of standard parallels and standard meridians will be used in the next chapter to help describe the conventional form of projections. It should be remembered, however, that the arrangement of the projection system so that standard great circles coincide with the equator or meridians, or so that the standard small circles coincide with parallels, is merely a great convenience; it is not a necessity.

The Employment of Map Projections

5.1 FACTORS INVOLVED IN CHOOSING AND USING A PROJECTION

The necessity to understand the character and uses of the various kinds of projections arises from the fact that there is a great variety of purposes to which maps may be put. Since the number of possible systems of projection is unlimited, the matching of a purpose or need with a system allows a wide range. Fortunately, in practice, the combination of purposes that recur frequently and the fact that a number of systems of projection combine several useful properties result in relatively few projections being commonly used. Anyone who uses maps or who finds it necessary to construct them should have a working knowledge of the character of those more frequently employed or encountered.

A map is a medium of communication constructed to show or make possible the derivation of relationships involving the factors considered in the previous chapter, viz., angles, distances, areas, and directions. The research geographer, historian, or ecologist is likely to be interested in examining the relationships among areas on the earth. He is less concerned with angles and distance; hence he will ordinarily be concerned with the class of projection that delineates the sizes of regions with an accuracy commensurate with his needs. On the other hand, the navigator, meteorologist, aviator, and engineer is usually more concerned with precise measurements or delineation of angles, distances, and directions. These two groups then have quite different needs, the one usually for equivalent projections, the other generally for conformal or azimuthal projections. Combinations of other specific needs dictate the selection of other systems of projection.

A large class of maps (and map users) is concerned not with the portrayal of some one or combination of the facts of spherical geometry but more with the widest possible uses of the map. In this class would be atlas makers, whose reference maps serve a wide clientele.

One of the more important factors involved in selecting projections to be used for general maps is the manner in which the deformation inherent in the projection is arranged with respect to the area covered by the maps. Certain general classes of projections have specific arrangements of the deformation values, and the knowledge of these patterns helps considerably in both choosing and using a particular system.

Maps to be made in series, such as sets for atlases or even topographic series, have dif-

ferent requirements from those made as individual maps. For example, a most useful attribute of some projections is the fact that any portion of it can be cut from the whole and provide a segment, which is in itself a relatively good selection for the smaller area, with good symmetry and deformation characteristics. Any projection in which the meridians are straight lines that meet the parallels at right angles satisfies this requirement. With such a projection it is possible, for example, to make a map of the entire United States and then trace from it separate, overlapping maps of each state, centered in the middle of neat projections.

Consideration of geometrical needs, expediency, methods of subdivision, etc., all play a part in the selection of a system of projection that will give the best result.

A great many maps demand more from the map projection than one or a combination of the major properties of projections (equivalence, conformality, azimuthality). Such projection attributes as parallel parallels, localized area deformation, and rectangular coordinates frequently become greatly significant to the success of a map. For example, a map of some sort of distribution that does not require equivalence may have a concentration of the information in the middle latitudes. In a case of this kind a projection that expanded the areas of the middle latitudes would be a great help by allowing relative detail in the significant areas. Any small-scale map of temperature distributions is made more expressive if the parallels are parallel and even more so if they are straight lines allowing for easy north-south comparisons. A map for which indexing of places is contemplated is more easily done with rectangular coordinates than with any other kind.

The over-all shape of an area on a projection is likewise of great importance. Many times the shape (format) of the page or sheet on which the map is to be made is prescribed. On one map projection the area may fit this format, and on another it may not; but each may have the desirable properties. By utilizing the projection that will fit a format most efficiently a considerable increase in scale can be effected, which may be a real asset to a crowded map.

Because the selection of a projection involves such diverse elements as expediency, publication format, geometric property, and many others, there is likely to be a tendency, common among those who do not quite appreciate the nature of projections, to think of them as but poor representations of an actual globe surface. The selective process then proceeds on the basis of "the least of the evils." Such an attitude leads to the conviction that one projection is intrinsically better than another. Nothing could be farther from the truth. Projections are commonly advantageous for reasons other than the fact that it is cheaper to make a flat map than a globe map. The majority of projections enable us to map distributions and derive and convey concepts that would be quite impossible or at least undesirable on a globe. The truth of the matter is that regardless of how much one is concerned with "deformation," "alteration," "distortion," and all the other concepts used in analyzing, comparing, and describing projections, a projection is a triumph of ingenuity and is a positive, useful device.

The notion that one projection is by nature better than another is as unfounded as saying pliers are better than wrenches. Each (tool or projection) is a device to use for a particular purpose, and some will be good for one purpose and bad for another. There are some projections for which no useful purpose is known, but there is no such thing as a bad projection—there are only poor choices.

5.2 THE CLASSIFICATION OF PROJECTIONS

Since there is an unlimited number of systems for transforming the sphere to a

plane, it would be desirable to be able to classify them in some manner so that their understanding, recognition, and choice would thereby be made easier. Like many other phenomena, however, the classification of projections is "easier said than done." The various methods of projection overlap and shade into one another in so many ways that any single classification leaves much to be desired.

The usual classification of projections is based on construction principles, and that approach is used in the following chapter concerned with the construction of projections. Theoretically, and sometimes actually, projections are constructed on "developable surfaces." These surfaces are those geometric forms capable of being flattened such as a cone or a cylinder (both of which may be cut and laid out flat) or a plane (which is already flat). The grid of the earth is "projected" geometrically or mathe-

matically onto the surfaces which are then developed, that is, flattened. Conventionally, the axis of the earth is aligned with the axes of the cylinder and cone (see Fig. 5.1), so that in a projection based upon a cone, meridians converge in one direction and diverge in the other, and on the flattened cylinder meridians are straight parallel lines. Projections on a plane are not so conventionally aligned, and no generalizations can be made about their appearance. Such a constructional grouping of projections results in categories called cylindrical, conic, azimuthal (plane), and miscellaneous (those based on no geometric form). Occasionally, the cylindrical group is called rectangular. Whatever the terminology employed the grouping is, strictly speaking, not a classification but a listing.

The choice of projections is generally based primarily upon their major property. Each property, for example, equivalence, is

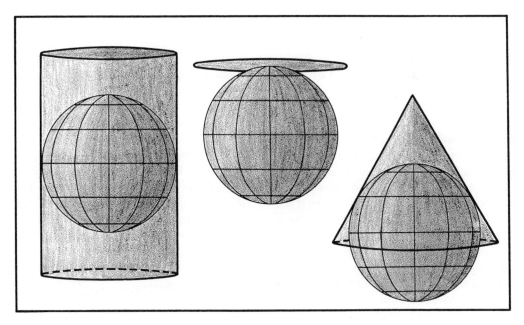

FIGURE 5.1. Some of the surfaces on which the earth's grid may be projected. The origin of the projecting lines may assume various positions. For example, it may be at the center of the earth, or at the antipode of the point of tangency of the plane.

of sufficient significance so that it is usually the first distinguishing characteristic with which the cartographer begins to make his choice. The properties of projections are not entirely mutually exclusive, for there are some azimuthal projections that are also conformal or equivalent. Hence, properties cannot easily be used as a basis for classification. The inherent qualities of the projections in that group which has a particular property are, however, relatively distinctive, and when one such projection is chosen on a utilitarian basis the fact that it has other properties is usually of minor significance.

5.3 TERMS USED TO DESCRIBE PROJECTIONS

Some unfamiliar terminology is necessary to describe adequately some of the elements of the different projections. Some of the terms have been mentioned and their meanings at least implied in the foregoing analysis of the kinds of deformation inherent in projections, but for the sake of completeness they have been included in the following discussion.

Many of the terms will be much clearer if the student will visualize the projection process as consisting of two steps: (1) the reduction of the earth sphere to a globe of a given size or scale, and (2), the projection system then being applied to this scaled-down globe. This enables one easily to compare the various dimensional characteristics of the map and the globe because the RF of the map is the same as that of the globe. If this RF, whatever it may be, is called unity, then one may ignore the complications of small fractions which would be introduced if actual scale values were employed.

(1) *Equivalence* is that quality of a projection in which the product of the quantities *a* and *b* (see Article 4.9) is everywhere the same on the projection. Hence, areas of any size will be represented on the pro-

jection in correct proportion to one another.

(2) *Conformality* is that quality of a projection in which the quantities *a* and *b* are at every point equal but change from point to point. Angles around every point are thus correctly represented.

(3) *Azimuthality* is that quality of a projection in which the angle between any straight line from *A* to *B* on the earth and the meridian at *A* is shown as the same angle as that which would occur on the globe between a meridian at *A* and the great circle arc from point *A* to point *B*.

(4) *Linear scale* refers to the ratio of distance in some direction on the map compared to distance along that same direction on the globe. Where they are the same, the scale is said to be "correct" or "true." Departures from correspondence in linear scale, when stated in numerical terms, are indicated by reference to unity on the reference globe. True scale would therefore be 1.0, enlargement would be indicated by a number greater than 1.0, and reduction correspondingly by one less than 1.0.

(5) *Area scale* is the ratio of areas on the map to areas on the globe. Relative area scales from one place to another are obtained by computing the *S* values referred to in Article 4.9. True or correct area scale (as on the globe) is also unity or 1.0.

(6) *Standard lines* are those great or small circles on the projection which have along them a uniform true linear scale as defined. In the conventional arrangement of the projection system with respect to the globe surface the lines of true scale are commonly represented by parallels or meridians of the earth coordinate system. Hence it is usual to refer to *standard parallels* or *standard meridians*. It is not, however, necessary that standard lines coincide with elements of the earth's coordinate system.

(7) The *central meridian* is the meridian which on the map divides it, or the projection, in equal parts. In many conventional

projections it is the straight line, which may or may not be a standard line, around which the projection is symmetrical, that is, the projection on one side of the central meridian is the mirror image of the other side.

(8) *Angular deformation* (ω) is the change in angular relationships that occur at a point. Since the amount of deviation that takes place varies from 0° to a maximum and then back to zero within any quadrant at any point (see Article 4.9), one cannot state that there is an average value at a point. The maximum angular deformation that could occur at a point is twice the amount that could occur in one quadrant. It is symbolized by 2ω, which is stated in degrees.

(9) *Pattern of deformation* is the arrangement of either S or 2ω values on a projection. It is most easily symbolized and visualized by thinking of the values as representing the "elevations" of an S or 2ω third dimension above the projection. Then "contours" drawn on this surface (see Article 4.9) will show the arrangement of the relative values and by their closeness the gradient or rate of change (see Chapter 10). Most of the projections illustrated in this chapter show such lines of equal deformation, and the lighter shading indicates less deformation. Certain classes of projections have similar patterns of deformation:

(a) A *cylindrical pattern* occurs on all projections which in fact or in principle are developed by transforming the spherical surface to a tangent or an intersecting cylinder. In all cases the lines of equal deformation are straight lines parallel to the standard lines, the least deformation being along the line of tangency or intersection (see Fig. 5.2).
(b) A *conic pattern* results if the transformation is made to the surface of a true cone tangent at a small circle or intersecting at two small circles on the sphere. Lines of equal deformation parallel the standard small circles (Fig. 5.3).

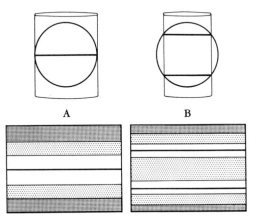

FIGURE 5.2. Cylindrical patterns of deformation. Diagram A shows the pattern when the cylinder is tangent to a great circle; B, when the cylinder is secant and the standard lines are parallel small circles. The darker the shading the more the deformation.

(c) An *azimuthal pattern* occurs if the transformation takes place from the sphere to a tangent or an intersecting plane.* The trace of the intersecting plane and sphere will of course be circular. Lines of equal deformation are concentric arcs around the point of tangency or the center of the circle of intersection (see Fig. 5.4).

Deformation will increase in all these instances away from the standard lines (or point). The greatest gradient will be along a line normal (perpendicular) to the standard line.

(10) *Mean deformation,* either maximum angular or area (2ω or S), is the arithmetic mean of the values that occur over the projection. When derived for similar areas on different projections, a comparison of the mean deformation values provides an index of the relative efficiency of the forms of projection.

* When an intersecting form (cylinder, cone, or plane) is used in the transformation process the resulting projection is commonly termed a *secant* projection. The term is usually applied to the conic forms.

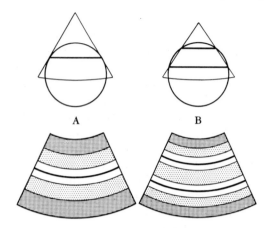

FIGURE 5.3. Conic patterns of deformation. Diagram A shows the pattern when the cone is tangent to one small circle; B, when it intersects along two small circles.

5.4 THE EMPLOYMENT OF EQUIVALENT PROJECTIONS

For general map use the quality of equivalence or near equivalence is perhaps more necessary than any other quality. Although the proper display of certain angular or distance relationships is indispensible for certain uses to which maps are put, the success of the majority of maps in atlases and books does not depend upon geometric relationships. For research tools and for the presentation of results in the geographic, economic, historical, and political fields the map is more than merely a graphic record. The framework of boundaries, rivers, and other base data provides a kind of correlative background for study, and of the elements needed for this background, proper delineation of relative sizes probably takes precedence.

In the presentation of many kinds of distributional data the property of equivalence becomes more than a passive factor. The mapping of some types of statistical and other kinds of information specifically requires that the reader receive the correct visual impression of the relative sizes of the areas involved. If he does not he is likely

to gain an erroneous impression of relative densities. This, of course, is fatal to the purpose of the map which is to present correct visual densities. An example of how this can come about is illustrated in Fig. 5.5.

Many of one's general impressions of the relative extent of various regions are gained subconsciously through frequent experience. Because nonequivalent projections have been so frequently used for general maps in the past, most people think Greenland is considerably larger than Mexico (nearly the same size) and that Africa is smaller than North America (Africa is more than 2,000,000 square miles larger).

It is, of course, clear that if any area measurement, for example, by planimeter, is contemplated, the projection must have a uniform area scale.

The choice among equivalent projections depends upon two important considerations:

(1) The size of the area involved.
(2) The distribution of the angular deformation.

There are a great many possibilities from which to choose, and if the cartographer

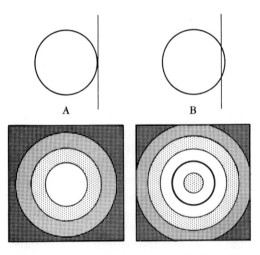

FIGURE 5.4. Azimuthal patterns of deformation. Diagram A shows the pattern when the plane is tangent to the sphere at a point; B, when it intersects along a circle on the earth.

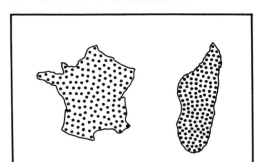

FIGURE 5.5. These two areas (France, left; Madagascar, right) are nearly the same size on the earth. Areas were considerably altered, however, on the projection from which these two outlines were traced, so that France appears larger than it should by comparison to Madagascar. The same number of dots has been placed within each outline, but the apparent density is not the same, although it should be.

will but keep these two elements in mind he will rarely make a bad choice.

In general, the smaller the area to be represented the less significant is the choice of projection for a general map. Any equal-area projection will contain areas of relatively little angular deformation. Consequently, if the area is not large a projection may be chosen with fortuitous deformation relationships for the area involved, and the representation will be practically unassailable. For large areas or the whole earth the distribution of the deformation becomes of paramount significance. The areas of topical importance on the map should be represented in the best fashion possible by the choice of a projection with an advantageous distribution of deformation.

A few representative types of equivalent projections are shown and brief notes on their employment given. Most of the illustrations show lines of equal angular deformation so that the pattern of deformation will be apparent. Since the values of the lines vary on the different illustrations, it is necessary for the reader to note the values carefully if he wishes to compare the various projections. The areas shown with lighter shading on the drawings are the areas of lesser deformation. Because equivalent projections are often employed for world maps it is convenient to consider this class separately. Consequently, equivalent projections appropriate for areas of lesser extent are dealt with first, and then those appropriate for world maps are considered as a separate class. This is not entirely consistent; some parts of projections appropriate for world maps are also useful for specific types of smaller areas.

The Albers projection (Fig. 5.6) has two standard parallel small circles (usually parallels of the coordinate system) along which there is no angular deformation. Because it is conically derived, deformation zones are arranged parallel to the standard lines as shown. Any two small circles in one hemisphere may be chosen as standard, but the closer together they are, of course, the better will be the representation in their immediate vicinity. Because of the low deformation value and the neat appearance in its conventional form with straight meridians and concentric arc parallels which meet the meridians at right angles, this is a good projection for any middle-latitude area of greater east-west extent and a lesser north-south extent. Outside the standard parallels the scale along the meridians is progressively reduced. Parallel curvature ordinarily becomes excessive if the projection is extended for much over 100° longitude. In recent decades the Albers has replaced other projections (notably the Polyconic) as the common choice for many kinds of maps of the United States. Its obvious superiority for maps of political subdivisions and for those on which to plot and study geographical distributions has led to its selection as the standard base map by many governmental agencies such as the Bureau of the the Census or the Bureau of Agricultural Economics.

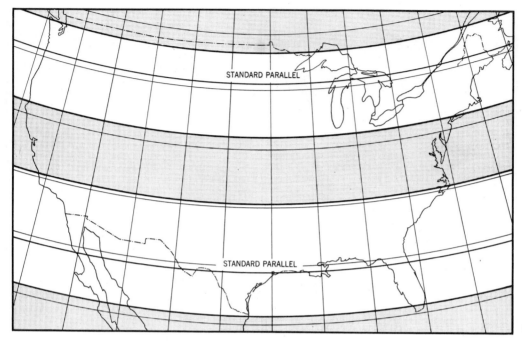

FIGURE 5.6. The Albers conic projection. Values of lines of equal maximum angular deformation are 1°.

The Bonne projection (Fig. 5.7) has a standard central meridian along which there is no deformation. Any parallel may be chosen on which to center the projection and all the others will parallel it. The representation decreases in angular quality outward from the central meridian and away from the central parallel. This projection is a better choice for an area of somewhat greater north-south extent than east-west extent because the parallels are all standard and the linear scale along the meridians is not excessively enlarged near the center. The Bonne projection formerly enjoyed great popularity and was commonly used as the projection for many of the earlier topographic series of Europe. The increasing significance of angular qualities for the military as well as other uses of topographic maps has made a substitution desirable. Although it is still seen in general atlas maps, its use is decreasing.

The Lambert equal-area projection (Fig. 5.8) is both azimuthal and equivalent. Its azimuthal properties are described in Article 5.8. Since deformation is symmetrical around the central point, which can be located anywhere, the projection is useful for areas which have nearly equal east-west and north-south dimensions. Consequently, areas of continental proportions are well represented on this projection. It is limited to hemispheres. As a base for general maps it is replacing the formerly much used Bonne projection.

5.5 EQUIVALENT PROJECTIONS USED FOR WORLD MAPS

The surface area of the earth may be plotted in equivalent fashion within the bounding lines of almost any kind of plane figure. Numerous possibilities have been tried out, but most of them have had more

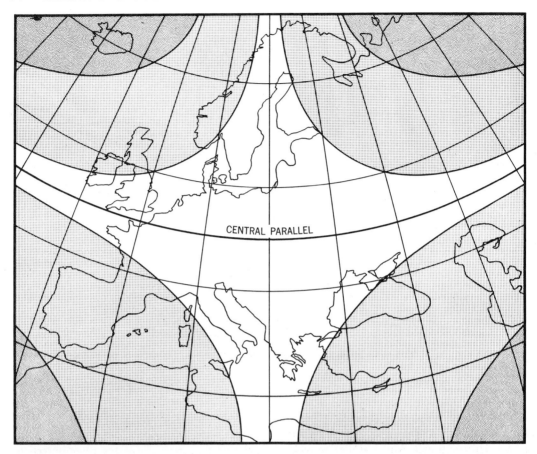

CENTRAL PARALLEL

**FIGURE 5.7. The Bonne projection. Values of lines of equal maximum angular deformation are 1°
and 5°.**

theoretical interest than practical utility.
Only a few examples can be examined here.

Any world equal-area projection will
necessarily have considerable angular deformation, for the modification of angular
relationships necessary to maintain the
relationship of $ab = 1$ over the entire projection is great. The value of the mean
maximum angular deformation is an index
of relative quality in this respect; but, because "general appearances" and some
rather illogical concepts seem important in
the selection of world map projections, this
kind of index has not gained much favor.
For example, the notion is very strong that

the pole is in reality a "point of beginning" on the earth. As a result, a projection that shows meridians converging to an
actual point is likely to be more favored
than one which gives this spot some dimension, even though the over-all representation
may not be so good. Such other factors as
the appearance of parallel parallels, or a
straight line equator, or true spacing of
parallels on a central meridian may well
transcend considerations of over-all angular deformation.

The cylindrical equal-area projection
(Fig. 5.9) is one example of this method of
projection that is capable of variation like

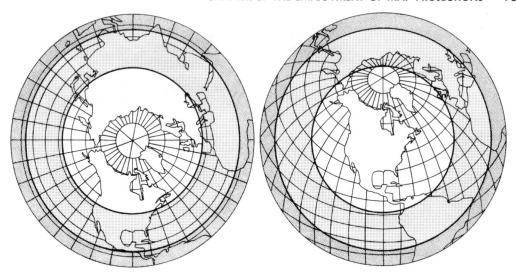

FIGURE 5.8. The Lambert azimuthal equal-area projection. Values of lines of equal maximum angular deformation are 10° and 25°.

the Albers conic. That is, the projection is constructed on the basis of two parallel standard small circles, usually parallels of latitude. The two parallels may "coincide," so to speak, and be the equator, or they may be any others so long as they are homolatitudes (the same parallels in opposite hemispheres). Deformation is ar-

ranged, of course, parallel to the standard small circles. Although for a variety of reasons this projection "looks peculiar" to many people, it does in fact provide, when standard parallels just under 30° are chosen, the least *mean* deformation of any equal-area world projection!

The sinusoidal projection (Fig. 5.10) when

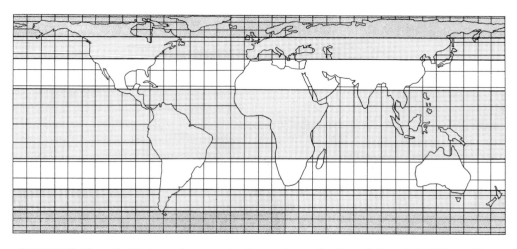

FIGURE 5.9. The cylindrical equal-area projection, with standard parallels at 30°. Values of lines of equal maximum angular deformation are 10° and 40°.

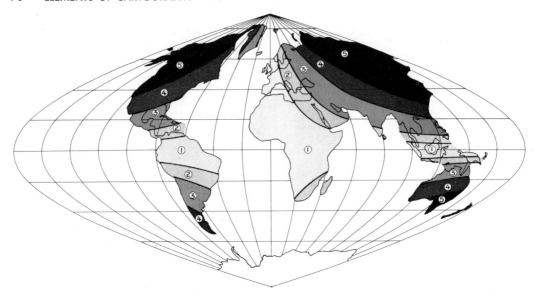

FIGURE 5.10. The sinusoidal projection excluding Antarctica. Values of zones of angular deformation are (1) 0°–10°, (2) 10°–20°, (3) 20°–40°, (4) 40°–60°, and (5) over 60°.

conventionally oriented has the merit of a straight central meridian and equator, along both of which there is no angular deformation. Because of the excessive shearing in the higher latitudes this projection has the largest mean angular deformation of any of the familiar world equal-area projections. On the other hand, a merit of this projection is that the parallels are the same "vertical" distance apart, giving the *illusion* of proper spacing so that it is useful for representations where latitudinal relations are significant. The sinusoidal, because of its small angular deformation along the equator and central meridian, is particularly suitable when properly centered for maps of less-than-world areas such as South America for which the deformation distribution is especially fortuitous.

The oval Mollweide projection (Fig. 5.11) does not have the pointed polar areas of the sinusoidal and thus it appears a bit more realistic. In order to attain equivalence within its oval shape it is necessary to decrease the north-south scale in the high

latitudes and increase it in the low latitudes. The opposite is true in the east-west direction. Shapes are modified accordingly. The two areas of least deformation in the middle latitudes make the projection useful for world distributions when interest is concentrated in those areas.

The Eckert IV (Fig. 5.12) is the best known of several similar equivalent projections. The pole is represented by a line half the length of the equator instead of by a point, so that the polar areas are not quite so compressed in the east-west direction as on the preceding two projections. This takes place, however, at the expense of their north-south representation. As in the Mollweide the equatorial areas are stretched in the north-south direction. Deformation distribution is similar to that of the Mollweide.

A recently devised projection (Fig. 5.13) utilizes a polar line one-third the length of the equator instead of one-half as in the Eckert IV. It has been called the flat polar quartic authalic (equal-area). As might be

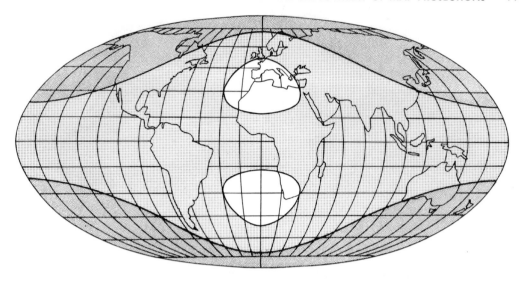

FIGURE 5.11. The Mollweide projection. Values of lines of equal maximum angular deformation are 10° and 40°.

inferred from a comparison between the mean deformations of the Sinusoidal, Eckert IV, and the cylindrical equal-area, the value of the mean deformation for the flat polar quartic equal-area projection lies between the Eckert IV and the Sinusoidal.

Mention should also be made of the possibility of combining different projections in order to utilize the better parts of each. One of these is called the homolosine projection developed by the late Professor J. Paul Goode of the University of Chicago.

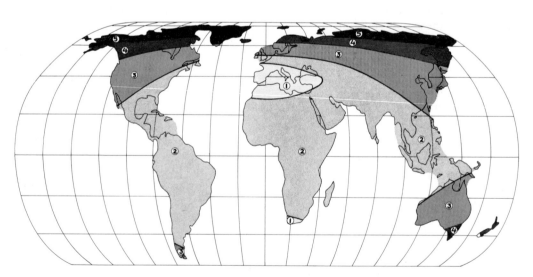

FIGURE 5.12. The Eckert IV projection. Values of zones of equal maximum angular deformation are (1) 0°–10°, (2) 10°–20°, (3) 20°–40°, (4) 40°–60°, and (5) over 60°.

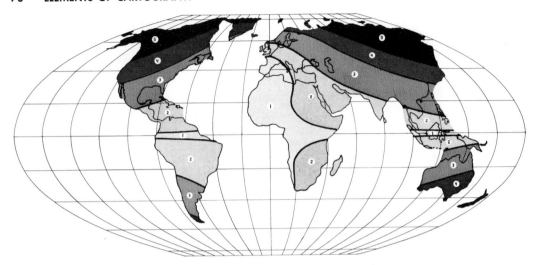

FIGURE 5.13. The flat polar equal-area projection. Values of zones of angular deformation are (1) 0°–10°, (2) 10°–20°, (3) 20°–40°, (4) 40°–60°, and (5) over 60°. (Courtesy *Annals of the Association of American Geographers.*)

This projection is a combination of the equatorial section of the sinusoidal and the poleward sections of the Mollweide; thus, it is equal-area. The Mollweide is sometimes called the "homolographic," hence the combined form homolo + sine. The two projections, when constructed to the same area scale, have one parallel of identical length* along which they may be joined. It is usually used in interrupted form (see the next article), and has been widely employed in the United States, although its over-all quality as shown by a comparison of mean values of deformation is not appreciably better than the Mollweide alone.

5.6   THE INTERRUPTION OF WORLD PROJECTIONS

In order to display better the land areas of the earth on an equal-area world projection, it is possible to interrupt the projec-

---

* J. Paul Goode, "The Homolosine Projection: A New Device for Portraying the Earth's Surface Entire," *Annals of the Association of American Geographers,* 1925, Vol. 15, pp. 119–125.

tion, that is, construct the projection in such a way as to repeat the zones of lesser deformation.

All that is necessary to interrupt and re-center a projection constructed in the conventional manner is that the parallels be uniformly subdivided by the meridians, or, to put it another way, that the linear scale along each parallel be uniform. Any number of central meridians may be chosen and the grid constructed around each; no central meridian need extend any particular latitudinal distance; the central meridians in opposite hemispheres need not match; and, as a matter of fact, a "central meridian" may even be displaced from latitude to latitude. In spite of these almost unlimited possibilities, cartographers have been relatively conservative in presenting interrupted projections. Professor Goode popularized the interruption process, applying it to his homolosine projection. Many projections that lend themselves to interruption have not been so treated.

The majority of the projections that have been interrupted have been equivalent pro-

jections. Without interruption the property of uniform *area* scale, so useful to the student of earth distributions, puts such a strain on the *linear* scale relationships that all these projections have a relatively high degree of angular deformation. The angular alteration is, of course, least along the lines of minimum linear scale discrepancy or, in such cases as the Mollweide and Eckert IV, for example, around the points of minimum linear scale discrepancy. When, through interruption and recentering, these lines or points are duplicated on the presentation, then no land area need be far removed from the area of least angular alteration. Thus, the deformation of the significant parts of the map, usually the land, may be considerably reduced. This is evident from even a cursory consideration, and it is rather surprising, to say the least, that so simple a method for reducing angular alteration was not thought of earlier.*

* Arthur H. Robinson, "Interrupting a Map Projection: A Partial Analysis of its Value," *Annals of the Association of American Geographers*, 1953, Vol. 43, pp. 216–225.

A comparison of Fig. 5.14, an interrupted flat polar quartic equal-area projection, with the uninterrupted form of Fig. 5.13 shows how the representation of the land has been improved by repetition of the better areas. The mean maximum angular deformation is reduced by nearly one-half. An analysis of before-and-after values shows that there is a considerable difference among the mean values of uninterrupted projections, but that after interruption in the manner illustrated, there is little to choose among them from the point of view of angular deformation.

Another operation which is commonly applied to world equal-area map projections is to condense them, that is, cut away the unnecessary water areas (if the land is the concern). This does not improve the deformation aspects, but it obviously does make it possible to employ a larger scale within a given format. Figure 5.15 shows this result.*

* This condensed form of the flat polar quartic equal-area projection was employed as the base for world maps in Finch, Trewartha, Robinson, and Hammond, *Elements of Geography*, 4th Ed., McGraw-Hill Book Co., New York, 1957.

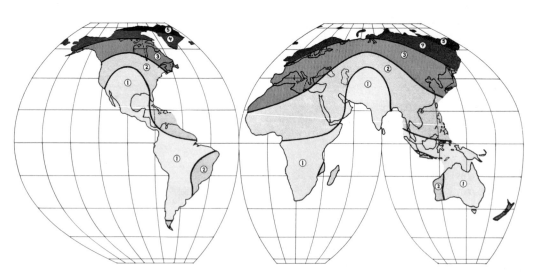

FIGURE 5.14. An interrupted flat polar equal-area projection. The values of the zones of angular deformation are the same as in Fig. 5.13. (Courtesy *Annals of the Association of American Geographers*.)

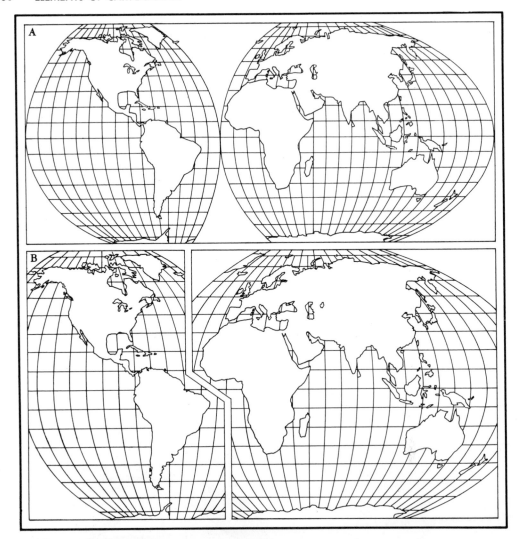

FIGURE 5.15. An interrupted, flat polar quartic equal-area projection (A) compared to one which has been condensed as well as interrupted (B).

5.7   THE EMPLOYMENT OF CONFORMAL PROJECTIONS

Maps which are to be used for analyzing, guiding, or recording motion and angular relationships require the employment of conformal projections. In these categories fall the navigational charts of the mariner or aviator, the plotting and analysis charts of the meteorologist, and the general class of topographic maps. For topographic maps the property of conformality is not quite so indispensable as it is for maps to be used for the other purposes, since topographic maps serve many needs that do not require conformality. The average topographic map covers such a small area of the earth's curved surface that any departure from reality will ordinarily be negligible. When precise measurements are made on

topographic maps, it is usually angular measurement; hence it is natural that such maps would be made on conformal projections if at all possible.

Just because, by definition, the property of conformality implies true angular relationships around all points it must not be assumed that the directions between points some distance apart are likely to be correct if the map covers any significant part of the earth's surface. Because there is no angular deformation at any point on a conformal map the notion is widespread that shapes of countries and continents are well presented on projections having this quality. Although it is correct to state that very small areas on conformal projections are practically perfect, it is also true that in order to retain angular representation it is necessary to alter the area relationships. Thus, on conformal projections the area scale varies from point to point, and consequently large areas are imperfectly represented with respect to shape.

It is difficult to express deformation on a conformal projection, for, in a sense, there is nothing deformed since all angular relationships at each point are retained. All that changes is the linear scale, and one point is as "accurate" as another; only the scales are different. Thus one may refer to the standard lines or points as having a particular scale and then refer to the other areas as being *relatively* exaggerated or reduced.

Some of the conformal projections together with some notes on their qualities follow.

The Mercator projection (Fig. 5.16) is one of the most famous projections ever devised. It was introduced in 1569 by the famous Dutch cartographer as a device for navigation, and it has served this purpose well. It has the property that all loxodromes are represented as straight lines, an obvious advantage to one trying to proceed along a compass course. Except for the meridians and the equator, directions (great-circle courses) are not straight lines, so this projection does not show "true direction"; but such courses

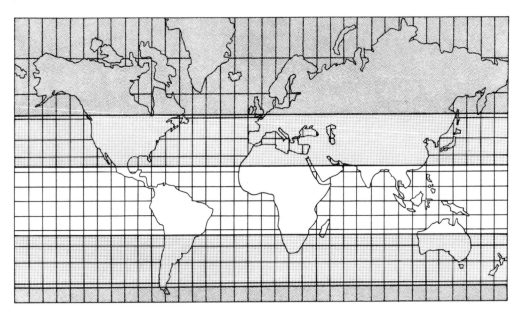

FIGURE 5.16. The Mercator projection. Values of lines of equal area exaggeration are 25% and 250%.

can be easily transferred from a projection (gnomonic) that does so. A series of straight "chords" or rhumb lines can thus approximate a great circle. It is apparent that the projection enlarges (not distorts) areas greatly in the higher latitudes, so it is of little use for purposes other than navigation. Also the poles cannot be represented for they are "at" infinity on the conventional Mercator. This is a distinct handicap in these days when the polar areas are of more than usual significance. The Mercator projection is particularly useful for navigation in the equatorial and middle latitudes. Almost all nautical charts are made on this projection.

The Lambert conic projection (Fig. 5.17) is very similar in appearance to the Albers equivalent projection, for it too has concentric parallels and equally spaced, straight meridians that meet the parallels at right angles. Like the Albers it has two standard parallels, but the spacing of the other parallels on the Lambert increases away from the standard parallels. Area exaggeration between and near the standard parallels is relatively small, and thus the projection provides exceptionally good directional and shape relationships for an east-west latitudinal zone. Consequently, the projection is much used for air navigation in intermediate latitudes (4° to 72°) and for meteorological charts.

The stereographic projection (Fig. 5.18) belongs also in the azimuthal group. Like the other azimuthal projections the deformation (in this case area exaggeration) increases outward from the central point symmetrically. As in the case of the equivalent azimuthal this is desirable when the area to be represented is more or less square or of continental proportions. In addition to being conformal and azimuthal the stereographic has an additional attribute which no other projection has. All circles on the earth remain as circles on the projection. It is possible therefore to plot the ranges of radiating objects, from radio

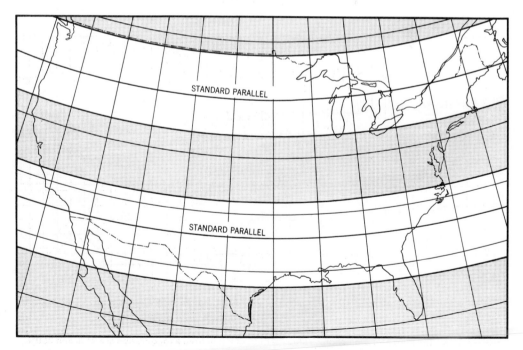

STANDARD PARALLEL

STANDARD PARALLEL

FIGURE 5.17. The Lambert conformal conic. Values of lines of equal areal exaggeration are 2%.

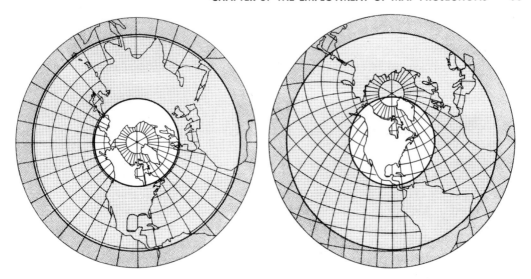

FIGURE 5.18. The stereographic projection. Values of lines of equal areal exaggeration are 30% and 200% (approximately).

waves to airplanes, merely with a compass. This projection, centered on a pole, is much used for navigation in the very high latitudes.

It bears repeating that recent practice has turned to the selection of conformal projections for topographic maps. Each of the mentioned three projections is so used in one form or another. The most widely used are the Lambert conic and a transverse form of the Mercator. The latter is of considerable significance because it has been chosen as the projection for at least twenty of the modern topographic series. In addition, it is the basis for a rectangular grid system employed for military purposes. It is also called the Gauss conformal after the mathematician who first devised it. The manner in which a projection is "transversed" is considered in Article 5.10.

5.8   THE EMPLOYMENT OF AZIMUTHAL PROJECTIONS

The azimuthal projections have long been known but only recently have they been resurrected to a position of prominence, or perhaps notoriety, among map projections.

The popular notion that we have entered an "air age" provided many map makers with the need for displaying the earth on projections that were better fitted for the requirements of this modern era. They commonly choose the azimuthal projections. It may turn out that the choice of just any azimuthal in many cases was not a wise selection. Like the other categories the azimuthal group has a number of types, each with quite different properties.

All azimuthal projections do have, however, certain qualities which are peculiar to this class. The projections are theoretically (or actually) "projected" upon a plane perpendicular to a line passing through the center of the sphere. Such a line may, of course, meet the surface of the sphere at any point; consequently, these projections are symmetrical around a chosen center. The scale variation (and it must vary either linearly or areally) in all cases radiates from the center at the same rate in every direction. If the plane is made tangent to the sphere, there is no deformation of any kind at the center. Furthermore, since all these projections are "projected" on a plane parallel to a tangent to the sphere, all great

circles passing through the center point will be straight lines on the projection and will show the correct azimuths from the center to any point. It should be emphasized that only azimuths (directions) *from the center* are correct on an azimuthal projection.

At the center point all azimuthal projections of the same scale are identical, and the variation among them is merely a matter of the linear scale differences along the straight great circles that similarly radiate from the center. Figure 6.10 illustrates this relationship. Any azimuthal projection may be changed to any other one by changing the scale relations along the azimuths. There is no angular deformation at the center, and the fact that the deformation radiates symmetrically makes this class of projections useful for areas having more or less equal dimensions in each direction, or for maps in which interest is not localized in one dimension. Because any azimuthal projection can be centered anywhere and still present a reasonable appearing grid the class is rather more versatile than others. We frequently see an azimuthal projection with the north pole as the center, for it is easy to draw and provides an illusion of reality because of the regularity of the grid. Except for the basic properties the other qualities of azimuthal projections so centered are somewhat wasted.

The gnomonic projection (Fig. 5.19), like the Mercator, is one of the most used projections of any class. It has the unique property that all great-circle arcs are represented *anywhere on the map* as straight lines. Therefore the navigator need but join the points of departure and destination with a straight line and his course is determined. Because compass directions constantly change along a great circle, the navigator transfers the course from the gnomonic grid to the Mercator grid and then approximates it with a series of loxodromes which are straight lines on the Mercator. The deformation, both angular and areal, increases rapidly away from the center so that the projection is not much good for any purpose other than showing great circles as straight lines. Because projection is from the center of the earth on the tangent plane, less than a hemisphere can be constructed.

The azimuthal equidistant projection (Fig.

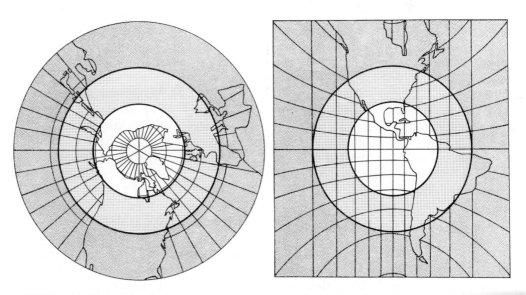

FIGURE 5.19. The gnomonic projection. Values of lines of equal angular deformation are 10° and 25°. Areal exaggeration, extreme toward the peripheries, is also present.

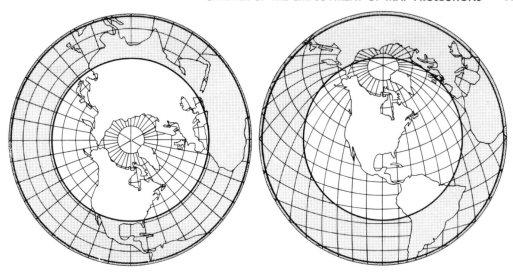

FIGURE 5.20. The azimuthal equidistant projection of a hemisphere. Values of lines of equal maximum angular deformation are 10° and 25°. Areal exaggeration is also present.

5.20) has become popular in recent years. It has the unique quality that the linear scale does not vary along the radiating azimuths from the center. Therefore the position of every place is shown in consistent relative position and distance *from the center.* Directions and distances between points whose connection does not pass through the center are not shown correctly. It is apparent, then, that unless movement from the center outward is of major significance, the azimuthal and equidistant qualities may be wasted and some other projection might be a better choice. Any kind of travel that emanates from a center is well shown on this projection. The projection has an advantage over many of the other azimuthal projections in that it is possible to show the entire earth on the projection (see Fig. 5.21). Most azimuthals are limited to presenting a hemisphere or less.

The orthographic projection (Fig. 5.22) looks like a photograph of the earth grid taken from a considerable distance although it is not quite the same. For this reason it might almost be called a visual projection in that the deformation of areas and angles, although great, is not particularly apparent

to the viewer since it appears the same as though he were looking at a portion of the globe. On this account it is useful for presenting some kinds of directional concepts (for example, Europe as seen from the south), illustrative maps, and for those maps wherein the sphericity of the earth is of major significance.

The employment of the stereographic projection, a conformal azimuthal, was considered in Article 5.7, and the Lambert equal-area azimuthal, in Article 5.4.

An infinite number of azimuthal projections are possible and many have been devised but not widely used. A vertical air photograph is an azimuthal projection as is a photograph of the heavens.

5.9   THE EMPLOYMENT OF OTHER SYSTEMS OF PROJECTION

There are any number of projections possible which have none of the precise relationships considered in the previous sections. Some of them are very useful indeed. In this group would fall those projections which have extremely little linear, angular, or areal scale error for small areas but which can be

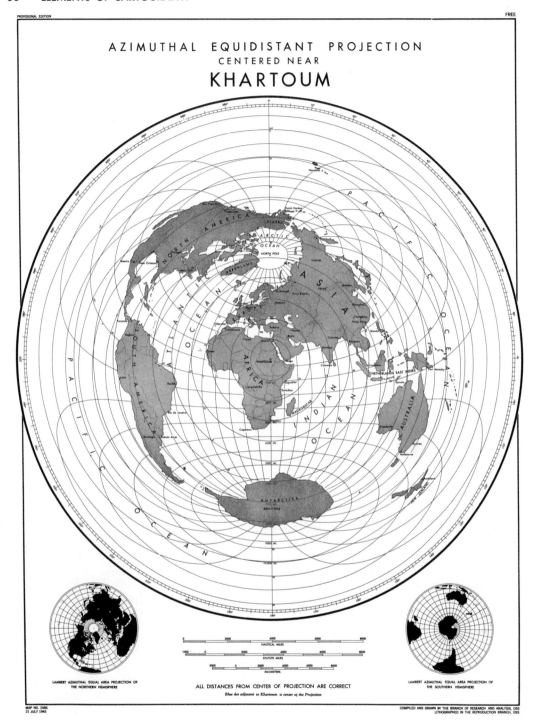

FIGURE 5.21. An azimuthal equidistant projection of the world centered near Khartoum. Note the excessive deformation around the margin. The outer circle is actually a point, the antipode of the center.

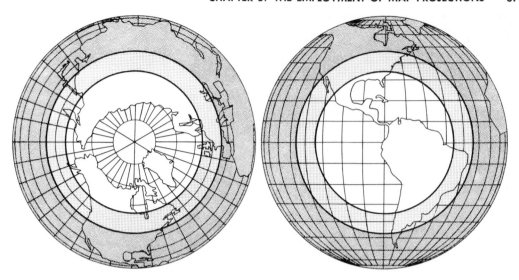

FIGURE 5.22. The orthographic projection. Values of lines of equal maximum angular deformation are 10° and 25°. Areal deformation is also present.

quickly constructed. Similarly, a projection system that can be developed for individual sections of the earth in such a manner that individual sheets will fit precisely but which have the same pattern of deformation on each sheet is very useful. In this class are the polyconic, the modified polyconic, and a number of others.

The polyconic was first widely used in the United States by the Coast and Geodetic Survey, and it was subsequently adopted as the projection for the standard topographic series of the U. S. Geological Survey. Figure 5.23 shows a polyconic development for a considerable area on which its general characteristics are more easily seen. It has a straight central meridian along which the linear scale is correct. The parallels are arcs of circles, but each is a standard parallel in the sense that it is truly subdivided by the meridians and each is drawn with the proper radius for its cone and hence with its own center. Thus the parallels are not concentric. The linear scale along each parallel is correct, but the scale along the curved meridians increases with increasing distance from the central meridian. The projection

is, of course, neither conformal nor equivalent. On the other hand, when it is used for a small area, bisected by a central meridian, both these qualities are so closely approached that the departure is very small. For the mapping of a large area on a large scale the development of each small section on its own polyconic projection is therefore desirable. Each small section will fit perfectly with the adjacent ones to the north or south, but on account of the curved meridians they will not fit together east-west. The scale error within the usual 15' quadrangle of the standard topographic map of the United States is insignificant and usually less than that which results from paper shrinkage or expansion. Although it is admirably suited for individual maps covering small areas, it is clearly not suited for maps of larger areas. A number of others are definitely preferable for an area even the size of a midwestern state in the United States.

The polyconic used for the so-called Millionth Map or International Map of the World was modified by making the meridians straight instead of curved, and by making two of them, instead of one, stand-

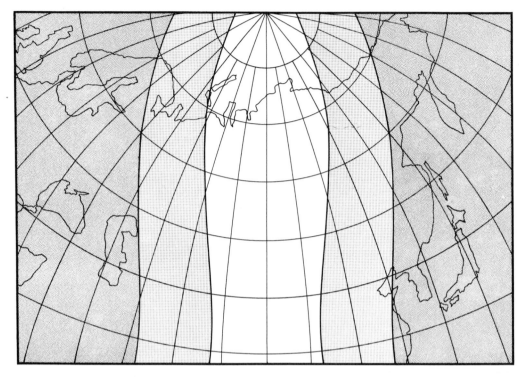

FIGURE 5.23. The polyconic projection of a large area. Values of lines of equal maximum angular deformation are 1° and 5°. Areal deformation is also present.

ard on each sheet. Whereas in the ordinary polyconic all parallels are standard, in the modified polyconic only the bottom and top one in each sheet are standard. This makes it possible to fit sheets together east-west as well as north-south at the slight expense of some linear and area scale variation. The diagonal sheets cannot fit. On the ordinary map sheet 4° of latitude by 6° of longitude the scale errors are considerably less than 1 in 1,000.

The equirectangular projection (Fig. 5.24) is one of the oldest and simplest of map projections. It is useful for city plans or base maps of small areas. It is easily constructed, and for a limited area has small deformation. All meridians and any chosen central parallel are standard. It may be centered anywhere.

The conic with two standard parallels

(Fig. 5.25) is similar in appearance to the Albers and Lambert conic projections but it has no special properties. It does not distort either areas or angles to a very great degree if the standard parallels are placed close together and provided the projection is not extended far north and south of the standard parallels. It is frequently chosen for areas in middle latitudes of too large an extent for an equirectangular projection, and for maps not requiring the precise properties of equivalence or conformality.

There are numerous other map projections which have no special properties. Only the major forms have been illustrated here, but there are many other modifications which have been made for special purposes. For example, O. M. Miller of the American Geographical Society devised a spacing of parallels for a rectangular projection which

would allow the poles to be shown but which would have neither the excessive areal exaggeration of the Mercator nor provide the appearance of excessive angular deformation of the rectangular equal-area.

5.10 TRANSVERSE AND OBLIQUE PROJECTIONS

There is no absolute need for the spherical surface of the earth to be represented by the system of projection in the conventional manner so that the set of the great and small circles that form the earth's coordinate system will appear as regular or smooth lines on the projection. Although it is conventional and usually desirable, it is not necessary. Projections are systems of transformation of the sphere to a plane, not systems of transformation of the earth grid to a plane. That this is so is easily demonstrated by reference to the azimuthal class of projections (and to their illustrations shown) which may be centered anywhere. Although the earth's coordinate net appears differently, depend-

ing upon the location of the center, the angular and areal relations of the projected surface will not vary because the surface of a sphere does not vary and neither does the surface of the plane on which it is projected.

One way of visualizing an arrangement other than the usual one for projections is to think of the coordinate system as being loose on the sphere while the land and water bodies remain stationary. Then it would be possible to slide or shift the grid in any way desired. One might even go so far as to turn it 90° so that the equator of the grid coincides with a former meridian and runs through the Arctic and Antartic regions, whereas the poles of the loose grid remain antipodal points, both now located where the former equator used to be, as in Fig. 5.26. If one then were to construct an ordinary Mercator projection symmetrical around the new equator, the result would be a projection which is, of course, conformal. But, instead of representing the areas in the tropics in the best fashion, it would present the

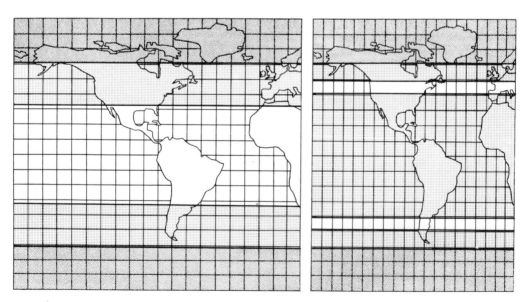

FIGURE 5.24. The plane chart or equirectangular projection. On the left the standard parallel is the equator; on the right, 45°. Values of lines of equal maximum angular deformation are 10° and 40°. Areal deformation is also present.

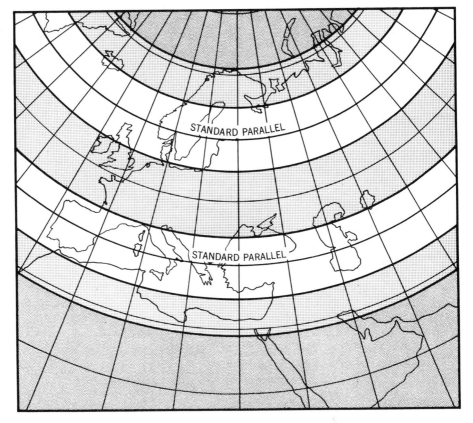

FIGURE 5.25. The conic with two standard parallels. Values of lines of equal maximum angular deformation are 1° and 2° (approx.). Areal deformation is also present.

areas along a meridian and across the poles in the best fashion (Fig. 5.27). It should be pointed out that most loxodromes would not be straight lines on this form of the Mercator.

Projections of the earth that are not conventionally oriented with respect to the earth grid are usually called *oblique* (Fig. 5.28) if the grid has been shifted less than 90° from its normal position and *transverse* if the full 90° shift has been made. Sometimes the transverse is also termed *polar*.

Any projection may be treated this way, and since the structural relations of the projection are not changed, regardless of the appearance of the grid, many cartographic representations of earth relations can be bet-

tered by "shifting the land masses" to bring about a better distribution of the deformation pattern with respect to the areas of interest.

5.11   THE TRANSVERSE MERCATOR PROJECTION

One of the commonly used projections of this type is the transverse Mercator referred to previously. It has been widely used to provide a conformal projection base for topographic maps. Because the scale departures are uniform along lines that parallel the standard great circle it is possible to construct over the map area a rectangular coordinate reference grid that has the merit that a given X value will have a uniform

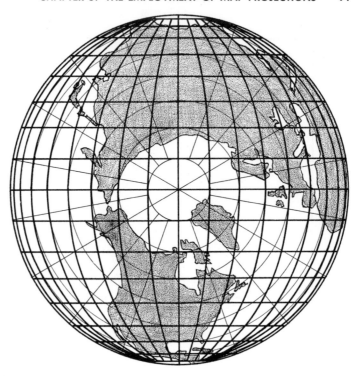

FIGURE 5.26. A polar ortho-graphic projection with an equatorial grid. Since the earth is spherical, the coordinate system will "fit" it in any position.

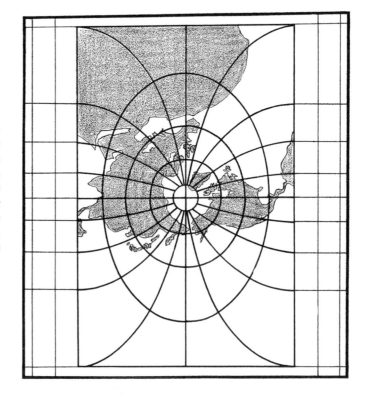

FIGURE 5.27. The transverse Mercator. This form of the Mercator gives a conformal representation with the least deformation along the meridian chosen as the "equator." It would be useful, for example, for an air chart of a route in a north-south direction. The conventional grid is shown on the sides.

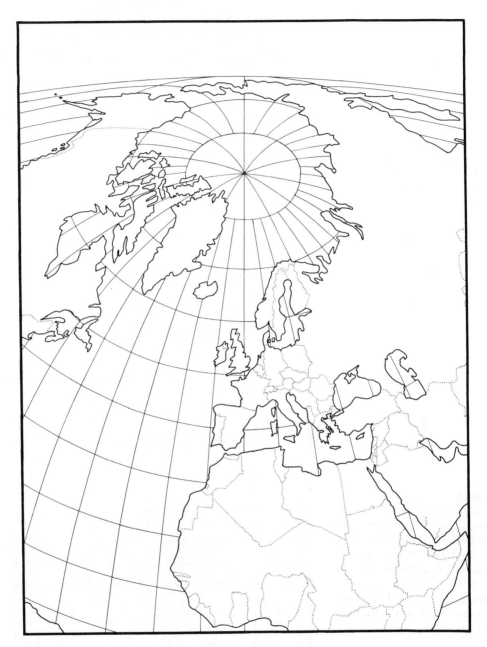

FIGURE 5.28. A portion of an oblique Mollweide. This is exactly the same projection system as shown in Figs. 5.11 and 6.19. North Atlantic relations are well presented on this representation, which gives somewhat the appearance of a portion of a globe, but is, of course, equal-area.

scale characteristic at any Y value. Such a rectangular coordinate reference system has many practical advantages over the ordinary geographical grid reference system involving latitude and longitude. Figure 5.29 shows how the grid is arranged with the vertical lines parallel to the central meridian and the horizontal lines perpendicular to it. Because the Mercator projection is cylindrical in concept the lines of equal deformation are small circles paralleling the standard great circle. In the conventional Mercator the standard great circle is the equator and the parallel small circles are, of course, parallels of latitude. In the transverse Mercator the projection has been turned 90° and a meridian is the standard great circle. The

parallel small circles, which were actually parallels in the conventional Mercator, are then represented by the vertical parallel lines on the rectangular grid system. The horizontal lines of the grid system are equally spaced great circles that cross the central meridian at right angles. They correspond to the earth meridians on the conventional Mercator.

In order to improve the scale characteristics the theoretical cylinder of the transverse Mercator is assumed to intersect the earth's surface along two of the small circles instead of being tangent at the central great circle. This distributes the deformation more evenly over the map as shown in Fig. 5.30.

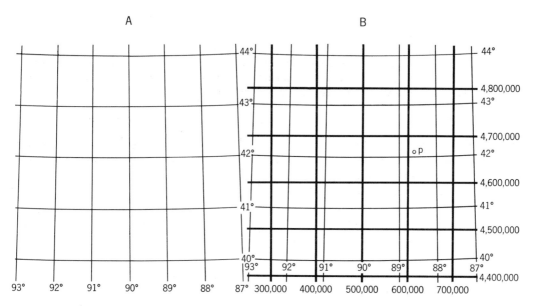

FIGURE 5.29. The diagram on the left (A) shows the earth's coordinate system as represented on a transverse Mercator projection. Diagram B shows a transverse Mercator rectangular coordinate system placed over the geographic grid and arranged so that the vertical lines are parallel, and the horizontal lines are normal, to the lines of equal scale departure on the projection. To make all grid references positive a false origin is assumed to the southwest outside the map. The geographic coordinates of point p are **42°07′30″ north latitude and 88°37′30″ west longitude.** The rectangular coordinates are simply ^{6}13,655–^{4}664,356 (reading to the right and then up). In actual use a map would cover only a small area so that a much smaller number of digits would be necessary in the grid reference.

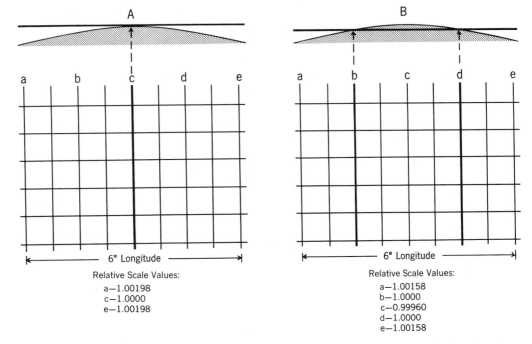

Relative Scale Values:
a—1.00198
c—1.0000
e—1.00198

Relative Scale Values:
a—1.00158
b—1.0000
c—0.99960
d—1.0000
e—1.00158

FIGURE 5.30. Instead of a single line being standard as in A, two are made standard on the Universal Transverse Mercator grid used for rectangular grid reference purposes. Each grid zone covers 6° of longitude and extends about 400 kilometers on each side of the central meridian. The standard lines are 180 kilometers east and west of the central meridian.

The United States employs what is called the Universal Transverse Mercator (UTM) grid system in its military mapping program. It consists of a series of identical projections around the world in the intermediate latitudes, each covering 6° of longitude. The stereographic is used in the polar areas.

Many nations are employing the transverse Mercator for their newer topographic series because of its conformality, its small scale error in a limited space, and because of the ease with which a useful rectangular grid may be superimposed.

The Construction of Projections

6.1 THE CLASSIFICATION OF PROJECTIONS FOR CONSTRUCTION

In the previous chapter, when considering the employment of projections, it was helpful to categorize them according to their properties. It was apparent, however, that projections having similar properties were markedly different in terms of the mechanics of the systems of transformation, some being based on cones, planes, or cylinders, and some not on actual geometry at all. Many of the diverse systems of projection have certain procedures in common, and it is convenient to approach their construction by these common characteristics. These are based upon the practical fact that in order to transform the spherical surface to a plane surface it is necessary to establish a series of points on the spherical surface and then to transfer these points to the plane surface according to the particular system being employed. Thus, by locating the points properly on the plane the system is "defined" by the points and all intervening spaces will conform. Because the earth's coordinate system is convenient for this purpose the parallel and meridian system (more particularly their intersections) provides the medium for the location of homologous points on the two surfaces.

Many projections may be visualized as being the result of a kind of geometric transfer of the grid from the spherical form to some kind of surface that may then be developed into a plane. Thus, one may wrap a cylinder around a globe, in some fashion "project" the grid to the inside of the cylinder, and, finally, cut the cylinder lengthwise which allows it then to be flattened. Similarly, the grid may be projected to a cone perched on the globe or to a tangent plane. The lines of tangency or intersection of the sphere with the cylinder, cone, or plane are the *lines* or *points of origin*. Because such lines will in all cases be either great or small circles, it is also convenient to arrange the surface of projection so that these circles will correspond to great or small circles of the earth's coordinate system. This ordinarily results when the axes of the cylinder and cone and the perpendicular to the plane are made to coincide with the earth's axis of rotation.

The equator or a pair of parallels north and south of it are usually the lines of origin for cylindrically based projections, and one or two parallels in the same hemisphere usually become the lines of origin in conically conceived projections. This is not necessary—it is merely convenient. Projections based upon a tangent or intersecting plane are not so commonly oriented in this fashion.

In any case, when the conventional method of orientation is followed it is often necessary only to calculate the lengths, the radii, and the scales along these lines of origin, and then to construct the projection around them. The remainder of the area will, so to speak, fall into place automatically. Even the oval projections can be thus constructed.

Because of similarities of construction methods and in order to enable the student to make comparisons more easily, projections for construction purposes will be grouped according to whether they are cylindrical, conic, oval, or azimuthal. The grouping is merely an expedient.

6.2   THE CONSTRUCTION OF PROJECTIONS TO SCALE

Scale in map projections is an elusive thing, for only in equivalent projections is there such a thing as consistent scale all over the projection. In *all* projections the linear scale varies in some way from place to place. On all conventional cylindrical projections, for example, since the parallels are all the same length it is obvious that not more than two of the parallels can be their true lengths. To construct a projection at a given linear scale along some line requires, at least in principle, a quite different operation from the construction of one at a given areal scale. In any case, projections should usually be constructed to a preconceived scale.

A number of the common projections may be graphically derived to fit a format, and provided (after construction) with a graphic bar scale. A numerical scale, or RF, for such a projection would be a very uneven number in most cases, such as 1:11, 453, 421, which would be inconvenient and hardly worth noting. Whenever possible it is better practice to construct the grid to a "round number" scale. This has the merits of promoting accuracy of construction (distances, etc. on the map may be more easily checked for accuracy with known values);

and it provides the map user and reader with an even, readily understood, and usable fractional scale.

A projection constructed so that the scale along a standard line bears the given scale relationship to that line on the sphere is said to be constructed at a linear scale. The length of the line segment on the projection in relation to the length of the same line on a spherical earth is the scale. To determine this is very easy, of course, for if D represents the diameter, then (1) the length of a great circle (the equator or a pair of meridians) on the sphere is πD, and (2) the length of a parallel is the cosine of the latitude (ϕ) × the circumference of the sphere ($\cos \phi \times \pi D$). These may be determined either by (1) first calculating their true lengths on the earth and then reducing the values by the desired ratio or (2) by first reducing the earth (radius or diameter) by the chosen ratio to a globe and then calculating the map lengths desired.

The construction of projections to a given area scale is accomplished in precisely the same way except that the scale of the map will actually be the square of the linear scale along a standard line. For example, a globe having a diameter at a scale of 1:40,000,000 would have an area in relation to the earth as 1 is to 40,000,000². Care must be exercised in working with the oval equivalent world projections, for most of them are constructed by using the equator and one meridian as axes of construction. In most cases these are not standard lines but instead bear a specified length ratio to the radius (R) or the diameter (D) of a globe of the given scale.

6.3   TECHNIQUES OF CONSTRUCTION

Projections may be mechanically constructed in a number of ways depending upon the system of projection and the complexity of the grid to be produced: (1) those which can be derived geometrically can be constructed by working from an elevation

of the globe drawn to the proper scale, and then the grid may be derived by transfer methods; (2) they can be constructed by calculating the radii of curves and spacings of parallels and meridians; (3) they can be constructed by consulting tables showing the *X* and *Y* plane coordinates of the intersections of given parallels and meridians, and then joining the points thus established by smooth lines to form the grid.

In many cases it is convenient to begin the construction by first drawing one or two of the grid lines and then using them as lines of reference. Most conventional projections are drawn around a *central meridian*, which is a straight line, with the projection being symmetrical on each side of it. It is necessary therefore to draw only one side of the projection; the other side will simply be the reverse and may be copied from the first.

The directions which are given in the following sections are meant to be used only for the construction of moderately sized projections suitable for exercises and small-scale maps. Large-scale maps wherein considerable precision is desired should be drawn on projections which have been derived from more extensive tables readily available in the standard treatises on map projections. Mention should also be made that for precise mapping of the earth the spheroidal shape of the earth must be considered. To simplify this in constructing equal-area projections the latitudes on the spheroid have been projected to a true sphere of equal area. These corresponding latitudes, called *authalic latitudes*, may then be used and the resulting projection will "automatically" be of the spheroid.*

The tables which are available for the construction of map projections frequently are given in some unit of distance (meters, miles, minutes of longitude at 0° latitude,

* A table of authalic latitudes for every 30' on the earth is available in U. S. Coast and Geodetic Survey *Special Publication No. 67.*

etc.) calculated at a scale of 1:1, that is, actual earth size. To construct to scale it is necessary (1) to reduce each unit by the scale ratio, and (2) convert the tabular unit of measure to a convenient unit for plotting, for example, centimeters or inches. It should be remembered that the scale relationship is simply an arithmetic linear relationship between the actual radius of the earth and the radius of the globe of desired scale which is being projected.

6.4 THE CONSTRUCTION OF CYLINDRICAL OR RECTANGULAR PROJECTIONS

All conventional rectangular projections may be constructed with a straightedge, dividers, scale, and a triangle. In these projections all meridians are the same length and all parallels are the same length; merely their spacing varies. In practice, the length of the equator or standard parallel and the length of a meridian are determined. These are drawn at right angles to one another. The standard parallel is then subdivided for the longitudinal interval desired. The meridians are drawn through these points as parallel lines. The spacing of the parallels is then plotted along a meridian, and the parallels are drawn.

6.5 THE MERCATOR PROJECTION

Numerous tables of the spacing of the parallels on the Mercator projection are available. The values in Table 6.1 are taken from *Special Publication No. 68* of the U. S. Coast and Geodetic survey, which shows values of the distance of each minute of latitude from the equator. A 5° grid interval is here presented. For any smaller interval it is necessary to consult the original table.

The values of Table 6.1 are given in minutes of longitude on the equator, which is simply a convenient unit of distance. The scale of the table is, of course, 1:1, making it necessary to reduce the values to the scale

desired. In addition to the reduction in scale it is also necessary to convert the values to inches or centimeters for plotting purposes. How this is done will be illustrated in the following discussion. A similar procedure can be followed for values in other tables.

TABLE 6.1

DISTANCES OF THE PARALLELS FROM THE EQUATOR ON THE MERCATOR PROJECTION IN MINUTES OF LONGITUDE AT THE EQUATOR (From Deetz and Adams, *Elements of Map Projection*)

0°	000.000	50°	3 456.581
5°	298.348	55°	3 948.830
10°	599.019	60°	4 507.133
15°	904.422	65°	5 157.629
20°	1 217.159	70°	5 943.955
25°	1 540.134	75°	6 947.761
30°	1 876.706	80°	8 352.176
35°	2 230.898	(The pole is in-	
40°	2 607.683	finitely dis-	
45°	3 013.427	tant)	

Note: Values for each minute of latitude are given in the reference from which the above abbreviated table is taken.

Suppose it were desired to construct a conventional Mercator projection from the values in Table 6.1 with a linear scale along the equator of 1:50,000,000. To divide each value in the table by 50,000,000 would give the map distances in "minutes of longitude at the equator," which would be useless for plotting purposes. Suppose further, then, that it were desired also to have the values converted to inches at the chosen scale. The procedure is as follows:

(1) The circumference of a globe at a scale of 1:50,000,000 is calculated by dividing the actual circumference in miles by 50,000,000 and then multiplying by the number of inches in a mile (24,899 ÷ 50,000,000 × 63,360). The result is about 31.55 inches.

(2) Since there are 21,600 minutes of longitude in a circle (360° × 60'), dividing 31.55 inches by 21,600 gives the length of 1

minute of longitude in inches on a globe at a scale of 1:50,000,000, about 0.00146 inch.

(3) Each value in the table, therefore, need only be multiplied by 0.00146, and the result can be plotted directly in inches on the map.

One could also proceed by finding the length in inches of a minute of longitude (73,037 inches) and divide it by the denominator of the scale ratio.

$$(73,037 \div 50,000,000 = 0.00146)$$

6.6   THE PLANE CHART

This projection is more precisely called the equirectangular projection, the name plane chart being reserved for the phase wherein the equator is standard. In any case its construction is relatively simple.

A standard parallel is chosen, and its length is calculated or determined from tables. The length of any parallel (ϕ) may be calculated by multiplying the circumference of the earth by the cosine of the latitude. It may also be obtained by referring to the table of lengths of the degrees of the parallel (Table D.1, Appendix D) and multiplying the value given for the latitude by the number of degrees the map is to extend. It must then, of course, be reduced to scale. The results, however determined, are then marked on a straight horizontal line. This is the standard parallel. Vertical lines are drawn through the points to establish the meridians. The other parallels are determined by pointing off the actual distance between the parallels (reduced to scale) as determined from the table of meridional parts (Table D.2, Appendix D).

If the equator is made the standard parallel, the projection will be made up of squares; any other standard parallels will make rectangles whose north-south dimension is the long one; if the poles were made the "standard parallels" the "projection" would be but a straight vertical line!

6.7 THE RECTANGULAR EQUAL-AREA PROJECTION

The rectangular equal-area projection is, like all rectangular projections, relatively easy to construct, requiring only a straight-edge, dividers, scale, and a triangle. The equator alone or any pair of parallels spaced equally from the equator may be chosen as standard. Since the angular deformation is zero along the parallel or parallels chosen as standard, these may be selected so that they pass through the areas of significance. If the projection is desired for only a portion of the earth rather than the whole, the projection is designed merely as a part of a larger, incomplete world projection.

This projection requires some calculation, but the formulas are elementary and are accomplished merely through the use of arithmetic. The general formulas for any form of the projection are:

(1) Length of all parallels is $2R\pi \times \cos\theta$.
(2) Length of all meridians is $2R \div \cos\theta$.
(3) Distance of each parallel from equator is $R \sin\phi \div \cos\theta$.

R is the radius of the generating globe of chosen *area scale;* θ is the standard parallel; ϕ is the latitude.

The procedure for construction is similar to that for other rectangular projections. Perpendicular lines are drawn to represent the equator and a meridian (Fig. 6.1). The length of the parallel chosen as standard (*ab*) is marked off on the equator. The length of a meridian (*cd*) is determined. These dimensions define a rectangle forming the poles and the bounding meridian of the projection. The distances of the parallels from the equator are then laid off on a meridian, and the parallels are drawn parallel to the equator as in quadrant *C*, Fig. 6.1. The parallels are, of course, equally subdivided by the meridians as in quadrant *D*.

6.8 THE CONSTRUCTION OF CONIC PROJECTIONS

Conic projections may be constructed either from tables which provide X and Y plane coordinate values with which to locate the intersections of the grid, or by the use of a straightedge and some sort of compass capable of drawing large arcs. In the latter procedure it is necessary to determine the

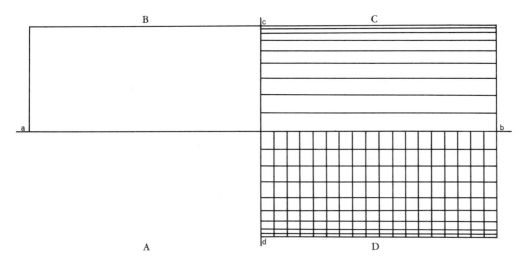

FIGURE 6.1. Construction of the rectangular equal-area projection.

radii of the arcs representing the parallels
and the spacing of the meridians on the
parallels. In most conventional conic projections the meridians are equally spaced
along each parallel, and the parallels are
arcs of circles which may or may not be
concentric; the meridians are usually
straight lines.

All conic projections are symmetrical
around the central meridian. Thus, it is
only necessary to draw one side of the projection; the other side may be copied by
either folding the paper or copying it onto
another paper with the aid of a light-table.
Another easy procedure is to place a sheet
of tracing paper over the projection and
prick the intersections with a needle. The
paper may then be "flopped over" and the
points pricked through in their proper place
on the other side of the central meridian.

6.9   THE CONIC WITH TWO STANDARD
PARALLELS

As was pointed out in the previous chapter the earth's surface may be projected to
a cone assumed to be set upon the sphere
and of course tangent at one small circle,

usually a parallel. If a limited latitudinal
segment is being mapped, the deformation
away from the standard parallel does not
reach serious proportions. Nevertheless, a
projection better in every way can be made
by assuming the cone to intersect the earth's
surface so that two small circles or parallels
are standard. This is sometimes called a
secant conic projection. As can be seen
from Fig. 6.2, the scale would not be correct
along the meridians if the surface were
actually projected from some one point. If
the point were the center of the sphere, the
parallels would be too close together between the standard parallels and too far
apart outside them. It is better to construct
the projection so that the scale is more
nearly correct along all the meridians.
There are other ways of constructing this
sort of projection, but only one will be illustrated here, viz., the conic with two standard parallels in which all the meridians are
standard.*

* The interested reader is referred to an analysis of simi-
lar projections, John Leighly, "Extended Uses of Polyconic
Projection Tables," *Annals of the Association of American
Geographers,* Vol. XLVI, 1956, pp. 150–173.

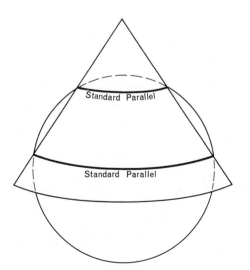

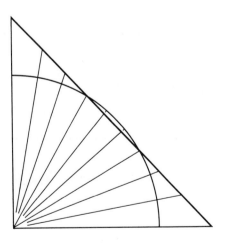

FIGURE 6.2. The basis of a geometrically projected secant conic with two standard parallels.

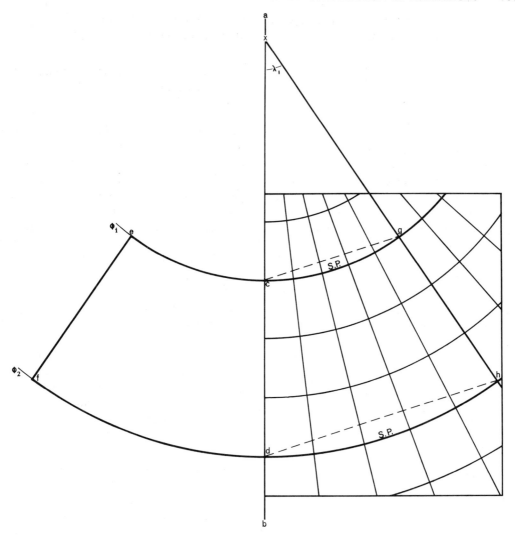

FIGURE 6.3. Construction of the conic with two standard parallels.

To construct the conic projection with two standard parallels first draw a vertical line, *ab* in Fig. 6.3, in the center of the paper. Select the two parallels, ϕ_1 and ϕ_2, to be made standard, and determine their actual distance apart on the generating globe of the desired linear scale. If *c* and *d* are then positions on *ab,* and if the radius, *R,* of the globe to be projected at scale has been determined, distance *cd* may be determined by

$$cd = 2\pi R \frac{\phi_1 - \phi_2}{360}$$

This distance may also be determined by reducing to scale the actual spacing on the earth. Points *c* and *d* should be placed in a convenient location on the paper so that the developed projection will be centered properly. Points *c* and *d* being the intersections of the standard parallels with the central meridian, it is next necessary to determine the position on *ab* of the center, *x,*

from which the two concentric arcs may be drawn. This may be done by

$$\frac{xc}{cd} = \frac{\cos \phi_1}{\cos \phi_2 - \cos \phi_1}$$

or

$$xc = \frac{\cos \phi_1 \times cd}{\cos \phi_2 - \cos \phi_1}$$

Draw arcs with x as the center through c and d. Extend these arcs (ecg and fdh) a distance equal to the length of the standard parallels which is to be included between the extreme meridians of the map. Space the arcs of the other parallels equally on ab.

The meridians are equally spaced on the parallels and are correctly spaced on the two standard parallels. The most nearly accurate means of doing this is by first determing the chord distances of the bounding meridian, chord cg on ϕ_1 and chord dh on ϕ_2.

To determine the chord distance cg on ϕ_1:

(1) Determine longitude on ϕ_1 to be represented by cg, for example, 25°.
(2) The length of ϕ_1 on the sphere of chosen scale $= 2\pi R \cos \phi_1$.
(3) Let xc be radius r. The circumference of a circle with radius $r = 2\pi r$.
(4) Therefore, angle λ_1 (angle cxg on Fig. 6.3) may be determined by

$$\lambda_1 = \frac{2\pi R \cos \phi_1}{2\pi r} \times 25° = \frac{R \cos \phi_1}{r} \times 25°$$

(5) Chord distance $cg = 2r \sin \dfrac{\lambda_1}{2}$

Lay off the chord distance cg. Determine in similar fashion chord distance dh. Subdivide the parallels in question (with dividers) into the desired number of equal parts for the meridians. Join homologous points with straight lines.

Linear distances along the meridians and along the standard parallels are correct, but the projection has no special properties. For a limited area, however, it has little distortion, and its ease of construction and neat appearance make it a useful projection.

6.10   THE LAMBERT CONFORMAL CONIC PROJECTION

This projection is similar in appearance to the Albers and the simple conic. It too has straight-line meridians that meet at a common center; the parallels are arcs of circles, two of which are standard; and the parallels and meridians meet at right angles. The only difference is in the spacings of the parallels and meridians. In the Lambert conic they are so spaced as to satisfy the condition of conformality, that is, $a = b$ at every point.

The calculation of this projection requires mathematical computations and facility beyond the average cartographer. On account of its relatively wide use for air-navigation maps, many tables for its construction with various standard parallels have been published. For example, a table for the construction of a map of the United States with standard parallels at 29° and 45° is given in the U. S. Coast and Geodetic Survey *Special Publication No. 52*. It is advisable, if a satisfactory distribution of scale error is desired, to space the standard parallels so that they include between them about two-thirds of the meridional section to be mapped.

A Lambert conic with standard parallels at 36° and 54° is useful for middle-latitude areas. Table 6.2 gives the radii of the parallels in meters for a map at a scale of 1:1. It is, of course, necessary to reduce each value to the scale desired.

To construct the projection draw a line, cd in Fig. 6.4, which will be the central meridian. The line must be sufficiently long so that it will include the center of the arcs of latitude. With a beam compass describe arcs with radii, reduced to scale, taken from Table 6.2.

To determine the meridians it is neces-

TABLE 6.2

TABLE FOR THE CONSTRUCTION OF A LAMBERT CON-FORMAL CONIC PROJECTION. STANDARD PARALLELS 36° AND 54° (From Deetz and Adams, *Elements of Map Projection*)

Lat.	Radii, meters	Lat.	Radii, meters
75°	2 787 926	40°	6 833 183
70°	3 430 294	35°	7 386 250
65°	4 035 253	30°	7 946 911
60°	4 615 579	25°	8 519 065
55°	5 179 774	20°	9 106 796
50°	5 734 157	15°	9 714 516
45°	6 283 826		

sary to calculate the chord distance on a lower parallel from its intersection with the central meridian (0°) to its intersection with an outer meridian. This is done by the following formula:

$$\text{chord} = 2r \sin \frac{n\lambda}{2}$$

where $n = 0.7101$; λ = longitude out from central meridian; r = radius of parallel in question.

This procedure is similar to obtaining the length of a chord that subtends an actual central angle (p. 47). The formula introduces a factor n to take into account the special meridian spacing.

Example. On parallel 30° the chord of 45° (see Fig. 6.4) out from the central meridian =

(1) $0.7101 \times 45° = 31° \, 57' \, 14'' = n\lambda$; therefore

(2) $n\lambda/2 = 15° \, 58' \, 37''$.

(3) Sin $15° \, 58' \, 37'' = 0.27534$.

(4) $2r = 15{,}893{,}822$ meters.

(5) $15{,}893{,}822 \times 0.27534 = 4{,}376{,}200$ meters.

The value thus determined, *ab* in Fig. 6.4, is reduced by the desired scale ratio and measured out from the intersection of the parallel and the central meridian to the bounding meridian. If point *b*, thus located, is connected by means of a straight-edge with the same center used in describing the parallels, this will determine the outer meridian. If a long straightedge is not available, the same procedure may be fol-

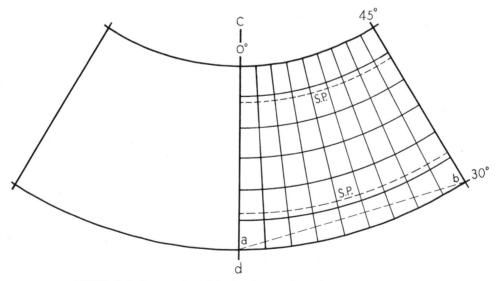

FIGURE 6.4. Construction of the Lambert conformal conic projection.

lowed (determining the chord) for another parallel in the upper part of the map, and the two points, thus determined, joined by a straight line. This will produce the same result. Since the parallels are equally subdivided by the meridians, the other meridians may be easily located.

6.11 THE ALBERS EQUAL-AREA PROJECTION

The construction procedure for this projection is essentially the same as for the preceding projection, the Lambert conic. Like the Lambert, the Albers conic, in conventional orientation, is suited to representation of an area predominantly east-west in extent in the middle latitudes.

Table 6.3 gives the radii of the parallels and the lengths of chords on two parallels for a map of the United States with standard parallels 29° 30′ and 45° 30′. The scale of the table is 1:1, and the values are in meters. As in the preceding projection, reduction to the desired scale is necessary.

6.12 THE POLYCONIC PROJECTION

In general the polyconic is not suitable for small-scale maps. On account of its balance of error and ease of construction it is primarily a survey projection, and this book is concerned more especially with smaller-scale cartography. Consequently, procedures for constructing the polyconic are not included. The student who may have need to construct one is referred to the directions in the U. S. Coast and Geodetic Survey *Special Publication 68*, p. 60, and the tables in *Special Publication 5*.

6.13 THE BONNE PROJECTION

The Bonne projection is a useful projection when an easily constructed equal-area projection is desired for a limited area but when one does not have available the tables for constructing an appropriate case of an Albers. The Bonne is, like most useful

TABLE 6.3

TABLE FOR CONSTRUCTION OF ALBERS EQUAL-AREA PROJECTION WITH STANDARD PARALLELS 29° 30′ AND 45° 30′ (From Deetz and Adams, *Elements of Map Projection*)

Latitude	Radius of parallel, meters
20°	10 253 177
21°	10 145 579
22°	10 037 540
23°	9 929 080
24°	9 820 218
25°	9 710 969
26°	9 601 361
27°	9 491 409
28°	9 381 139
29°	9 270 576
29° 30′	9 215 188
30°	9 159 738
31°	9 048 648
32°	8 937 337
33°	8 825 827
34°	8 714 150
35°	8 602 328
36°	8 490 392
37°	8 378 377
38°	8 266 312
39°	8 154 228
40°	8 042 163
41°	7 930 152
42°	7 818 231
43°	7 706 444
44°	7 594 828
45°	7 483 426
45° 30′	7 427 822
46°	7 372 288
47°	7 261 459
48°	7 150 987
49°	7 040 925
50°	6 931 333
51°	6 822 264
52°	6 713 780

Chord Distances in Meters		
Long. from central meridian	On Latitude 25°	On Latitude 45°
1°	102 185	78 745
5°	510 867	393 682
25°	2 547 270	1 962 966
30°		2 352 568

conic forms of projection, modified in that it cannot actually be projected on an enveloping cone.

To construct the projection draw a vertical line, *cb* in Fig. 6.5, that is long enough to include the latitudinal extent desired and the center (*c*) of the central parallel.

Theoretically, a cone is made tangent to the parallel (*φ*) which is selected near the center of the area to be mapped. The radius (*r*) of this central parallel on the map will be

$$r = R \cot \phi = oc$$

in which *R* is the radius of the generating globe of the desired area scale. Describe an arc for this parallel through *o* with *oc* as the radius. Plot points on *cb* north and south of *o* spaced correctly at scale for the other parallels. Through these points draw arcs with *c* as their center. The radius of each parallel may easily be found by subtracting or adding the appropriate meridional distance (as found in Table D.2, Appendix D), from the *r* value used for the central parallel. This will provide parallels of concentric arcs properly spaced on the central meridian.

Each parallel of the Bonne projection is standard, that is, the linear scale along it is correct, and therefore the meridians are equally spaced on any given parallel. The positions of the meridians must be separately determined on *each* parallel; then smooth curves are drawn through homologous points. It is easiest to determine the chord distance for *each* parallel from the central meridian (*cb* in Fig. 6.5) to one meridian near the edge of the map and then divide the intervening space along the parallel equally with dividers. The chord distances may be determined in the manner outlined in Article 3.11, *but* the central angle λ to be used in the computation must first be calculated. It will not be the actual angle on the earth between the meridians; instead it will be λ_1 which is the actual angle on the projection which corresponds to λ on the parallel circle of the earth. For example, if the position of the meridian 30° from *cb* in Fig. 6.5 is desired on parallel ϕ_1, then λ_1 (which represents 30° in the general formula for a chord distance) is obtained by

$$\lambda_1 = \frac{R \cos \phi_1}{r} \times 30°$$

in which *φ* is the latitude, and *r* = *co* plus the distance on the projection between *φ* and ϕ_1.

6.14 THE CONSTRUCTION OF OVAL PROJECTIONS

Most useful oval projections are equivalent, and they are constructed to an area scale. The linear dimensions, for construction purposes, of an oval projection depend upon the shape of the bounding meridian which encloses the projection. It is obvious that the axes of two dissimilar shapes would be different if both shapes enclose the same area, that is, if they were the same area scale. Most oval projections

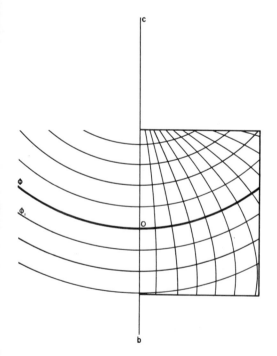

FIGURE 6.5. Construction of the Bonne projection.

have a vertical axis half the length of the horizontal axis; and, in the conventional equatorial phase, this is the relation to be expected between a meridian and the equator. The relationship between the generating globe and the particular projection being constructed is merely one that states the length of the central meridian on the projection compared to the radius (R) of the generating globe of the same area scale. The equator being twice the length of the central meridian, no further calculation is necessary.

On the majority of the oval projections the meridians are equally spaced along the parallels. The spacing of the parallels along the central meridian varies from projection to projection. These values are available in tabular form.

6.15 THE SINUSOIDAL PROJECTION

The sinusoidal projection is particularly simple to construct, since the spacings of the parallels and meridians are the same (to scale) as they are on the earth. The length of the central meridian is 3.1416 times the radius (R) of a generating globe of equal area. The equator is twice the length of the central meridian.

To construct the projection a horizontal line representing the equator, *ab* in Fig. 6.6, is drawn twice the length of the central meridian. The equator is bisected, and at point *o* a perpendicular central meridian (*cd*) is constructed. The positions of the parallels on *cd* are determined by spacing them as they are on the globe. For a small-scale projection this means equally; for a large-scale projection the exact spacings may be taken from Table D.2, Appendix D. Through the points thus established the parallels are drawn parallel to the equator as in quadrant *B*. The lengths of the various parallels are their true lengths (to scale) as on the earth and may be determined by multiplying the length of the equator (*ab*) by the cosine of the latitude. One-half this value is plotted on each side of the central meridian. The meridians are

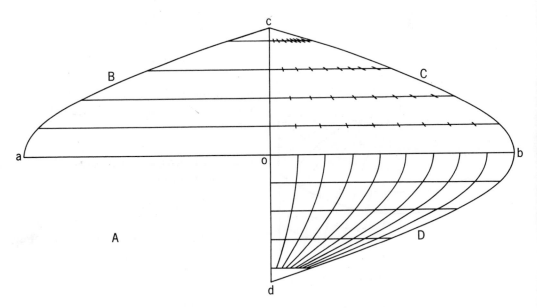

FIGURE 6.6. Construction of the sinusoidal projection.

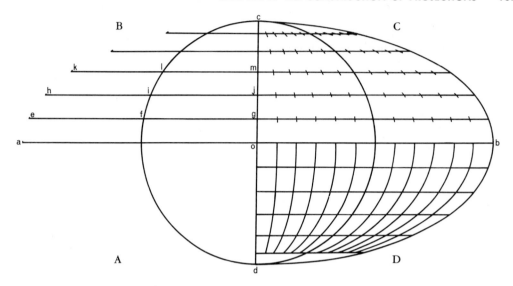

FIGURE 6.7. Construction of the Mollweide projection.

drawn by subdividing, as in quadrant *C*, each parallel equally, with dividers, and drawing smooth curves (with a French curve) through homologous points as in quadrant *D*.

The linear scale along the parallels and the central meridian is correct (same as the generating globe), and is the square root of the area scale; that is, if the area scale is 1:50,000,000² the linear scale along the parallels and the central meridian will be 1:50,000,000. This is the only equivalent oval projection in which this relationship exists, although some others come close to it.

6.16   THE MOLLWEIDE PROJECTION

The Mollweide projection does not have the simple relationship to the sphere that characterizes the sinusoidal. The meridians of the sinusoidal are sine curves which produce a pointed appearance near the poles, whereas in the Mollweide the meridians are ellipses, which provide a projection shape that is somewhat less of a radical departure from the globe impression. The length of

the central meridian is 2.8284 times the radius (*R*) of a generating globe of equal area. The equator is twice the length of the central meridian.

To construct the projection a horizontal line representing the equator, *ab* in Fig. 6.7, is drawn twice the length of the central meridian. The equator is bisected, and at point *o* a perpendicular central meridian (*cd*) is constructed. A circle whose radius is *oc* is constructed around point *o*. This contains a hemisphere. The spacing of the parallels on the central meridian is given in Table 6.4, in which *oc* equals 1. These positions are plotted on the central meridian, and the parallels are drawn through the points parallel to the equator. Each parallel is extended outside the hemisphere circle a distance equal to its length inside the circle. Thus, in quadrant *B* of Fig. 6.7, *ef* = *fg*, *hi* = *ij*, *kl* = *lm*, etc. Each parallel is subdivided equally with dividers, as in quadrant *C*, to establish the position of the meridians. The meridians are drawn through homologous points, as in quadrant *D*, with the aid of a curve.

TABLE 6.4

DISTANCES OF THE PARALLELS FROM THE EQUATOR IN THE MOLLWEIDE PROJECTION (oc = 1) (From Deetz and Adams, *Elements of Map Projection*)

0°	0.000	50°	0.651
5°	0.069	55°	0.708
10°	0.137	60°	0.762
15°	0.205	65°	0.814
20°	0.272	70°	0.862
25°	0.339	75°	0.906
30°	0.404	80°	0.945
35°	0.468	85°	0.978
40°	0.531	90°	1.000
45°	0.592		

6.17   THE ECKERT IV PROJECTION

The Eckert IV projection is representative of a large group of projections in which the pole is represented by a line half the length of the equator, rather than by a point, as in the case of the Mollweide and the sinusoidal. The rather excessive shearing of the higher latitudes is somewhat lessened by this device, at the expense, however, of increased angular deformation in the lower latitudes. As in the other oval projections the length of the central meridian is half the length of the equator. In the Eckert IV projection the length of the central meridian is 2.6530 times the radius (R) of a generating globe of equal area.

To construct the projection a horizontal line representing the equator, *ab* in Fig. 6.8, is drawn twice the length of the central meridian. The equator is bisected, and at point *o* a perpendicular central meridian (*cd*) is constructed. On each side of the central meridian a tangent circle is drawn. In quadrant *B* the center of one circle (*e*) is on *ab* and midway between *a* and *o*. The pole is a line (*fg*) perpendicular to *cd* and equal in length to *ao* and *cd*. The spacing of the parallels on the central meridian is given in Table 6.5, in which *oc* = 1. These positions are plotted on the central merid-

ian, and the parallels are drawn through the points parallel to the equator as in quadrant *B*, Fig. 6.8. Each parallel is subdivided equally with dividers, as in quadrant *C*, to establish the position of the meridians. The meridians are drawn through homologous points, as in quadrant *D*, with the aid of a curve.

TABLE 6.5

DISTANCES OF THE PARALLELS FROM THE EQUATOR IN THE ECKERT IV PROJECTION

(oc = 1)

0°	0.000	50°	0.718
5°	0.078	55°	0.775
10°	0.155	60°	0.827
15°	0.232	65°	0.874
20°	0.308	70°	0.915
25°	0.382	75°	0.950
30°	0.454	80°	0.976
35°	0.525	85°	0.994
40°	0.592	90°	1.000
45°	0.657		

6.18   THE FLAT POLAR QUARTIC EQUAL-AREA PROJECTION

This projection is representative of a group in which a line represents the pole, like the Eckert IV, but in which that line is less than half the length of the equator and the bounding meridian is a complex curve. On this account neither the spacing of the parallels nor their lengths can be easily derived by construction. A table of lengths or X and Y coordinates is necessary. Tables 6.6 and 6.7 list the necessary information to construct the projection with a 5° grid interval. In the flat polar quartic equal-area projection the length of the central meridian is 2.6513 times the radius (R) of a generating globe of equal area. The equator is 2.2214 times the length of the central meridian and the length of the line representing the pole is one-third the length of the equator.

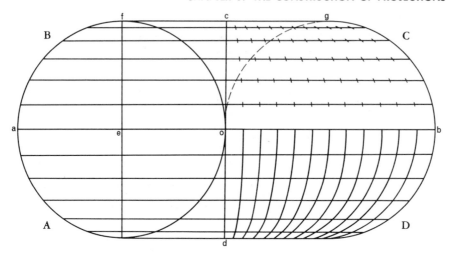

FIGURE 6.8. Construction of the Eckert IV projection.

TABLE 6.6

DISTANCES OF THE PARALLELS FROM THE EQUATOR IN THE FLAT POLAR QUARTIC EQUAL-AREA PROJECTION

(oc = 1)

0°	0.000	50°	0.668
5°	0.070	55°	0.727
10°	0.140	60°	0.784
15°	0.209	65°	0.837
20°	0.278	70°	0.886
25°	0.346	75°	0.930
30°	0.413	80°	0.966
35°	0.479	85°	0.991
40°	0.544	90°	1.000
45°	0.607		

To construct the projection draw a vertical line, *cd* in Fig. 6.9, representing the central meridian to scale. Draw a perpendicular *ab* through *o* midway between *c* and *d*. Lay off distance *ao* equal to 1.1107 *cd.* Length *ob* = *ao*. Draw *fg* parallel to *ab* at *c*. Distances *fc* and *cg* = ⅓ *ao*. From Table 6.6 determine the distance of each parallel from the equator on the central meridian. In the table length *oc* = 1. These positions are plotted on the central meridian and through these points parallels to *ab* are drawn as in quadrant *B*. The length of

each parallel is obtained from Table 6.7 in which it is shown as a proportion of length *ob*. Subdivide each parallel equally with dividers as in quadrant *C* of Fig. 6.9 to establish the positions of the meridians. The meridians are drawn through homologous points, as in quadrant *D,* with the aid of a curve.

TABLE 6.7

LENGTHS OF THE PARALLELS IN THE FLAT POLAR QUARTIC EQUAL-AREA PROJECTION

(ob = 1)

0°	1.000	50°	0.752
5°	0.998	55°	0.700
10°	0.990	60°	0.643
15°	0.979	65°	0.581
20°	0.961	70°	0.517
25°	0.939	75°	0.453
30°	0.911	80°	0.394
35°	0.879	85°	0.350
40°	0.842	90°	0.333
45°	0.800		

A complete table for the construction of the projection with a 1° grid by means of *X* and *Y* coordinates is given in Coast and Geodetic Survey, *Special Publication No.*

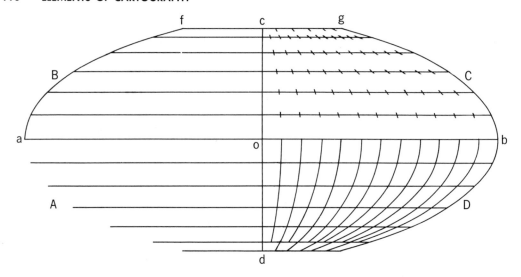

FIGURE 6.9. Construction of the flat polar quartic equal-area projection.

245, by F. Webster McBryde and Paul D. Thomas, by whom the projection was devised. The values in the tables shown are based upon those in this reference.

6.19   THE CONSTRUCTION OF AZIMUTHAL PROJECTIONS

Although azimuthal projections seem to have more in common with each other than any other class of projections, the uses and common methods of construction are quite varied. Some can be easily constructed geometrically; some cannot in any way be constructed geometrically. Some are most expeditiously put together by using X and Y coordinates to locate grid intersections; others by transforming one projection into another. It is this last method that is the key to understanding these projections. Any azimuthal projection can be transformed into any other by merely relocating the grid intersections along their azimuths from the center of the projection, for the projections vary only as to the radial scale from the center of the projection (see Fig. 6.10).

There are a great many azimuthal projec-

tions (theoretically, an infinite number are possible), but only a few have desirable properties. Of these few, one, the gnomonic, is used primarily as a planning map in connection with navigation, and a cartographer is rarely called upon to construct it. The remaining common azimuthal projections, the Lambert equal-area, the orthographic, the stereographic, and the azimuthal equidistant, are much in demand in these days of "one-world" consciousness, and methods for their construction are suggested here. In the interests of brevity not all the possibilities will be detailed, and the reader is referred to any of the standard works on map projections for a fuller account of possible procedures.

Since the azimuthal projections can, theoretically at least, be projected on a tangent plane, and since the point of tangency may be anywhere on the sphere, it is evident that each projection may have many different appearances. The names *equatorial, meridional, oblique,* and *polar* are variously employed to refer to them. It is perhaps better and clearer practice when labeling to name the projection, as Lambert equal-area, and follow it with a statement as to where it is

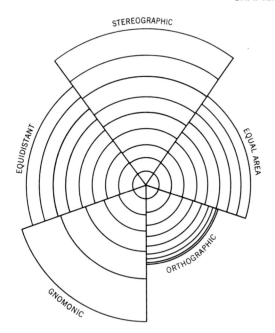

STEREOGRAPHIC

EQUIDISTANT

EQUAL AREA

ORTHOGRAPHIC

GNOMONIC

FIGURE 6.10. Comparison of azimuthal projections centered at the pole. Note that the only variation is in the spacing of the parallels; in other words, the only difference among them is the radial scale. The relationship obtains wherever the projections may be centered.

centered, since changing the point of tangency does not change in any way the structural quality of the projection.

6.20   THE STEREOGRAPHIC PROJECTION

The stereographic projection is the conformal graticule in the azimuthal group of projections. In addition to being conformal, it has a quality shared by no other projection, namely, that all circles on the earth are represented by circles on the projection. This being the case, the parallels and meridians in the stereographic are arcs of circles, which makes the projection relatively easy to draw. As is true in all azimuthal projections, great circles passing through the center of the projection are represented by straight lines. They may be considered as arcs of circles whose radii are of infinite length. Because it is a projection

composed of straight lines or arcs of smaller circles, all that is necessary to draw this projection, centered anywhere, is a straightedge and a compass, preferably a beam compass.

It is relatively easy to calculate the values necessary to center the projection anywhere. The method is given in Appendix F, together with tables for constructing the projection at 10° latitude intervals. The table for centering the projection at 40° is included here to illustrate the construction procedure. It is much easier and quicker to construct the projection from calculated tables, and such procedure also eliminates errors that usually creep in when one works with a maze of construction lines, protractors, and the like.

Table 6.8 has been calculated for a globe the diameter (D) of which is unity. This means that the values (and those in Appendix F) need only to be multiplied by the number of inches, or other units, contained in the diameter of the generating globe of chosen scale.

To construct the projection first draw a vertical line, ab in Fig. 6.11. Locate on ab the center of the projection (o), in this case 40°, and with o as the center describe a circle the diameter of which is twice the diameter of the generating globe. The parallels are drawn by locating on ab the upper (U) and lower (L) points of each parallel. The center of the circle representing the parallel is midway between the points U and L for each parallel. For example, from Table 6.8 the upper intersection with ab for the parallel of 20° is 1.73205 above o and is at U in Fig. 6.11. The lower intersection is 0.17633 below o (shown by the minus sign) and is located at L. Midway between these points is the center of the circle representing the parallel of 20°.* The other parallels are similarly located and drawn with a compass.

* It should be noted that any circle on the earth is found on the projection by plotting first the ends of its diameter on a great circle through the projection center. Midway between these points is the *construction* center of the circle, but not the actual center on the earth.

TABLE 6.8

TABLE FOR CONSTRUCTING THE STEREOGRAPHIC PRO-JECTION CENTERED ON 40°

(D = 1)

Parallels	Upper		Lower
North Pole		0.46631	
80°	0.57735		0.36397
70°	0.70021		0.26795
60°	0.83910		0.17633
50°	1.00000		0.08749
40°	1.19175		0.00000
30°	1.42815		−0.08749
20°	1.73205		−0.17633
10°	2.14451		−0.26795
0°	2.74748		−0.36397
10°	3.73205		−0.46631
20°	5.67128		−0.57735
30°	11.43005		−0.70021
40°	−0.83910	−0.83910	−0.83910
50°	−1.00000		−11.43005
60°	−1.19175		−5.67128
70°	−1.42815		−3.73205
80°	−1.73205		−2.74748
South Pole		−2.14451	

Homolatitude = −0.83910

Meridians	Bow	Center
10°	0.11421	7.40335
20°	0.23018	3.58658
30°	0.34986	2.26104
40°	0.47513	1.55573
50°	0.60872	1.09537
60°	0.75368	0.75368
70°	0.91406	0.47513
80°	1.09537	0.23018
90°	1.30541	0.00000

The centers of the arcs representing the meridians are all located along a straight line, *cd* in Fig. 6.11, perpendicular to *ab* which is the homolatitude of the center of the projection. The homolatitude of any point is the same latitude in the opposite hemisphere. In Fig. 6.11, the homolatitude is located 0.83910 below *o*. The *bow* distance is the distance from the central meridian (*ab*) along the homolatitude (*cd*) to the intersection of the meridian with the homolatitude. The center distance is the

distance along the homolatitude, on the opposite side of *ab*, to the center of the arc that represents the meridian. In Fig. 6.11, the bow distance for the meridian of 30° is 0.34986 and the intersection is at *w* on *cd*. The center distance is 2.26104 on the other side of *ab* and is located at *R*. The arc drawn through *w* must pass through the pole. The other meridians are drawn in similar fashion, first for one side and then repeated for the other side. They may, of course, be numbered in any desired sequence, depending upon what part of the earth is being mapped.

It will be observed that the spacing of the parallels on the central meridian increases away from the center. Since the parallels are evenly spaced on the earth, this establishes the radial scale for the projection. The scale is the same from the center to the periphery in any direction.

6.21   THE ORTHOGRAPHIC PROJECTION

The orthographic projection is a view of the globe as it would appear (if it could be seen) from infinity; that is to say, it is projected upon a plane with parallel lines. In this sense it is like an architect's elevation. The principle of its construction can be seen in Fig. 6.12, where the latitudinal spacing on the globe is projected by parallel lines to the central meridian of the projection. Being an azimuthal projection all great circles through the center are straight lines and azimuths from the center are correct. When the pole is the center all great circles that pass through it are meridians; hence, all meridians on the projection are straight lines and are correctly arranged around the pole.

The construction of the projection centered on the equator is no more involved. The procedure is illustrated in Fig. 6.13. The parallel spacing on the central meridian is the same as in the polar case, but the parallels are horizontal lines. The positions of the meridians on the parallels is carried

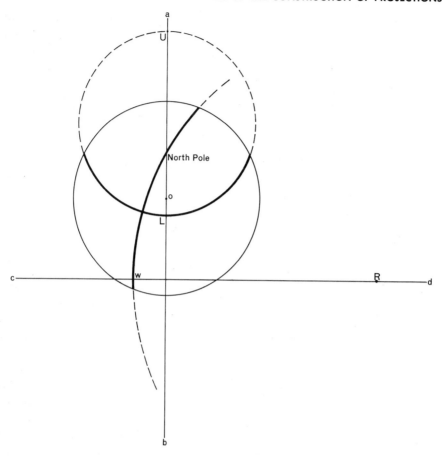

FIGURE 6.11. Construction of the stereographic projection.

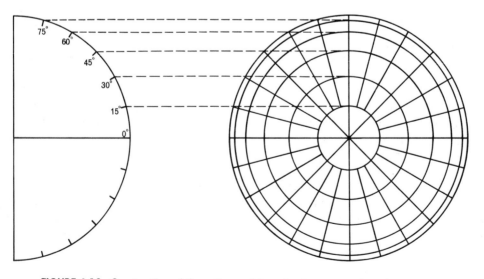

FIGURE 6.12. Construction of the orthographic projection centered on the pole.

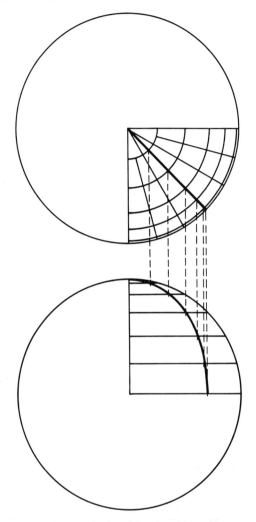

FIGURE 6.13. Construction of the orthographic projection centered on the equator.

It may also be drawn by using the equatorial case as a nomograph as described in Article 6.24. A third method is to trace a photograph of the globe centered at the desired spot. A photograph of the globe is not a true orthographic, for some perspective convergence is bound to occur in the photographing, even when the camera is at a considerable distance. Nevertheless, the result is a true azimuthal projection and is very nearly the same as the orthographic. Since the only useful precise property is its azimuthality, nothing is lost by using a photograph.

6.22   THE LAMBERT EQUAL-AREA PROJECTION

Like the orthographic, the Lambert azimuthal equal-area projection is most useful when centered in the area of interest, although the projection is frequently seen in the polar case to accompany other projections that distort areas considerably. The polar case is easily constructed as illustrated in Fig. 6.15. A segment of the globe is drawn with R as the radius of the generating globe of chosen area scale. The chord distances from the pole to the parallels are carried up to a tangent with a compass and establish the positions of the parallels on the projection. The meridians, as in other azimuthal projections, are straight lines through the poles.

The equatorial case of the projection is somewhat more difficult to construct graphically and is more easily accomplished by plotting the X and Y coordinate positions of the grid intersections from tables. Table E.1 in Appendix E gives values for every 10°.

As with most of the azimuthal projections the oblique case centered on some area of interest is the most useful. The oblique case may be derived from the equatorial by using the latter as a nomograph in the manner outlined in Article 6.24. Coordinates

over from the polar case as illustrated. Since all four quadrants are images of one another only one need be drawn. The others may be traced.

The orthographic projection centered on the pole or the equator is seldom used. It is more often centered on some point of interest between the pole and the equator. This may be accomplished by employing a polar and equatorial case as in Fig. 6.14.

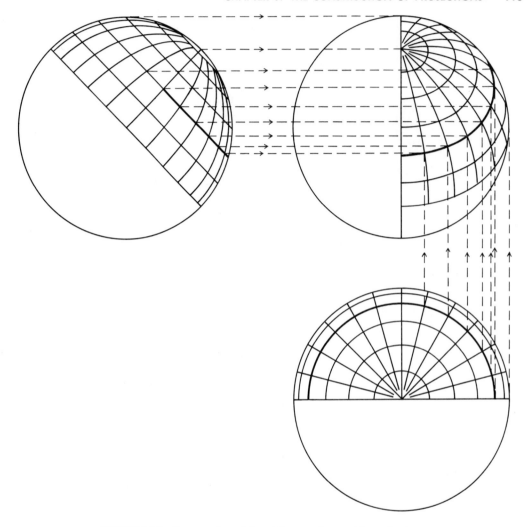

FIGURE 6.14. Construction of the oblique orthographic projection.

are given in Appendix E for a grid centered at latitude 40°, which is an appropriate place for maps of the United States or North America, among others, to be centered.

Since this projection is equal-area it should be constructed to an area scale. The tables just referred to have been prepared on the basis of $R = 1$, so that each value in the tables needs only to be multiplied by the length of the radius of the generating globe of chosen area scale.

6.23   THE AZIMUTHAL EQUIDISTANT PROJECTION

The azimuthal equidistant projection is a most useful projection when directions or distances from a particular point are of interest, and it is not difficult to construct the projection centered on any spot. The polar case is constructed by first drawing an appropriate set of meridians and then constructing equally spaced circles concen-

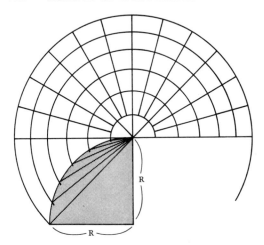

FIGURE 6.15. Construction of the Lambert equal-area projection centered on the pole.

the stereographic may be located in the following manner. When the equidistant hemisphere has been completed, the stereographic is no longer needed. The position of every point on the earth is obviously 180° from its antipode; each point and its antipode lie on a great circle through the center of the projection; the diameter of the hemisphere is 180°; and the scale is uniform from the center. Thus, all that is necessary is to mark on a straightedge the diameter of the hemisphere, and keeping the edge on the center of the projection, locate all the outer intersections from their antipodes in the inner hemisphere.

tric around the pole. This may be extended to include the whole earth, in which case the bounding circle is the opposite pole as in Fig. 6.16. As may be seen the area and linear distortions become large as the periphery is approached. A world map centered on a pole is not a very appropriate use of the azimuthal equidistant projection for reasons outlined in Article 5.8.

For an oblique case the simplest procedure is to prepare first a stereographic projection centered at the desired latitude. This may then be transformed (to any other azimuthal projection) by merely relocating the positions of the intersections of the new grid along their azimuths from the center. This is accomplished by marking off on one edge of a strip of paper the radial scale of the stereographic and on the other edge the radial scale of the equidistant. The strip is then placed on the stereographic, and the distance of a grid intersection from the center noted. This distance is transferred to the radial scale of the equidistant and the position plotted *along the same azimuth.* Figure 6.17 illustrates this procedure. Of course, the scale of the new projection may be changed, if desired, at the same time.

Positions outside the inner hemisphere of

6.24   SHIFTING THE CENTER OF THE PROJECTION

In the previous chapter it was shown that each projection has a specific pattern of inherent deformation. Most distribution maps of hemispherical or world-wide extent have a sort of "center of gravity" of distortion, and it is frequently desirable to "balance" the projection around this distribution,

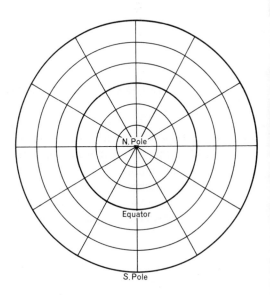

FIGURE 6.16. The azimuthal equidistant projection centered on the pole.

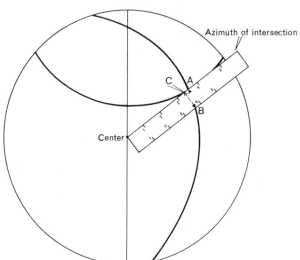

Azimuth of intersection

Center

FIGURE 6.17. The transformation of one azimuthal to another. **A** is the distance from the center to a point according to the radial scale of the stereographic. **B** is the distance of the same point according to the radial scale of the equidistant. **C** is the location of the point along the same azimuth on the equidistant.

rather than merely constructing it in its conventional equatorial or polar orientation. This was suggested in the section on azimuthal projections, but it is by no means limited to that class of projections.

There are several ways of changing the "viewpoint" of a projection, that is to say, of centering it anywhere on the sphere. The general procedure involves locating the positions of the grid intersections on the sphere when the earth grid has been "shifted" in the manner suggested in Article 5.10. This is relatively easy when working with the azimuthal projections, and the procedure for viewing the sphere in any fashion has been treated in those sections. It is frequently the case, however, that one is desirous of producing an "oblique" azimuthal without the necessity of going through the process of transformation from the stereographic. If one has available the *equatorial* case of the projection desired, it is possible to do this by employing an ingenious nomographic process best described by R. E. Harrison. The following explanation is slightly modified from his paper which appeared in *The Geographical Review*, 1943.

To illustrate the procedure the construction of an orthographic projection centered at 35°N is here described. The same procedure is followed in making any azimuthal projection, with only minor and rather obvious differences.

First, the circular nomograph (the equatorial case) is placed on a drawing board and covered with a rectangular piece of tracing paper that overlaps the nomograph on the sides but not at the top and bottom. The tracing paper is fixed to the board. A needle or round-shanked thumbtack is thrust firmly through tracing paper and nomograph at the center of the latter. As the needle or tack remains in position until the new grid is completed, it is well first to reinforce the nomograph at the center with cellulose tape or similar material. The nomograph is positioned so that its equator is vertical (stage I, Fig. 6.18). The intersections of the equator and the central meridian with the bounding circle are then lightly marked on the tracing paper. Thirty-five degrees are counted off below the center along the equator of the nomograph; the meridian passing through this point becomes the equator of the new grid. This is traced, and the intersections of the parallels of the nomograph with the new equator are marked at the desired interval of the grid. This should be done so that the angles of the intersections are correctly preserved, because of a remarkable feature of the nomographic method: instead of providing horizontal and vertical coordinates to establish the points of crossing as in mathematical and other

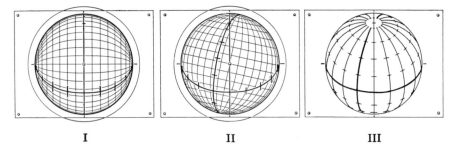

I   II   III

FIGURE 6.18. Three stages in the construction from a nomograph of an orthographic grid centered at 35°. Light lines show the nomograph, heavy lines construction on the tracing paper. (Courtesy of *The Geographical Review,* published by the American Geographical Society of New York.)

graphic procedures, it gives not only the point but the correct angle of any intersection on the projection. Before changing the orientation of the nomograph, the North Pole is marked by counting 90° from the new equator along the upright center line. (When making an azimuthal equidistant or equal-area projection, the South Pole is also marked.)

At this stage the North Pole and the equator (with the meridional intersections) are located (stage I, Fig. 6.18). All the meridians may now be added to the map grid. This is accomplished in the same manner as finding a great circle nomographically, namely, by rotating the nomograph until the North Pole and the meridional intersection of the equator are on the same nomograph meridian or occupy the same relative position between two meridians. The meridian is drawn in its entirety, and while in this position the appropriate crossings of the parallels (with their proper angles of intersection) are noted on the meridian (stage II, Fig. 6.18). Since the intersections rarely coincide exactly with the parallels on the nomograph, it is generally necessary to interpolate. However, in working with a one-degree nomograph the proper intersections will be so close to a parallel that they can be drawn directly with little loss of accuracy. Furthermore, one often finds a simple means of checking the accuracy of the interpolations. For example, on the orthographic projection advantage can be taken of the fact that all lines connecting the intersections of parallels along any two meridians are parallel. With a parallel ruling device the intersections along any meridian can be ticked off from the corresponding intersections along the central meridian, since these are already established.

The nomograph is then rotated to obtain the next meridian, and so on until all are drawn in. At this stage the grid consists of an equator and a complete set of meridians marked with the crossings of the parallels (stage III, Fig. 6.18), and it is a simple matter to complete the parallels, since these crossings form an almost continuous curve. The grid can be drawn in first in pencil and later in ink, or it can be inked directly. It is a most satisfying experience to draw a brand-new grid in ink without the necessity for any previous pencil drawing, to say nothing of not having to erase horizontal and vertical construction lines.

The accuracy of the method is limited only by the accuracy of the nomograph and the ability of the draftsman.

The nomographic method can be used with other classes of projections such as the cylindrical, but it is not quite as simple a procedure as it is with the azimuthals.

Another method of transforming the centering of a projection is by calculation of coordinates. For example, if one wished to "shift" the earth grid of a Mollweide projection so that the equator of the conventional projection coincided with another great circle, it would be the same as shifting the earth so that the pole of the grid was at some other point on the earth's surface (see Fig. 6.19). If the "loose grid" were thus shifted on the earth, all the intersections of the new grid positions could be located and expressed in terms of latitude and longitude

on the old grid. The calculations are not difficult, and their appearance should frighten no one. Nothing but arithmetic is necessary, for tables of sines and cosines are available. The procedure is as follows, assuming the central meridian is 0° longitude in both old and new grid:

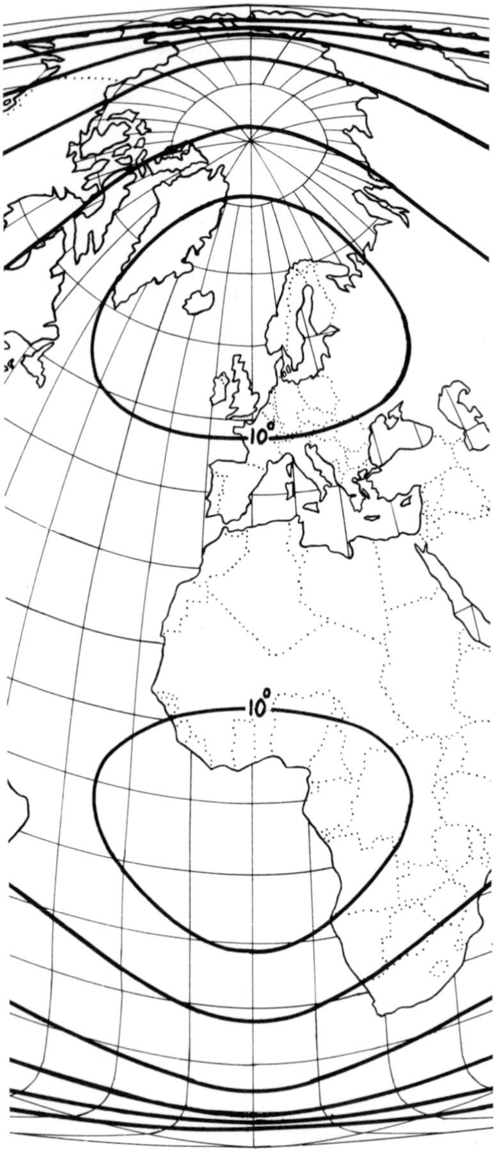

ϕ = the number of degrees the grid has been shifted (90° minus the position of the new pole).

θ = latitude in new system.

λ = longitude in new system.

θ' = latitude in old system.

λ' = longitude in old system.

The problem is to find the latitude (θ') and longitude (λ') on the conventional projection of the *same* latitude (θ) and longitude (λ) of the new system. The formulas are:

$$\sin \theta' = \sin \theta \cos \phi - \sin \phi \cos \theta \cos \lambda$$

$$\sin \lambda' = \frac{\sin \lambda \cos \theta}{\cos \theta'}$$

Tables of the position of θ' and λ' have been computed for every 5° of shift of the grid and are available in E. Hammer, *Über die geographisch wichtigsten Kartenprojektionen...*, Stuttgart, 1889.

6.25   INTERRUPTING AND RECENTERING A PROJECTION

Any projection which, in its conventional form, has the parallels evenly divided by the meridians and the parallels constructed as straight lines may be interrupted and recentered (see Article 5.6). Interruption involves using several central meridians in place of one, and it results in a lobate kind of projection with the continental masses (or oceans) being shown separately on either side of a single equator. Recentering merely means not placing central meridians in opposite hemispheres opposite one another. Even those projections with a line for the pole instead of a point may be interrupted. It should not be inferred that the conventional form (straight-line equator, etc.) is necessary. After interruption

FIGURE 6.19. A portion of a "tilted" Mollweide projection. The lines of equal angular deformation show that the structural characteristics of the projection do not change no matter where the projection may be centered. Compare with Fig. 5.11.

any projection could then be "tilted" in the manner described in the last section of the previous article, although, except to satisfy one's curiosity, it is hard to imagine a use for such a map which would be worth the effort involved.

The process of interruption involves constructing the chosen central meridians and then duplicating the projection around each as far to each side as is necessary. This provides several "points or axes of strength" in place of the one or two on the uninterrupted projection. In practice only the minimum necessary section of the conventional projection need be constructed, and then the appropriate sections or lobes may each be traced in its proper position.

The Map Base: Compilation and Generalization

7.1 THE MAP BASE

There is a fundamental difference between those maps which are constructed to show the distributions of various earth phenomena such as population, precipitation, or tectonic activity, and those which delineate the earth's surface itself. In the latter class fall the topographic map, the coastal chart, various forms of aeronautical charts, and other classes of maps in which there is no great distinction as to the relative importance of the various kinds of information being shown. Such a twofold classification is difficult to justify on purely logical grounds because the two classes shade into one another, and the differences are, in a sense, in the eyes and minds of the users of the maps, not in the maps themselves. Nevertheless, the difference exists and is indicated by the fact that all cartography is commonly divided into two kinds, viz., large-scale cartography and small-scale, "special purpose" or geographic cartography. In small-scale maps the subject data of the map are presented against a background of earth features selected to help show the place-correlation of the mapped data. Small-scale maps are compiled maps in that their data are gathered from a variety of other maps and written sources.

Large-scale maps, 1 : 150,000 and larger, are not usually compiled maps, but are maps made from surveys ranging from photogrammetric to field plane-table survey. Their planimetric accuracy, that is, the correctness of position in the horizontal plane, is controlled as carefully as possible, and within the limits of definition, scale, and human error they are correct. Some medium-scale maps are made by tracing selected data from the larger-scale maps and reducing the result photographically. These are essentially mechanical processes, and relatively little interpretation and generalization take place.

The special-purpose or small-scale map is quite a different operation. The subject matter of the map is presented against a background of locational information which is called the base data. This base map is compiled first, and the accuracy with which it is made determines in large part the accuracy of the final map. This is because of the practical requirement that the cartographer must compile much of the subject-matter data by using the base data as a skeleton on which to hang it. Base data, consisting of coasts, rivers, lakes, and political boundaries, are available from larger-scale, generally accurate, survey maps, and it is absolutely necessary that the cartog-

rapher take special pains to be accurate in his compilation of the base data.

The compiling of base data requires using many maps from which to gain the desired information. They may be on different projections; they may differ markedly in level of accuracy; the dates of publication may vary; and their scales will probably be different. The cartographer must pick and choose, discard this, and modify that, and all the while he must place the selected data on a new projection, locating each item precisely by eye. For although it is possible to transform by tracing and photography a 1:50,000 map into one at 1:250,000, it is quite impossible to transfer mechanically between scales of a much greater range. This is easily understood if one but remembers that 1 square inch at a scale of 1:62,500 will occupy only 0.01 square inch at a scale of 1:625,000. The latter is still a fairly large scale for special-purpose maps.

The process of compilation requires that the selected data be transferred by eye. The projection grid in each case constitutes the guide lines, and all positions must be estimated. Lest the reader be concerned about the accuracy of such a process he should remember that 90% of all small-scale maps have been compiled in this manner. Since the projections commonly differ between those of the sources and that of the base being compiled, it is necessary for the cartographer to become adept at imagining the shearing and twisting of the grid from one projection to another and to modify his lines accordingly. He must continuously be generalizing and simplifying. The difficulties occasioned by projection differences between the sources and the compilation can be largely eliminated by making the projection grids comparable. That is to say, the same grid interval on each will greatly facilitate the work (see Fig. 7.1). One should, whenever possible, compile from larger to smaller scale, because to enlarge the generalizations of a smaller scale map can only result in relative inaccuracies and poor generalization.

Compilation is most easily undertaken by first outlining on the new projection the areas covered by the source maps, as in Fig. 7.2. This outlining is similar to the index map of a map series. The sheet outlines may be drawn, and the special grid spacing of each source (5°, 2°, etc.) may be lightly drawn on the base.

It is worth reiterating that the care with which the cartographer approaches this part of his task will, in large part, determine the accuracy of the final map.

7.2 THE IMPORTANCE OF BASE DATA

The importance of including on the finished map an adequate amount of base data cannot be overemphasized. Nothing is so disconcerting to a map reader than to see a large amount of detail presented on a map and then be confronted with the realization that there is no "frame" of basic geographic information to which he can relate the distributions.

The amount and detail of the base data will, of course, vary considerably from map to map. The usual special-purpose map must have on it the coastlines, the major rivers and lakes, and at least the basic civil divisions. The projection grid, in most cases, should also be indicated in some fashion. The purpose of the map will dictate the degree of detail required, but it is a rare map that can be made without this kind of information to aid the reader to appreciate the relationships presented.

The compiling of these kinds of base data is not always easy. As was observed in the first chapter, there are different kinds of surveys according to the definitions and assumptions made by the survey organization. Cadastral survey is commonly done for a limited area, and because the curvature of the earth's surface is relatively insignificant over a small area, it may not be

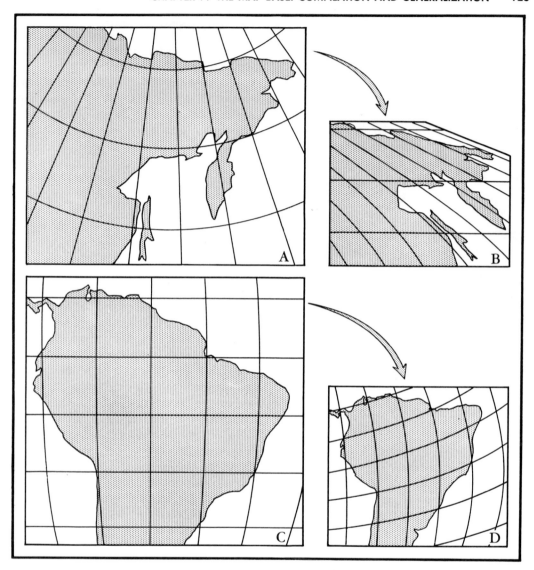

FIGURE 7.1. Changing shapes in the compilation procedure.   Maps B and D are derived from A and C.

taken into account. The boundary lines of such a survey are marked out on the ground with a compass and, perhaps, with the aid of a little astronomic observation. The lines thus established are defined by direction and distance measured on the ground. These do not coincide, to a greater or lesser degree, with directions determined by a survey which defines the area surveyed as a geodetic or three-dimensional surface rather than as a plane surface.

Most plane-survey and cadastral maps do not show much physical data. Compilations of many special-purpose kinds of maps have been made on one or the other kinds of bases and if the map being made requires the union of the two kinds of data, the cartographer may be hard put to it to resolve

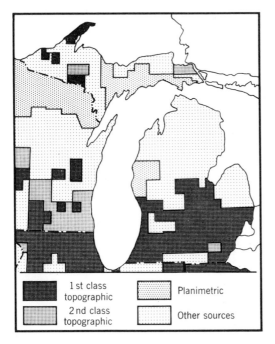

1st class topographic

2nd class topographic

Planimetric

Other sources

FIGURE 7.2. Indexing of sources preliminary to compilation. This makes it possible for the cartographer to see immediately what gaps in source material there may be. It also aids him in pursuing the task systematically.

the differences. For example, if one wishes to make a map showing up-to-date information concerning (1) the streams, lakes, and swamps, and (2) the roads of a region, he may find the first category on topographic maps (of different dates!), but not the second; the second category will be on county or state road maps, but they may not show the first category. The two sources will be essentially "accurate" according to the definitions used in their mapping, but they will not match one another. In general, the practical significance of these kinds of problems varies according to the scale of the map being compiled; the smaller the scale the less the difficulties, since positional discrepancies diminish and the desirability of generalization increases with reduction in scale.

7.3 DETERMINING THE SCALE

All maps must, of course, be drawn to a scale. In actual practice most special-purpose maps are drawn to fit a prescribed format, the format being the size and shape of the sheet on which the map will appear. The format may be a whole page in a book or an atlas, a part of a page, a separate map requiring a fold, a wall map, or a map of almost any conceivable shape and size. Whatever the format may be the map must fit within it.

The first operation in planning the map is to arrive at a layout. (See Article 12.9.) The layout need not be in precise final form, but should be sufficiently exact so that the cartographer may proceed with the base map.

As has been observed the shapes of areas vary considerably, depending on the projection upon which they are plotted. Hence the first concern of the cartographer regarding scale is the projection on which the map will be made. If the map is one for which almost any projection could be used, the cartographer need concern himself only with the dimensions of the format. This circumstance is not, however, likely to occur, or at least it ought not to occur frequently, for it is difficult to imagine a map that would be equally presentable on any projection. When the projection choice has been narrowed to a smaller class or group of projections, then the variations in the shapes of the mapped area on the different projections must be matched against the format in order to see which will provide the best fit and maximum scale.

The easiest way to do this is to establish the vertical and horizontal relationship of the format shape on a proportion basis and then compare the proportion against representations on the various projections. The proportion can be set on a slide rule or plotted on graph paper, so that for any one dimension the other may be readily deter-

mined (see Fig. 7.3). With the proportion established, any scale projection can be used to test for shape fit.

When the projection has been selected that best fits the purpose and format of the proposed map, the necessary scale may be determined. This, of course, may be done in a number of ways, but the simplest is to calculate the scale from the length in degrees of the central meridian.

The cartographer must also decide at this stage whether he is going to compile on an already drawn projection or base map, or construct his own projection and compile on it. Most projections may be used more than once by simply copying the projection and renumbering the longitude. One must be careful, however, not to use a projection that has been copyrighted or patented unless permission is obtained. As a general rule it is far better to construct the projection

to fit precisely the purpose of the map. Most projections are not difficult to construct except in special phases, and it is poor practice to produce an inferior map "projection-wise" in order to save a few hours' time. Frequently mapped areas such as continents or countries have, however, appeared on most of the appropriate standard projections, and if available there is no reason why a good projection already available should not be used. One should, however, always test such a projection to be certain that it has not been improperly constructed.

7.4   REDUCTION

Most maps are made for reduction by photography. This is not always the case, for some processes of reproduction cannot change the scale, but whenever reduction of the fair drawing is possible its advantages make it desirable. The amount of reduction will depend upon the process of reproduction and upon the complexity of the map. It will also depend upon whether definite specifications have been determined for the reproduction, as may be the case with maps of a series. In general, maps are made for from one-quarter to one-half reduction in the linear dimensions. It is unwise to make a greater reduction, for the design problem then becomes difficult.

Whatever the reduction, it is frequently necessary to change the scale of a base map or an already prepared projection. This is unnecessary, of course, if the projection is being constructed, for it may be initially computed and drawn at the larger scale.

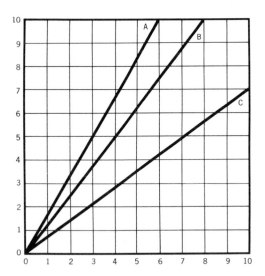

FIGURE 7.3. Dimension proportion graph. The ratio is constant along each line. A defines a rectangle with sides in a 5:3 ratio; B, a 5:4 ratio; and C, a 7:10 ratio. Whatever pair of values is obtained by reading the ordinate and abscissa of any point on one line, the defined shape will always be the same.

7.5   CHANGING SCALE

The scale of a base map, a source map, or projection may be changed in a number of ways, viz., by projection, by photography, by pantography, or by similar squares.

Many larger-scale special-purpose maps such as soils maps, geologic maps, and maps for engineering purposes require great precision. Commonly they are prepared by combining materials from many sources and it has been found that mechanical projection provides the fastest, easiest, and most accurate method of fitting the parts together. A variety of devices has been developed and most cartographic establishments have installed one of them. There are a number of types, but their use is basically similar. They consist of an overhead, opaque projector with an adjustable focus downward to a drawing surface. A source map is placed in the projector and by adjustment, the projection of the image to the drawing surface may be changed in scale and position so that it fits precisely on the map being compiled. The desired information may then merely be traced in position. Needless to say, if the projections of the source map and the map being compiled are much different, the opaque projector cannot be used.

Changing scale by photography is the easiest for the cartographer, but, as might be expected, it is the most expensive. It may be accomplished either by photographic enlargement or reduction through the use of the conventional film process or by several kinds of photocopy processes, for example, Photostat (see Chapter 14). Formerly photocopy was cheaper, but there seems to be less difference at this writing between the costs. Photography provides a little more precision than does photocopy, and there is likely to be less distortion around the edges of a photograph than a photocopy. It is necessary to specify the reduction or enlargement of some types of photocopy work by a percentage ratio, such as 50% or 75% reduction. Change of scale is usually accomplished by adjusting the machine on a percentage scale. Care should be exercised in specifying the percentage change, since 50% reduction or enlargement means one-half in the linear dimension and is usually the most that can occur in one "shot." A change of more than 50% requires repeating the process. To reduce something by 75% in the linear dimension would require two exposures of 50% each, not one at 50% and another at 25%. Photocopy paper is ordinarily limited to 18 × 24 inches, and anything larger may need to be done in sections. It is difficult to match the sections since the paper commonly changes shape unevenly in the developing and drying.

Photographic enlargement or reduction using film negatives may be made somewhat more precisely, since the image may be projected (if enlarged) or viewed in the camera (if reduced), and thus dimensions can be scaled exactly. All the cartographer need do is to specify a line on the piece to be photographed and then request that it be reduced to a specific length. The ratio can be worked out exactly, and the photographer needs only a ruler to check his setting. Any clearly defined line or border will serve as the guide. If none is available he may place one on his drawing. The sizes available are limited only by the photographer's equipment and paper stock.

The pantograph is an ancient device for enlarging and reducing, the common form of which is illustrated in Fig. 7.4. Simple

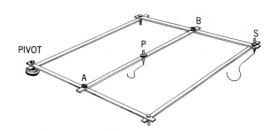

FIGURE 7.4. A pantograph. Stylus (S) and pencil (P) are interchangeable for enlargement or reduction. Adjustment to the desired ratio is made by moving arm AB parallel to itself while the pencil or stylus on AB is adjusted so that it, the pivot point, and S are kept in a straight line.

wooden pantographs cost but a few dollars; large, metal precision models cost much more. They are easy to operate for reduction, but enlargement is relatively difficult and accuracy is hard to obtain.

If a pantograph is unavailable, and if the projection of a map one wishes to copy is either too difficult or not indicated, then one may change scale by similar squares. This involves drawing a grid of squares on the original and drawing the "same" squares, only larger or smaller, on the compilation. The lines and positions may then be transferred from the one grid system to the other (see Fig. 7.5). With care it is quite an accurate process, for it is the same as compilation.

Occasionally a cartographer is called upon to produce a large wall-size chart or map that involves greatly enlarging a base. In most cases, extreme accuracy is not required. If the outlines cannot be sketched satisfactorily because of their intricacies, it is possible to accomplish an adequate solution by projection. A slide or film positive (in some cases, a negative will do) may be projected to paper affixed to the wall and the image traced thereon. If an opaque classroom projector with a large projecting surface (that is sufficiently cool in operation) is available, it may be used directly so that the necessity of making a slide is eliminated.

7.6   COMPILATION PROCEDURE

Perhaps nothing helps the mechanical process of compiling so much as a transparent or translucent material with which to work. A tracing medium of some sort (paper, plastic, etc.) enables the compiler to accomplish a number of things in addition to the convenience of being able to trace some data. He may lay out lettering for titles, etc., and move the layout around under this compilation worksheet (see Article 12.12). If he wishes to draw a series of lines, or letter at an angle, or place dots regularly, he need only place some cross-section paper under the tracing paper. The use of a lightweight material such as tracing paper occasions, however, the problem of maintaining size, for paper contracts and expands with changes in humidity and temperature. Plastic materials are more stable.

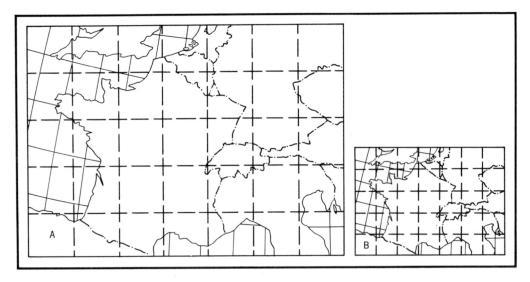

FIGURE 7.5. Changing scale by similar squares. Map B has been compiled from map A.

If registry, that is, the matching of several drawings, is a problem, a dimensionally stable material should be used.

Compilation may be done in any colors and inks the cartographer desires. The main problem is to put all the desired data on the worksheet in such a way that each item is clear and will cause no confusion in the drafting process; thus hydrography, coastlines, boundaries, and other elements of the base data may each be compiled in a different color.

7.7 COASTLINES

The compiling of coasts for very small-scale maps is not much of a problem, for they usually require so much generalization that detail is of little consequence. This is not the case when compiling at medium scales where considerable accuracy of detail is necessary.

Perhaps the major problem facing the cartographer is the matter of source material. It is well to bear in mind that some coasts will be shown quite differently on different maps, yet both may be accurate. Hydrographic charts are made with a datum, or plane of reference, of mean low water, whereas topographic maps are usually made with a datum of mean sea level. The two are not the same elevation, and it is to be expected that there will be a difference in the resulting outline of the land. In parts of the world with higher tides and with special planes of reference the differences will be greater. Another difficult aspect of dealing with source materials is that the coloring of the charts and maps may be quite different. Swamp land, definitely not navigable, is usually colored as land on a chart. The compiler would assume it to be land by its appearance. All low-lying swamp on a topographic map is colored blue as water, and only a small area may be shown as land. On many low-lying coasts the cartographer is faced with a decision as to what is land; the charts and maps do not tell him.

Through the years some coasts change outline sufficiently so that it makes a difference even on medium-scale maps. Figure 7.6 shows the north coast of the Persian Gulf in the past and at present, and Fig. 7.7, a portion of the Atlantic coast. If one were making maps of an historical period he should endeavor to recreate the conditions at the period of the map. This problem is particularly evident on coastal areas of rapid silting, which in many parts of the world seem to be important areas of occupancy.

Another problem of considerable concern to the cartographer is the representation of coasts on maps wherein the scale varies considerably over the map. For example, at 60° latitude on the conventional Mercator projection everything is much larger (twice linearly, four times areally) than similar features at the equator. Bays, inlets, fjords, etc., in the higher latitudes take on a great apparent significance on such maps and look more detailed and complex than they

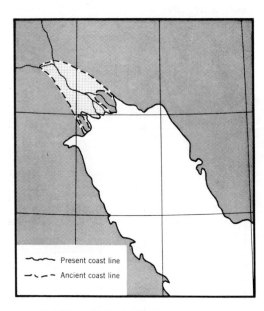

Present coast line
Ancient coast line

FIGURE 7.6. Major changes in coastlines occur over long periods of time, which are significant even on small-scale maps. A portion of the Persian Gulf.

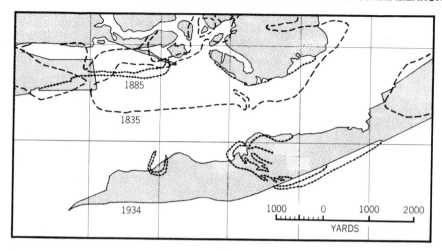

FIGURE 7.7. Frequent changes have occurred in some areas. The various lines show the positions of the shoreline of Rockaway Inlet, Long Island, at several periods in the past. (Modified from Deetz, Cartography, Special Publication 205, U. S. Coast and Geodetic Survey.)

should if the coast is not the focus of interest. It may be necessary to vary the simplification and generalization according to the scale variations of the map. Of course, this would never be done on a topographic or chart series.

In a number of areas of the world, notably in the polar regions, the coastlines, like many other elements of the map base, are not well known. They vary considerably from one source to another. On some maps a particular region may appear as an island; on others, as a series of islands; and on still others, as a peninsula. On simple line maps a broken or dashed line suffices for unknown positions of coastlines, but it becomes a larger problem when the water is to be shaded or colored, for no matter what type of line is used to delineate the coast the value or color change outlines it clearly.

7.8   DRAFTING COASTLINES

Coastlines may be drawn with a crow quill pen or any other fine nib if care is taken to maintain a uniform thickness of line. It is an aid to have the paper loose on the drafting table so that it may be turned

around freely and lines drawn toward the cartographer. Occasionally, it is desirable to draw a lighter line in a complex area, and a slightly heavier line in a simple area in order that the two coastlines may appear more nearly uniform as shown by *A* in Fig. 7.8. Likewise, embayments, estuaries, etc., may sometimes be drawn with a line lighter than the main trend of the coastline, as shown by *B* in Fig. 7.8. This is especially desirable for the thick coasts of wall maps.

Coastlines may also be drawn with a pen that makes a uniform line no matter what direction it is moved on the paper, such as the LeRoy et al., shown by *C* in Fig. 7.8. This is much faster than using a quill pen, but it is not so precise for detailed work, for no points can be made with these "round-pointed" pens. It is also difficult to vary the width of line, and a very thin line cannot be drawn.

7.9   POLITICAL BOUNDARIES

Compiling political boundaries for base data is sometimes a complex problem, for the boundaries must be chosen for the purpose and date of the map data to be placed

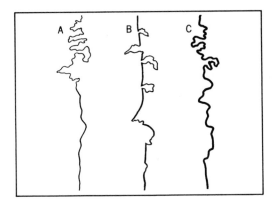

FIGURE 7.8. Various kinds of coastlines. Letters refer to Article 7.8.

on them.   The problem becomes more difficult as the area covered by the map increases.   Almost all boundaries change from time to time, and it is surprising how difficult it is to search out the minor changes. For example, a population map of the distribution of languages in central Europe prior to World War II, but also showing present boundaries, raises these problems: (*a*) international boundaries today and (*b*) census division boundaries as of the dates of the enumerations in the various countries.

The major difficulties are twofold.   The first is that of finding maps showing enumeration districts that show latitude, longitude, and other base data so that the boundaries may be transferred to the worksheet in proper position.   The second is that of placing present international boundaries in correct relation to the enumeration boundaries.

It is not uncommon for official civil division boundary maps to be without any other base data, even projection lines. Such a condition should impress on the cartographer who uses such deficient maps the need for him to provide base data for the users of his maps.

7.10   DRAFTING BOUNDARIES

As in drawing other linear symbols, boundaries on base maps are most easily made with a pen that will draw a uniform line no matter which direction it is moved. As shown in Fig. 7.9, such a line cannot, however, have sharp corners, and this is sometimes a disadvantage when boundaries are shown with a dot-dash symbol. One way to overcome this defect is illustrated in Fig. 7.9, where a solid line is first drawn and then broken into the symbol desired by brushing across it with white paint. This is a good way to clean up corners and other junctions, but it can be done *only when the map is to be photographed on relatively slow film*.

A large variety of symbols may be used to show boundaries, some of which are illustrated in Fig. 7.10.   There is no generally accepted standardization of boundaries, but many agencies and governments have standardized boundary symbols for their own official maps.   Generally speaking, decreasing significance of boundaries on a map is accompanied by a decrease in width of line and an increase in complexity of line.

One difficulty the cartographer occasion-

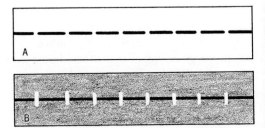

FIGURE 7.9.   A line drawn with a round pen (A) has round corners; B shows one method of sharpening such corners with white paint. They may also be drawn with a stub-type pen, or the corners may be sharpened by touching them up with a crow quill.

ally encounters is the problem of symbolizing the boundary along a water course also shown as base data. Some possible solutions are shown in Fig. 7.11.

7.11 HYDROGRAPHY

The compiling of rivers and lakes on the base map is an important process. These elements of the physical landscape are the only relatively permanent interior features on many maps, and they provide helpful "anchor points" both for the compilation of other data and for the map reader's appreciation of the significance of the distribution mapped.

The selection of the rivers and lakes depends, of course, upon their significance to the problem at hand. On some maps the inclusion of well-known state boundaries makes it unnecessary to include any but the larger rivers. Maps of less well-known areas require more hydrography, for the drainage, which indicates the major topographic structure of an area, is sometimes a better known phenomenon than the internal boundaries. Care must be exercised to choose the main "stream" of rivers and the major tributaries. Often this depends not upon the width, depth, or volume of the stream but upon some economic or other

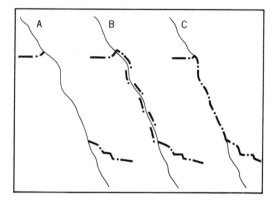

FIGURE 7.11. Some methods of showing boundaries along rivers. A and C show only that the boundary follows the river. It may be on either bank or in the middle of the stream. B shows that it is in the middle. If it is necessary to show that the boundary follows one bank it may be drawn parallel to the stream on the appropriate side.

element of significance. Oftentimes it is necessary to eliminate relatively important rivers or lakes because they will interfere with the planned use of the maps. For example, Lake Winnebago in Wisconsin becomes a visual focus on many maps to the detriment of the map data. Frequently it need not be included.

Just as coastlines have characteristic shapes (see Article 7.13) so do rivers, and these shapes help considerably on the larger-scale maps to identify the feature. The braided streams of dry lands, intermittent streams, or the meandering streams on flood plains are examples. On small-scale maps it frequently is not possible to include enough detail to thus differentiate between stream types, but the larger sweeps, angles, and curves of the stream's course should be faithfully delineated. Likewise, the manner in which a stream enters the sea is important. Some enter at a particular angle, some enter into bays, and some break into a characteristic set of distributaries. Examples of streams are shown in Fig. 7.12.

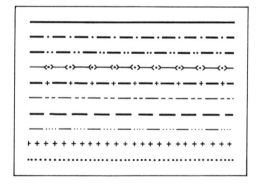

FIGURE 7.10. Some examples of kinds of boundary symbols.

Swamps, marshes, and mud flats are commonly important elements of location on the base map. They may be represented by various symbols, examples of which are shown in Fig. 7.12.

7.12 DRAFTING HYDROGRAPHY

It is usually desirable when representing streams to draw them so that they grow from thin to thicker lines near their mouths. This is most easily done with a flexible, fine pen nib which spreads with increased pressure. It requires a bit of practice to keep the spreading uniform around curves and angles in the stream. It should be pointed out that streams do not always become larger or wider downstream. In dry land areas of the world the reverse is usually true, the streams being larger near their sources. This is also occasionally the case even in humid regions; for example, the Congo River is wider in its middle course than near its mouth.

On all but the largest-scale maps it is im-

possible to represent the width of a river truly, and, consequently, the width of line chosen is an important consideration. When the existence of a river is known but not its precise location, its unknown portion may be represented by a dashed line the same width as the known course.

Patterns for lakes, swamps, intermittent lakes, etc., may either be drafted or obtained in preprinted form.

7.13 GENERALIZATION

To make a map implies the reduction of the features to a smaller size in order to be able to view a larger area than can be encompassed by an individual's range of vision. Reduction of scale is accompanied by inescapable changes: widths and lengths of the earth's features are reduced in the ratio of the reduction; intricacies are increased in similar proportion; crowding of adjacent items increases; and legibility in general is reduced. The effective limit of exact representation on maps of earth phenomena having dimension (roads, rivers, etc.) is at a fairly large scale. The limiting scale varies somewhat, of course, depending on the item to be represented. Certainly, however, at any scale smaller than the topographic it becomes necessary (1) to make a selection of the objects to be shown, (2) to simplify their form, and (3) to evaluate the relative significance of the items being portrayed in order to make the appearance of the important items more prominent. The combined process is called cartographic generalization. Every small-scale map and every special purpose map must be products of generalization.

Many cartographers have attempted to analyze the processes of generalization, but so far it has been impossible to set forth a consistent set of rules that will prescribe what should be done in each instance. It seems likely that cartographic generalization will remain forever an essentially creative process, and that it will escape the

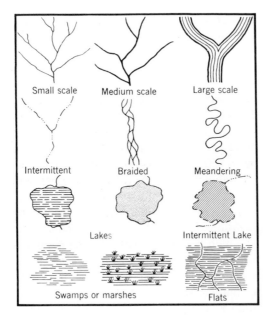

FIGURE 7.12. Some examples of kinds of symbols used for hydrography.

modern tendency toward standardization which seems, even in cartography, to be an unfortunate corollary of technical development and specialization. It is helpful to distinguish in this creative process between what may be called intellectual generalization as opposed to visual generalization, although in practice they clearly overlap and each includes elements of selection, evaluation, and simplification.

Intellectual generalization refers to that part of the process that involves the selection and portrayal of map items in the manner which satisfies *the purpose of the map.* If the map being made is a reference map, then the data must be placed as accurately as possible within drafting and legibility limits. If, on the other hand, the map is for a special purpose, some of the base data may be simplified to a considerable degree. Intellectual generalization often requires apparent inconsistencies on the part of the cartographer whenever elements of "importance" enter into the choice of items to be portrayed. One cannot, for most special-purpose maps, make a selection of features, for example, rivers or cities, on purely objective grounds such as size. Importance is a subjective quality; a selection of cities on a map of the United States which included only those of more than 100,000 inhabitants would eliminate many in western United States that are far more "important" in their region than many of those included in more populous eastern United States. A thorough knowledge of the subject matter of the map and of the area being mapped is indispensable to good intellectual generalization. A Swedish cartographer, Gösta Lundqvist, has observed that it always *seems* easier to generalize faraway places; and he stated a familiar and revealing reaction when he pointed out that "I always find . . . that other peoples' maps are extremely good—except for their treatment of Sweden"!

In visual generalization the cartographer is concerned with the visual effect of the character of the line on the viewer. It is particularly important in designing lines to represent coasts and boundaries when the reference value of the line itself is slight, as is the case with a great many maps on which boundaries and coasts appear.

As a general rule we may say that any visual form that appears more complicated than the surrounding forms will draw attention to itself, simply because it is more interesting to the eye. The fjorded coast of Norway is an example. If the reader will refer to Fig. 7.13 he will at once see that *A,* the more complicated representation of the coast, catches his eye. This is partly due to the fact that the degree of complexity also makes the coastal region a dark value area. By simplification the map maker can help the reader refrain from giving attention to details that are extraneous to the purpose of the map.

It is not enough merely to smooth out coasts and ignore islands. The basic shapes and outlines must be retained and emphasized in their simplicity, for the eye will not quibble with the representation if the general shapes are as expected.

The cartographer must be careful not to overdo the simplification, for, as has been abundantly shown in many newspaper maps, too much simplification makes a representation of a known shape appear ridiculous.

While the cartographer is learning, and for some time afterward, it would be wise for him to test his generalization by drafting a small portion of the planned map before compilation has progressed far. In this way he may decide upon the generalization needed for his compilation. It will also help him in his design plan.

Good generalization requires many qualities on the part of the cartographer, chief among which are a thorough knowledge of his subject matter, a clear understanding of the purpose of his map, and essential intellectual honesty. The latter is particularly important. A distinguished cartographer

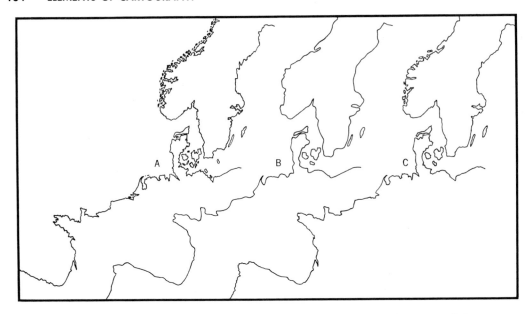

FIGURE 7.13. Generalization of coasts. A and C are least generalized; B, the most. All, however, are greatly simplified from reality.

and geographer, John K. Wright, puts it thus:*

Fundamental among these qualities is scientific integrity: devotion to the truth and a will to record it as accurately as possible. The strength of this devotion varies with the individual. Not all cartographers are above attempting to make their maps seem more accurate than they actually are by drawing rivers, coasts, form lines, and so on, with an intricacy of detail derived largely from the imagination. This may be done to cover up the use of inadequate source materials or, what is worse, to mask carelessness in the use of adequate sources. Indifference to the truth may also show itself in failure to counteract, where it would be feasible and desirable to do so, the exaggerated impression of accuracy often due to the clean-cut appearance of a map.

7.14   RELIABILITY

One of the most difficult tasks of the cartographer is to convey to the map reader

some indication of the reliability of the information on his map. When writing or speaking, words such as "almost," "nearly," and "approximately" can be included to indicate the desired degree of precision of the subject matter. It is not easy to do this with map data. It is unfortunate that this is the case, for a well-made map has about it an aura of truth and exactness that might not be warranted if the facts concerning its accuracy were known.

There are several ways to combat this. One, of course, is to include in the legend a statement concerning the accuracy of any item about which such is necessary. Another, and more common method on larger-scale maps, is to include a reliability diagram (Fig. 7.14) which shows the relative accuracy of various parts of the map.

It is also good practice to include in the legend, if warranted, such terms as "position approximate," "generalized roads," or "selected railroads," in order that an idea of the completeness and accuracy may be given the reader.

* From "Map Makers Are Human . . . ," *The Geographical Review*, 1942, Vol. 32, p. 528.

COVERAGE DIAGRAM

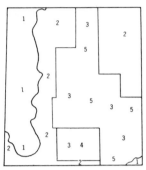

1. USC&GS Charts, (Reliable survey)
2. Luzon, 1:63,360 (Trigonometric
   survey - reliability fair)
3. PIC&GS Charts
   (Compiled map - reliability fair)
4. Luzon Island, 1:200,000
   (Reconnaissance map - reliability fair)
5. Sectional Aeronautical Chart, 1:600,000
   (Compiled map - reliability fair)

FIGURE 7.14. Coverage diagram from a map of the Lingayen Gulf area, Philippine Islands, giving an annotated list of sources together with an index. (Courtesy of the Army Map Service.)

7.15   COPYRIGHTS AND CREDITS

It is beyond the purpose of this book to suggest sources of compilation materials, but the cartographer, regardless of what sources he uses, must always give proper credit for materials gathered and presented by others. It is necessary to do this for it is the honest way of doing things. But this does not mean that he must identify the source of every single item on a reference map, even though it is obvious that he could not have gathered any of the material himself in the field by original survey. It does mean that he should identify the source of any material that is not generally common knowledge or does not obviously come from good public authority. He may, however, wish to identify such sources of well-known information in order to justify the quality of his map.

Equally important for the map maker is the problem of copyright protection and the use of materials that have been copyrighted. This is a particularly difficult problem in cartography, for there has never been a clear definition of the way in which the copyright laws apply to maps. In general, no copyrighted map may be used as a source without permission, for the precise manner in which the material is arrayed and generalized is protected. Most United States government maps and publications may be used, but in the case of specialized materials containing judgments and opinions, it is not only courteous but wise to request permission, for the material may have been copyrighted by the authors separately or some of it may have come from copyrighted sources.

Generally speaking, survey maps of the topographic variety, census material, and the like may be used freely. Actual reproduction or strict copying of private and many public materials *must* be accompanied by permission from the holder of the copyright. Even some projections are copyrighted, but this is not much of a problem to the cartographer for there are many from which to choose.

Symbolizing and Processing Map Data

8.1 THE MAP AS A SYMBOL

The entire map is a symbol, as well as its parts, and it is not quite correct to designate only certain components as symbols. A coastline is actually a line of equal value (a contour), and has no existence at all, being but an imaginary line between water and land. Similarly, everything, from the lines used to represent the imaginary earth graticule to the marks employed to represent base or specialized data, cannot be shown as it actually is but must be symbolized. This is one of the major ways in which a map differs from an air photograph. The data on a map are selected and symbolized in order to tell a story, to make clear one or a series of relationships. A photograph of a portion of the earth is a record, unsymbolized and unselected, of what is "seen" by the camera. One of the major duties of the cartographer, then, is to understand the relations among symbols, their relative effectiveness, and their relative suitability for the purpose for which the map is being constructed.

The symbolism of cartography has developed over the centuries; consequently, traditions and conventions regarding map representation have gained general acceptance. Symbols constitute a kind of code by which the cartographer can present the most

effective story in the limited space available. In a sense, the symbolism of small-scale cartography has become standardized over the years, but the great possibilities of variation have, however, effectively prevented any rigid standardization, although in the case of large-scale maps standardization is more nearly approached. The cartographer who works with small-scale maps must of necessity be critical and imaginative, and adjust the representation and symbolism to the special purpose of his map.

Standardization of symbols can and must be accomplished for a set of maps at a given scale, such as a topographic set, but such standardization is likely to be useful only at that scale and in that combination. On the other hand, special purpose maps vary so widely in terms of scale and purpose that a large part of the cartographer's job is concerned with the effectiveness of the symbols he selects or designs. In the balance of this chapter the various kinds of symbols appropriate to represent facts other than base data are discussed, along with some of the fundamental principles underlying their use. Needless to say, all their possible variations or opportunities of employment cannot be touched upon here. The reader is advised to examine closely the numerous examples of distribution maps

appearing in books and periodicals in order to acquire a broader understanding of the manifold utility of cartographic symbolism.

8.2   KINDS OF SYMBOLS

Map symbols may be separated into two major categories, qualitative and quantitative, according to whether they represent kinds of phenomena, on the one hand, or amount as well as kind, on the other. Within each of those two major divisions the range of possible symbols falls into three subcategories, namely, *point, line,* and *area* symbols. Within each of these subcategories there are possible variations. The range is illustrated by representative examples in Fig. 8.1. Their characteristics and major utility are considered separately in the following articles.

It is important for the cartographer to be fully aware of the fact that all geographical quantities are associated with places; otherwise they would not be geographical. John K. Wright has pointed out that when geographical or place quantities are reduced to dimensional terms, every place is either a *point* (location only), a *line* (one dimensional), an *area* or surface (two dimensional), or a *volume* (three dimensional).* These are the kinds of data the cartographer is called upon to represent on maps. The first three geographical quantities may be shown relatively easily with the three kinds of marks that can be placed on a plane, that is, point, line, and area symbols. On the other hand, the fourth, geographical volume, has three space dimensions, but must somehow be reduced to two dimensions on the map plane. Needless to say, the discrepancy between the number of kinds of geographical quantities (4) and the number of cartographic symbols available

to represent them (3) causes confusion to the beginner. This will be considerably clarified if, when thinking about the representation of geographical data, he takes care to maintain a clear distinction between the kind of geographical quantity with which he is concerned and the kind of map symbol he may use to represent it. Plane symbols on the map can be classified systematically, that is, in mutually exclusive categories, only as to whether their place connotation on the map refers simply to location or to magnitudes in one or two dimensions. They cannot be classified systematically in terms of the kinds of geographical quantities they represent, because three types of marks must be made to serve four classes of quantities.

Almost as important as the inherent qualities of a symbol is its design, for, as has often been stated (but less often heeded), the map symbol that cannot be seen or read is wasted and is but a useless encumbrance. The appearance of a visual item may be varied by size, shape, and color contrasts. Dots may be large or small, regular or irregular, dark or light or colored. Lines may vary similarly. As is pointed out in Chapter 12, contrast of any of these qualities or combinations of them is the key to visibility. The possibilities of variation are large indeed, and the cartographer would do well to exercise his ingenuity and experiment with possibilities before settling upon any one design or kind of symbol.

8.3   POINT SYMBOLS

Point symbols such as dots, circles, spheres, cubes, or any of the other varieties may represent any phenomenon having territorial extent or simply location. A dot may represent a city; a triangle, a triangulation station; a circle, the population of a city or the production of an industrial plant. The variations and uses are legion. Thus, a point symbol may represent either simply

* John K. Wright, "Crossbreeding Geographical Quantities," *The Geographical Review,* Vol. 45, No. 1, 1955, pp. 52–65.

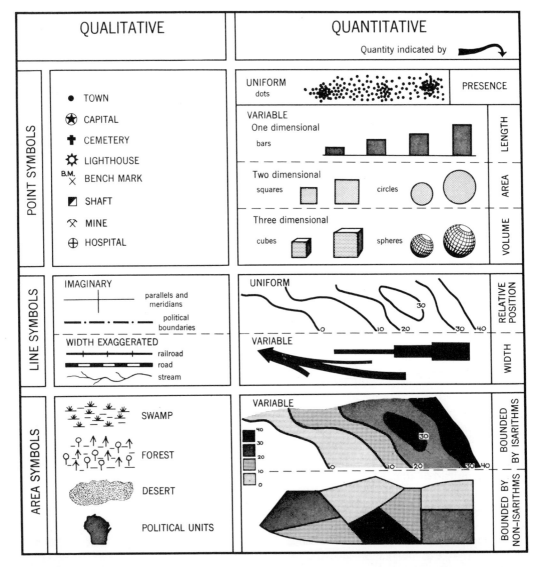

FIGURE 8.1.   Illustrative outline of point, line, and area symbols. (Modified from John K. Wright by permission of *The Geographical Review*, published by the American Geographical Society of New York.)

kind as in the case of a capital city or both *kind* and *amount* as in the case of a graduated circle representing the population of the city. The point symbol is not adaptable for showing directly a ratio or relationship.

Representation of *kind* by point symbols merely requires that the symbol design be characteristic enough to be seen and understood by the map reader.

Representation of *amount* by a point symbol may be accomplished either by repeating a uniform symbol, so that the aggregate number represents a total, or by varying the size (area or apparent volume)

of each symbol in proportion to the amount at each location.

8.4 LINE SYMBOLS

There are many kinds of line symbols. The most familiar are those that are qualitative in nature, that is to say, those that show a *kind* of feature, such as a river or a road. Although such line symbols are fundamentally alike in that they represent the qualitative nature of the feature without ordinarily indicating any quantitative value, they may be used for many kinds of purposes. For example, a line may represent a road and show exactly where it lies on a topographic map, whereas at a smaller scale it may be drawn merely to show that two places are connected by a road. Another line, for example a boundary, may be used merely to separate unlike areas. Thus, a line can be used qualitatively to join things, a line along which there is some constant quality; or it may be used to separate things, a line along which there is no constant quality.

Still another kind of line is one along which a specified quantitative value changes. Such lines are used to show movement and variable *amount*, separately or in combination. Traffic flow or commodity flow between areas is frequently represented in this fashion. An arrow alone may represent nothing but movement; but a line of varying width may show differences in capacity, without showing any movement, such as roadbed load limits. As a matter of fact, the tapering line of a river on a map is actually a flow line, although it is usually thought of as being a qualitative rather than a quantitative symbol.

Another kind of line symbol showing amount is the line along which the same value of some phenomenon exists from place to place on a map. The earliest use of such lines, other than for a coastline, was by Edmund Halley who joined points on a map which had the same compass declination. Since then many other kinds of data, varying in amount from place to place, have been symbolized by these kinds of lines. Perhaps the best known is the line of equal elevation above sea level; it is sometimes called an isohypse, but it is best known by its common name, the contour. To the prefix *iso* (Gr. *isos,* equal) is commonly added the term describing the phenomenon being mapped. Thus lines of equal compass declination are called isogones (Gr. *gonia,* angle), lines of equal elevation are called isohypses (Gr. *hypso,* height). The generic term, or the name of all such lines, is *isarithm* (Gr. *arithmos,* number).

In addition to symbolizing at various map locations the values of the data being mapped, the systematic use of isarithms allows the representation of a third dimension. This allows the map reader to deduce certain derivatives of the relation between the change of quantity and the change of place, such as the ratio of quantity change with distance, that is, gradient. Because they are so important in scientific cartography the employment of isarithms to represent the third dimension is the main subject treated in Chapter 10.

8.5 AREA SYMBOLS

Area symbols, like line and point symbols, may be used to represent either qualitative or quantitative data. Qualitative area symbols are those such as simulated grass for marshes, patterns to show vegetation, soil, or terrain types, and a host of others. They differentiate *kind,* and each symbol used should be sufficiently varied from the others so that no confusion can result. Many qualitative symbols have become conventional through long use.

Quantitative area symbols to show *amount* are employed to convey data in two ways. They may either consist of the application of some coloring or shading to symbolize

the range of amounts between two isarithms, as in the case of the familiar elevation map, or they may be used to symbolize different amounts in areas, the boundaries of which have no actual numerical value (see Fig. 8.1).

There is a wide range of prepared area symbols available, and the ultimate range is limited only by the imagination of the cartographer. Basically, area symbols may vary either in terms of pattern (lines, dots, etc.) or in terms of visual value (their relative darkness or lightness). Parallel lines tend to cause the viewer to have disturbing eye movements (see Article 12.7), and it is generally good practice to use parallel lines sparingly. Dot patterns are visually more stable and differentiate areas more clearly. Naturally, when a large number of patterns is required, parallel lines must occasionally be utilized. They should be surrounded by other kinds of patterns as frequently as possible.

Qualitative area symbolization should be accomplished by variation in pattern, whereas quantitative variation should generally utilize value changes. The range from dark to light automatically gives the impression of varying amount, with the darker standing for the greater amount.

8.6   DISTRIBUTION MAPS

In a general sense, any map is a distribution map, for it is impossible to present relative location without showing distribution. Nevertheless, a large group of maps containing point, line, or area symbols are commonly termed distribution maps in contrast to atlas maps, topographic maps, historical maps, and the other categories in the commonly employed, loose, and overlapping classification of kinds of maps. Many distribution maps employ statistical data; but because distributions may be non-numerical in the statistical sense, it would not be proper to call them statistical maps. These are the kinds of maps that show, for example, areas predominately inhabited by Moslems or the distribution of important fishing grounds.

Maps showing quantitative distributions are one of the cartographer's stock in trade. They are capable of surprising variety and can be used to present almost any kind of data. Few maps can be made that do not in some way present quantitative information, even if the amounts involved result from so simple an operation as grading the symbols for cities of different size for an atlas map. Column after column of numbers in tables frequently are excessively forbidding, and the statistical map often can present the same material in a more understandable and interesting manner. Tabular materials of various kinds, ranging from a federal census to reports of commissions (for example, Interstate Commerce) and from the reports of industrial concerns to the results of one's own tabulation, exist in staggering variety. With such a wealth of material, it is to be expected that the cartographer finds a large percentage of his effort is devoted to preparing this type of map.

It is necessary for the student to have well in mind that figures can lie, cartographically at least, if they are not properly presented. Hasty evaluation of data, or the selection of data to support conclusions unwarranted in the first place, results in intellectually questionable maps. Their production is vicious, for they may be, and unfortunately sometimes are, used by their authors or others to support the very conclusions from which they were drawn in the first place. The exhortation, occasionally implied or stated in this book, "to make the map tell the story desired by the author" is not contradictory to the preceding. It is merely a matter of integrity. Another dangerous source of error in cartography is that of providing an impression of precision greater than can be justified by the facts. To keep from making this serious kind of

mistake the cartographer is often forced to invent symbols such as dashed lines or patterns of question marks, which may detract from the appearance of the map, but which will serve the more important purpose of preventing the map reader from falling into the common trap of "believing everything he sees."

The examples found in this book of kinds of distribution maps by no means complete the list, for the number of possibilities of combination and presentation are almost infinite. Included, however, are the major types of presentation techniques commonly used by geographers, meteorologists, economists, and other social and physical scientists. To categorize them precisely is all but impossible, for the various kinds shade into one another almost imperceptibly. Nevertheless, some useful generalizations can be made concerning classes of distribution maps and the kinds of problems that commonly arise when certain sorts of data are being mapped.

Some maps are clearly *qualitative* in that their function is to show the distribution of differences of kinds of phenomena, such as kinds of precipitation, types of rock, or predominant races. Their fundamental purpose is to present the location of the characteristics, and consequently adequate base information is imperative for such maps. Different from that class are *quantitative* maps which present data expressable as numbers, such as amounts of precipitation, depth of rock formations, or numbers of people. They cannot escape being somewhat qualitative since they must display a kind of phenomenon, but their major function is the presentation of variations in amounts. This class is much more complex than the qualitative class, for the possibilities of manipulation of the data are much greater. Base data requirements are usually not quite so great for quantitative maps, because it is not unusual that the major focus of interest is on the numerical varia-

tions within the phenomenon being mapped rather than on its precise location.

8.7 QUALITATIVE DISTRIBUTION MAPS

One of the major tasks of the cartographer is to select ways of presenting qualitative data. The types of data he may need to present run a long gamut, from such qualitative facts as religions, dominant livelihoods, or racial characteristics to rock types, vegetation characteristics, or dominant agricultural practices.

Qualitative maps generally utilize area symbols, and are distinguished by presenting the cartographer with a problem for which there is no easy solution. When the distribution of qualities is mapped in its entirety, it is immediately evident that qualitative areas are generally not mutually exclusive. Consequently, the cartographer is forced to devise a means of showing overlap. This may be done in a number of ways, as suggested in Fig. 8.2, none of which is suited to all circumstances.

If the map is a color map it is possible to choose colors that give the impression of mixture. For example, a red and a blue when superposed appear purple, and that color looks like a mixture. On the other hand, a color produced by mixing red and green does not look like a mixture of its components.

The selection of area symbols for qualitative maps poses the problem, common to all qualitative distribution maps, of symbolizing without much value contrast. As is explained in Chapter 12, clarity and visibility are the result of contrast, and, of the various kinds of contrast, value (degree of darkness) is probably the most important. Value changes are, however, inappropriate on a qualitative map because of the universal tendency to assign quantitative meaning to value differences. Thus a darker area symbol looks more "important" to the map reader. Of course, such emphasis

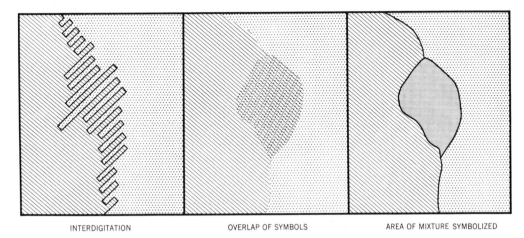

INTERDIGITATION   OVERLAP OF SYMBOLS   AREA OF MIXTURE SYMBOLIZED

FIGURE 8.2. Methods of showing mixture and overlap.

could be used to advantage if the cartographer were desirous of drawing attention to one or more of the various qualitative elements he is mapping. The use of color complicates the problem even further.

Quantitative information may be combined with the qualitative to present details of distribution. This may be accomplished in two ways: (1) by showing ratios or a proportion of the whole and (2) by symbolizing totals and showing percentages thereof. Figure 8.3 shows the ratio between two components. It should be noted that the presentation gives no indication of the total numbers involved. The total amount may be included in the presentation by using pie charts in which the area of the circle represents the total, and each circle is subdivided to show the relative amount of each component of the total. Such a map is illustrated in Fig. 9.13.

8.8   QUANTITATIVE DISTRIBUTION MAPS

The cartography of the past two hundred years has been characterized by many major changes, not the least of which is that it has seen the introduction of quantitative symbolization. When man became conscious of the variety of phenomena on the earth it was only natural that he should also have been interested in variations in amount from place to place. His observations were generally so incomplete and unreliable that it was not possible to map the results in any consistent fashion until comparatively recently. Almost all the symbolization employed on quantitative maps has come into use in less than two centuries, and the great majority, including most point and line symbols, is not much over one hundred years old. Each year has seen a greater production of these kinds of maps and it is to be expected that the rate of increase will continue to rise. Consequently, it is imperative that the cartographer become adept at selecting appropriate methods of presenting quantitative data.

All quantitative maps fall in one of two classes. In one group may be put all those representations of a single category of data; the values are those observed and they are expressed on the map in absolute terms. In the second group are those maps that show derived values (for example, averages, percentages, densities, etc.); on these the mapped values express a summarization or some sort of comparison of two kinds of data. In the first class many combinations are possible, and two or more kinds of

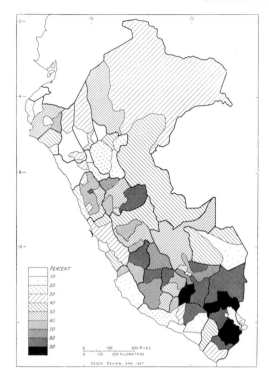

FIGURE 8.3. Quantitative-qualitative population map showing the percentage of "Indians" to total population of Peru by provinces. (Courtesy *The Geographical Review*, published by the American Geographical Society of New York.)

values may be presented at once; but in no case are the data expressed as a relationship, except as the amount or kind of data may vary from place to place, thus providing the basis for a kind of visual correlation. The second group, showing derived rather than absolute values, includes three general classes of relationships.

The first, and probably the most common, are the maps of measures of *central tendency,* for example, averages, which are obtained by the reduction of large amounts of statistical data, such as weather observations, well records, or numbers and sizes of farms.

The second class includes all those maps of proportions and percentages in which some element of the data is singled out and compared to the whole. These are illus-

trated by maps of the percentage of rainy days or the proportion of all cattle that are beef cattle.

The third class is more closely related to the land than the others and such maps are commonly called *density* maps. In this class the divisor is a measure of area and the dividend a summation of data for a statistical unit of some kind. Thus, 5000 persons in an area of 100 square miles is a density of 50 persons per square mile. The data for density maps are made relative to the total area (or to a significant part) of the divisions for which the distribution data are available. The specific value that results is a kind of density index, showing numbers per unit area, and it requires some mental calculation on the part of the reader to appreciate the concept.

The most common density map is that which shows the number of things per square mile, or some other areal unit such as square kilometer. The "things" may be any phenomena which may be counted as units, from people to railroad stations or road intersections. Such a map provides the reader with a summary of the characteristics of the distribution, but from which specific numerical values are also available. In many instances a density value derived from the (1) total number within and (2) the total area of a statistical unit is not so significant as one which expresses the ratio between more closely related factors. For example, the relation of the number of people to productive area in predominately agricultural societies is frequently found to be more useful than is a simple population to total area ratio. If the data are available one can easily relate population to cultivated land or to productive area defined in some other way. Figure 8.4 illustrates a map of this kind.

The concept of simple density assumes an even spread of the mapped units over the area of the statistical divisions used in deriving the mapping values. Instead of

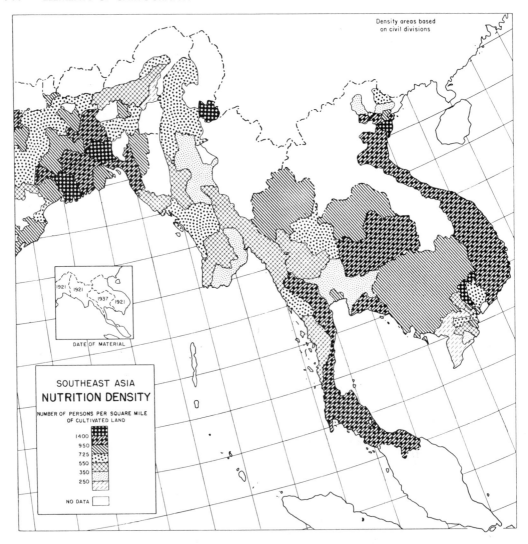

FIGURE 8.4. A "nutrition" map. Note the inclusion by the cartographer of the helpful index to the date of the information. (Map by W. Zelinsky, courtesy of the *Far Eastern Quarterly*.)

being expressed as a number-per-unit-area value the same initial data may be converted to an average-distance-between value by the use of the following formula:

$$\overline{S} = 1.0746\sqrt{A \div n}$$

where A is the area in square units such as miles or kilometers, and n the number of units in the area, and $\overline{S}$ is the average spacing of the items, or the mean distance be-

tween them (in linear values of the same units used for A). The values of $\overline{S}$ for each unit area can be plotted, and either isarithms can be drawn or area symbols can be used to differentiate the unit categories.

When working with densities the cartographer is limited in the detail he can present by the sizes of the statistical units for which the enumeration of numbers of items has been made. As a general rule, the

larger the units (such as townships, counties, or states) the less will be the differences among the density values. In many cases the initial data must be supplemented by other sources in order to present a distribution as close to reality as possible.

8.9   ESTIMATING DENSITIES OF PARTS

Observation of supplementary data frequently shows that one part of a unit area has a higher total than another, yet only the average concentration for the whole area may be available directly from the statistics. John K. Wright has presented a relatively simple system for calculating the values of parts. His explanation follows:*

Assume, for example, a township with a known average density of 100 persons to the square mile. Assume, further, that examination of topographic maps and consideration of other evidence have shown that this township may be divided into two parts, *m,* comprising 0.8 of the entire area of the township and having a relatively sparse population, and *n,* comprising the remaining 0.2 of the township and having a relatively dense population. If, then, we estimate that the density of population in *m* is 10 persons to the square mile, a density of 460 to the square mile must be assigned to *n* in order that the estimated densities *m* and *n* may be consistent with 100, the average density for the township as a whole.

The figure 460 for the density in *n* was obtained by solving the following fundamental equation:

$$\frac{D - (D_m a_m)}{1 - a_m} = D_n$$

or

$$\frac{100 - (10 \times 0.8)}{0.2} = 460$$

where D is the average density of population of the township as a whole, D_m the estimated density in *m*, a_m the fraction of the total area of the township comprised in *m*, $1 - a_m$ the fraction comprised in *n*, and D_n the density that must accordingly be assigned to *n*.

D_m and a_m are estimated approximately. It

* John K. Wright, "A Method of Mapping Densities of Population with Cape Cod as an Example," *The Geographical Review,* 1936, Vol. 26, pp. 103–110.

is not necessary to measure a_m accurately, since the margin of error in a rough estimate is likely to be less than the margin of error in the best possible estimate of D_m.

Study of neighboring townships sometimes gives a clue to a value that may reasonably be assigned to D_m. For example, the topographic map may show what would appear to be similar types of population distribution prevailing over T_m, or part of one township, and over the whole of S, an adjacent township. It would be reasonable, therefore, to assign to T_m a density comparable with the average density in S.

Having assigned estimated but consistent densities to two parts [of an area], one may then divide each (or one) of these parts into two subdivisions and work out densities for the latter in the same manner; and the process may be repeated within each subdivision.

The method is merely an aid to consistency in apportioning established [values], either of population or of other phenomena, within the limits of … territorial units for whose subdivisions no statistical data are available. Obviously it should not be applied in mapping densities of population within counties in the United Sates, since census figures are published for the townships and other minor civil divisions within the counties.

On the other hand, it can easily be applied in the large-scale mapping of any phenomena for which statistics are available only by larger units. Table H.1, in Appendix H enables one to solve the fundamental equation without either multiplication or division. Figure 8.5 shows the refinement that can be made.

8.10   REFINING AND PROCESSING
THE RAW MATERIALS

The basic approach to refining and processing data for statistical maps is by way of the kinds of symbols or techniques that may properly be used to convey the information. The range of symbols was discussed in a preceding section of this chapter, and it is only necessary here to reiterate the fact that the cartographer has a wide choice indeed. Consequently, his first action, after selecting or preparing the map base, is to decide upon the mode of presentation. He must

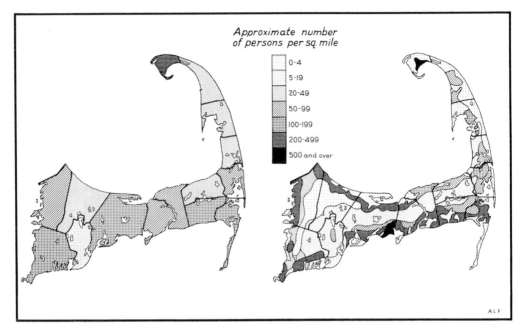

FIGURE 8.5. The left-hand map shows the density according to whole civil divisions, and the right-hand map shows the refinement that can be developed by this system. (Redrawn from *The Geographical Review*, published by the American Geographical Society of New York.)

decide if it is to be a static (all the data as of one period or place) or a dynamic (change of time or place) map, and he must select the symbolism (point, line, or area, or combination). The next step is to process the crude statistics in such a fashion that they become usable for the system of presentation that has been selected.

When data are obtained from a variety of sources it usually is necessary to equate them so that they provide comparable values. For example, different countries use different units of measure such as long tons or short tons, U. S. gallons or Imperial gallons, hectares or acres, and so on. Frequently the units must be further equated to bring them into strict conformity. If, for example, one were preparing a map of fuel reserves, it would not be sufficient only to change the tonnage units to comparable values, but it would also be necessary to bring the tonnage figures into conformity

on the basis of their Btu rating. It is also frequently necessary to process the statistics so that unwanted aspects are removed. A simple illustration is provided by the mechanics of preparing a density map of *rural* population (persons per square mile) based on county data. The total populations and areas of minor civil divisions and the totals for counties may be available. If that is the situation, the areas and populations of incorporated divisions must be subtracted from the county totals. Another illustration is provided by the well-known regional isothermal map. If only the relationships between temperatures, latitudes, air masses, etc., are desired, the local effects of elevation must be removed from the reported figures. This involves ascertaining the altitude of each station and the conversion of each temperature value to its sea-level equivalent.

After the statistical data have been made

comparable the next step is to convert them to mappable data. This may, of course, not be necessary for many maps such as the isothermal map referred to above, because in that case the data need merely be plotted and isarithms drawn. On the other hand, ratios, per acre yields, densities, percentages, and indices must be calculated before plotting. Some kinds of symbols, such as graduated circles or spheres, require determination of logarithms or roots. Many of these operations may be most efficiently handled by various kinds of calculating aids.

A desk calculator which can add, subtract, multiply, and divide is of constant use to a cartographer working with distribution and statistical maps. Their operation is relatively simple. If very large numbers or more difficult calculations are required it is well worth the initial tabulating time to process the data with the aid of punch cards for subsequent machine calculation. It is not necessary that the cartographer learn to operate the high-speed calculating machines; they are the responsibility of experts. An increasing amount of census records, weather observations, etc., is becoming available in punch-card form. With the aid of mechanical sorters and punchers the cartographer need only obtain copies of the "decks" of cards containing the necessary information. The entire processing can be done by machine and the result can be printed tabulations that need only be plotted. Effort spent in initial search for data in the form easiest to process will often save considerable total expenditure of time.

Probably the most frequently used calculating aids are the slide rule and mathematical tables of roots, logarithms, and conversions. Quite acceptable accuracy can be attained with the slide rule, and percentages, ratios, division, and multiplication can be computed almost as fast as the cartographer can read the figures. The manipulation of the slide rule for these purposes can be learned in a short time. Square roots and cube roots can also be derived from the slide rule, or can be determined from mathematical tables such as those in Appendix C.

If a large number of calculations involves the same kinds of units on a variable scale, it is frequently a saving of time to prepare a *nomograph*. Nomographs should be reserved for calculations involving two or more variables, as, for example, when data are (1) population and (2) acres, and the desired result is persons per square mile. Figure 8.6 illustrates a nomograph of this type. Another type is used to derive plotting values from data such as are shown in Fig. 8.7.

Figure 9.6 is a more complex kind of nomograph. Practically any kind of calculation involving variables can be set up on a nomograph, and the student may refer to any standard work on nomography for ideas.

8.11   STATISTICS IN CARTOGRAPHY

An increasing amount of a cartographer's effort is devoted to mapping data that require statistical manipulation in order to obtain descriptive measures such as averages and relationships. Much of the data with which he works consist of samples obtained in a variety of ways and, as is illustrated in Chapter 10, realistic portrayal and use of these data cannot be accomplished unless the cartographer has a clear understanding of their relative reliability as descriptive devices. Furthermore, in the manipulation of the data, in the selection of categories of data, and in the planning of the symbolization, the map maker must use the simpler techniques employed by the statistician. The accomplished cartographer, therefore, finds it necessary to be familiar with some of the basic concepts of descriptive and inference statistics.

It is clearly not possible in an introductory book, where the main theme is cartog-

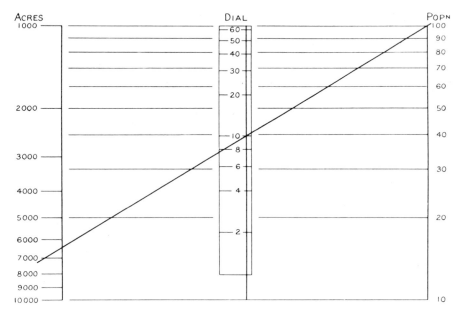

FIGURE 8.6. A nomograph for calculating population density per square mile from acres and popu-lation. Logarithmic paper is used. On the one margin is plotted *area in acres*, the plotting being done on a strip of logarithmic graph paper pasted upside down so that the smaller quantity ap-pears at the top. On the opposite margin is plotted *population*, with the smallest quantity at the bottom. Halfway between these scales and parallel to them is pasted the dial, a strip of two-cycle logarithmic paper that is labeled and scaled (beginning at the bottom) to indicate *density per square mile*. To determine how far up the sheet to paste this dial, a thread is stretched between 6400 on the area scale and 100 on the population scale. As an area of 6400 acres (10 square miles) with 100 people would have a density of 10 people per square mile, the middle strip should be adjusted so that the thread crosses it at 10. Calculations can then be made by merely stretching the thread between a point on the area scale and one on the population scale, the point where the thread crosses the dial being the density per square mile. (From Alexander and Zahorchak, courtesy *The Geographical Review*, published by the American Geographical Society of New York.)

raphy rather than statistics, to go into much detail concerning all the statistical tech-niques the cartographer might find useful. Nevertheless, the representation of quanti-tative data usually requires familiarity with the general concepts involved. The student is urged to acquire an elementary book on statistical methods to use as a reference. A number of titles are included in the bibli-ography.

Among the more common descriptive measures employed by the cartographer are the various kinds of rates, ratios, and per-

centages. A rate or ratio is a quantity ex-pressed in relation to some other quantity. Thus 12 persons per square mile is a ratio obtained by dividing the total number of people by the total number of square miles. It has also, therefore, the characteristics of an average. This kind of average ratio is the basis of the familiar density map. Rates and ratios need not be quantities related to the land since any significant factor may be used as the denominator. For example, an ordinary density map, on a county basis, might be made from the total number of

dairy cows divided by the total square miles; on the other hand, innumerable other kinds of maps could be prepared by retaining the numerator and using other kinds of denominators, such as number of farms, number of farm operators, or total cattle. These would result in maps showing the number of dairy cattle per farm, per farm operator, or the proportion of dairy cattle to total cattle. It is often convenient to multiply the result by 100 to present it as a percentage, that is, the number of dairy cattle per 100 cattle.

These kinds of maps are made to show variations from place to place in the relationship mapped; consequently they are usually prepared from summations of statistical data either over area or through time. The appropriateness of the derived

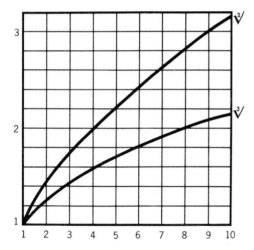

FIGURE 8.7. A nomograph to provide plotting values. The nomograph in this example is constructed to show the square or cube roots of the plotting range on the horizontal axis. Of course, the range may extend to any limit. The vertical scale is determined by the actual drawing scale. Thus, all that is necessary is to find the appropriate point on the horizontal scale, and the distance from the base to the curve is the proper map distance. When a large number of values need to be plotted it usually saves time to make up such a nomograph. One can be made for any series that varies systematically.

number obviously depends upon the use to which it is being put, but a few words of caution are in order. Percentages and ratios, when mapped on the basis of enumeration units, are usually assumed by the reader to extend more or less uniformly throughout the enumeration unit. If the phenomenon being considered does not so occur, then the ratio mapped may be quite misleading, just as it may if too few of the items occur. Thus a value of 100% of farms with tractors may be the result of only one farm with one tractor in a large area. Quantities which are not comparable should never be made the basis for a ratio. For example, one ought not calculate the number of tractors per farm by dividing the total number of tractors by the number of farms in a county unless the farm sizes (or some such significant element) are relatively comparable. Common sense will usually dictate ways to insure comparability.

8.12   MEASURES OF CENTRAL TENDENCY

The arithmetic mean is the most frequently used measure of central tendency in cartography. Most of the maps of temperature, pressure, precipitation, and other elements common in physical geography are based upon means derived in one way or another. Their significance in cartography is not in the manner of their derivation; this is a matter of accuracy and substantive appropriateness which is, theoretically at least, not directly of cartographic concern. The cartographer is, however, likely to be concerned with the derivation of means *from* maps of distributions and, more especially, in the correct symbolization of the mean values on maps. For these purposes he must be familiar with the concept of the weighted mean.

The ordinary average or arithmetic mean is obtained by summing the values of the items and dividing by the number of items. This procedure may be followed if the items

are strictly comparable, but if the data are grouped in any way, then the items must be weighted. In the geographic analysis of problems, by means of maps, one is often required to obtain means from mapped data in which totals are difficult if not impossible to obtain. For example, suppose one wished to obtain from a map of elevation the average elevation above sea level. The data exist in the form of an ordinary contour map. Figure 8.8 may be used as an illustration, and it is assumed to be a perfectly conically shaped island, whose form and elevations are shown by evenly spaced contours at a 100 foot interval. It is clear from inspection that different elevations occur more or less frequently. The geographic frequencies of earth distributions are the relative areas of the occurrences; consequently it is necessary to obtain the areas of the spaces between the contours. This can most accurately be done by measuring them with a planimeter (see Article 3.12). One could also place a geometric grid over the map and count the number of grid points between each contour, and thus determine

the area values by means of sampling. In any case, the results obtained are expressed in any convenient square units, such as square inches. The measurements obtained from the original drawing of Fig. 8.8 (before reduction for printing) are shown in the first two columns of Table 8.1. The mean elevation may be determined in two ways: by calculation or by graphic analysis.

TABLE 8.1

CALCULATION OF THE MEAN ELEVATION OF THE ISLAND SHOWN IN FIG. 8.8

Elevation classes— feet	Mid-value of elevation classes—feet	Map areas of elevation classes— square inches	Cumulated areas—square inches	
(X)	(X_m)	(a)	aX_m	$(a_1+a_2+a_3...)$
0–100	50	3.32	166	3.32
100–200	150	2.92	438	6.24
200–300	250	2.55	638	8.79
300–400	350	2.18	763	10.97
400–500	450	1.79	806	12.76
500–600	550	1.37	754	14.13
600–700	650	0.99	644	15.12
700–800	750	0.59	443	15.71
800–900	850	0.20	170	15.91
Total	—	15.91	4 822	—

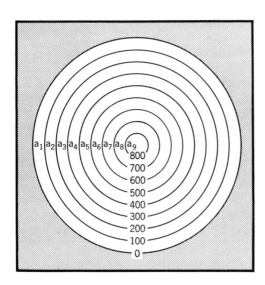

FIGURE 8.8. A conical island delineated by 100 foot contours.

The general expression for any mean is

$$\overline{X} = \frac{\Sigma X}{N}$$

in which $\overline{X}$ represents the mean of the X values, N represents the total number of X values, and the Greek letter Σ is the summation sign, that is, ΣX means the sum of all the X values. In geographical distributions whenever the X values are in any way related to areal extent, they must be weighted for their frequency. This is most easily done by multiplying each X value by the area of its extent, summing these products, and then dividing the sum by the total area. The general expression for any geographic mean is, therefore,

$$\overline{X} = \frac{\Sigma aX}{\Sigma a}$$

in which ΣaX represents the sum of the products of each X value multiplied by its area. From Table 8.1

$$\overline{X} = \frac{4822}{15.91} = 303.1 \text{ feet}$$

When one wishes also to use a *cumulative frequency graph* for other purposes (see Article 10.10), it may be desirable to accomplish the result graphically instead of arithmetically. A cumulative frequency graph is constructed by plotting the X values of the distribution on the vertical axis in the order of their value against the extent of their progressively cumulated areas on the horizontal axis. The paired data from the first and last columns of Table 8.1 are placed on the graph shown in Fig. 8.9 by plotting the value of the upper class limit of the first elevation category, X_1 (100) on the Y axis and the area a (3.32) on the X axis.* The next pair, X_2 (200) and $a_1 + a_2$ (6.24) are similarly plotted. The addition of each area value to the sum of the preceding areas (after arranging them in the ascending order of X values) assures that the curve, which results from joining the plotted points with a smooth line, will rise to the right. The area under the curve (bounded by the curve, the base line, and an ordinate drawn at the final value of the summed areas) may then be measured by whatever means is available (preferably a planimeter) and expressed in square units, such as square inches. When this value is divided by the length of the base line from the origin to the total area (measured on the graph in linear terms of the same units used

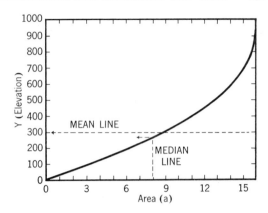

FIGURE 8.9. A cumulative frequency graph. The light horizontal dashed line is the top of a rectangle of the same area as that included by the curve. The height of the rectangle on the Y axis is the geographic mean. The light vertical dashed line is erected at the midpoint of the cumulated areas plotted along the base. The Y value of the curve at the point of intersection is the geographic median.

to express the area under the curve), the quotient is the height of a rectangle with the same area as that under the curve, one side of which is the length of the base line. The height of the rectangle when plotted on the Y axis of the graph is the mean height of the curve and is the geographic mean. In Fig. 8.9 the area under the curve (on the original drawing, before reduction) is 9.63 square inches. The length of the base as plotted was 6.36 inches. Division of the area by the base $\left(\frac{9.63}{6.36}\right)$ results in a quotient of 1.51 inches. This value measured on the Y axis from the base gives a rectangle with a height having an elevational value of 302 feet which is the geographic mean. In Fig. 8.9 this height is shown by the light dashed horizontal line. The difference of not much over 1 foot between the mean determined arithmetically (303.1 feet) and the mean determined graphically (302 feet) results from the graphic process and the consequent rounding of numbers, as well as the fact that

---

* Note that the X values of the distribution are plotted on the Y axis of the graph. Unfortunately, for this illustration, it is customary to symbolize the values of any single distribution with X, while the vertical axis or ordinate of the cartesian system is designated as Y. It is convenient to plot a cumulative frequency graph in the above manner, in spite of the awkwardness of the designations.

mid-values of classes were used in one computation, whereas upper class limits were used in the other. This kind of graph is also occasionally called a hypsographic curve because it has been used to determine mean land heights (mean hypsometric values) exactly as illustrated here. It may, of course, be applied to any other kinds of data varying in quantitative value and having actual or assumed continuous areal extent.

The cumulative frequency graph may also be employed to determine geographic percentiles, quartiles, etc., and the geographic median. The geographic median is determined by erecting an ordinate (a line perpendicular to the base) at the midpoint of the base line and reading the Y value of its intersection with the curve. The median elevation of the island on Fig. 8.8 as derived from the graph in Fig. 8.9 is close to 280 feet, that is, half the map area is shown as above and half below that elevation. Percentile and quartile values are similarly obtained by subdivision of the base and determining the Y values of ordinates erected at such points. The curve can also be used to find the total area of all those sections lying above or below any given elevational value.

Many problems of cartographic analysis include data with open-end classes, that is, the top or bottom class may be only available on a "less than . . ." or a "more than . . ." basis. This is the case with the series of elevations shown by the contours on the island in Fig. 8.8 wherein the contour of highest value is 800 feet. By definition the area inside that contour is above (that is, more than) 800 feet, but by exactly how much is not shown. In other cases, the neat line or map edge may cut through a statistical unit area and produce a similar result. When the limits of all classes are not given, the mean value cannot be accurately ascertained, but judicious estimate and interpolation will usually make significant errors unlikely.

8.13   THE STANDARD DEVIATION

Any quantitative distribution when analyzed as an array of numbers exhibits a dispersion of the values which may or may not be well described by a measure of central tendency. For example, to state that the mean elevation of the island shown in Fig. 8.8 is slightly over 300 feet does not in any way indicate anything about the distribution of the elevations. It could be a cliffed island with a flat top such that very little of its horizontal extent had any elevation very far from 300 feet. Similarly, the statement that the mean population density of a state is 16.3 persons per square mile tells nothing of the variations which together result in the mean. There are many measures of dispersion useful in the statistical analysis of distributions, such as the range, the average deviation, the standard deviation, and descriptions of the form of the distribution such as its peakedness and symmetry. Most of these are not commonly used in general cartography; but one, the *standard deviation,* is especially important, because of (1) its descriptive utility, (2) its wide employment, (3) its use in the evaluation of the reliability of measures computed from samples, and (4) its utilization as an aid in the location of isarithms.

When many measurements are made of many kinds of phenomena it has been found that there is a similarity in the frequency with which particular values occur in the series. The values that occur with the greatest frequency are usually those near the mean of the series. The greater the difference (or deviation) of a value from the mean of its series, the less frequently that value is likely to occur.* When an "ideal" series is graphed by plotting the frequencies against

* Although a great many phenomena show a "normal" distribution of values, some do not. A description of "abnormal distributions" is a topic for more advanced statistics.

the values, the result is a *normal curve* of a *normal distribution.* It is illustrated in Fig. 8.10 by an ordinary (not cumulative) frequency graph on which the frequency of occurrence of the values is plotted on the Y axis against the values on the X axis. Of particular significance in mapping data which have been obtained by taking samples is the fact that if a series of random samples were taken from a normal statistical "population," the means of the individual samples also tend to have a normal distribution. The standard deviation is a way of describing the dispersion of the values in a normal distribution.

The standard deviation is the range on either side of the mean value which includes approximately two-thirds (68.27%) of all the values in the series. For example, the standard deviation of the elevations on the island in Fig. 8.8 is 211 feet. This means that about two-thirds of the island has an elevation within 211 feet of the mean; or, stating it another way, about two-thirds of the island lies above approximately 92 feet $(303 - 211$ feet) and below approximately 514 feet $(303 + 211$ feet), that is, lies between those two elevations.

There are several ways to compute the standard deviation from a list of values depending upon the nature of the data.* Any statistics textbook will illustrate several procedures. If one is working with original values and does not wish first to calculate the differences between each value and the mean of the distribution he may proceed as follows:

$$ s = \sqrt{\frac{\Sigma X^2}{N} - \left(\frac{\Sigma X}{N}\right)^2} $$

in which s is the standard deviation and X represents the original values. As was pointed out in connection with the determination of the mean, when the data occur in varying frequencies, as they do in geographic distributions, then it is necessary to take this into account. The easiest way to do this is to use the areal extent as the frequency.

As an illustration the standard deviation of the elevations of the island shown in Fig. 8.8 is calculated below. The necessary data are shown in Table 8.2 and it will be seen that mid-values are employed. The expression then becomes

$$ s = \sqrt{\frac{\Sigma a X^2}{\Sigma a} - \left(\frac{\Sigma a X}{\Sigma a}\right)^2} $$

in which $\Sigma a X^2$ is obtained by first squaring each X value, then multiplying it by the area it represents, and then summing the products. The term $(\Sigma a X/\Sigma a)^2$ will be recognized as the square of the geographic mean.

$$ s = \sqrt{\frac{2,171,975}{15.91} - \left(\frac{4822}{15.91}\right)^2} $$

$$ = \sqrt{136,516 - 91,857} = \sqrt{44,659} $$

$$ = 211 \text{ feet} $$

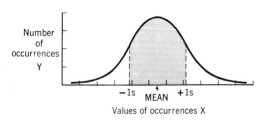

Number of occurrences Y

−1s   MEAN   +1s

Values of occurrences X

FIGURE 8.10. A frequency curve of a normal distribution. The number of occurrences are plotted on the Y axis and the values on the X axis. The shaded area shows the proportion (68.27%) of the occurrences which occur within one standard deviation on either side (plus or minus) from the mean.

* The standard deviation is the square root of the mean squared deviations from the mean, that is, the difference (deviation) between the mean of the distribution and each value is squared; the squares are summed; the mean square is obtained by dividing the sum by the number of values; and the square root of the mean square is the standard deviation.

TABLE 8.2

CALCULATION OF STANDARD DEVIATION (s) OF ELEVATIONS ON THE ISLAND SHOWN IN FIG. 8.8

Mid-value of elevation class—feet X_m	Map (or actual) area of class— sq. in. a	aX_m	X^2	aX^2
50	3.32	166	2 500	8 300
150	2.92	438	22 500	65 700
250	2.55	638	62 500	159 375
350	2.18	763	122 500	267 050
450	1.79	806	202 500	362 475
550	1.37	754	302 500	414 425
650	0.99	644	422 500	418 275
750	0.59	443	562 500	331 875
850	0.20	170	722 500	144 500
Total	15.91	4 822		2 171 975

The standard deviation has wide use in both descriptive and inference statistics. In cartography and geographical research it has considerable descriptive utility as an index of the effectiveness with which a mean value describes a particular series of numerical values. When one is drawing isarithms to symbolize a distribution based on mean values (see Article 10.8), a high standard deviation indicates that isarithms should be generalized. In addition, many maps are made of distributions wherein the data are obtained by sampling. For example, a map of average temperatures is based upon temperature records for a particular period and thus is but one sample of the time through which such temperatures have occurred. The particular sample available will not provide an accurate mean because it contains only a portion of the total of all possible values, and random occurrences included in the mean can be expected to make it too high or too low. The likelihood of the mean being too high or too low can be inferred from the standard deviation of the values in the sample. This inference is made by calculating the standard deviation of the mean. It is usually called the *standard error* of the mean and is symbolized by $\sigma_{\bar{x}}$. It is obtained by dividing the standard deviation of the sample values by the square root of the number of the sample values which were used in calculating the mean. Its expression is

$$\sigma_{\bar{x}} = \frac{s}{\sqrt{N}}$$

where s is the standard deviation of the values of X, $\bar{X}$ is the mean of X, and N is the number of X values which entered into the calculation of the mean of X.* It is clear that the smaller the number of values used to arrive at a mean the larger will be the standard error, that is, the greater the likelihood that the mean is incorrect. The cartographer must keep in mind the variations in the reliability of the means whenever he is drawing isarithms based on data having different degrees of quality. This topic is considered in greater detail in Article 10.8.

---

* In descriptive statistics the standard deviation is sometimes symbolized by s; in inference statistics it is usually symbolized by σ. The differentiation is not particularly important, however, and some statisticians do not bother to make the distinction; it is done here to acquaint the student with both signs. Lower case *sigma* (σ) is the most common sign.

Mapping Quantitative Point, Line, and Area Data

9.1 SYMBOLIZING GEOGRAPHICAL QUANTITIES

In the preceding chapter some of the basic attributes of the more familiar cartographic symbols were considered. It was pointed out that the kinds of data from which maps are made fall into four basic categories: point, line, area, and volume data. These are mutually exclusive, and the four categories are depicted on flat maps by but three categories of graphic symbols: point, line, and area symbols. Some of these serve double duty in that they are regularly used to delineate two or more kinds of distribution data, as for example the line symbol. Lines as qualitative symbols show connection and location of kinds of linear features, and they are also commonly used as a device to show the surface topography of a solid or imaginary volume distribution. To try to classify with systematic precision all the variations in the geographical concepts symbolized by the large variety of graphic symbols is all but impossible because the multiplicity of categories would reach astronomic numbers. Consequently, one cannot illustrate in a practical manner the variety of ways a given symbol may be used. Instead, this and the following chapter will illustrate the means by which the various classes of data (point, line, area, and volume) are usually repre-sented. It will be left to the student, if he be interested, to attempt the analysis of such intellectually teasing problems as how many different ways can a single symbol, for example, an isarithm (a line symbol) be employed to represent specific kinds of geographic data.*

When approached from the point of view of frequency of use, the symbolization in cartography becomes relatively simple since only a few types of symbols are used on the great majority of maps. The qualitative symbol is not much of a problem since differences in kind can be represented merely by changing the appearance of the symbol, as was illustrated in connection with base data in Chapter 7. On the other hand, the symbol used to express variations in quantity generally cannot be so treated. Instead, since it shows variations in the amounts of a single class of data it is usually desirable to employ for each distribution only one form of graphic device and then somehow vary it in terms of size, frequency, or visual value to show the variations in quantity from place to place. This chapter will be concerned with the commoner

---

* Start (and probably stop!) with the coastline on a topographic map. It is a contour; it separates two different sorts of surfaces; in combination with other contours on the topographic map it helps to represent value; etc., etc.

techniques used to symbolize variations in quantity of those distributions which are essentially two dimensional or less in character, that is, the primary purpose of the map is to show differences in amounts at different locations. The symbolization of continuous spatial three-dimensional distributions, both actual and abstract, is dealt with in Chapter 10.

A large share of statistical maps use point symbols, such as dots or circles, to show place variations in quantity. The most frequently used point symbol is the dot.

9.2   THE DOT MAP

The simplest of all maps using point symbols is the one wherein the data are presented by varying numbers of uniform dots, each representing the same amount. It is possible, of course, to substitute little drawings of men, or sheep, or cows (or whatever is being represented) for the simple dot. This generally reduces the amount of detail which may be presented, but it is sometimes desirable for rough distributions or for maps for children. This kind of map, called a dot map, is a great favorite among geographers, because, given the data, it is capable of showing more clearly than any other type of map the details of location of many phenomena. It provides a visual impression of relative density, easily comprehended by the reader, but it does not provide him with any absolute figures. Theoretically, it would be possible to count the dots and then multiply the number by the unit value of each dot to arrive at a total, but in practice it is almost never done.

A second advantage is the relative ease with which such maps may be made. No computation is ordinarily necessary beyond that of determining the number of dots required, which merely necessitates dividing the totals for each civil division by the number decided upon as the unit value of each dot.

Dot maps ordinarily show only one kind of data; for example, population or acres of cultivated land, but by using different-colored dots or different-shaped point symbols it is sometimes possible to include two different distributions on the same map. Of course, if there is no mixing of two types of data they both may be shown on the same map.

9.3   THE SIZE AND VALUE OF THE DOT

If the visual impression conveyed by a dot map is to be realistic the size of the dot and the unit value assigned must be carefully chosen. The five dot maps shown here have been prepared from the same data; only the size or number of dots used has been changed. The maps show potato acreage in Wisconsin in 1947.

If the dots are too small, as in Fig. 9.1, then the distribution will appear sparse and insignificant, and patterns will not be visible. If the dots are too large, then they

FIGURE 9.1. A dot map in which the dots are too small so that an unrevealing map is produced. Each dot represents 40 acres in potatoes in 1947.

will coalesce too much in the darker areas, as in Fig. 9.2, and give an overall impression of excessive density that is equally erroneous. It appears in Fig. 9.2 that there is little room for anything else in the region.

Equally important is the selection of the unit value of the dot. As a matter of fact the two problems (size and value of the dot) are inseparable. The total number of dots should neither be so large that the map gives a greater impression of accuracy than is warranted nor should the total be so small that the distribution lacks any pattern of character. These unfortunate possibilities are illustrated in Figs. 9.3 and 9.4.

The selection of unit value and size of dots should be made so that in the denser areas (of a dense distribution) the dots will just coalesce to form a dark area. Figure 9.5 is constructed from the same data as the preceding examples in this article but with a dot size and unit value more wisely chosen.

FIGURE 9.3. A dot map in which the unit value of the dot is too large so that too few dots result; a barren map revealing little pattern is produced. Each dot in this example represents 150 acres.

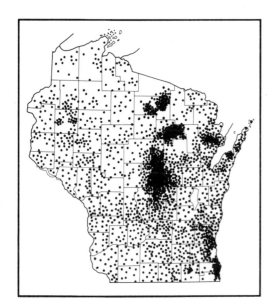

FIGURE 9.2. A dot map in which the dots are too large so that an excessively "heavy" map is produced. An erroneous impression of excessive potato production is given. The same data and number of dots are used as in Fig. 9.1.

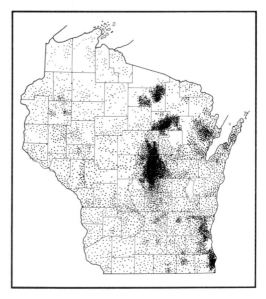

FIGURE 9.4. A dot map in which the unit value of the dot is too small so that too many dots result; an excessively detailed map is produced. The dots are the same size as those in Fig. 9.3. Each dot in this example represents 15 acres.

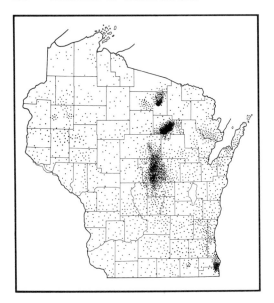

FIGURE 9.5. A dot map in which the dot size and dot value have been more wisely chosen than in the preceding examples. Each dot in this example represents 40 acres.

Of course, if the distribution is a sparse one even in the relatively dense areas, as would be the case (to use an extreme example) with areas of marketable saw timber in North Dakota, then even the relatively dense areas should not appear dark.

The data for dot maps consist of the enumeration of the number of items to be mapped in unit areas. These are usually civil divisions used as census statistical units. However the data may have been obtained, each unit area contains a total number of the phenomena to be symbolized within that map area. Rarely is it possible to employ so large a map scale that each item may be shown by a dot, although theoretically the farmhouses on a topographic map might be termed a kind of dot map; rather, it is usually necessary to assign a number of the phenomena to each dot. This is called the unit value of the dot and is obtained merely by dividing the total number

of items in each statistical division by the chosen unit value. For example, if a county had a total of 16,000 acres in corn, and a unit value of 50 acres per dot had been chosen, then 320 dots would be placed in the county to symbolize the corn acreage.

Professor J. Ross Mackay developed an ingenious nomograph to assist in determining the desirable dot size and unit value.* This graph, shown in Fig. 9.6, requires a knowledge of the sizes of dots that can be made by various kinds of pens. This information is presented in Table 9.1. By varying the relation between dot diameter and unit value, the cartographer can choose the relationship that will best present the characteristics of the distribution.

The nomograph may be used in several ways, but perhaps the easiest is first to select three unit areas on the proposed dot map which are representative of (1) a dense area, (2) an area of average density, and (3) an area of sparse density. A tentative unit value is then selected and divided into the totals for each of the three statistical divisions. The map area of one of the divisions is estimated in terms of square inches, and the number of dots per square inch is deduced. As in the previous example, assume a county contains 16,000 acres of corn; a unit value of 50 acres per dot is chosen which results in 320 dots to be placed within the boundaries of the division; and assume further that the statistical division on the map covers one-half square inch. This would mean that the dots would be placed on the map with a density of 640 dots per square inch. An ordinate at 640 is erected from the X axis of the nomograph. A radial line from the origin of the nomograph to a given dot diameter on the upper and right-hand scale will intersect the ordinate. The location of the intersection on the in-

* J. Ross Mackay, "Dotting the Dot Map," *Surveying and Mapping*, 1949, Vol. 9, pp. 3–10.

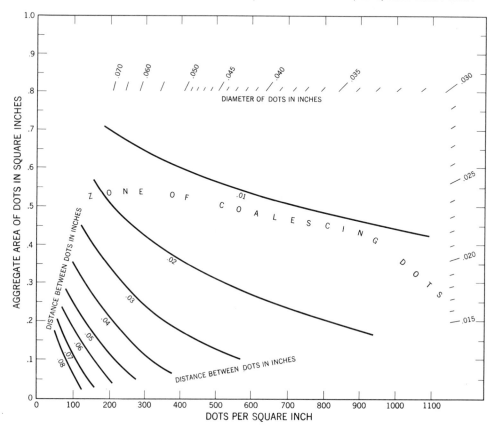

FIGURE 9.6. A nomograph showing the effects of varying the relation between dot size and dot density. Any combination of numbers of dots and diameters of dots that falls in or beyond the "zone of coalescing dots" will produce dots on top of one another. (Courtesy J. Ross Mackay and *Surveying and Mapping*.)

terior scale will show the average distance between the dots if they were evenly spaced. The height of the intersect on the Y axis will indicate what proportion of the area will be black if that dot diameter and number of dots per square inch were used. Also shown is the "zone of coalescing dots," at or beyond which dots will fall on one another.

If the initial trial seems unsatisfactory for each of the three type areas selected for experimentation, either the unit value or the dot size, or both, may be changed. One can enter the graph with any of several as-

sumptions and determine the derivatives. It is good practice while using the nomograph to dot the areas (on a piece of tracing paper) in order to see the results and to help visualize the consequence of other combinations.

The cartographer should remember that the visual relationships of black to white ratios, and the complications introduced by the pattern of dots, make it difficult, if not impossible, for a dot map to be visually perfect. The best approach is by experiment after narrowing the choices by use of the nomograph.

TABLE 9.1

DOT DIAMETERS OF VARIOUS PENS

Pen type	Pen number	Dot diameter (line width) in inches
Barch-Payzant	8	0.012
	7	0.018
	6	0.025
	5	0.036
	4	0.046
	3	0.059
	2	0.073
	1	0.086
Leroy	00	0.013
	0	0.017
	1	0.021
	2	0.026
	3	0.035
	4	0.043
	5	0.055
	6	0.067
	7	0.083
Wrico	7	0.018
	7A	0.018
	6	0.025
	6A	0.025
	5	0.027
	5A	0.027
	4	0.036
	4A	0.036
	3	0.048
	3A	0.048
	2	0.062
	2A	0.062

Note: See Fig. 3.11 for width sizes of Pelican-Graphos nibs.

9.4   LOCATING THE DOTS

Theoretically the ideal dot map would be one with a large enough scale and with the data sufficiently well known so that each single unit could be precisely located. Ordinarily, however, it is desired that the map be of a small enough scale so that a larger area can be shown in order to indicate more

clearly the pattern of distribution. Sometimes, if the data are sparse enough, a unit value of one (for example, paper mills) can still be used on a small-scale map and come close to presenting a true picture. If, however, it is necessary to make the unit value of the dot greater than one, the problem then arises of locating the one point symbol that represents several differently located units.

It is helpful to consider the several units to be represented as having a kind of center-of-gravity, and then to place the symbol as nearly as possible at that point. For example, an area of uneven distribution will have more dots in the dense region and less in the sparse region, although all the cartographer knows from the original data is the total number of dots to place in the area. Consequently he must draw upon every available source of information to assist him in placing the dots as accurately as possible. Such aids as topographic maps, other distribution maps which he knows correlate well with the one being prepared, soil maps, climatic maps, and many others, as well as a good knowledge of the area being mapped, are indispensable. The level of quality and completeness depends upon the ability of the cartographer to bring all the pertinent evidence to bear on the problem of where to put the dots.

Considerable detail can be introduced in the map if the map is made on the basis of the smallest civil divisions and then greatly reduced. Placing the dots with reference to minor civil divisions can be easily done by using tracing paper, cloth, or plastic for the map and putting under it a map of the minor civil divisions as a guide. Only the larger administrative units need then be shown on the map. Care must be exercised so as not to leave the guiding boundary areas blank, for they will show up markedly in the final map as white lines. Care must also be taken that the dotting does not in-

advertently produce lines and clusters of dots that do not occur in actuality. Such regularity can easily occur and is quite noticeable by contrast to its amorphous surroundings. Figures 9.7 and 9.8 were made in the same office and present nearly the same dot distributions. Figure 9.7 was prepared by a relatively inexperienced cartographer who placed the dots a bit too geometrically within the minor civil divisions.

An undesirable over-all pattern of regularity resulted. Figure 9.8 was made by a more experienced cartographer who, by "looking ahead," placed the dots in the minor civil divisions so that a more desirable, smoother pattern resulted.

A dot map in which the dots are evenly spread over the unit areas, although numerically correct, could better use some other symbol than dots.

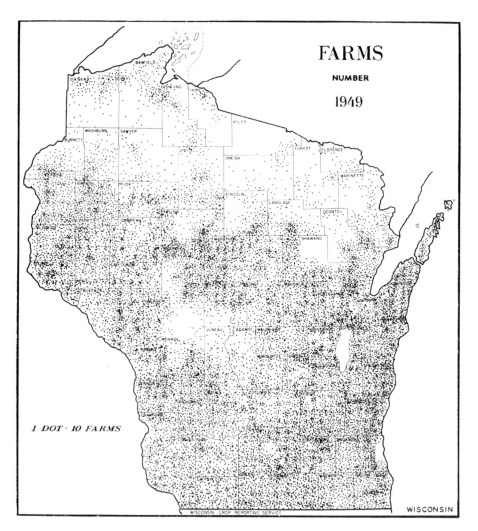

FIGURE 9.7. An undesirable pattern on a dot map. See text for explanation. (Courtesy Wisconsin Crop Reporting Service.)

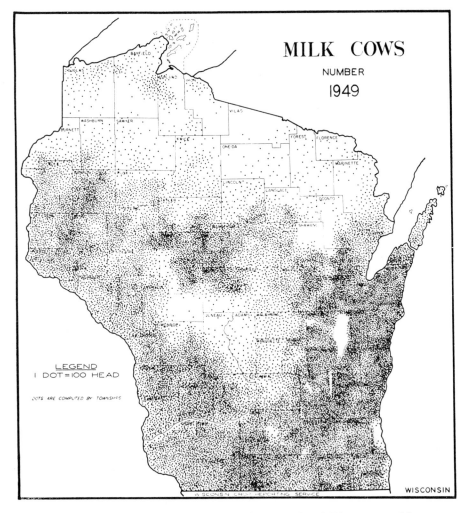

MILK COWS

NUMBER

1949

LEGEND
1 DOT=100 HEAD

DOTS ARE COMPUTED BY TOWNSHIPS

WISCONSIN

FIGURE 9.8. Nearly the same distribution as that shown on Fig. 9.7 but prepared by a more experienced cartographer. See text for explanation. (Courtesy Wisconsin Crop Reporting Service.)

9.5   THE GRADUATED CIRCLE

The graduated circle is one of the oldest of the quantitative point symbols used for statistical representation. Near the beginning of the nineteenth century it was used in graphs illustrating the then new census materials. So far as is known the earliest use of graduated circles on maps was in the third decade of that century to show the relative populations of the cities and towns of Ireland.* Since that time it has been near the top of any list of quantitative point symbols in the frequency of its use, and its ease of construction and interpretation makes it likely that it will continue to be widely utilized.

Graduated circles (or squares) are used

* Arthur H. Robinson, "The Maps of Henry Drury Harness," *The Geographical Journal,* Vol. 121, 1955, pp. 440–450.

for presenting amounts when the totals of statistical units are of more interest than details of location. Thus, they are useful (1) when the units represented exist in close proximity but are large in aggregate number, such as the population of a city, or (2) for representing aggregate amounts for relatively large territories. In the latter instance the territory is considered only as a location even though it has areal extent. This is another example of the apparent inconsistencies that result between a logical classification of map symbols and one of geographical quantities. The cultivated area of a statistical unit is obviously a two-dimensional geographical quantity. When symbolized by a circle in combination with other circles for similar statistical units it has, in a sense, been transformed into a locational or point value for mapping purposes.

When the graduated circle was first used, the variations in the actual *areas* of the circles were made uniformly comparable to the numbers they represented. For example, if two statistical units had values to be represented that were in a 1:2 ratio, that is, the population of the second city was twice that of the first, the second circle was constructed so that its area was exactly twice that of the first. This is easily accomplished since the area of a circle is πr^2; since π is constant, the method of construction is to extract the square roots of the data and then construct the circles with radii or diameters proportional to the square roots. The unit radius value by which the square roots are divided may represent any desirable unit, such as tenths or hundredths or an inch, and is selected so that the largest circle will not be "too large," and the smallest, not "too small." As long as the same unit is used for all circles, their areas will be in strict proportion to the sizes of the numbers they represent. If the cartographer does not wish to show relative sizes of each individual statistical quantity he can classify the range and then show all individuals in one class by a "standardized" circle constructed to the size of the midpoint of that class.

9.6   THE RATIO OF CIRCLE SIZES

Recent extensive research by James J. Flannery has demonstrated that the visual appearance of circular areas is not a linear function; instead the ordinary observer tends to underestimate the sizes of larger circles in proportion to the smaller ones.* For example, to use the previous illustration, if the populations of two cities were in a 1:2 ratio and the areas of two circles representing them were in the same ratio, then a map reader would not think the second city was twice the size of the first. When one makes the areas of the circles strictly proportional to the numbers they represent, he has, therefore, in effect reduced the *apparent size* of the larger circles in relation to the smaller. This would appear, on the surface, to be an advantage to the cartographer who is regularly plagued by a large range of data, since it would help him to fit all the circles on the map. On the other hand, if he were to increase the sizes of the larger circles, they may not fit together on the map so well. To look at it another way, it increases the visual significance of the smaller circles relative to the larger. It should be remembered, however, that the purpose of making such a map is certainly not to demonstrate how to cram together symbols representing an inconveniently large range of numbers; it is, instead, to symbolize geographical quantities so that the map reader will obtain a realistic impression of the distribution being mapped.

The research by Professor Flannery en-

* James J. Flannery, "The Graduated Circle: A Description, Analysis and Evaluation of a Quantitative Map Symbol," Ph.D. Dissertation, University of Wisconsin, 1956.

abled him to determine the scale of sizes which should be employed so that the correct visual impression would be conveyed to the reader. Instead of extracting the square roots of the data and making the radii of the circles relative in length to the square roots, the procedure is (1) to determine the logarithms of the data, (2) multiply the logarithms by 0.57, (3) determine the antilogarithms, and (4) divide the antilogarithms by the chosen unit value for the radii of the circles.* An illustration that follows demonstrates the procedure.

The first four columns of Table 9.2 show the calculations needed to determine the numbers which, when divided by the chosen unit radius value, will give the plotting radii of the circles. It should be pointed out that the logarithms of n (whatever is being represented) must be multiplied directly by 0.57, that is, the logarithm of 0.57 should not be used in this step.* The antilogs provide directly the plotting values and need only be converted to map dimensions by dividing by some convenient unit value. The map shown in Fig. 9.9 has been constructed from the data shown in Table 9.2, using a unit radius value chosen so that the circles do not overlap.

The cartographer often finds that with a desirable unit radius value for the map as a whole, the circles in one part may fall on top of one another if their centers are placed approximately at the locations of the data they are to symbolize. Two of several ways to approach this problem are shown in Fig.

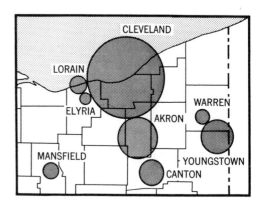

FIGURE 9.9. The relative sizes of some cities in northeastern Ohio prepared from the data in Table 9.2.

9.10. The two small maps are taken from the same data as that for Fig. 9.9, but the unit radius value has been enlarged.

The selection of the unit radius value with which to scale the circles is important and should be done with the aid of some preliminary experimentation. The ideal value is one which will result in the greatest visual contrast between the smaller and larger circles but which provides a map

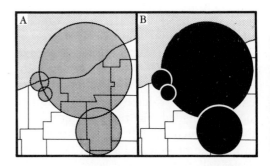

FIGURE 9.10. Two ways of solving the problem of overlapping circles. The data are the same as those used for Fig. 9.9, but the unit radius value for the circles is smaller than that chosen for Fig. 9.9, resulting in larger circles. In A the circles are allowed to overlap, being "transparent." In B smaller circles are "above" larger circles.

* The square root of $\log n = \dfrac{\log n}{2}$ or $\log n \times 0.5$.

Multiplying the logarithms by 0.57 instead of 0.5 serves proportionately to increase somewhat the sizes of the larger circles so that they *appear* in proper relation to the smaller ones.

* Log n + log 0.57 will in effect multiply n by 0.57. One may proceed logarithmically: log log n + log 0.57 will provide the correct result but it is hardly worth the effort, especially if a calculator is available.

TABLE 9.2

1950 POPULATIONS OF THE CITY OF CLEVELAND AND OTHER CITIES OVER 30,000 IN NORTHEASTERN OHIO OUTSIDE THE CLEVELAND METROPOLITAN DISTRICT

City	(1) 1950 Population (n)	(2) log n	(3) log n × 0.57	(4) Antilog of log n × 0.57	(5) Drafting radii of circles. Unit radius value: 300 = 0.10 inch. Col. 4 ÷ 300
Akron	274 605	5.43872	3.10007	1 261	0.42
Canton	116 912	5.06785	2.88867	774	0.26
Cleveland	914 808	5.96133	3.39796	2 500	0.83
Elyria	30 307	4.48159	2.55451	359	0.12
Lorain	51 202	4.70927	2.68428	483	0.16
Mansfield	43 564	4.63909	2.64428	441	0.15
Warren	49 856	4.69775	2.67772	476	0.16
Youngstown	168 330	5.22616	2.97891	953	0.32

which is neither "too full" nor "too empty." For example, Figs. 9.11 and 9.12 show the area of land available for crops in some counties. When too small a unit radius is chosen, then the circles are too small to show much, as is illustrated in Fig. 9.11. Also, the impression is given that there is practically no cultivated land in those counties. When too large a unit radius is chosen, then the circles are too large. Again, the representation does not reveal much, and the impression is given that practically all the land is cultivated, as in Fig. 9.12.

9.7 THE PIE CHART

More than one kind of data can be shown with the same graduated circle by making it into a pie chart. Thus, to use the illustration of cultivated land in a county, any part of the cultivated-land total may be shown by segmenting the circle in the manner in which a pie is cut. Any relation of a part to the whole can be shown visually by the pie chart. For example, Figs. 9.13 and 9.14 show the total amount of farmland in each county and at the same time

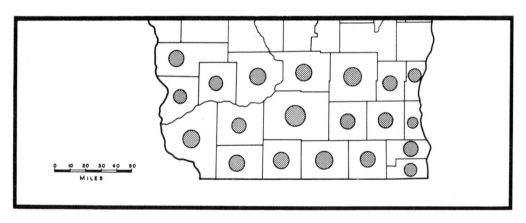

FIGURE 9.11. Area available for crops by counties. The unit radius is too small.

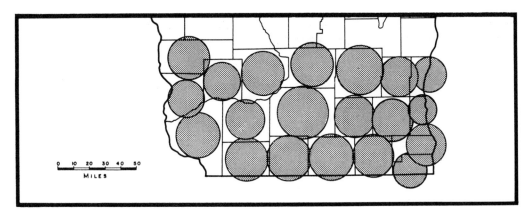

FIGURE 9.12. Same data as in Fig. 9.11, but the unit radius is too large.

show what percentage of that total is available for crops. The procedure merely requires that the percentage be determined and that, then, by using a "percentage protractor" the various values be marked off on each circle.

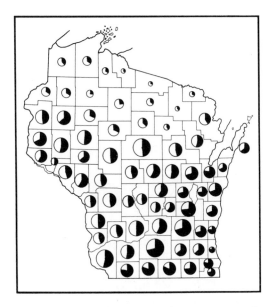

FIGURE 9.13. Land in farms and percentage available for crops in Wisconsin by counties. The circle represents the land in farms. The percentage *available* for crops has been blacked in on each circle.

A "percentage protractor" may be constructed by drawing a circle and then subdividing the circumference according to percentage in the desired detail with dividers. A small hole at the center will make it possible to place the center of the protractor over the center of each graduated circle. The appropriate per cent can be marked off at the periphery.

It is important that the subdivision of each circle begin at the same point; otherwise, the reader will have difficulty in comparing the values. Also important is the selection of the portion to be shaded or colored. As is illustrated in Figs. 9.13 and 9.14, this can have considerable influence on the effect gained by the reader.

If the two classes of data being represented by a pie chart are of equal importance to the purpose being served by the map, one may cover the background with a neutral tone so that the contrasts of the two segments of each circle with the background are approximately equal. Figure 9.15 has been constructed in this manner, although the background tone in this illustration is a bit too dark. It may be done relatively easily by using a prepared shading film for the background. This is applied after the remainder of the map has been drafted. The circles can easily be cut out with divid-

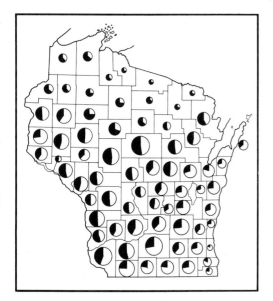

FIGURE 9.14. Same data as in Fig. 9.13, but in this map the percentage *not available* for crops has been blacked in on each circle.

ers or by replacing the pencil in a small compass with a sharp needle.

A kind of map similar to the pie chart can be constructed by employing one or more concentric circles to represent portions of the total. These interior circles are scaled according to the original data in the same manner as the circle representing the total. The visual impression is not very commensurable since percentages are not easily read.*

9.8   THE GRADUATED VOLUME SYMBOL

Occasionally the cartographer is faced with a range of data so large that he cannot effectively show both ends of the range by graduated circles. If he makes the circles large enough to be differentiated clearly in the lower end of the scale, then those at the

* This procedure has been followed in the *Atlas of Economic Geography*, by Johannes Humlum, Meiklejohn and Son, Ltd., London, 1955, pp. 88, 89, 91, 112.

upper end will be too large. A solution, if these kinds of data *must* be presented on a map, is to symbolize the data with apparent *volume* rather than area. This is done by making a comparable dimension of each symbol proportional to the *cube roots* of the data, in the same way in which the areas of two-dimensional graduated circles can be made strictly proportional to one another (see Article 9.5).

One kind of device used occasionally is the sphere-like symbol. An illustration of its use is shown in Fig. 9.16. Another type of graduated volume symbol is the cube or the block pile, developed by Erwin Raisz, illustrated by Fig. 9.17. Volume symbols, being prepared so that their apparent values are proportional to the cube roots of the data, have the effect of actually lessening the plane area of the large symbols on the map. This, of course, is what makes it possible to map a larger range of data by this method. It has the marked disadvantage, however, that the smaller values cover a relatively larger map area, so that this portion of the data is magnified somewhat, unless the reader takes care to appreciate the volume aspect. Three-dimensional symbols such as sphere-like and cube-like symbols may be very graphic, especially if the visual impression is intensified by good execution and design. This tends to offset somewhat the danger of the reader misinterpreting the relationship of these volumetric symbols.

9.9   QUANTITATIVE LINE SYMBOLS

Quantitative line symbols are of two kinds: there are those which symbolize by position some locational amount and those which represent a variable amount along their course. The first are isarithms such as contours which are numbered on the map and simply show location of amount by connecting points which actually have or are assumed to have the same value.

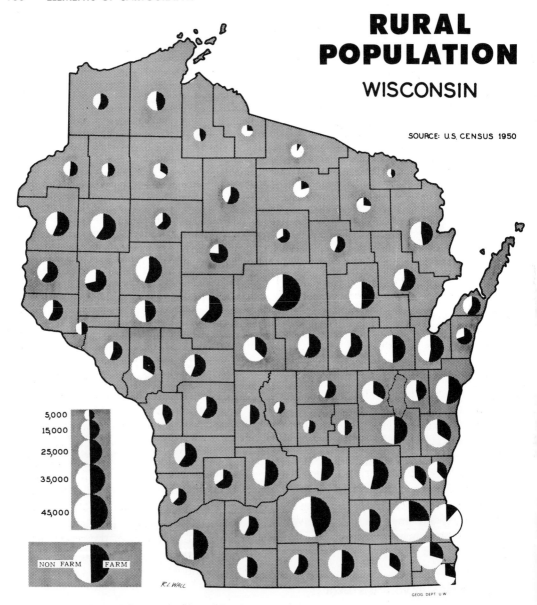

RURAL POPULATION

WISCONSIN

SOURCE: U.S. CENSUS 1950

5,000
15,000
25,000
35,000
45,000

NON FARM   FARM

R.L WALL

GEOG DEPT U W

FIGURE 9.15. Proportion of rural farm and rural nonfarm populations in counties. The sizes of the circles are scaled in proportion to the total rural population. (Map by Robert L. Wall.)

Ordinarily, the amounts themselves are of lesser significance than the delineation of derivatives of the relation between the amounts and their locations. Consequently, these kinds of symbols are more often used to show change from place to place and rates of change or gradient. In so doing they are intended to portray a three-dimensional geographical quantity or a statistical surface. Because the concepts underlying their use and the techniques involved in their construction require considerable ex-

planation and illustration, these types of quantitative line symbols are considered in detail in the next chapter.

The second type of quantitative line symbol is commonly called a flow line; usually of variable width, they show movement along the route of the line or between the terminal points connected by the line. The flow line need not be variable in width, but the thickness of the line is usually proportional (linearly) to the quantity represented at each point along the line. This type of line symbol came into use a little over a century ago during the period when Europe was becoming "statistics conscious." The development of rail transportation and the rapidly increasing movement of goods by both rail and canal, together with the rise of statistical symbolism, contributed to the

use of this easy-to-understand symbol. To-day flow lines are used in the same fashion to represent the flow or movement of everything from mineral raw materials to automobile traffic.

9.10   FLOW LINES

The techniques used in the construction of flow maps are easily observed from well-made examples such as those illustrated here. The symbolism is accomplished by merely graduating the thickness of the lines in proportion to the values by using a convenient unit width. The unit width is selected so that division of the data by the unit width results in a number representing a map dimension in inches or millimeters, in the same fashion that a unit value is used

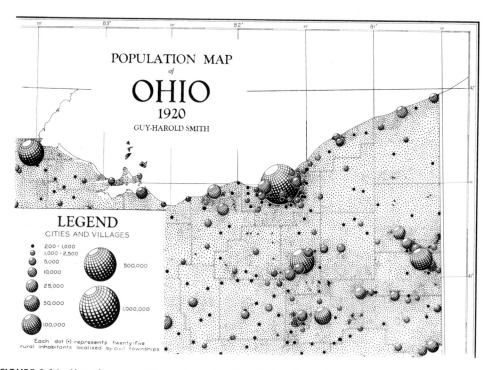

FIGURE 9.16. Use of apparent three-dimensional symbols. (From Population Map of Ohio by Guy-Harold Smith.) Note that the legend has been relocated for purposes of illustration. (Courtesy of Guy-Harold Smith and *The Geographical Review*, published by the American Geographical Society of New York.)

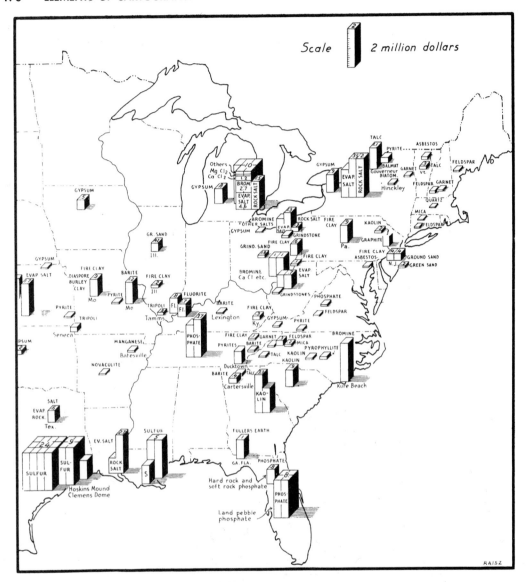

FIGURE 9.17. Another form of three-dimensional symbols, called block piles, developed by Erwin Raisz. (From a map by E. Raisz, taken from *Mining and Metallurgy*, AIME, March, 1941.)

to determine the drafting sizes of graduated circles. Lines may be shown as smooth curves as in Fig. 9.18 or as angular lines as in Figs. 9.19 and 9.20.

Actual movement along the route may be represented, or, as in "origin and destination" maps, the terminal points may simply be connected. Arrowheads at the ends of

lines are often used to show the directions of movement, although the varying thickness and angle with which "tributaries" enter frequently show flow adequately. Arrows may be placed along the lines as in Figs. 9.18 and 9.19 to show the direction or even to show relative movement in opposite directions as in Fig. 9.19. Lines can in-

crease or decrease in width as the values change, but between tributaries a line should maintain a uniform width. Tributaries should, of course, enter smoothly in order to enhance the visual concept of movement. In some instances the range of the data is so large that a unit width value capable of allowing differentiation among the small lines would render the large ones much too large. It is, consequently, sometimes necessary to symbolize the smaller lines in some way, such as by dots or dashes (see Fig. 9.18). Volume flow lines are also possible. Numbers may be placed alongside the lines to convey more exact information.

9.11   QUANTITATIVE AREA SYMBOLS

Geographical quantities which exist over area exist in vast array and range from the simple to the complex, including many very useful abstractions. No less bewildering is the cartographer's problem of representation. The difficulties arise because many kinds of data can be considered in two or more conceptual classes from a cartographic point of view, even though the numbers representing the data are the same. For example, many of the phenomena which are frequently mapped, such as temperature, exist continuously both in space and in time. The relation of the phenomena from one place to another is that of a continuous variable. Not only may the values at points be important, but derivatives of the spatial relationships, such as rates of change, are equally significant.

Quite different are many ratios and percentages which are also useful in the analysis of the geographical aspects of phenomena.

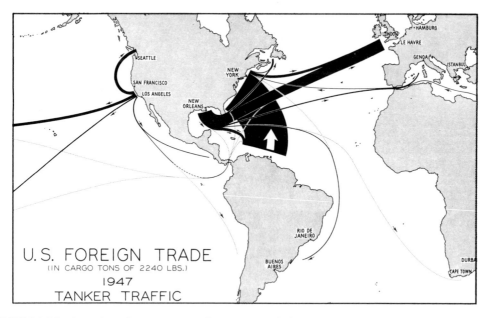

FIGURE 9.18. A portion of a quantitative flow map symbolizing 1947 tanker traffic of the United States. The widths of the lines are proportional to the tonnage. Since the thickest line represents well over 20,000,000 tons, small values of less than 200,000 tons cannot be adequately shown by proportional thickness. Consequently they are symbolized by line character (dots or dashes). (Map drawn by R. P. Hinkle. The map appears in Edward L. Ullman, *American Commodity Flow*, University of Washington Press, Seattle, 1957.)

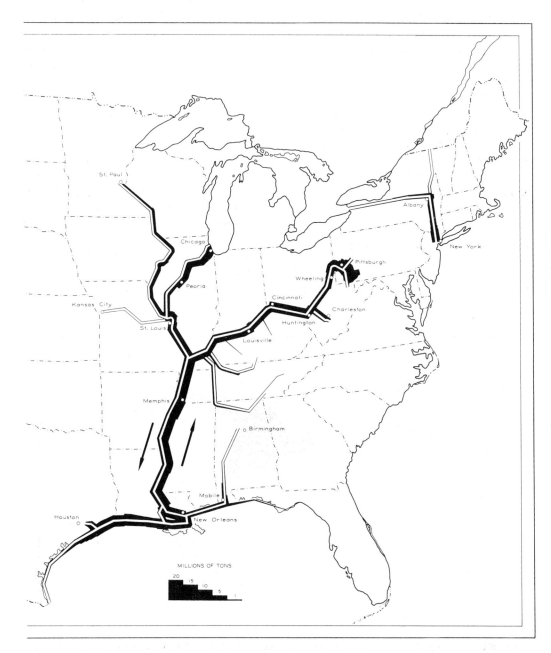

FIGURE 9.19. A portion of a quantitative flow map showing 1949 tonnage of barge and raft traffic in the United States. The legend has been moved. Note how direction of movement is indicated. (From Edward L. Ullman, *American Commodity Flow*, University of Washington Press, Seattle, 1957.)

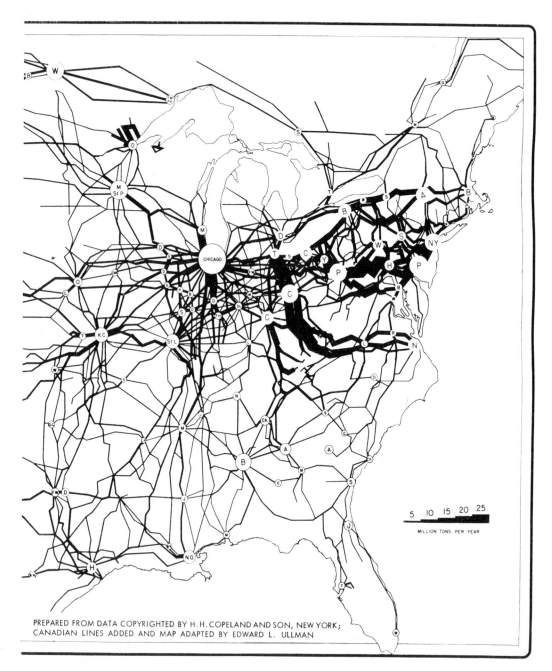

PREPARED FROM DATA COPYRIGHTED BY H. H. COPELAND AND SON, NEW YORK;
CANADIAN LINES ADDED AND MAP ADAPTED BY EDWARD L. ULLMAN

FIGURE 9.20. A portion of a map showing tonnage per year of railway traffic on lines of class one railways hauling over 1,000,000 net tons per mile per year in northeastern United States adjusted to 1929 traffic levels. (Map prepared and copyrighted 1956 by Edward L. Ullman.)

For example, one may derive the ratio or density between numbers of persons and the areas in which they live. This is done by utilizing statistical unit areas, as previously described, as a basis for density values. Such ratios may be thought of merely as individual values related only to the areas they represent. On the other hand, in spite of the fact that one of the factors (population) is obviously discrete, that is, not continuous, the assemblage of ratios may also be considered in an abstract fashion as constituting a continuously distributed phenomenon similar to a temperature distribution. Consequently, the representation of a density such as persons per square mile may be treated cartographically in either of two ways, depending upon whether the interest is (1) in the specific ratio values of individual unit areas, or (2) in the rate and direction of change of ratio values from place to place. Needless to say, before one can select a method of representation he should have clearly in mind the function of the map.

The nature of the phenomenon being mapped or the efficiency of the unit areas employed to derive ratio values may make it necessary to employ a third system of representation in which an assumption is made that is neither quite that of assuming the distribution to constitute a continuous variable nor that of concentrating the attention on the values within the statistical unit areas. Some kinds of phenomena do not extend, even when abstractly conceived, across certain kinds of areas. Neither do they have distributional characteristics like those associated with the sloping-surface-concept associated with a continuously changing set of values. For example, agricultural population density at a large scale in a region of extreme variation in character of agricultural land is likely to show relatively uniform high density in favorable areas coupled with a very rapid change to sparse occupance in unfavorable areas. Changes are rapid at boundaries which are not likely to be those of the enumeration units.

The preceding three kinds of areal data, or the assumptions made regarding the cartographic treatment of a body of areal data, are sufficiently diverse so that their mapping methods are quite different. Figure 9.21 shows, by means of a hypothetical density distribution, the difference in map appearance. Diagram A in Fig. 9.21 is made on the assumption that the density in question appears as a continuous variable. The lines are isarithms and each of the area symbols represents a sloping surface with the upper and lower values those of the bounding isopleths. Diagram *B* in Fig. 9.21 is made from exactly the same data as diagram *A*, but in this case the delineation is primarily for the purpose of exhibiting the actual ratios in the statistical units, and the boundary lines of the minor civil divisions have no numerical value. This kind of map is called a *choropleth* map. Diagram *C* is also prepared on the assumption that the distribution is not a continuous variable; but an additional assumption is made, namely, that the conceptual error that would result from bounding the area symbols by the boundaries of the political units would be excessive. Instead, therefore, the distribution is assumed to have the characteristics of a steplike variable, that is, areas of relative uniformity are bounded by zones of rapid change to another area of relative uniformity. The bounding lines of the area symbols are located where the values change rapidly, but the lines have no numerical value. This is called a *dasymetric* representation.

9.12   CHOROPLETH AND DASYMETRIC MAPS

The choropleth map requires the least analysis on the part of the cartographer, for it involves little more than locating the areas

FIGURE 9.21. Three ways of using area symbols: A, an isarithmic map; B, a choropleth map; C, a dasymetric map. See Article 9.11 for explanation of terms. Note the unconscious application, by the reader, of greater value to the darker areas.

to which tabular statistics apply. This technique may be used for many kinds of ratios and when the statistical units are small it provides sufficient variability in the map (if there is variability among the data) to take on some of the visual character of an isarithmic map. Ordinarily, however, it is employed when the problems of interpolation make an isarithmic or dasymetric map out of the question. For example, when mapping at a large scale the cartographer may not know enough about the details of the distribution or, at a small scale, the regional variations may be too inconsistent. In effect, the choropleth map attempts to present only the spatial organization of the statistical data, with no effort being made to insert any inferences into the presentation.

The dasymetric map, although made from exactly the same initial data used for the choropleth map, assumes the existence of areas of relative homogeneity. By subdivision of the original statistical unit areas additional detail is added to the presentation. The subdivision is made on the basis of whatever knowledge the cartographer has

respecting the data. This may be founded on field knowledge or any other kinds of data the cartographer may obtain. The arithmetic involved in making the numerical assumptions consistent with the original data has been explained and illustrated in Article 8.9. It should be emphasized that there is nothing in the data itself which will indicate to the cartographer the kinds of subdivision he should make; instead, this kind of interpretation must come from other knowledge concerning the spatial relationships between the data and other geographical distributions.

9.13   THE CLASS INTERVAL

Class intervals must be chosen to represent the data displayed on choropleth and dasymetric maps since the original numbers of the mapped data are usually not shown. Each class interval, such as 25 to 50 persons per square mile, lumps together all the values lying anywhere between the class limits. Obviously, therefore, the map reader will see only those values revealed by the

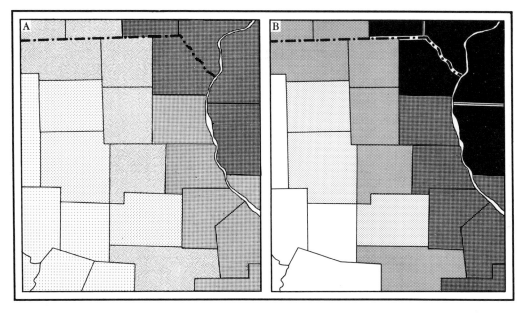

FIGURE 9.22. The same data are used in choropleth maps A and B, but the data are symbolized with different spreads of visual values.

cartographer's choice of class intervals. As J. Ross Mackay has pointed out, class intervals are the mesh sizes of cartography with the chosen values forming the screen wires.*

He further points out that it is necessary to choose the mesh size wisely so that the "size-sorting" of the distributional data is most effectively accomplished. The class intervals should neither be so small that unimportant detail confuses the map, nor should they be so large that important differences within the distribution are lost.

It is difficult, if not impossible, to select class intervals merely from inspection of the data. It is usually necessary, for all except the simplest of maps, first to evaluate the distribution of the data areally and especially to employ graphic aids in analyzing the

numerical and areal characteristics of the data. Several kinds of graphic aids may be useful, such as the ordinary frequency graph, the cumulative frequency graph, and the clinographic graph.* Of these, the most generally useful is the cumulative frequency graph. Its construction and utility as an aid to the choice of intervals are described in Articles 8.12 and 10.10.

Inasmuch as the data are numerical, it is appropriate to symbolize them with area symbols which vary in visual value, that is, with variations from dark to light in either black and white or color maps. The tonal values selected for categories on a map of graded intensities are extremely important. The same map with the same data may be made to appear quite different by changing the spread of values, as is illustrated in Fig. 9.22. The range appears much greater in map *B* than in map *A*.

* J. Ross Mackay, "An Analysis of Isopleth and Choropleth Class Intervals," *Economic Geography*, Vol. 31, 1955, pp. 71–81.

* Mackay, op. cit.

The general tendency is for one to assume that, within any gradation, black is "complete" and white is "empty." Consequently, the positions on the value scale should be chosen to bear a reasonable relation to the spread of the data. If the visual range is great, the reader cannot help but infer a great data range.

The eye cannot accommodate much more than six or eight steps from black to white, and even in this limited range considerable confusion can result from the juxtaposition of different values, as is pointed out in Article 12.6. Consequently, if the grading requires that the tonal value steps be too close together on the gray scale or in terms of hue, the cartographer may introduce numbers or patterns to aid in differentiation, as is illustrated in Fig. 9.23.

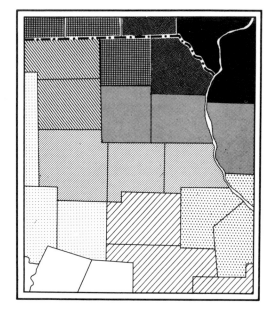

FIGURE 9.23. Pattern aids when values are too close together.

Mapping
Three-Dimensional Data

10.1 MAPPING GEOGRAPHICAL
VOLUME DATA

It was observed previously that geographical data could be categorized as being made up of point, line, area, or volume quantities, and that one- and two-dimensional symbols could adequately portray the first three without any particular strain on the imagination of the map reader. The portrayal of volume data is a somewhat different matter, because the map plane has a maximum of two dimensions, whereas a volume has three. Volumes that exist at what may be considered points, for example, the population of a city, can be symbolized by a two-dimensional plane figure, such as a circle, or by a drawing which looks like a three-dimensional figure, such as a sphere. On the other hand, actual or abstract volumes that have continuous extent, such as atmospheric heat energy (temperature) or population density are not so easily displayed. Most distributions which belong to this category cannot usually be well communicated by point or area symbols. To be sure, if the concern with the distribution is (1) concentrated on the values at individual places, or (2) if the major interest is focused on the location of areas of relative uniformity, then either the choropleth or dasymetric technique may be appropriately utilized as

described in the previous chapter. If, however, the emphasis is to be placed on the *form* of the distribution, that is, the rate and magnitude of the change from place to place, then a different technique of symbolization is necessary.

In order visually to comprehend a volume it is obviously necessary to see the outside surface enclosing it. A geographical volume is consciously or unconsciously thought of as resting upon an underneath surface such as the land, or upon some smooth, defined surface such as mean sea level. The values of the distribution, which define the volume, are therefore departures from the assumed or actual base. In most cases, these values are thought of as positive magnitudes lying above the assumed base.* Together these values define a three-dimensional surface. From the geometric form of this surface one can infer the extent of the volume resting on the base. In many instances the actual *volume* itself is less interesting and of less concern than the form of its surface. This is not always the case; for example, a road engineer is greatly concerned with actual volumes as in cut-and-fill problems. Never-

---

* Sometimes the reverse is true, for example, when one thinks of the volume of the sea, he visualizes magnitudes *below a surface.*

theless, the character of a three-dimensional geographical distribution is most clearly mapped by delineating its surface.

The symbolization of a three-dimensional surface is the most difficult problem of representation in cartography, and, no doubt, more time and effort have been devoted to it than to all other problems of symbolization put together. The principles involved in delineating such a surface are best illustrated by beginning with a familiar example, such as the surface of the land. This sometimes steep, sometimes almost flat, and usually not level surface, exists continuously; and all traverses over it consist of series of connected points all lying on a never-ending undulating surface. Because the land surface is so intimately connected to man's life, its character and delineation are of outstanding significance; consequently, numerous ways of depicting its undulations have been devised for various purposes (see Chapter 11). In the course of time it has developed that the most useful way is a technique that enables one not only to visualize its three-dimensional form, but which also makes possible the derivation of a variety of useful data from the symbols used, such as slope or gradient, elevation, ridges or troughs, flat plains, etc. The familiar contour which, through analysis, reveals all these and many other interpretations is but one member of the large and increasingly important cartographic family of symbols called isarithms.

10.2 ISARITHMS

An isarithm is a line which passes through, and therefore "connects," all points on a map that have the same quantitative value. The geometry of the construction of any isarithm is most easily demonstrated with the example of the contour, which is merely the common name for an isarithm which connects all points of equal elevation above some defined level such as mean sea level.

If the undulating land surface has been mapped in terms of *planimetry,* that is, the relative horizontal position of all points on the land, it is evident that there exists an infinity of points, each of which has, by reason of its location, an x and a y coordinate position (cf. longitude and latitude) on the horizontal map plane to which the earth's surface has been projected. The land surface undulates, and by definition is at all points either above or below some smooth assumed reference elevation, called a *datum.* It follows, therefore, that each of the infinity of points on the land must have a third coordinate position measured in a direction perpendicular to the datum plane in which the x and y coordinates lie. This third coordinate at each point is called the z coordinate. If a plane parallel to the projection plane and a given z distance from it is assumed to pass through the undulating surface, it must intersect with the land surface at all points having that z value. The *trace,* or the line of intersection, of these two surfaces (the z plane and the land) will be a closed line. When this line is orthogonally viewed, that is, perpendicularly projected to the map plane, it shows by its position the x and y locations of the points which have the particular z value it represents.

Figure 10.1 shows, in perspective, a hypothetical island, evenly spaced z planes, and below, an isarithmic map of the distribution of these z values on the surface of the island. In this case, z is elevation above the average level of the sea, which is defined as 0; it is, therefore, a contour map. The lowest or outer isarithm represents the average position of the shoreline. The next isarithm in Fig. 10.1 is the trace of the plane spaced 20 z units above 0; it is in the same location as the average shoreline would be were the sea 20 z units higher.

The shapes of the undulations of a three-dimensional surface are well indicated by characteristic shapes and patterns of spac-

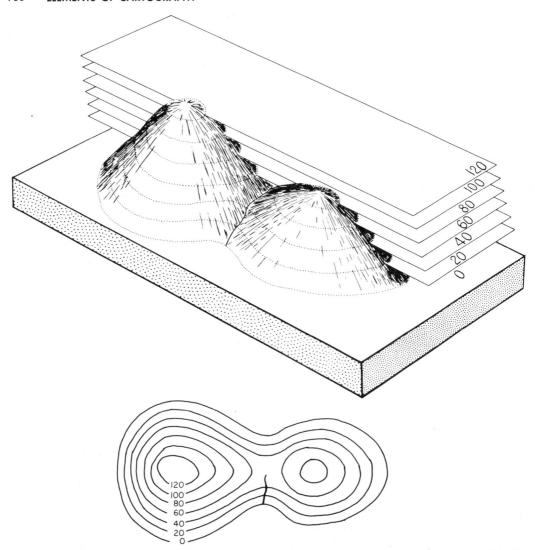

FIGURE 10.1. In the upper diagram horizontal planes of given z values are seen passing part way through a hypothetical island. The traces of the intersections of the planes with the island surface are indicated by dotted lines. In the lower drawing the traces have been mapped orthogonally on the map plane and constitute the representation of the island by means of isarithms (contours).

ings of isarithms, especially when the intersecting z planes are equidistant from one another. Smooth, steep, gentle, concave, convex, and other simple kinds of slopes and combining forms may be readily visualized from isarithmic maps, as indicated in Fig. 10.2. For example, the bends of con-

tours always point upstream when they lie athwart a valley; they always point down slope when crossing a spur (see Fig. 10.3). The angle of slope, that is, the gradient or rate of change of elevation, of the land is shown by the spacing of the contours made from equally spaced z planes. The

steeper the slope the closer will be the contours representing it. Profiles of the land surface along a traverse, or along a road or railroad, can easily be constructed from a contour map by working backward from the map to the profile. The recognition of detailed topographic forms and even genetic structural details are readily revealed by the patterns of the contours on topographic maps.

It is not necessary that the *z* surface to be represented by isarithms be an actual visible, tangible surface, such as the land; any three-dimensional surface may be mapped in the same way. For example, the undulations of a defined pressure surface in the atmosphere, such as the 500 millibar surface, may be mapped by passing planes of given pressure values through the atmosphere. The shapes in nature are not visible, but the patterns of the isarithms, in this case called

isobars, show the gradients, the troughs, and the ridges of the surface in the same way that contours show the ups and downs of the land. The three-dimensional surface may even be an abstraction. For example, the *z* values may consist of some sort of ratio or proportion, such as persons per square mile. Anything that varies in magnitude and either actually exists or can be assumed to exist in continuous fashion over area constitutes a statistical surface. Its undulations can be mapped isarithmically.

10.3 DEFINING THE STATISTICAL SURFACE

In order to map the traces of the intersections of horizontal planes with a statistical surface it is necessary, as in following the proverbial recipe for rabbit stew, first to "catch" the statistical surface. This is easier said than done.

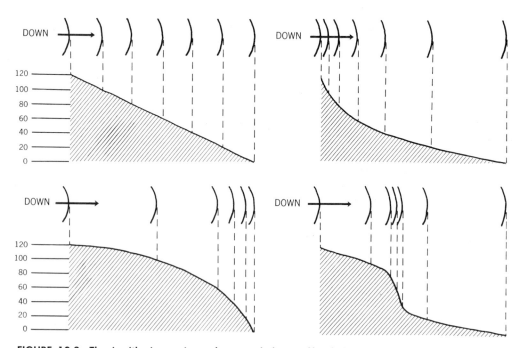

FIGURE 10.2. The isarithmic spacings above and the profiles below show in each diagram the manner in which the spacings of the isarithms show the nature of the undulations of the form from which they result. All the forms may be described as variations of the general rule that, if the isarithms are the traces of equally spaced planes, the closer the isarithms the steeper the slope.

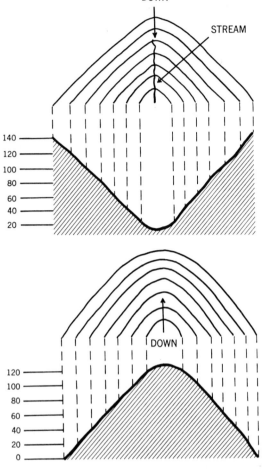

FIGURE 10.3. Whenever isarithms, in this case contours, cross a sloping trough on a surface, the apex of their bends points in the direction of the higher elevation; when they cross a spur, they bend toward the lower elevation.

Only recently, with the development of stereoviewing equipment for air photographs, has it been possible to define in its entirety the infinity of points on the land, each of which has its *z* value of relative elevation. In *all* other cases the statistical surface must be defined by a limited number of *z* values, and the totality of the surface *must be inferred* from these. In a very real sense the infinity of *z* values constitutes a statistical population or universe, but because of practical limitations only a sample

of these points is usually available. Since one cannot know precisely the characteristics of the universe from which the sample has been taken, any extension of the characteristics of the sample to the universe or to a particular part of it constitutes but an inference, the validity of which cannot be tested by direct means.

An example will clarify the foregoing. If air temperature is simultaneously observed at a series of weather stations, then the temperatures at the given station positions constitute the sample of *z* values. If it is desired to make a synoptic (instantaneous view) map of the total distribution of temperatures (by means of *isotherms*, that is, "contours" of temperature), it can be done only by making assumptions and inferences as to the nature of the temperatures that existed at the infinity of points in between the stations, for which actual *z* values are not available. The validity of the inferences will depend upon a variety of factors. The most important of these is (1) the cartographer's knowledge of the general characteristics of air temperature, and (2) his knowledge of its covariation characteristics, that is, its behavior in relation to a variety of other factors known to affect it, such as, elevation, the *xy* positions and the *z* values of which are known. In any case, the assumed positions of the traces of intersecting isothermal *z* planes will be but hypothetical positions of the isarithms. It is apparent then that the accuracy and representativeness of the given sample values, which the cartographer uses to locate the traces, are of considerable significance to the inference he draws of the total statistical surface. Various aspects of the probable validity of sample values are considered in subsequent sections.

10.4   THE CLASSIFICATION OF STATISTICAL SURFACES

The nature of any statistical surface depends upon the inherent characteristics of

the *z* values which make up the sample that defines it. There are several classes of *z* values which vary in terms of the precision with which they define a statistical surface: (1) actual values that can occur at points, (2) derived values that can occur at points, and (3) derived values that cannot occur at points.

Actual values that can exist at points are exemplified by such data as elevation above or depth below sea level, a given actual temperature, the actual depth of precipitation, thickness of a rock stratum, etc. These kinds of values do exist at points, and at any moment there is an infinity of such *z* values making an accurate synoptic view theoretically, if not actually, possible. Only actual errors in observation or in the specification of the *xy* positions of the observation points can affect the validity of the sample values. If accurate quantities were known for all points, then each isarithm resting on the statistical surface could have only one position on the map.

Derived values that can exist at points are of two kinds. One kind consists of various measures of central tendency or dispersion, such as means, medians, standard deviations, and other sorts of numbers derived from a time-series of observations made at a point. One can calculate an average monthly temperature, an average retail sales figure, or an average land value for some particular place; the resulting numbers, although representative of magnitudes at the point in question, cannot, by their very nature, actually exist at any moment. They are subject to various kinds of inherent error, particularly with regard to the extent of the sampling from which the derivation was made. A second kind of derived value that can occur at points is illustrated by the variety of ratios and percentages of point values that may be convenient to describe or study. Examples of these are the ratio of dry to rainy days that occurred at a particular place, or the percentage of total precipitation that fell as snow. Such ratios are also incapable of existing at any instant, but they do represent the quantities at the point for which they are derived. Like measures of central tendency or dispersion they are generally subject to more error than simple actual values. If they are rigorously defined and uniformly derived, they approach the validity of actual point values.

Quite different in concept is the derived value that cannot occur at a point. Representative of this class are percentages and other kinds of ratios that include area in their definition directly or by implication, such as persons per square mile, the ratio of beef cattle to total cattle, or the ratio of cropland to total land in farms. Therefore, only a mean value for a given unit of surface area can be derived. Consequently, although it is perfectly legitimate to assume a statistical surface defined by these kinds of quantities, such a surface can be described only by a series of mean values for *unit areas*. Since each unit area represents a larger or smaller aggregate of *xy* points, no single point can have such a value. Nevertheless, in order to symbolize the undulations of the statistical surface by isarithms it is necessary to *assume* the existence of such *z* values at singular points.

Because of the fundamental differences in the concepts of these three kinds of statistical surfaces, it is conventional to make a distinction among the isarithms employed to display their form. Different names are applied to them, and considerable confusion in definition and spelling exists in the literature. The following terminology seems to be consistent with present-day usage.

An *isarithm* is any trace of the intersection of a horizontal plane with a statistical surface. It is thus the generic term; it may also be called an *isoline* or *isogram*. Isarithms showing the distribution of actual or derived values that can occur at points (in which there is relatively little error) are called *isometric lines*. This is a rather awkward term, and often they are given instead

individual names which indicate their function, such as *isotherm* (equal temperature) or *isobar* (equal pressure). Those isarithms displaying the undulations of statistical surfaces that are based upon values that cannot exist at points, and which are likely to be subject to a somewhat larger inherent error of position, are commonly called *isopleths.*

An observation is in order here. Much less confusion will result if the student will transfer the distinctions just made from the symbols to the surfaces they delineate. An isarithm is defined as the trace made by the intersection of a horizontal plane with *any* three-dimensional surface. Whatever the nature of the surface may be, the function of the trace as a cartographic symbol is the same. Consequently, the "difference" between an isopleth and an isometric line is in reality an attempt to distinguish between the precision of two kinds of surfaces, rather than a distinction between kinds of cartographic symbols.

Isarithmic maps serve two purposes: (1) they may provide a total view of the undulations of the statistical surface, for example, the form of the land, and (2) they may serve as devices for the graphic portrayal of a series of quantities, for example, elevations at points. The ability with which they perform these functions is dependent upon the validity and reality of the surface. For example, one can safely obtain values of elevations by interpolation from a contour map, within a certain margin of error. On many isarithmic maps this cannot be so readily done; this is especially true of very large-scale isoplethic maps. In such maps the isopleths serve more as "form lines": to delineate the ups and downs of the surface and less as a method of portraying specific values at points.

When one is called upon to prepare an isarithmic map, whether the surfaces are isometric or isoplethic, he follows much the same procedure. In all cases, except when plotting contours with stereo plotting equipment, the cartographer works from either a limited series which constitutes but a sample of the infinity of values, or from a limited series of mean values representing finite areas. In each case the numbers on his map, constituting the series of z values, are spaced some distance apart; and he must, by assumption, inference, and estimate, produce isarithms representing a continuous statistical surface.

10.5   THE LOCATION OF THE CONTROL POINT

The location of each z value of the assumed statistical surface is called the *control point.* The xy positions of and the z values of the control points constitute the statistical evidence from which the locations of the isarithms are inferred. If the z value of the control point is correct but the xy position is incorrect, then a displacement of the isarithm will result. If the xy position is correct but the z value is in error, the same thing will happen if a sloping surface with the same gradient is assumed. This is illustrated in Fig. 10.4. Clearly both the position of the control point and the validity of the value at the control point have considerable effect on the location of the statistical surface and hence on the position of the isarithm.

The problem of choosing a location for the control point is not difficult when the statistical surface is one based upon actual or derived quantities that occur at points. The location of each observation is then the location of the control point. This is not the case, however, when mapping distributions derived from ratios, percentages, and the like that involve area in their definition, such as, for example, the density of population (persons per square mile). These kinds of values are derived from two sets of data based on civil divisions, other units of area, or portions thereof. The resulting numbers, upon which the ultimate locations of the isarithms depend, refer to the whole areal unit employed, and each is "spread,"

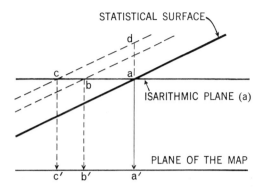

STATISTICAL SURFACE

ISARITHMIC PLANE (a)

PLANE OF THE MAP

FIGURE 10.4. If a' is the xy location of a control point with z value a, and if the isarithmic plane has the value a, then a' will be the orthogonal position on the map of the isarithm. If the z value a is incorrect and really should be d, then the a isarithmic plane would intersect the surface at c and the isarithm on the map would be located at c'. If the a value were correct but the xy position of a should be at b, then b' would be the map position of the isarithm.

of the center-of-gravity and center-of-area for uniform and variable distributions, with a dot map of rural population used as an example. They serve also to illustrate the problem of locating the control point in regularly and irregularly shaped divisions. In A, which is rectangular, the center-of-gravity and center-of-area would, of course, coincide at the intersection of the diagonals. Because the distribution is even, the centers in B also coincide, but they lie outside the irregularly shaped area at some point that is more representative of the whole division than any point within it. The distributions are uneven in C and D, so the center-of-gravity is displaced away from the center-of-area. In each case, however, the center-of-gravity is probably the more accurate location for the control point.

10.6   THE ASSUMPTION OF GRADIENT ON ISARITHMIC MAPS

Generally, the selection of the isarithm as the kind of symbol with which to represent

so to speak, over the entire area of the unit. Therefore, there can be no *points* at which the values used in plotting the isopleths exist. Nevertheless, the lines must be located somewhere and upon some basis. In order to do this, positions of control points are assumed.

When the distribution is uniform over an area of regular shape the control point may be chosen as the center. If the distribution within the unit area is *known* to be uneven, the control point is shifted toward the concentration. Center-of-area may be considered as the balance point or the geographic median of an area having an even distribution of values without any unevenness of the distribution taken into account. The center-of-gravity takes into account any variation of the distribution and is the likely location of the geographic mean. Figure 10.5 illustrates the concept.* The four diagrams of statistical divisions show possible locations

* J. Ross Mackay, "Some Problems and Techniques in Isopleth Mapping," *Economic Geography*, 1951, Vol. 27, pp. 1–9.

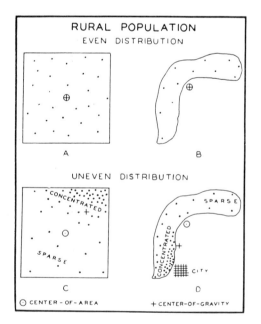

FIGURE 10.5. Placing control points. (From Mackay, courtesy of Economic Geography.)

a quantitative distribution has one important consequence, namely, it indicates that the cartographer has made the assumption that the sample values (z values) at their control point locations define some sort of *continuously undulating* statistical surface. If, instead, the assumption were made that the statistical surface consisted of a series of more nearly horizontal planes, having different z elevations separated by "escarpments," then another technique, the dasymetric, would be more appropriate (see Article 9.12). The isarithmic surface on a map is therefore assumed primarily to be composed of slopes, the gradients of which are derivatives of the distances between the control points and the z values at those control points.

The surface of the land is visible either by stereo-photogrammetric methods or in the field. The infinity of z values can, therefore, be directly or indirectly employed as a guide for the delineation of the form by the isarithms. The gradients are not unknown, and through long familiarity with the nature of the land surface an experienced cartographer can infer the multiplicity of slopes and changes in gradients that occur in the spaces between control points. The character of most other statistical surfaces is known only imperfectly, and an assumption is necessary as to the kinds of gradients between the z values at control points. When nothing is known to the contrary the gradient between control points is assumed to be *linear*.

A cross section of a statistical surface which shows a profile along the top is an ordinary graph in which z is the ordinate and xy is the abscissa. A linear slope or gradient is represented on an ordinary graph by a straight line. Consequently, as is illustrated in Fig. 10.6, if two z values at different xy positions are represented, then the linear gradient between them is represented by the straight line a connecting them. The dotted lines b or c, in Fig. 10.6

may actually represent the true slope; but unless other evidence is available to indicate that z varies in a curvilinear relation with change in xy, such an assumption is obviously more complex. In science whenever several hypotheses can fit a set of data, the simplest is chosen. As previously pointed out, the slopes of the actual land surface are known, in most cases, to bear certain kinds of a curvilinear relationships to xy position on the land. On the other hand, for most other statistical data distributed over the earth, this is not known. There are theories in some cases, such as that population density tends to be curvilinear (for example, b in Fig. 10.6), but their validity has not yet been generally demonstrated. Consequently, in the majority of cases a linear gradient is assumed in the construction of isarithmic maps.

10.7 THE INTERPOLATION OF ISARITHMIC POSITION

Interpolation is the name for the process of estimating the magnitude of intermediate values in a series. The control points of a statistical surface to be mapped by isarithms constitute the series, and the magnitudes and locations of intermediate values, such as the positions of individual isarithms, are accomplished by interpolation. When no

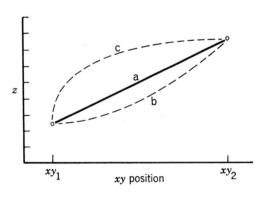

FIGURE 10.6. Three kinds of gradient between two control points.

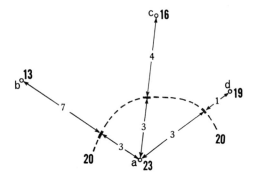

FIGURE 10.7. Interpolation between control points.

evidence exists to indicate a nonlinear gradient between control points, interpolation becomes merely a matter of estimating linear distances on the map in proportion to the difference between the control point values. For example, Fig. 10.7 is a map on which are located z values at xy positions a, b, c, and d. If the position of the isarithm with a value of 20 is desired, it will lie $\frac{3}{10}$ of the distance from a to b, $\frac{3}{7}$ (or approximately $\frac{4}{10}$) of the distance from a to c, and $\frac{3}{4}$ of the distance from a to d. Lacking any other data, the dotted line representing the 20-isarithm would be drawn as a smooth line through these three interpolated positions.

Professor J. Ross Mackay has illustrated one of the common problems that arises in interpolation when using control points that are located in a rectangular pattern due to circumstances beyond the control of the cartographer.* Many isarithmic ratio maps are based upon the rectangular minor civil divisions of the United States and Canada, and many other census and sampling surveys use more or less rectangular subdivisions. When control points are arranged in a rectangular pattern, it is usual that alternative choices will arise concerning the location of an isarithm when one pair of

diagonally opposite z values forming the corners of the rectangle is above and the other pair below the value of the isarithm to be drawn. Figure 10.8 illustrates the problem that is involved in interpolating a 20-isarithm with reference to rectangular z values of 25, 18, 33, and 16.

A careful examination of other relevant information may help to indicate which choice of the two alternatives is the better. If this is not possible, averaging of the interpolated values at the intersection of diagonals will usually provide a value which will remove the element of choice (see Fig. 10.9). One is forced, in the absence of other data, to assume the validity of the average.

If the cartographer has control over the shapes of the unit areas, he can prevent the problem of alternative choice by designing the pattern of unit areas so that the control points have a triangular pattern, such as

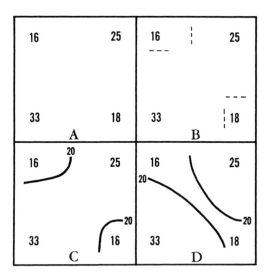

FIGURE 10.8. In A the z values are arranged rectangularly. In B the positions of the 20-isopleths between adjacent pairs have been interpolated. Diagrams C and D show the two ways the isopleth of 20 could be drawn through these points. (Redrawn, courtesy of Mackay and *The Professional Geographer*.)

* J. Ross Mackay, "The Alternative Choice in Isopleth Interpolation," *The Professional Geographer*, Vol. V (New Series), 1953, pp. 2–4.

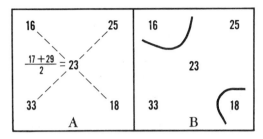

FIGURE 10.9. If the average of the interpolated values at the center is assumed to be correct, the isopleth of 20 would be drawn as in B. (Redrawn, courtesy of Mackay and *The Professional Geographer.*)

would result from unit areas that are rhombic or hexagonal or composed of staggered rectangles as are shown in Fig. 10.10. The cartographer can do this if he is "gridding" a map preparatory to deriving unit area values from which to prepare a subsequent isarithmic map of the derived statistical surface.

Another related kind of problem, which is just as significant when interpolating from isarithmic maps, results from the fact that the steepest gradients on an undulating form twist and turn over the surface. Thus, the line representing the most direct gradient on a curved surface will be a line normal (at right angles) to the isarithms and will be curved when orthogonally projected to the map plane. In Fig. 10.11 diagram *A* shows two straight parallel isarithms. Because the surface between those two isarithms must be a plane (with the assumption of linear gradient) the value of point *a* is interpolated merely by the relative distances to the adjacent isarithms. In diagram *B* point *a'* would be interpolated by the relative distances along the smooth curve which passes through *a'* and lies normal to the isarithms. Therefore, when the cartographer is plotting isarithms on a map he should "look ahead" and determine by the arrangement of *z* values the nature of the

curvature of the surface and plot the positions of the isarithms accordingly.

10.8   THE VALIDITY OF THE CONTROL POINT VALUE

As was illustrated in Fig. 10.4 any error in the *z* value at a control point can have as much effect upon the location of an isarithm as changing the location of the control point. There are several kinds of factors which affect the validity of the control point value, and hence the certainty with which the cartographer can locate the isarithm. Whenever there is a question concerning the accuracy of the *z* value, this

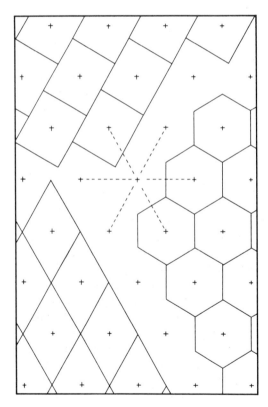

FIGURE 10.10. Control points arranged in triangular fashion remove the problem of alternative choice. (From Mackay, courtesy of *The Professional Geographer.*)

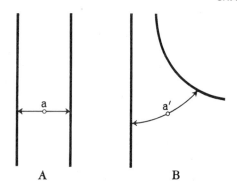

FIGURE 10.11. Interpolation of point a' in B is done by estimating distances along a smooth curve normal to the isarithms.

doubt is automatically projected to the map; it there becomes transformed to a question as to the xy position of the isarithm. There is, therefore, always a zone on the map within which any isarithm may be located, depending upon the certainty of the z values. The width of this zone depends upon the amount of error in the z value, assuming that the control point (the xy position) is correct.

There are three kinds of statistical errors that commonly affect the reliability of the z values from which an isarithmic map is made: (1) *observational error*, (2) *sampling error*, and (3) *bias or persistent error*. A fourth kind of question as to the reliability of an isarithmic map is related not so much to actual error as it is to the validity of the concept being presented by the map. This may be called for the lack of a better term *conceptual error*. Each of these is briefly considered.*

Observational error refers to the method used to obtain the z values. If they are de-

* For an excellent, detailed, and illustrated discussion of the first three kinds of statistical error the reader is referred to David I. Blumenstock, ''The Reliability Factor in the Drawing of Isarithms,'' Annals of the Association of American Geographers, Vol. 43, 1953, pp. 289–304, upon which much of this summary is based.

rived by means of instruments operated or read by humans there is usually some inaccuracy, both in the instruments and in their reading by the observers. Observational error is not limited to instruments, however. A considerable amount of statistical data is based upon various kinds of estimates, as, for example, a farmer's estimate of the extent of his cropland, the yield per acre, the extent of soil erosion, etc. Most statistical data are subject to observational error of one sort or another.

Sampling error is of several kinds. The most obvious is that associated with any map which purports to represent the distribution of an entire class of data, only a sample from which is known. Any map of mean climatological values, which is not specifically for a particular period, is, in effect, attempting to describe a total average situation (or *statistical population*) from only one relatively small sample. For example, temperatures have occurred for thousands upon thousands of years, but man's records cover only the comparatively short modern period. From this small sample must be inferred the long-term average. Many kinds of data in censuses are collected by a sampling procedure. In this case, the statistical population exists at one time, but the cost of ascertaining it in its entirety is too great; thus a sample is taken.

Another kind of sampling error is involved in the uneven spacing of control points and in the sizes of the statistical units for which mean values are computed. The farther apart the control points are, the less may be inferred about the nature of the distribution between the points, that is, the less valid is each z value as a sample of all the possible z values within the area to which it refers. On an undulating surface which is subdivided into statistical units for which means are computed, it is apparent that the larger the statistical unit the more likely it is to contain extreme values which will be

merged into one average. The actual variations of a given undulating statistical surface will therefore be progressively diminished as the number of sample means is diminished.

Bias or persistent error may be of many kinds. Instruments may consistently record too low or too high; the majority of weather stations may be in valleys or on hilltops; people show preferences for certain numbers when estimating or counting; and so on. Bias is difficult to ascertain but may have considerable effect upon z values.

Conceptual error in the z value may be illustrated by the use of mean values computed from a series of observations with which to make a map of mean monthly temperatures. When one computes a mean value it is apparent that the mean may not describe very well the actual fact since the dispersion of the values around the mean may be large. For example, the standard deviation of mean December temperatures in central United States is around 4° F. This indicates that approximately one-third of the time an individual December mean will be more than 4° above or 4° below the average of the December means. A map that purports to show by isarithms the distribution of mean December temperatures will, therefore, show each isarithm located only near the center of a map zone or band represented horizontally by several degrees of temperature gradient. Furthermore, it is necessary to realize that if individual year-to-year maps had been made, approximately one-third of the time the isarithm would lie outside the zone delineated by 8° of temperature gradient. On even a small-scale map such a zone would be of noticeable dimensions. It follows that minute isorithmic wiggles and sharp curves would be an affectation of accuracy not supported by the nature of the data.

It is extremely important to take into account the various kinds of possible error in the validity of the z values. Sometimes a careful determination of the extent of error would be more time-consuming than the results would be worth, but reasonable estimates can usually be made without undue effort. In many cases, some of the kinds of sampling error have already been ascertained and need only be obtained from the sources, as for example the U. S. Census of Agriculture. Standard deviations and standard errors of the mean are often available or are not difficult to compute. Simple logic and common sense will often provide enough of an answer for highly generalized maps.

Except when the infinity of z values is known, and this is possible only with respect to elevation (with modern photogrammetric methods), the total effect of all the possible sources of error and inconsistency from one part of the map to another can function toward only one end, viz., *to smooth out the isarithms.*

10.9   THE ISARITHMIC INTERVAL

Probably the most important problem the cartographer must face in employing isarithms is the choice of the interval between the lines actually drawn, that is, the z distance between the horizontal planes passed through the statistical surface. Theoretically, of course, an infinite number of lines is possible; in practice, a selection must be made. This selection is based upon a number of factors considered in this and the following article.

The most significant element, of course, is the intended purpose of the map. As noted previously, the cartographer can employ isarithms for two quite different purposes: he may be concerned with presenting the distribution of the z values graphically in lieu of their tabular distribution, or he may attempt the delineation of the form of the statistical surface as revealed by the sample of z values with which he has to work. These aims need not be mutually

exclusive, but unless the numbers involved are fortuitously distributed he must ordinarily decide which is the more important. The revelation of form by isarithms is most easily done by means of a regular interval, whereas showing the locations of particular values does not require, and usually precludes, a regular interval.

The recognition of form from the patterns made by the isarithms, such as concave or convex slopes, hills or valleys, escarpments, and the like, on the statistical surface is difficult, if not impossible, when irregular intervals are used. Figure 10.12 illustrates how the nature of slopes is easily revealed by the spacings of lines from a regular

arithmetic interval in the one case and almost completely hidden by an irregular interval in the other. In some cases, when interest is concentrated in one portion of the range of values, a regular, but not strictly arithmetic interval, may be employed. An arithmetic interval is one in which values change by a constant amount, such as 2, 4, 6, 8, 10, etc. A geometric interval is one in which the values change by a constant *ratio*, such as 0, 1, 3, 7, 15, and it may progress either "up" or "down," as, for example, 15, 14, 12, 8, 0. An arithmetic isarithmic interval provides the easiest recognition of the form of the statistical surface. An increasing or decreasing geometric interval requires

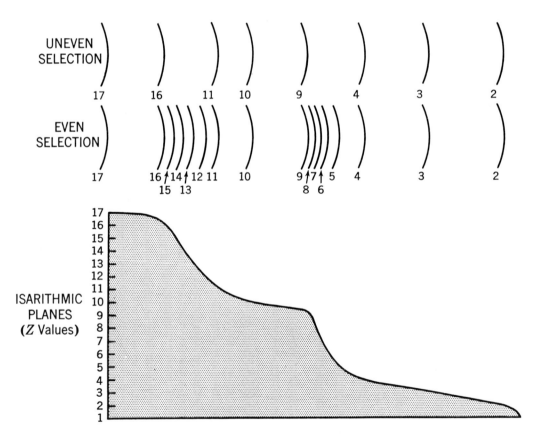

FIGURE 10.12. Only when an even selection of z value isarithmic planes, that is, a uniform interval, is chosen does the pattern of isarithms clearly reveal the shape of the statistical surface as is shown by comparing the profile with the isarithmic map sections above.

more mental effort on the map reader's part when he tries to infer the form of the surface, but it allows the cartographer to concentrate detail in one portion of the range, as illustrated in Fig. 10.13. A non-arithmetic and nongeometric interval provides the poorest representation of the form of the statistical surface.

10.10   GRAPHIC AIDS TO SELECTING AN INTERVAL

Occasionally, the problem of selecting an interval is difficult because of (1) the range

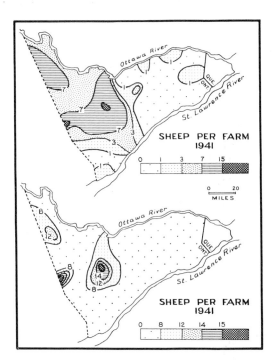

FIGURE 10.13. These two maps have been pre-pared from the same ratios but employ different isopleth intervals. The intervals in the top map increase in steps of 1, 2, 4, and 8, whereas those in the bottom map increase in the reverse order, 8, 4, 2, 1. The result is to provide detail and accentuate differences at the lower end of the scale in the top map and to reverse this relation-ship in the bottom map. (Redrawn from Mackay, courtesy of *Economic Geography*.)

of the data, (2) the scale of the map, or (3) the fact that certain portions of the distri-bution may be inherently more significant than others for the purpose at hand. It is frequently desirable to select lines and in-tervals which have some significance, either in themselves or in the areas they delimit. It is also considered desirable to select the interval in such a way that few isolated spots result on the map. For these purposes graphic aids may be employed.

The most useful aid is a cumulative fre-quency graph (see Article 8.12). Its prepa-ration and use in cartography involves only the understanding that frequency in the geo-graphic sense means areal extent of occur-rence. How a cumulative frequency graph is used to select isarithmic intervals is best explained with the aid of an example. Table 10.1 shows in column (1) the rural farm population density in 1950 of some counties in Nebraska. The areas of the counties are shown in column (2). The counties have been arranged in order of their popu-lation density, that is, they have been ranked according to z value. In column (3) the areas have been cumulated as follows: the area of each county, beginning at the top has been added to the sum of the areas of the preceding counties above it in the rank-ing. The z values of column (1) have been plotted on a graph (shown in Fig. 10.14) against the cumulated area shown in col-umn (3), in the manner illustrated in Article 8.12. The z values are plotted on the Y axis and areas on the X axis. A map of the area showing the counties and their means is shown in Fig. 10.15.

An analysis of the graph allows a number of inferences. The curve is relatively smooth. From this one may infer that, in general, there is not likely to be a major escarpment on the z surface. Consequently, assuming no unusual geographical grouping of the values, population density over the area will probably show a fairly regular change. Therefore, it may be assumed that an even

TABLE 10.1

RURAL FARM POPULATION 1950 AND AREAS OF
SOME COUNTIES IN NORTH CENTRAL NEBRASKA

County	(1) Rural farm population— persons per square mile—1950	(2) Area— miles^2	(3) Cumulated area
Hooker	0.4	722	722
Cherry	0.7	5,982	6,704
Thomas	0.8	716	7,420
McPherson	0.8	855	8,275
Blaine	1.1	711	8,986
Logan	1.5	570	9,556
Rock	1.6	1,012	10,568
Loup	1.7	574	11,142
Brown	1.8	1,218	12,360
Wheeler	1.9	576	12,936
Keya Paha	2.1	769	13,705
Garfield	2.5	570	14,275
Lincoln	2.6	2,523	16,798
Holt	3.1	2,408	19,206
Custer	4.0	2,562	21,768
Boyd	5.1	538	22,306
Greely	5.3	570	22,876
Valley	6.4	570	23,446
Dawson	6.6	979	24,425
Sherman	6.8	570	24,995
Buffalo	7.4	952	25,947
Howard	7.4	566	26,513
Knox	7.8	1,124	27,637
Antelope	7.8	853	28,490
Nance	8.3	438	28,928
Boone	8.9	683	29,611
Merrick	8.9	467	30,078
Hall	9.2	540	30,618
Pierce	9.7	573	31,191
York	10.3	577	31,768
Polk	10.4	433	32,201
Hamilton	10.8	541	32,742
Madison	11.0	572	33,314
Platte	11.9	672	33,986

arithmetic interval would show the form of the distribution without "hiding" very much of significance between the isarithms. The greatest slope occurs between the approximate z values of 4 and 6, so that if the interval 2, 4, 6, 8, 10 were chosen this

slightly steeper section of the statistical surface would be well shown. Stated another way: there is more change in population density per unit distance in those areas that have densities between 4 and 6 than there is in those areas having densities less than 4 and more than 6. Hence, these are likely to be more revealing values than any others in the area. From this one may generalize that z values at the base and top of escarpments on cumulative frequency graphs are generally more useful as isarithmic values because they tend to outline areas of different z value gradient.

In spite of the fact that there is not a great deal of difference in gradient in this area, Fig. 10.16, a map showing the isarithms of rural farm population density, clearly reveals that the greatest average slope on the undulating statistical surface is in the vicinity of the areas between 4 and 6 persons per square mile.

The cumulative frequency graph may be used to determine other intervals. As described in Article 8.12 one may determine from it the geographic mean, the geographic median, or such other functions of z value over areas as quartiles or deciles. Since the X axis of the graph from the origin to the opposite edge of the graph represents the total area of the map, an ordinate erected halfway on the X axis to the curve will give the Y value that divides the map area into two equal parts, that is, the geographic median of the distribution. Inspection of the graph shows that the median occurs at a z value of approximately 3 persons per square mile and reference to Fig. 10.16 shows that if a 3-isarithm were interpolated, it would in fact nearly divide the area into two equal parts. Other ordinates at given X values would provide quartiles, etc.

Ordinary frequency graphs in which z values of unit areas are plotted against frequency of occurrence, for example, numbers of counties, may be quite erroneous if either the sizes of the areal units or the spread of

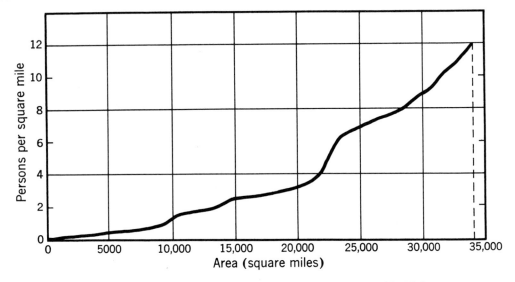

FIGURE 10.14. A frequency graph based on the data in Table 10.1.

the sample points is uneven. In such a case an extraneous item such as the frequency of county boundaries may affect the graph more than the z values. If the unit areas are about the same size or if the distribution of sample points is relatively even, then frequency graphs of number of occurrences or even cumulated occurrences may be used.

Although theoretically one can have as small an interval as he wishes, there is, on the other hand, the matter of accuracy which acts as a brake against choosing too small an interval. Small intervals and numerous lines may give an impression of accuracy not warranted by the nature of the data. On the other hand, large intervals may not show sufficient detail. The cartographer must analyze the quality of his data and the purpose of the map, and select his interval accordingly.

FIGURE 10.15. A group of counties in north central Nebraska. The z values are the number of persons per square mile (rural farm population) in 1950 (U. S. Census).

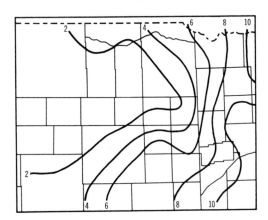

FIGURE 10.16. Isarithms of the distribution shown in Fig. 10.15 employing an even arithmetic interval.

Mapping the Terrain

11.1 REPRESENTING THE TERRAIN

In Chapters 8 to 10 various techniques of symbolism were discussed according to the principles underlying their utility. Another approach to the same problem would be to consider separately the various categories of geographic information commonly presented on maps and then to discuss the various techniques by which each can be symbolized. The difficulty with such an approach is that there is considerable similarity in the methods of representing such phenomena as population data, agricultural data, manufacturing data, and so on, which would necessarily result in a great deal of repetition. There is, however, one category of geographical data that is so different from the others as to make it almost imperative that it be treated separately. This is the category concerning the surface of the land. The data in this category also may be represented by point, line, or area symbols, or by combinations of them.

The representation of the three dimensions of the earth's surface has always been of special concern to cartographers, but the earliest maps and even those of the Middle Ages showed little of this, probably because of the paucity of knowledge about land forms. To be sure, mountains were shown as piles of crags, and ranges appeared as "so many sugar loaves"; but until precise

surveying provided the elevational and positional data upon which the cartographer could base his drawings, land forms could not be well represented. As soon as surveying did provide the basic information, the representation of terrain became almost of primary concern.

There is something about the three-dimensional surface that intrigues cartographers and sets it a little apart from the other symbolization techniques. First, it requires a bit more skill. Moreover, it is a continuous phenomenon; that is, all portions of the earth above the sea have a three-dimensional form, and as soon as the land is represented *all* of it must be represented, at least by implication. It is also the one phenomenon the cartographer works with that exists as an impression in the minds of most map readers, and the reader is therefore relatively critical in his approach to its representation on the map.

Because of its universal spread, and because of the relative importance to man of minor land forms, the representation of terrain has also been a great problem to the cartographer. If he shows the surface in sufficient detail to satisfy the local significance of the land forms, then the problem arises of how to present the other map data. If he shows with relative thoroughness the nonland-form data, which perhaps are more

important to the purpose of the map, he may be reduced merely to suggesting the land surface, an expedient not likely to please either the map maker or the map reader. And, to make matters worse (or better, depending on how one looks at it), the development of aviation has made the effective and precise representation of terrain a most important task. The pilot must be able to recognize the area beneath him, and the passenger has naturally become more interested than he formerly was in the general nature of that surface, for he may now see it. His height above it provides a reduction similar to that of a map.

The story of the development of landform representation is a recital of the search for symbolizations suitable to a variety of purposes and scales. On large-scale maps the desirable symbolization is one that appears natural and at the same time is capable of exact measurement of such elements of the land surface as slope, altitude, volume, and shape. The major problem arises from the fact that, generally speaking, the most effective visual presentation is the least commensurable, whereas the most commensurable is the least effective visually. One of the major decisions of every survey has been in what manner to balance these opposing conditions. Although it is somewhat early as yet to judge, there is some indication that advances in color printing have enabled the cartographer to reach a relatively effective combination, without undue sacrifice of either desirable end. The new, shaded relief, contour maps of the United States Geological Survey are a case in point (see Fig. 11.1).

Perhaps even more of a problem has been that of depicting land forms on smaller-scale maps. To the geographer and geomorphologist are reserved the specialized techniques for terrain appreciation and analysis. Small-scale land-form representation is a major problem for atlas maps, wall maps, and other general-purpose reference

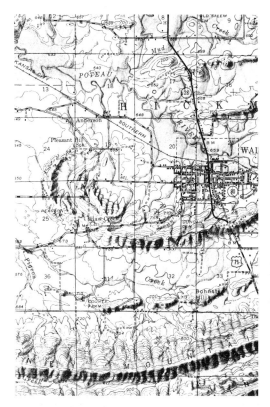

FIGURE 11.1. A small portion of a modern contoured topographic map. The terrain is emphasized by colored shading. This black reproduction, reduced to two-thirds original scale, cannot do justice to the excellence of the original. (Waldron Quadrangle, Arkansas, United States Geological Survey, 1949.)

maps, as well as for those special-purpose maps in which regional terrain is an important element of the base data. The smaller scale requires considerable generalization of the land forms, which is no simple task, as well as the balancing of the surface representation with the other map data, so that neither one overshadows the other. (See Fig. 11.2.) No less a problem is the representation, in bolder strokes, of the land forms for wall maps, so that such important elements as major regional slopes, elevations, or degrees of dissection are clearly visible from a distance (see Fig. 11.3).

FIGURE 11.2. Drawing landforms for a modern atlas. Drawn in black for photography, the surface representation is printed in brown on the final map. (Courtesy Rand McNally and Company.)

Practically every conceivable technique, from brilliant coloring to the artists' shading, has been tried.

For many years to come the representation of land forms will be an interesting and challenging problem, for it is unlikely that convention, tradition, or the paralysis of standardization will take any great hold on this aspect of cartography. Particularly will this probably be true of terrain representation on special-purpose maps, for each such map will be a new challenge.

11.2 THE HISTORY OF REPRESENTING THE TERRAIN

The earlier representations of terrain were concerned mainly with undulations of some magnitude and consisted of crude stylized drawings of hills and mountains as they might be seen from the side, such as those depicted in Fig. 11.4. The perspective-like, oblique, or birdseye views became more sophisticated in the period from the fifteenth to the eighteenth centuries when the delineation of terrain developed along with the landscape painting of the period. The eighteenth century was the period when the great topographic surveys of Europe were initiated and for the first time map makers had factual data with which to work. Delineation of the form of the land shifted from an employment of the oblique view to the plan view, perhaps because of the availability for the first time of extensive planimetric data. Symbols with which to present the form of the land without planimetric displacement were developed.

In 1799 a kind of flow-line symbol called the *hachure* was advocated by Lehmann, an Austrian army officer. Each individual hachure is a line of varying width that follows the direction of greatest slope. By varying the widths of the lines according to the steepness of the slopes on which they lie, the steepness of the rise may be indicated. When many of them are drawn close together, they collectively show the slopes and "ups and downs" of the surface. This turned out to be particularly useful on the then recently initiated, large-scale, topographic military maps; and, for nearly a century, the hachure was widely employed. Figures 11.5 and 11.6 are examples of hachured maps. On small-scale maps or maps of poorly known areas, hachuring degenerated into the familiar "hairy caterpillars," an example of which is shown in Fig. 11.7. These worms are not yet extinct, and they still may occasionally be encountered.

Another line symbol, the *contour*, had been invented in the first half of the eighteenth century (1730), before the advent of the hachure. A Dutchman named Cru-

FIGURE 11.3. A much reduced portion of a modern wall map emphasizing surface. The detailed terrain is derived from photographing a carefully made, three-dimensional model. The map is reproduced by complex color printing analogous to process color. (Map by Wenschow, (Germany), courtesy Denoyer-Geppert Company.)

quius, being called upon to represent the bottom configuration of the Merwede River, did so by using isarithms representing depth. Others, perhaps independently, seized upon the idea of representing dryland surface with a similar type of line symbol; but it was not until relatively late in the nineteenth century that contours became a common method of depicting the terrain on survey maps. One development, which grew out of the use of contours on large-scale maps, was their extreme generalization on small-scale maps, resulting in the familiar "relief map," together with its layer coloring according to altitude, originally developed more than a century ago (1842). The colors, of course, are area symbols between isarithms.

After the development of lithography in the first half of the nineteenth century, it became possible easily to produce continuous tonal variation or shading. It was not until after about 1870, however, that this type of area symbol was utilized for the

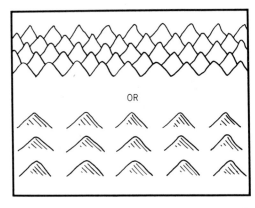

FIGURE 11.4. Crude, early symbolization of hills and mountains.

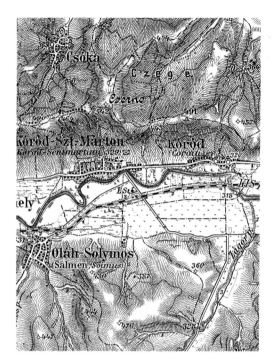

FIGURE 11.5. A section of a hachured topographic map with vertical illumination. Austria-Hungary, 1:75,000.

readily apparent. For the last several decades the problem has been one of how to combine the techniques to achieve both ends. The newer topographic maps are the most effective yet produced.

The representation of the land surface at large scales is concerned essentially with the three major elements of configuration, the slope, the height, and the shape of the surface formed by elevations and angles. The various methods outlined above, and their combinations and derivatives, seem to provide the answer, more or less, for the problem at large scales; but the representation of land surface at smaller scales is another matter. Here the generalization required is so great that only the higher orders of elevation and slope may be presented by contours or hachures, whereas

representation of the terrain, the shading applied being a function of the slope. Not long after, color gradations were combined with shading, and some truly "visual" maps of the land surface were forthcoming. Various techniques of shading and coloring were tried, but the general aim was to achieve the impression on the flat map of an actual third dimension. Warm and cool colors (yellow-red as opposed to blue-green) were combined with various kinds of shadows, so that the visual effect of the third dimension was most strikingly achieved.

By the beginning of the present century the basic methods of presenting terrain on large-scale topographic maps (contouring, hachuring, and shading) had been discovered, and the essential incompatibility between commensurability on the one hand and visual effectiveness on the other was

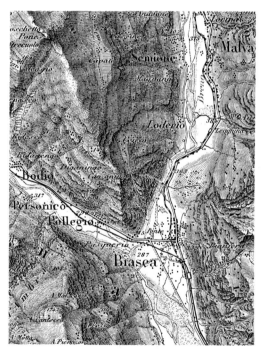

FIGURE 11.6. A section of the Dufour map of Switzerland in which obliquely lighted hachure shading is employed. Sheet 19, 1858, Switzerland, 1:100,000.

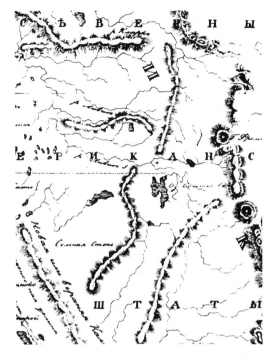

FIGURE 11.7. Genus *hachure*, species *woolly worm*. (From an old Russian atlas of western North America.)

detail, if shown, becomes so intricate that the map is useful for little else. To be sure, the exceptionally skillful cartographic artist can apply shading or hachuring effectively, but such skill is not easy to develop. As knowledge of the land surface of the earth has grown, so also has the need for a variety of methods of presenting effectively that surface at smaller scales.

No one method can satisfy all the small-scale requirements for land surface delineation. Consequently, with the growth of reproduction techniques and drawing media, the variety of the ways of depicting the land surface is steadily increasing, and it may be expected to continue to do so for some time to come. Some of the older methods are beginning to be discarded because of their rather obvious deficiencies.

Layer coloring, with or without spectral gradations between selected and generalized

contours, is one of the earliest devised techniques that has been most often employed, mainly because of its relative simplicity; but it leaves much to be desired. Character of surface is presented only be implications of elevation; the generalized contours show little except regional elevations, which are not very significant; and the problems of color gradation and multiple printing plates are sometimes difficult. The larger the scale, of course, the relatively more efficient the system becomes.

Hachures at small scales are likely to revert to the woolly worm, and the simple shading technique, without expensive multiple color plates, tends to become little else than an uneven background tone, which serves only to reduce the visibility of the other map data.

In lieu of simple layer tinting, hachuring, and shading at small scales, many other techniques have been tried. One of the more effective devices is that of drawing the terrain pictorially, as a kind of bird's-eye view with a slight perspective, as in Figs. 11.16 and 11.17. This may be done as a black line drawing, or as a continuous tone line drawing on Ross or Coquille board, or it may be rendered in wash or crayon for halftone reproduction. This sort of delineation requires a knowledge of landforms, considerable practice, and at least some manual skills. One who draws terrain must know what he is drawing, but he must also have the skill to interpret graphically the three-dimensional relationships he wishes to convey. The first requires training in such fields as landform analysis, geomorphology, and structural geology; the second requires more training in the visual arts than most cartographers have the good fortune to receive. There is practically no end to the combinations of perspective viewpoint, coloring, highlighting, shadowing, and line drawing that can be employed. Only some of the fundamentals can be treated in this book.

Many other systems of landform representation for special purposes have been tried or suggested. Most of them are relatively complex and intellectually involved. Their use is limited to the professional geographer and geomorphologist, whose knowledge of landforms is sufficient to interpret them. In this category would fall those methods which present certain aspects of the geometry of the land, such as the landform unit-area technique, the average-slope technique, and the relative-relief technique.

A thorough understanding of the small-scale possibilities for delineating terrain requires familiarity with the fundamentals of the three methods used to show terrain on topographic maps, viz., contours, hachures, and shading.

11.3 CONTOURS

Representation of the form of the land by means of contours is the most commensurable system yet devised. As described in Chapter 10, contours are the traces obtained by passing parallel "planes" through the three-dimensional land surface and projecting these traces orthogonally to the plane of the map. A contour is, therefore, an isarithm of equal elevation above some sea level or other assumed starting elevation. The assumed horizontal surface of zero elevation is called the *datum plane,* which is the surface of a particular earth spheroid projected beneath the land. This surface is essentially that which would be assumed by a worldwide ocean that was not modified by localized variations in gravity.* It is apparent that the spheroid surface is not a

* This concept is an expedient, for it is well known that the surface that would be assumed by a continuous ocean, with the present surface density and gravity differences retained, would not be that of a spheroid. Rather, it would have local undulations, and would instead be a geoid surface. It is the establishment of this surface that is one of the problems of geodesy.

flat surface but is curved in every direction. It is the problem of the mapper to establish the horizontal position on, and the vertical elevation above, this surface of a large number of points on the land. When enough positions are known and the curved datum surface has been transformed into a plane surface by means of a projection system, such as the polyconic, the map may then be made. The map reader *sees* the represented land surface orthogonally. Figure 11.8 illustrates these important relationships.

Contours on a topographic map are remarkably expressive symbols, if they have been correctly drawn and if the interval between them is relatively small. The most obvious expression is that of elevation. The elevation of all points on a map may be determined within one-half the contour interval. For example, if the interval between contours is 20 feet, and if any point not on a contour must necessarily be above the lower and below the higher of the two contours between which it is located, then a point can be reckoned to the nearest 10 feet. One must, however, bear in mind that not all contour maps are of the same order of accuracy. Before the acceptance of the air photograph as a device from which to derive contours, the lines were drawn in the field with the aid of a scattering of "spot heights" or elevations. Consequently, often they were by no means precisely located.

It is apparent that much of the utility of contours depends upon their spacing, and the choice of a contour interval is not an easy task. In areas of high relief the interval must necessarily be large, and as the interval is increased the amount of surface detail lost between the contours becomes correspondingly greater. If, owing to lack of data or scale, the contour interval must be excessive, other methods of presentation, such as hachures or shading, are likely to be preferable. In some cases, lack of data results in *form lines* being employed in place of contours. These are discontinuous lines

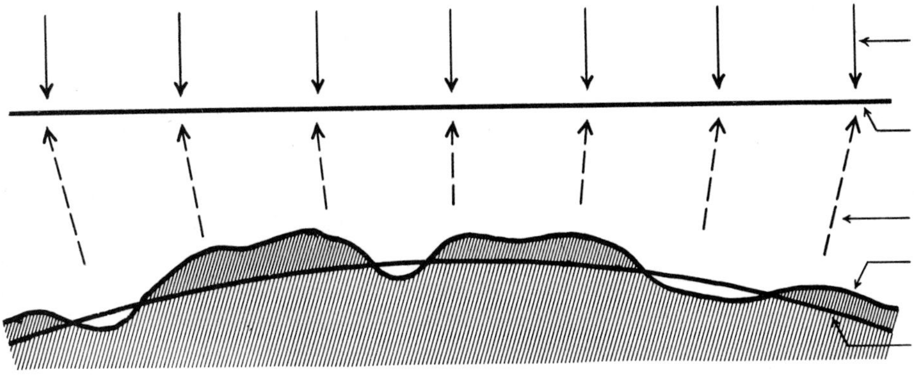

FIGURE 11.8. The building of a contour map. The curvatures are, of course, greatly exaggerated.

which, by their orientation, suggest shapes but from which precise elevations are not to be read.

Although contours do not present quite so clear a visual picture of the surface as does shading, the immense amount of information that may be obtained by careful and experienced interpretation makes the contour by far the most useful device for presenting the land on topographic maps.

11.4   HACHURES

Hachures are not commensurable as contours are, but for many purposes, especially at smaller scales, they provide a more readily visible picture of the land. The hachure is a line symbol drawn down the slope, and it is varied in width or spacing with the slope of the land on which it lies. The steeper the surface, the darker the representation. The original form of hachures was based on the assumption of a light source directly over each portion of the map in line with the reader. As the light shone upon the assumed three-dimensional land surface some of it would be reflected in the direction of origin (to the reader) in some proportion to the angle of the slope (see Fig. 11.5). A number of different slope-darkness relationships have been used. For example, the originator, Lehmann, established a system

wherein any slope 45° or more would appear black on the map.

The varying amounts of light and dark may be produced either by thickening lines, as in the Lehmann system, or by decreasing the spaces between lines of the same thickness. Many different combinations have been tried, but they all are based on the same general idea—a change of slope changes the amount of light reflected. Other variations have been incorporated in the system, such as having the light come from some angle other than vertical. Oblique lighting produced a more realistic picture, and some of the shaded hachure maps produced in this fashion are remarkably effective, as for example the Dufour map illustrated in Fig. 11.6.

The major difficulty experienced with hachures is that, although slope is their basis, it cannot practically be measured from the map, regardless of the precision underlying the representation. Flat areas, whether they are on the tops of uplands or in valleys, appear the same, and only streams or spot heights strategically placed make it possible for the reader to tell them apart. Another difficulty of hachuring is that its effectiveness, when printed in one color, is dependent in large degree upon the darkness of the ink. Thus, a considerable problem is created, for as darker inks are used

to make the terrain more effective the other map detail becomes correspondingly obscured.

It is interesting to note that precise, effective hachuring depends upon a considerable knowledge of the terrain. In actual practice, contours were often drawn on the field sheets of a survey, and the final map was hachured in the office from the contours. Thus the original French survey for the 1:80,000 map had contoured field sheets but was published only in the hachured form! In modern times hachures have been little used on topographic maps. They are still employed in smaller scales in atlases and on occasional special maps.

11.5 SHADING

Shading is the representation of the land surface by means of variations in light and dark. The variations, as in a chiaroscuro drawing, are applied according to a number of different systems. For example, the shading may vary according to the slope of the land as seen from above in a fashion similar to vertically lighted hachuring, or it may be applied according to the angles of light reflection that might occur if the light source were at some particular angle. In its simplest form, shading attempts to create the impression, appropriately exaggerated, one might gain from viewing a carefully lighted model of the land, as is illustrated in Fig. 11.9. Of course, the usual shaded map is not quite the same as an area seen from above, for the observer is, in theory, directly above all parts of the map; there is no perspective.

Not long after hachuring with vertical lighting was employed on topographic maps, it was discovered that a more realistic effect could be attained by varying the line widths to give the effect of light coming from the side. The Dufour map of Switzerland, started in 1833 and completed in 1866, and referred to in the previous article, is an out-

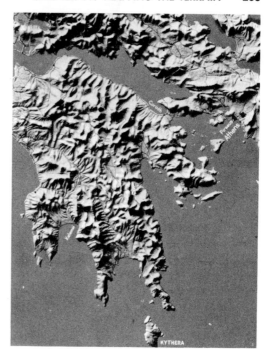

FIGURE 11.9. A much reduced portion of a topographic model. Reproduction by halftone.

standing example. This method was followed in other surveys as well. In such maps the graphic quality took precedence over the desire to indicate precise slope, although attempts to combine them were extensively investigated.

The versatility of lithography gave the cartographer of the nineteenth century a medium previously lacking, and he was quick to take advantage of it. Lithography allowed smoother and easier application of shading with a crayon, which was considerably faster than the tedious drawing of hachures, even if the hachures were not graded precisely according to slope categories. After the use of stone for lithography declined, the gradation of light and dark (continuous tone) was accomplished by halftoning. The "terrain plate" is usually prepared separately and is halftoned (see Article 14.15); the line work of the map is then either combined with it and printed as

a combination line and halftone, with one press plate, or it is printed separately, as two impressions with different inks. Continuous-tone drawing is generally decidedly preferable to photographing a model when the reproduction is to be a monochrome, because much more contrast and sharper detail can be attained in the drawing. The continuous-tone monochrome drawing may be done in wash (painted with a brush), by airbrush, by carbon pencil, charcoal, or crayon; in any case it must be reproduced by halftone, since it employs continuous tone. (See Fig. 11.10.)

The drawing or the photograph of the model may also be reproduced in color, and various other effects are thus possible. For example, several identical halftones may be separated during the retouching stage;

portions of them may then be printed in different colors, so as to achieve an effect of elevational layer tints, in addition to the realistic terrain. The coloring need not conform strictly to elevational lines, but may be employed simply to distinguish lowlands from uplands in any particular region.

It is, of course, not necessary that the vertically viewed terrain drawing be drawn in such a way that its reproduction requires the halftone process. The obliquely illuminated hachure map, exemplified by the Dufour map (Fig. 11.6), is one example of the kind of copy that could be reproduced by a line cut. Ross board and Coquille board may also be employed to the same end. (See Fig. 11.11.) The line-cut method reduces the cost considerably, but does not allow quite as much contrast or detail.

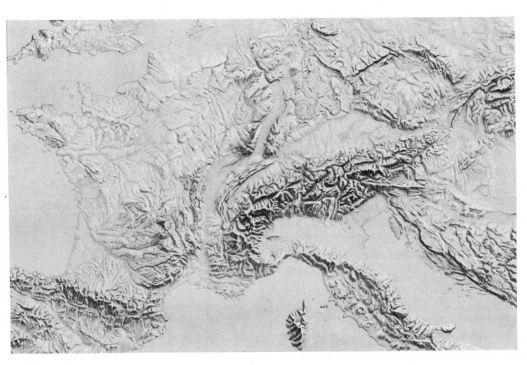

FIGURE 11.10. A portion of an expertly rendered, shaded, monochrome terrain drawing of Europe by Richard Edes Harrison. The drawing was prepared considerably larger than here shown. (From *Eurasia, of Lands and Peoples of the World,* copyright 1958 by Ginn and Company. Reproduced with permission.)

FIGURE 11.11. A portion of a reduced, vertically viewed terrain drawing, done with No. 60 Castell pencil and India ink on Ross board. (Drawn by Richard Edes Harrison.) Reproduction is by line cut. The lighting is from an angle, but the shading is also a function of elevation, as lowlands are systematically darkened. This is a portion of one-half of a split drawing used for the end paper of the book, *The Flying North*, by Jean Potter, copyright 1947. (Courtesy The Macmillan Company, publishers.)

One of the problems facing the cartographer, when he plans to employ vertically viewed shaded terrain, is the direction from which the apparent illumination is to come. A curious and not completely understood phenomenon is that under different directional illumination, depressions and rises will appear reversed. Consequently, the illumination direction must be chosen so that the proper effect will be obtained. Generally, when the light comes from the upper right, elevations appear "up" and depressions, "down." In addition to pro-

viding the correct impression of relief, the direction of lighting is important in illuminating effectively the terrain being presented. Many areas have a "grain" or pattern of terrain alignment that would not show effectively if the illumination were from a direction parallel to it. For example, a smooth ridge with a northwest-southeast trend would require the same illumination on both sides, if the light were to come from the northwest. Finally, the cartographer must select the direction of lighting so that the items of significance will not all be in the dark shadow areas.

The utility of shading as a visual vehicle for presenting landforms has long been appreciated. It was to be expected that there would be attempts to make it in some way commensurable as well as visually effective. The first such attempt was the hachure. A number of other possibilities have been suggested, but none of them has been tried beyond the experimental stage. For example, the late Max Eckert, one of Europe's foremost cartographers, attempted to use point symbols in the hachure-slope manner.* By using more carefully controlled dot sizes graded according to slope, he hoped to produce a map in which the amount of light that would be reflected from a vertical source would be accurately represented.

Two other proposals having to do with illuminated contours and a vertical lighting technique have been made by Professor Tanaka of Japan.* His latest suggestion is

* Max Eckert, *Die Kartenwissenschaft*, Berlin and Leipzig, 1921, Bd. 1, pp. 585–590; see also Arthur H. Robinson, "A Method for Producing Shaded Relief from Areal Slope Data," *Annals of the Association of American Geographers*, 1946, Vol. 36, pp. 248–252.

* K. Tanaka, "The Orthographical Relief Method of Representing Hill Features on a Topographical Map," *Geographical Journal*, 1932, Vol. 79, pp. 213–219; K. Tanaka, "The Relief Contour Method of Representing Topography on Maps," *The Geographical Review*, 1950, Vol. 40, pp. 444–456.

to illuminate contours systematically so that they provide an impression of shading with oblique lighting, as well as being commensurable. Figure 11.12 is an example.

11.6 PERSPECTIVE REPRESENTATION OF TERRAIN

Almost as soon as maps were drawn, the major terrain features were represented pictorially in crude fashion. As artistic abilities have increased and as knowledge of the character of the earth's surface has expanded, its perspective representation has become increasingly effective. Within the past fifty years this method of presenting the land features has made great strides. One reason for this has been the advent of the airplane, because the airplane has made man more conscious of the appearance of terrain, and

FIGURE 11.12. An example of Professor Tanaka's illuminated contour method. (Courtesy of The Geographical Review, published by the American Geographical Society of New York.)

the air photograph has provided a source of information hitherto unavailable.

There are in common use today many varieties of perspective delineation of the land. Most of them stem from the attempts made during the nineteenth century to illustrate the concepts which were being rapidly developed by the growing science of geology. The earlier geologists illustrated their studies and reports with cross sections in order to show the structural relationships. The top line of a cross section is a profile of the land, and it was only natural that some pictorial sketching was occasionally added to make the appearance more realistic. The next step was to cut out a "block" of the earth's crust and tilt it upward and sideways so that two sides as well as the top became visible. Although drawn by others nearly a century ago, the block diagram technique was most notably advanced by W. M. Davis, a renowned geomorphologist and teacher. Through his examples and those of his students, the block diagram has today become a standard form of graphic expression; and its utility has been extended to illustrate land use, land types, and other kinds of earth distributions. Almost any degree of elaborateness may be incorporated in a block diagram, ranging from the successive geologic stages in the development of an area to multiple cross sections of the structure. Uncomplicated block diagrams are not difficult to draw and even the simplest is remarkably graphic (see Fig. 11.13). For many examples of great variety the reader is referred to the many works of W. M. Davis, D. Johnson, and A. K. Lobeck. The latter produced a textbook which is required reading for anyone interested in developing his skill along this line.*

The block diagram, being obliquely oriented to the reader, is not a map in the

---

* A. K. Lobeck, *Block Diagrams and Other Graphic Methods Used in Geology and Geography*, 2nd Ed., Emerson-Trussell Book Company, Amherst, Mass., 1958.

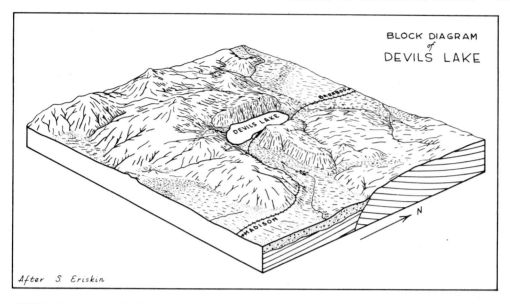

BLOCK DIAGRAM
of
DEVILS LAKE

DEVILS LAKE

BARABOO

MADISON

N

After S. Eriskin

FIGURE 11.13. A simple block diagram prepared for student field-trip use. The natural appearance of the surface forms on a perspective block makes the concepts easily understandable to anyone.

sense that a map is viewed orthogonally and its scale relationships are systematically arranged on a plane projection. From the block diagram, however, have come map types which combine the perspective view of the undulations of the land and the planimetric (two-dimensional) precision of the map. This is the physiographic diagram or the landform map developed primarily in the United States by cartographers who were greatly influenced by the teaching and example of W. M. Davis. The categorization of most phenomena tends to submerge gradations and the category of perspective terrain maps is no exception. Within this general class there is a large variety ranging from the essentially pictorial view placed on a realistically curved earth surface to the schematic landform map which uses symbolic methods on a plane projection. There is almost no limit to the number of possible combinations of viewpoint and execution which can be employed to meet an equally large variation in the purposes to which such maps are put.

11.7 PICTORIAL TERRAIN MAPS

Pictorial terrain on maps ranges from the relatively crude terrain commonly seen in newspaper maps to the scientifically accurate diagrammatic physiographic, or landform map; it may be line cut or halftone; and it may be monochrome or multicolor. Whatever its use and its form, all pictorial terrain drawings range between two extremes: (1) the perspective *drawing,* and (2) the perspective *map* (see Fig. 11.14).

The perspective drawing essays to show a portion of the earth as if seen from some distant point. On it the appearance of the whole is relative, as in a block diagram of a large section of the earth. It has become popular in recent decades (see Fig. 11.15). Drawings of this type are usually done on an orthographic projection (for very small scales), or on an "oblique" photograph of a portion of the globe. The terrain is then modeled so that the earth's curvature is simulated and so that the entire drawing provides the impression of a view of the

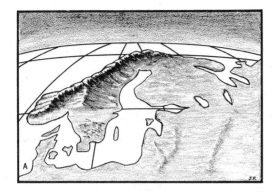

FIGURE 11.14. Sketches showing the fundamental difference between the perspective drawing (at top) and the perspective map (at bottom).

earth as seen from a point far above. Remarkably graphic effects can be created with this method of terrain representation. They are particularly useful as illustrations of national viewpoints and of strategic concepts in a world that is growing smaller each year.

The student should have clearly in mind why pictorial terrain cannot be realistic but must exaggerate to a tremendous degree. Actual departures of the earth's surface up or down from the spheriod are very small, relative to horizontal distances, and

they can hardly be shown at all at most medium and small scales. For example, the highest mountain on the earth, Everest, is a bit over 29,000 feet above sea level, or only about 5½ miles. If the terrain of the continent of Asia were represented pictorially and accurately on a map with a scale of 1:10,000,000, Mount Everest would be only about ⅓₀ inch high! Consequently, almost all pictorial-terrain representation must greatly exaggerate and simplify the terrain. This introduces problems of selection and generalization, which make it absolutely necessary that the cartographer be relatively competent in the field of the geography of landforms.

One of the more distinctive contributions of American cartography is the pictorial map in which the terrain is represented schematically on a base map. Although this type of map is not limited to cartographers in the United States, it has reached its highest development through the efforts of A. K. Lobeck, Erwin Raisz, Guy-Harold Smith, and a few others.

Many combinations of media and scales are used for the perspective map. Simple line drawings with or without shading and highlighting make effective *sketch maps* to illustrate the broader concepts of terrain relationships (see Figs. 11.16 and 11.17). More carefully made maps in which the pictorial terrain is treated more systematically are usually called physiographic diagrams or landform maps. The former attempts to relate the surface forms to their origin. The physiographic diagrams of A. K. Lobeck are of this type. In these are suggested, by varying darkness and texture, the major structural and rock-type differences having expression in the surface forms. They do not have a particularly realistic appearance and their name "physiographic *diagram*" is appropriate (see Fig. 11.18).

Landform or land-type maps are those in which more emphasis is placed on the ap-

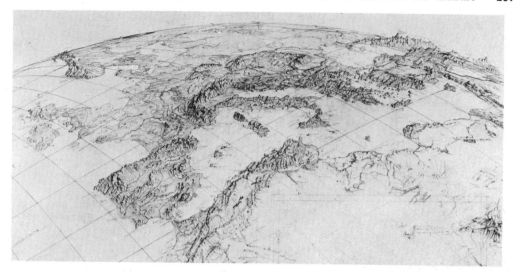

FIGURE 11.15. A much reduced worksheet or "scrub sheet" of a perspective drawing by Richard Edes Harrison. The map, for which this was the preliminary study, appeared in final form in *Fortune* magazine, 1942.

FIGURE 11.16. A small perspective map made with a combination of line and shading on Coquille board. Reproduced by line cut. (From Armin K. Lobeck, *Things Maps Don't Tell Us*, The Macmillan Company, New York, 1956.)

FIGURE 11.17. A portion of a small perspective map made entirely with line work. Compare with Fig. 11.16 in which little systematic symbolism is employed. In this map categories of terrain are given prominence by different treatments. (From Armin K. Lobeck, *Things Maps Don't Tell Us*, The Macmillan Company, New York, 1956.)

FIGURE 11.18. A portion of the small-scale *Physiographic Diagram of the United States* by A. K. Lobeck. Note the schematic treatment of the surface. (Courtesy of the Geographical Press, formerly at Columbia University Press, now at C. S. Hammond and Company, Inc.)

FIGURE 11.19. A portion of a small-scale landform map. Compare with Fig. 11.18. Note the inclusion of descriptive terms. (From *Landforms of Arabia* by Erwin Raisz.)

pearance of the surface forms with less concentration on their genesis. This type of map is exemplified by those of Erwin Raisz, who has developed a set of schematic symbols with which to represent various classes of the varieties of landforms and land types (see Fig. 11.19).* There is, of course, no sharp distinction between the physiographic diagram and the landform map. All possible combinations of representation of the underlying structures, rock types, and geomorphic processes may be employed.

* See E. Raisz, "The Physiographic Method of Representing Scenery on Maps," *The Geographical Review*, 1931, Vol. 21, pp. 297–304; E. Raisz, *General Cartography*, 2nd Ed., McGraw-Hill Book Co., New York, 1948, pp. 120–121.

Whatever the emphasis may be on such maps, the terrain is positioned on the map without perspective; but the terrain symbols are derived from their oblique appearance. All physiographic or landform maps have had one major defect in common; the side view of a landform having a vertical dimension requires horizontal space, and on the map horizontal space is reserved for planimetric position. For example, if a single mountain is drawn on a map as seen from the side or in perspective, the peak or base and most or all of the profile will be in the wrong place planimetrically (see Fig. 11.17). This fundamental defect in landform maps has, of course, been recognized by the cartographers who draw them, but has, prop-

FIGURE 11.20. A much reduced portion of a planimetrically correct terrain drawing of the Camp Hale, Colorado area. The map was drawn at a scale of 1:50,000 for printing in two drawings, one for culture and one for terrain. The terrain drawing was "opened up" for names and symbols; hence it appears "spotty" in places. (Drawn by Norman J. W. Thrower. Courtesy of *The Geographical Review*.)

erly, been justified on the ground that the realistic appearance obtained more than outweighs the disadvantages of planimetric displacement. On small-scale drawings the planimetric displacement is not bothersome to the reader and only occasionally causes the cartographer concern, especially when some feature of significance is "behind" a higher area. At large scales, however, the conflict of perspective view and the consequent error of planimetric position make it desirable to adopt another technique.

11.8 PLANIMETRICALLY CORRECT PICTORIAL TERRAIN

A vertical profile across the surface of the ground, when viewed from the side and placed on a map, utilizes planimetric position in two dimensions, yet the top and base of the profile are actually in the same

planimetric position on the earth. It is impossible, therefore, to utilize planimetric position to express vertical dimension without producing planimetric displacement. In order to overcome this fundamental difficulty it is desirable to replace the usual vertical or perspective profile across the land with a line which *gives the same appearance*, but which is not out of place planimetrically. This is done by passing a series of parallel *inclined* planes through the three-dimensional surface.*

* Much of the textual material and all the illustrations in Article 11.8 first appeared in Arthur H. Robinson and Norman J. W. Thrower, "A New Method of Terrain Representation," *The Geographical Review*, Vol. 47, No. 4, 1957, pp. 507–520, and are used with the permission of the American Geographical Society. The original study was sponsored by the Department of the Army, Quartermaster Research and Development Center, Environmental Protection Division.

When a single horizontal plane is passed through the land surface the contour is the trace, that is, the line of intersection, of the two surfaces. On the usual map the contour line is viewed orthogonally, that is, from directly above. If the plane is rotated on a horizontal axis, *ab* in Fig. 11.21 and the successive traces plotted, *and still viewed from above*, the traces produced run the gamut from the contour trace, *x*, to a straight line, *z*. The trace produced by the inclined plane, *y*, has the same appearance as the conventional vertical profile, *z*, if the latter were being viewed in perspective at an oblique angle. If the angle of inclination from horizontal is designated as θ, then when θ is zero, the trace of the ground with the plane *orthogonally* represented on a map is the conventional contour. When θ is 90°, the trace is a vertical profile, and its orthogonal representation is a straight line. When θ is greater than zero but less than

90° (*y* in Fig. 11.21), the trace is that of the ground with an *inclined plane*. A series of traces on parallel inclined planes produces an appearance of the third dimension while still retaining correct planimetry (see Fig. 11.20).

The construction of an inclined trace is not difficult. A conventional contour map is required; the contours are needed to define the land surface. The contour map is first ruled with horizontal lines spaced at equal intervals. Then the intersection of the lowest contour and lowest horizontal line is connected by a smooth line with the intersection of the next higher contour and the next horizontal line, and so on. The resulting line is the orthogonal projection on the map of the trace of the intersection of the land surface (as defined by the contours), with a plane passed through the land inclined away from the viewer upward toward the top of the map. Why this is so is explained as follows.

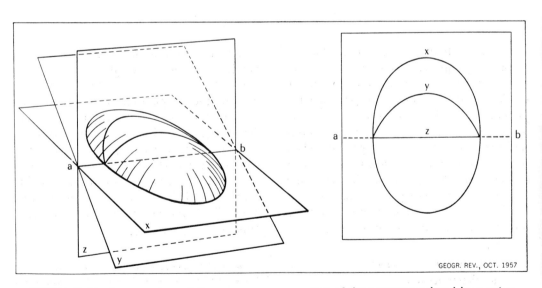

GEOGR. REV., OCT. 1957

FIGURE 11.21. A comparison of the appearance on a map of three traces produced by passing three differently oriented planes (x, horizontal; y, inclined; z, vertical) through a single landform. The drawing at left shows the relationships in perspective, and the drawing at right shows the successive traces as they would appear when projected orthogonally on a map. (Courtesy of *The Geographical Review*.)

If a series of parallel horizontal planes is passed through a single inclined plane one can construct a conventional contour map of the inclined plane, that is, the lines of contact between, or the traces of, the inclined plane and the several contour planes. These will appear as equally spaced parallel lines perpendicular to the direction of inclination. Diagram *A* in Fig. 11.22 shows a conventional contour map of a hill and a single inclined plane as seen from above, and *B* shows the hill and the plane as seen from the side in cross section. In *A* the horizontal lines are the contours of the inclined plane. On this double system of contours the intersections of contours of equal elevations can be located. These are shown as dots. These dots obviously must be the orthogonal representation of points of contact between the inclined plane and the ground. If a smooth line is drawn connecting these points in the order of their elevation, it will approximate the trace of the ground and the inclined plane as seen in orthogonal view. A succession of such traces, resulting from a *series* of equally spaced parallel inclined planes, provides the framework for a planimetrically correct terrain drawing.

In order to construct with minimum effort the orthogonal representations of the traces on a succession of inclined planes, it is necessary to arrange the planes in such a way that a single parallel line represents the succession of contour lines of *successive* elevations. Figure 11.23 is a cross-sectional side view of this advantageous relationship between the contour planes and the inclined planes. If the horizontal distance apart, *D*, of the inclined planes is made equal to h cot θ, where h represents the conventional contour interval, then a horizontal contour of the nth inclined plane will coincide planimetrically with the horizontal contours of the $n+1$ and the $n-1$ inclined planes where these have a difference in elevation

from the nth plane equal to h. Hence only *one* set of parallel lines is required to construct the orthogonal representation of a series of traces as shown in Fig. 11.24, which is merely an extension of Fig. 11.22 with the successive inclined planes added.

It was observed in the previous article that in terms of horizontal distance the vertical variations of the earth's surface are relatively insignificant. Many people are

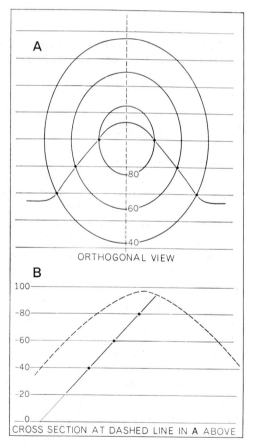

FIGURE 11.22. The circular lines are contours of the land in A. The straight lines are the traces or contours of one inclined plane sloping upward toward the top. This is seen in cross section from the side in B. (Courtesy of *The Geographical Review*.)

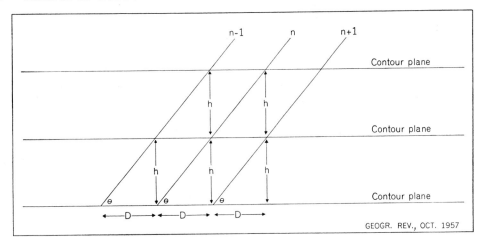

FIGURE 11.23. The spacing of the inclined planes so that one set of parallel lines on the map represents the contours of all the inclined planes. (Courtesy of The Geographical Review.)

familiar with the "flattening out" of rolling and hilly country when viewed from an airplane. Whatever the psychological reason may be, from man's relatively diminutive stature to the kinds of difficulties he experiences in traversing terrain, it is almost always necessary to exaggerate the vertical dimension when representing landforms perspectively or visually at most map scales. As is shown in Fig. 11.25 the traces of the ground and planes inclined at different angles, when orthogonally projected to the map, may range from a contour (when θ is 0°) to a straight line (when θ in 90°). In the drawing of terrain by this method the orthogonal representation of the trace establishes the *apparent* profile of each feature. Consequently, within obvious limits, the smaller θ is, the more elongated will the "profile" be and the greater will be the apparent exaggeration; when θ is 0°, there will be no "profile." There is, of course, no actual exaggeration in the representation, since all traces are orthogonally correct, but it is evident that a realistic appearance will be obtained by establishing θ somewhere in the middle range of the quadrant of possibilities.

The cartographer beginning a landform drawing has a set of conditions within which he must work. He has or makes a contour map at a given scale; he can change the scale of the map if he so desires, but the contours do not change relatively. Practically, his problem is to decide on the spacing of the horizontal lines (D in Fig. 11.23) by means of which he will construct the traces; for by the spacing of these lines he controls the degree to which the vertical dimension *appears* to be exaggerated. Since there is no formula that prescribes how much the vertical dimension should be exaggerated for each combination of map scale and relative relief, the cartographer must proceed by trial and error. All other things being equal, the closer together the horizontal lines, the "flatter" the terrain will appear, for the nearer θ will be to 90°. The relation between the angle of the planes from horizontal (θ), the contour interval in feet (h), and the scale denominator of the map (S) is

$$\frac{12h \cot \theta}{S} = D$$

where D is the distance in inches between

the parallel lines on the map. For example, if a cartographer were working with a map at the scale of 1:50,000 with a contour interval of 500 feet, and wished to pass the planes through the landforms at an angle of 45° from horizontal, the equation would be

$$\frac{(12 \times 500 \times 1)}{50,000} = 0.12 \text{ inch}$$

If in a critical trial area this did not seem to provide enough relief, he could employ a smaller angle for θ, which would provide a larger value for D. When D is very small, drawing one trace for each horizontal line may be too confusing. One may then start traces on alternate lines.

The first step in preparing a landform drawing is the compilation of conventional contour lines for the area. On some topographic maps, for example, those of the United States Geological Survey, the contour interval may be relatively small, so that in areas of great local relief the contour lines are close together. To use all available contour lines as a base for drawing traces on inclined planes would be an unnecessarily tedious operation; a selection can be made that will provide a base of sufficient accuracy.

Since three sets of construction lines (conventional contours, horizontal lines, and the traces of the inclined planes) are drawn on the same piece of paper (see Fig. 11.26 bottom), it is well to distinguish them. This can readily be done by using different colored pencils. Trace the selected contour lines from the topographic map in, for example, brown, and as nearly complete a drainage pattern as possible in blue. Then remove the tracing paper, rule the horizontal lines in green, and construct the inclined contours in red. A fresh piece of tracing paper for the terrain rendering can then be mounted over the construction sheet. Details of the landforms can then be drawn, with the framework of inclined traces as a

guide. This should be done in pencil. The most effective rendering is a "plastic shaded" map, produced by drawing more lines to the right and front of the features than to the left and rear (see Fig. 11.27). This will, of course, give the impression of terrain illuminated from the northwest. If the shading lines are drawn as controlled by the pattern of the inclined traces on the undersheet, the important attributes of unity and horizontality are preserved, that is, the landforms

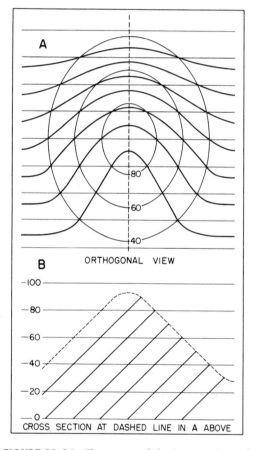

FIGURE 11.24. The traces of the intersections of the ground and a series of inclined planes are shown in A. The ground surface, the contour planes, and the inclined planes are shown in cross section in B. Compare with Fig. 11.22. (Courtesy of *The Geographical Review*.)

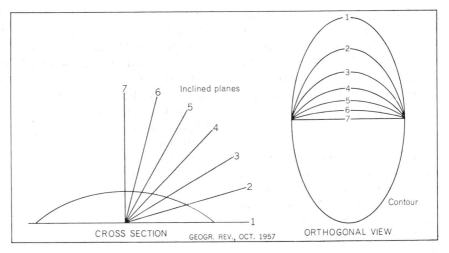

7   6   Inclined planes
5
4
3
2
1

CROSS SECTION   GEOGR. REV., OCT. 1957   ORTHOGONAL VIEW

1
2
3
4
5
6
7

Contour

FIGURE 11.25. The differing orthogonal appearances of traces of differently inclined planes. (Courtesy of *The Geographical Review*.)

are realistically placed in relation to one another, and features do not seem to be "falling off" the map.

The advantages obtained by using this method for large-scale landform map drawing do not hold for very small-scale maps. Instead, such maps should be considered more as diagrams in which the forms are being used as symbols. Nevertheless, the qualities of unity and horizontality should be maintained as far as possible.

11.9   OTHER METHODS OF DEPICTING LAND SURFACE

Perhaps the most widely used method of presenting land-surface information on wall maps, in atlases, and on other "physical" maps is that called by various names such as layer tinting, hypsometric coloring, or altitude tinting. This is the application of different area symbols (hue, pattern, or value) to the areas between the isometric lines (contours). On small-scale maps the simplification of the chosen contours must, of necessity, be large. Consequently, the "contour" lines on such maps are not particularly meaningful, and the system de-

generates, so to speak, into a mere presentation of categories of surface elevation. It is an obvious fact that surface elevation is in itself of little consequence with regard to the character of third-order landforms. For example, much of the great plains of the United States lies at an elevation between 2000 and 5000 feet; yet a considerable proportion of it is as flat as any coastal plain. In contrast, most of mountainous Norway lies at an elevation of less than 5000 feet. The conclusion is inescapable, namely, that layer tinting at small scales portrays little about the land surface except elevation zones. Such information is of value to an airplane pilot and to a number of others concerned with subjects, such as meteorology, wherein altitude is of some consequence. It is, however, of little value in presenting the significant differences or similarities of the land surface. It should be emphasized that the larger the scale, assuming a reasonable degree of contour simplification, the more useful the layer system. When the scale has been increased to the point at which the character of the individual isarithms and their relationships become meaningful, then the representation

graduates to being a contour map, which is a most useful map.

The one concept, besides elevation, that the relief map does help to portray for large areas is that of the second-order, three-dimensional structure of a region. Thus, a relief map of South America shows clearly a ridge of high land near and paralleling the western coast. This may be useful to one who is familiar with geographic interrelationships, for he can speculate with some certainty regarding the climate, vegetation, drainage, occupance, and other possible consequences. To the uninitiated, however, simple layer tinting may well be meaningless.

Colored layer tints at small scales, when combined with pictorial terrain or shading, nearly satisfy most of the landform requirements of the general map reader. It gives him the major structure as well as the detail. On the other hand, to do this is expensive, and it demands a skill not generally enjoyed by most cartographers. The Wenschow wall maps, previously mentioned, and the works of Richard Edes Harrison are outstanding examples of such combinations. Their reproduction is necessarily by process color, or some equally expensive method, and their reproduction cost effectively removes them from the endeavors of the average cartographer. Even the inclusion of a sample in this book is out of the question.

Because of the relative inadequacy of the layer-tinting method for showing detail, geographers and cartographers have been searching for ways to present a more useful representation of the land surface. Several methods have been suggested:

1. Terrain unit or descriptive landform-category method.
2. Relative-relief method.
3. Slope-value method.

With the possible exception of the first named, none has attained an acceptance for general maps that even approaches hachuring, shading, or layer tinting. The method of symbolization and presentation, which is the cartographer's major role, is straightforward; area symbols are used to reinforce either isarithms or dasymetric lines. The major problem, inherent in these methods, is the determination of what to present, not how to present it. Consequently, to utilize these methods himself the cartographer must be essentially a landform geographer, or he must simply present the work of others.

The terrain-unit method employs descriptive terms that range from the simple "mountains," "hills," or "plains" designations to complex, structural, topographic descriptions such as "maturely dissected hill land, developed on gently tilted sediments." The lines bounding the area symbols have no meaning other than being zones of change from one kind of area to another. This method of presenting landforms has been found useful in textbooks and in regional descriptions for a variety of purposes, ranging from military terrain analysis to regional planning. Its basic limitations are the regional knowledge of the maker and the geographical competence of the map reader (see Fig. 11.28).

In both Europe and the United States the concept of relative relief, as opposed to elevation above sea level, has been tried.* Relative, or local, relief is the difference between the highest and lowest elevations in a limited area, for example, a 5′ quadrangle (see Fig. 11.29). These values are then plotted on a map and isarithms may be drawn or the distribution may be symbolized in the choropleth manner. Area symbols, as in layer tinting, may also be applied. The method is of value when applied to areas of considerable size, for basic landform and physiographic divisions are emphasized; but it seems to be unsuited for differentiating important terrain details too

* See Guy-Harold Smith, "The Relative Relief of Ohio," *The Geographical Review*, 1935, Vol. 25, pp. 272–284.

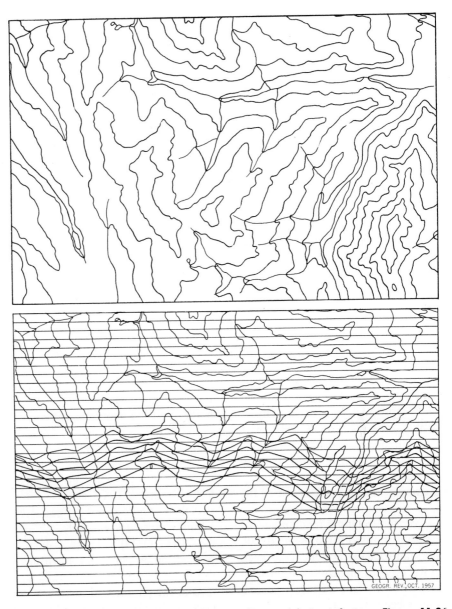

GEOGR. REV., OCT. 1957

FIGURE 11.26. Top—a conventional map with contour lines and drainage features. Figures 11.26 and 11.27 show successive stages in the construction of a landform drawing by means of traces resulting from inclined planes. The same area (the upper right-hand corner of Fig. 11.20) is shown in all four drawings. Bottom—here parallel construction lines and six ground-surface-inclined-plane traces have been added to the map shown at the top. Note the method of constructing these traces by means of smooth lines that connect the intersections of parallel lines and contour lines. (Courtesy of *The Geographical Review.*)

GEOGR. REV., OCT. 1957

FIGURE 11.27. Top—in this illustration the conventional contour lines and the parallel construction lines have been removed, leaving only the drainage features and the traces. This framework of lines, which itself gives an interesting impression of the three-dimensional surface, serves as a basis for the terrain drawing. Bottom—the completed rendering of the terrain, with additional detail supplied by aerial photographs, topographic maps, and field notes and sketches. More lines have been drawn to the right and front of the features to give the impression of terrain illuminated from the northwest. (Courtesy of *The Geographical Review*.)

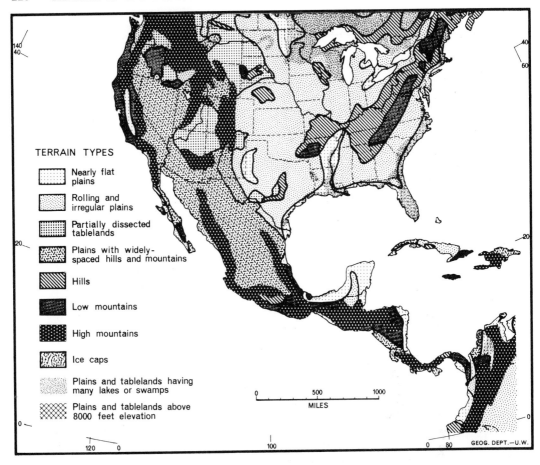

FIGURE 11.28. A section of a small-scale terrain type or terrain unit landform map. The terrain types here symbolized by area symbols are those determined by Edwin H. Hammond. (Courtesy *Annals of the Association of American Geographers.***)**

small to extend beyond the confines of the unit area chosen for statistical purposes. It is best adapted to relatively small-scale representation.

From the time the hachure became popular, the cartographer and geographer have been concerned with the representation of the slope of the land. Hachuring and shading, although not particularly commensurable, provide a graphic account of slopes on medium- and large-scale maps. The problem of presenting actual slope values on small-scale maps is not easily solved. One technique, suggested by Raisz and

Henry, is the slope-category method.* In this method, areas of similar slope are outlined and presented by means of area symbols in the dasymetric fashion (see Fig. 11.30). The system emphasizes detail, and the relationships between slopes and important minor topographic features are well

* E. Raisz and J. Henry, "An Average Slope Map of Southern New England," *The Geographical Review,* 1937, Vol. 27, pp. 467–472. See also Glenn T. Trewartha and Guy-Harold Smith, "Surface Configuration of the Driftless Cuestaform Hill Land," *Annals of the Association of American Geographers,* Vol. 31, 1941, pp. 25–45; see map of average slope, p. 27.

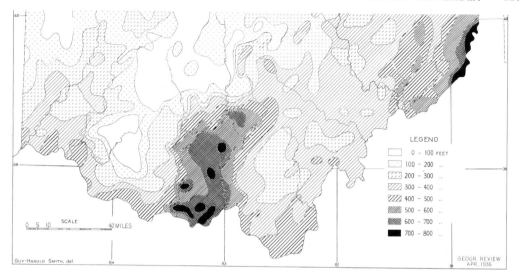

FIGURE 11.29. A portion of a relative- or local-relief map of Ohio. The values were obtained for each 5′ quadrangle. The lines are isopleths. (Drawn by Guy-Harold Smith. Courtesy of *The Geographical Review*.)

presented, at the expense, however, of the major topographic features. In this respect it is somewhat the opposite of the relative-relief technique. Other slope techniques, such as per cent of flat land per unit area have been tried, but, except for specialized teaching or research purposes, they have not been widely used.

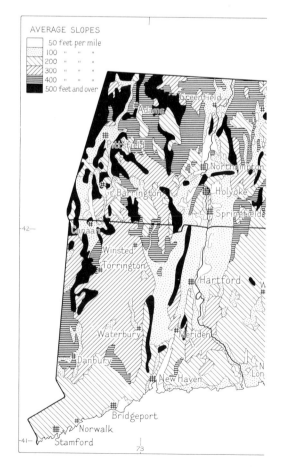

FIGURE 11.30. A portion of a slope-value map of southern New England by Raisz and Henry. The areas of similar slope were outlined on topographic maps by noting areas of consistent contour spacing. (Courtesy of *The Geographical Review*.)

Designing the Map

12.1 MAP DESIGN AND VISUAL SIGNIFICANCE

Of all the aspects of cartography, map design is perhaps the most complex. The manner of presentation of the many map components so that together they appear as an integrated whole, devised systematically to fit the purposes of the cartographer (and thus those of the reader), includes elements ranging from mathematics to art. Regardless of the essential accuracy or appropriateness of the map data, if the map has not been properly designed it will be a cartographic failure.

It is not necessary to be an artist to learn to design effectively. The basic elements of good design lend themselves to systematic analysis, and their principles can be learned. A fundamental requirement, however, is a willingness to think in visual terms, uninhibited by prejudices resulting from previous experience, or, to put it another way, a willingness to exercise imagination. The imagination must, of course, be disciplined to some extent, for, like many fields, cartography has developed traditions and conventions; to disregard them completely would inconvenience the user of the maps, which would in itself be proof of poor design. Cartography is not art in the sense that one may have complete freedom with techniques and media. The exercise of imagination

will soon reveal, however, that the possibilities of variation of shapes, sizes, forms, and other visual relationships of the map components are practically unlimited. The aim of cartographic design is to present the map data in such fashion that the map, as a whole, appears as an integrated unit and so that each item included is clear, legible, and neither more nor less prominent than it should be.

The myriad things seen every day vary from the visually important to the visually unimportant. Sometimes the striking things are interesting because of some special significance they may have, such as a new-model automobile or darkness at midday. Usually, however, the striking things are *visually significant*. That is to say, they appear so different from their surroundings that they excite the eyes. Since this is a common experience it is relatively easy to apply the underlying principles to cartography.

Suppose, for example, that one wished to attract the reader's eye to the water or hydrographic features of a map, perhaps even to the extent that he would notice little else. It would be a simple matter to color the water and rivers a bright red to the end that their brilliant and incongruous appearance would dominate. This is, of course, extreme, even for an example, but the principle has not been violated, namely,

that every item in a design has some place on the scale of visual significance. The estimation of how visually significant a thing may be is not, however, an easy task, for there are a number of factors which must be analyzed, such as:

(1) The degree to which an item departs from its expected appearance. The more it departs, the more visually interesting it is.

(2) The relative complexity of its delineation. The more complex the item is, the more visually interesting it is.

(3) The relative size of an item. The larger an item is, the more visually important it is.

(4) The relative brightness of an item. The brighter or lighter an item is contrasted with its surroundings, the more visually interesting it is.

(5) The position of an item with respect to the other components of the map. The nearer to the visual center of a presentation an item is, the more significant it is visually.

It may be seen from the list that each of the statements is concerned with some kind of varying relationship between an item and its surroundings. Consequently, it is possible to assess the design "strength" of an element, and, in a sense, to locate it on a scale of visual significance.

12.2 THE VISUAL OUTLINE

Just as when one plans to write something, he first prepares an outline, so is it also necessary to outline a visual presentation. Each item of the design should be evaluated in combination with the other elements in terms of its probable effect on the map reader. To do this requires a full and complete understanding of the purpose or purposes of the map to be made. One can scarcely imagine writing an article or planning a lecture without first arriving at a reasonably clear decision concerning (1) the audience to which it is to be presented,

and (2) the scope of the subject matter. With these well in mind, the writer uses them as a framework upon which to plan and as a yardstick against which to measure the significance of the items to be included.

It is impossible to categorize the kinds of maps that can be made in such a way that the rubrics will help provide more than a very general guide to design planning. It is true, however, that many maps generally fall into what might be called a class of "reference maps." These maps, common in atlases, are to be used like a dictionary; they are for the reader to find many kinds of information. Few, if any, of the represented items are more important than the others. Consequently, the elements of clarity and legibility are paramount; but at the same time no emphasis, no differing position on the scale of visual significance, is desirable, at least theoretically. A reference map is only one of many kinds of maps. Others show categories of information, such as roads, railroads, population, mineral resources, soil types, and so on; they may show several such kinds of information, and one kind of information may be more significant than another. Furthermore, many maps that are made for geographers, geologists, historians, planners, and the like are intended to make clear special relationships between two or among a number of items.

As an illustration of how the presentation may be outlined, A, B, C, and D in Fig. 12.1 have been prepared. The assumption is made that the planned map is to show two related hypothetical distributions in Europe. The fundamental elements of the visual outline are:

(1) The place, Europe.

(2) The data, the two distributions to be shown.

(3) The position of the data with respect to Europe.

(4) The relative position of the two distributions.

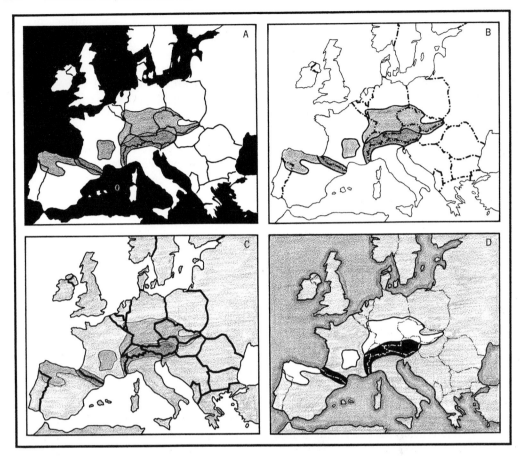

FIGURE 12.1. Examples of variations in the primary visual outline. Letters refer to Article 12.2.

Any one of these four elements may be placed at the top of the visual outline, and the order of the others following it may be varied in any way the author desires. In *A* in Fig. 12.1, the design places the items in the general order of 1-2-3-4; in *B*, 2-3-4-1; in *C*, 3-1-4-2; and in *D*, 4-2-3-1. Other combinations are, of course, possible. It should not be inferred that the positioning of elements in the visual outline can be as exact and precise as in a written outline. In the latter, the position is reasonably assured since the reader is more or less forced to start at one point and go systematically to the end, whereas in the visual outline he sees the items all at once, and it is up to the designer to attempt to lead him by applying the principles of visual significance.

It is appropriate at this point to digress slightly in order to emphasize one of the more difficult complicating factors a cartographer must face in cartographic design. Any component of a map has, of course, an intellectual connotation as well as a visual meaning in the design sense. It is difficult to remove the former in order to evaluate the latter, but many times it is not only necessary but definitely desirable. Artists turn their works upside down; advertising layout men "rough in" outlines, and even

basic lettering, as design units without "spelling anything out"; and because the intellectual connotation cannot always be predicted, cartographers, *for their own purposes*, will obtain better design if they do likewise, except for obvious, well-known shapes, such as continents and countries. To illustrate this the distributions in Fig. 12.1 and some other figures in this book have been made incomplete, purely hypothetical, or highly generalized.

Often a map maker is called upon to work with a cartographically untrained author or editor. The significance of design in all its complications usually requires that one or more "trial maps" be prepared in order that primary decisions may be made regarding various forms of symbolism, lettering styles, area patterns, consistency of layout, and many other important design elements. These trial maps should be made with great care to the end that the substantive aspects are as correct as they can be, even though such accuracy may confuse the design issues involved. Unfortunately, it appears to be difficult, if not downright impossible, for those inexperienced in design problems to ignore the intellectual aspects of a map. A map inaccurately made may not serve its purpose, even when the sole objective may be to consider design. The noncartographer, with seeming perversity, is likely to dwell upon any planned or inadvertent inaccuracies and fail to give the needed attention to the design problems. One experience in such a situation serves clearly to exemplify the fact that any map component has both an intellectual and a visual connotation; but it is an experience the cartographer can well avoid.

After the major elements have been decided upon, attention must be shifted to the second scale of visual significance. Just as is the case with a written outline, the major items, or the primary outline, are first determined, then the position of the subject matter within each major rubric is decided. In the case of a map, the visual presentation of the *detail* is primarily a matter of clarity, legibility, and relative contrast of the detail items.

The outlining of a map depends upon an understanding of the contrasts of lines, shapes, colors, brightness (value), and the principles of balance. These topics are treated in the succeeding articles.

12.3 CLARITY AND LEGIBILITY

To be effective any kind of communication must be clear and legible. The transmission of information by maps is no exception.

Clarity and legibility are broad terms, and many of the techniques and principles considered in other parts of this book are important factors in obtaining these qualities in a presentation. Furthermore, a considerable portion of the task of achieving clarity and legibility will have been accomplished if the map maker has made sure that the intellectual aspects of his map are not open to doubt or misinterpretation. In writing or speaking, the aim is to state the thought with the right words, properly spelled or pronounced, and clearly written or enunciated. In cartography, the symbol takes the place of the written or spoken word; their form and arrangement substitute for the spelling or pronunciation; and their delineation takes the place of writing or enunciation. It is apparent, then, that no matter what the form of a presentation may be, the principles behind clarity and legibility are much alike; only the "vocabulary" varies.

If it is assumed that the geographical concepts underlying the purpose and data of a map are clear and correct, then legibility and clarity in the presentation can be obtained by the proper choice of lines, shapes, and colors and by their precise and correct delineation. Lines must be clear,

sharp, and uniform; colors, patterns, and shading must be easily distinguishable and properly registered; and the shapes of symbols, coastlines, and other items represented must not be confusing.

One important element of legibility is size, for no matter how nicely a line or symbol may be drawn, if it is too small to be seen it is useless. There is a lower size limit below which an unfamiliar shape or symbol cannot be identified. This has been established as being a size which subtends an angle of about 1' at the eye. That is to say, no matter how far away the object may be, it must be at least that size to be identifiable. It is well to point out that this limit sets rather an ideal, for it assumes perfect vision and perfect conditions of viewing. Because of the unreasonableness of these assumptions, it is wise for the cartographer to establish his minimum size somewhat higher. Instead of the ideal of an angle of 1', it may be assumed that 2' is more likely to be a realistic value for average (not "normal") vision and average viewing conditions. Table 12.1 is useful in setting bottom values of visibility. It should be remembered that some map symbols have length as well as width, and in such cases, as for example with lines, the width may be reduced considerably since the length will promote the visibility. In similar fashion, other elements, such as contrasting colors or shapes, may enhance visibility and legibility, but even though the existence of a symbol on the map is made visible by such devices, if it does not stand at or above the sizes given in Table 12.1 it will not be legible. In other words, it might be seen (visibility), but it might not be read or recognized (legibility).

A second element regarding legibility is also operative in cartography. As a general rule, it is easier to recognize something we are familiar with than something that is new to us. Thus, for example, we may see a name in a particular place on a map, and,

although it is much too small to read, we can tell from its position and the general shape of the whole word what it is.

TABLE 12.1
APPROXIMATE MINIMUM SYMBOL SIZE FOR
VIEWING FROM VARIOUS DISTANCES

Viewing distance	Size (width)
18 inches	0.01 inch
5 feet	0.03 inch
10 feet	0.07 inch
20 feet	0.14 inch
40 feet	0.28 inch
60 feet	0.42 inch
80 feet	0.56 inch
100 feet	0.70 inch

The fact that symbols, lines, and the other elements of a map are large enough to be seen does not in itself provide clarity and legibility. An additional element, that of *contrast,* is necessary.

12.4   CONTRAST OF LINES AND SHAPES

No element of the cartographic technique is so important as contrast. Assuming that each component of the map is large enough to be seen, then the manner and the way in which it is contrasted with its surroundings determine its visibility. The degree to which a map appears precise and "sharp" is dependent on the contrast structure of the map.

Contrast is a subtle visual element in some ways, and in others it is blatant. The character of a line, and the way its curves or points are formed, may set it completely apart from another line of the same thickness. The thickness of one line in comparison to another may accomplish the same thing. The shapes of letters may blend into the background complex of lines and other shapes, or the opposite may obtain. If one element of the design is varied as to darkness, thickness, or shape, then the rela-

tionship of all other components will likewise be changed. It requires careful juggling of the lines, shapes, and brightness characteristics, on a kind of "trial and error" basis, to arrive at the "right" combination.

Most maps require the use of several kinds of lines, each symbolizing some geographic element or concept, such as coastlines, rivers, railroads, roads, various political boundaries, and so on. In order to make each clearly distinct from the next, it is necessary to vary in some way their character, design, or size. Figure 12.2 shows some of the many possible variations in line width. Figure 12.3 shows some of the various possibilities in line design. Figure 12.4 shows some possible variations in character of line. Only on the largest-scale maps does accuracy require an exact position for every part of a line. On smaller-scale maps the lines, if large enough to be seen, cover much more area than the element they represent on the earth. Therefore, they may be drawn precisely and firmly. A wobbly,

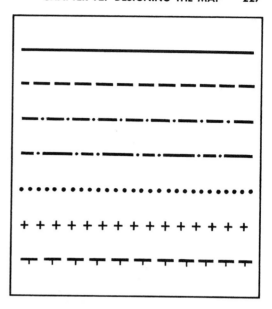

FIGURE 12.3. A few examples of design variations of lines. Others are, of course, possible.

wavering line looks weak and indecisive and should be avoided.

Just as lines may have an almost infinite variety, so also may larger shapes vary. Oftentimes shape is given by nothing but the bounding line, and there are some components of a map, such as the legend or title box, insets, labels, and so on, that are definite shapes without benefit of a geographic delimitation. Part of the ability of the eye to perceive and take note of the contents of such shapes is because of the way they contrast with their surroundings. Figure 12.5 shows some of the ways such shapes may be varied.

It is impossible, of course, to catalog all the ways in which lines and shapes may be varied and contrasted. In other portions of the book some specific elements, such as the shapes and lines of letter forms, the delineation of coastlines, and so on, have been considered. It is up to the student, however, to let his imagination roam and to consider critically those maps on which the

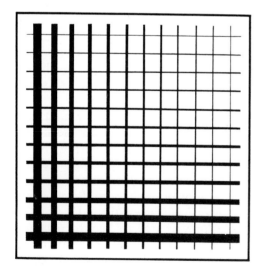

FIGURE 12.2. Size contrast of lines. Uniformity produces monotony. Note that a clear visual difference between sizes of lines requires considerable actual difference.

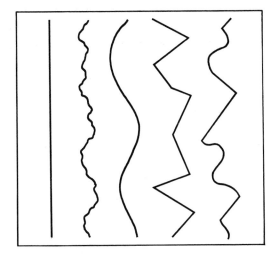

FIGURE 12.4. Variation of shape or character of lines. Irregular "wiggliness," such as the line second from the left, produces an impression of weakness.

line and shape structure appears well designed in order to become familiar with the range of possibilities.

12.5   COLOR IN CARTOGRAPHY*

Color is without doubt the most complex single medium with which the cartographer works. The complications arise from a number of circumstances, the major one being that even yet we do not know precisely what color is. We theorize about it, but exactly why color affects man's eyes the way it does is still a mystery. Recent investigations indicate that present theories seriously need revision. The complexity is due to the fact that, so far as the *use* of color is concerned, it exists only in the eye of the observer. The student may obtain an inkling of some of the consequent difficulties by imagining the problem of explaining the appearance of red to a "color-blind" person.

Even the use of a small amount of color seems to produce remarkable differences in legibility and emphasis on maps. Its importance was early realized, and, although facilities for printing color are relatively recent, old maps were laboriously hand colored—an index of the esteem in which color was held. During the last century printing techniques have developed to the point where is it possible to reproduce practically any kind of cartographic copy. Unfortunately, as the techniques have increased, so has the relative cost. As a result, it is to be expected that monochromatic techniques will be used for most maps, at least for most special-purpose maps. Although the majority of cartographers will have few opportunities to make colored maps for reproduction, they should be familiar with the bases for evaluating color use. Familiarity with principles of color use will also enable the cartographer to make an intelligent choice of the available alternatives, when economic considerations preclude the use of the ideal. For example, a range of shades or tints may be produced from a single plate in the flat-color process, whereas the best range might involve the more expensive requirement of several plates, or the four-color process.

The choice and use of color must obviously be primarily based on the normal reactions to color and the purpose behind the making of the map, for maps are to be read. When color is examined from the point of view of its effect on the observer it has several characteristics. First, to the eye, color varies as to hue, for example, blue or red. The normal person reacts in different ways to different hues, and a knowledge of these differences is necessary to the proper employment of colors. Second, each individual hue varies both in terms of its inherent brightness or value and in the

* Portions of this and following articles have been in part modified from Arthur H. Robinson, *The Look of Maps, An Examination of Cartographic Design,* University of Wisconsin Press, Madison, Wis., 1952.

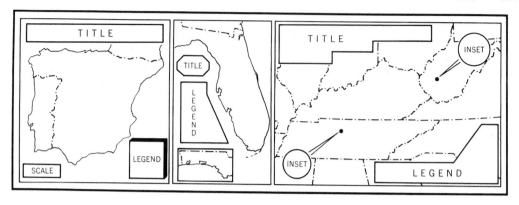

FIGURE 12.5. Variation of larger shapes. Note that no attempt has been made to create additional contrast by varying the brightness of the background.

degree of its intensity or the relative saturation of the color area. Just as the eye reacts differently to the various hues, so does it have varying sensitivity to value and intensity changes. Moreover, color always appears in an environment, and the environment seems to have a marked influence on its appearance. Also significant in color use are the conventions, preferences, and the traditional significance of colors, cartographic and otherwise. The cartographer must be familiar with all these considerations before he can effectively evaluate the color technique. He should also have some background in the basic elements of color science, as is suggested by some of the references in the bibliography.

It is fundamental to the consideration of color that it be clearly understood that, for practical purposes, color exists only in the eye of the observer. The physics of light is of importance in the investigation of the characteristics of color behavior. But the study of color, whether in the cartographic technique or in any other aspect of its use, is based fundamentally not on the physics of light, but on the sensations produced by the eye's reaction to colors.

Colors as eye sensations are difficult to describe. Most of the descriptive terms have a different meaning for each reader, depending upon his own particular experience. Such adjectives as tawny and rosy, or terms such as grass green, buff, azure, etc., are far from definite. On the other hand, color scientists have developed certain terms to describe the sensations of the eye to color which are relatively precise. The most commonly accepted are the terms *hue, value,* and *intensity.*

Hue is an eye sensation the reasons for which are not understood at present.* When one speaks of red, green, blue-gray, or chartreuse, he is attempting to describe a particular hue. Millions of hues are, of course, possible and, except in a general way, words are quite incapable of communicating exact meanings of hue. When passed through a prism, "white" light is changed, forming the familiar spectrum of the rainbow. Many of the descriptive terms use these colors as a basic ingredient and then attempt to qualify them as to what kind of blue, green, yellow, orange, or red is under consideration. Those hues that come relatively close to the colors of the spectrum are called spectral colors, and a progression of hues used as area symbols,

* Edwin H. Land, "Experiments in Color Vision," *Scientific American,* Vol. 200, No. 5, 1959, pp. 84–99.

when arranged in the same order as they appear in the spectrum, is called a spectral progression.

Value is the sensation of lightness or darkness of a color; for example, a red is usually darker than a yellow. The tones of the value scale range from black to white and are rated by reference to a *gray scale*. A gray scale precisely constructed on the basis of equal changes in black/white ratios is widely used in photography and printing (see Fig. 12.6). All colors, modified or pure spectral hues, have a value rating and can be matched in tonal value with one of the tones on a continuous gray scale.

Intensity is the most difficult to describe of the reactions of the eye to color. It is somewhat analogous to the brightness of the physicist, and bright or brilliant colors are commonly intense colors as contrasted with the less intense dull colors or lighter pastels. More precisely, intensity is varied by changing the ratio of gray and hue while maintaining a constant value rating. Thus, intensity also refers to saturation, that is, the "amount" of hue in a color. A scale of intensities would range from the pure hue at one end to a neutral gray at the other. At no place would it vary in value.

12.6   CONTRAST OF VALUE

It was stated in a preceding article that contrast is the most important visual element of the cartographic technique. It may be further asserted that the variation of light and dark, whether colored or uncolored, is the most important of all contrast elements. Value contrast may be termed either brightness contrast, as the physicist thinks of it, or tone contrast, as the photographer thinks of it. Lightness is termed high value, and white would be the maximum attainable.

Value contrasts are the most important element of seeing, and everyone is familiar with the ease with which it is possible to recognize objects represented in drawings or photographs merely by their tonal or value structure. Since anything that can be seen must have a value rating, and because anything must vary in value if it is to be easily distinguished from its surroundings, it follows that the contrast of values is one of the fundamentals of visibility.

Any object or group of objects on a map has a value rating. Widths of lines, shading patterns, names, blocks of lettering, the title, the legend, colors, and so on, are all value areas, and their arrangement within the map frame is a basic part of map designing. It is well for the student to keep in mind the generalization that *visibility and visual importance vary directly with value contrast.* Figure 12.1 illustrates in a limited way the significance of value contrast.

One of the more important ways in which the cartographer uses values is in presenting a graded series of information. Thus, for example, rainfall, depth of oceans, elevation of land, density of population, intensity of land use, and so on, are usually depicted by some technique that depends for a large

FIGURE 12.6. A value scale in which the steps are equal in terms of black/white ratios. The middle gray does not appear to be halfway between black and white. Note also the apparent "waviness" or induction. (From a *Kodak Grey Scale*, courtesy Eastman Kodak Company.)

portion of its effectiveness upon changing values.

The human eye is not particularly sensitive when it comes to distinguishing value differences. Eight shades of gray, between black and white, is about the limit, and consequently the cartographer must be relatively restrained in this respect. If a greater number of divisions in a series must be shown, he must add hue or some pattern, such as dots or lines, to the areas to aid the user to distinguish among them. Also important is the fact that physically equal fractional steps of black and white ratios from 0 (white) to 1.0 (black) do not appear equal to the eye. Figure 12.6 is a scale in which the differences between steps are equal in terms of changes in the black/white ratios.

Another characteristic of vision and its relation to value, hue, and intensity, which the cartographer must bear in mind, is a general phenomenon of vision called simultaneous contrast. In value contrasts it is particularly important. A basic generalization regarding the employment of any color is that the value, hue, and intensity rating of a color is markedly modified by its environment. When analyzed with respect to value, we find that a dark area next to a light area will make the dark appear darker and the light appear lighter. This specific effect, called induction, makes it difficult for a reader to recognize a given value in various parts of a map when it is surrounded by or adjacent to different values. Figure 12.6 illustrates one aspect of induction. The "wavy" appearance of the value blocks causes the recognition of values to be difficult, and the difficulty increases in direct ratio to the similarity of the values. The effects of induction may be largely removed by separating adjacent values with a white space or by outlining the areas with black lines. In Fig. 12.7 the gray spots are the same, but the one on the dark block appears

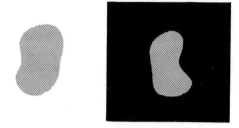

FIGURE 12.7. How environment modifies appearance. The two gray areas are exactly the same line pattern.

much lighter, and the reverse is true of the other. It is obvious that a reader would have difficulty in recognizing values under such a situation.

The precise ratios of black to white in a series of grays that will result in a gray scale of *equal visual steps* have been a question under study for some time. In general, it appears that there is a tendency for the human eye to overestimate the value ratings and differences in the lighter end of the gray scale and perhaps to underestimate them in the darker end. The effects of induction and the normal rather wide variation among the reactions of individuals merely emphasize the necessity for the cartographer to use as few pure grays as possible if they are to be used for quantitative purposes. Patterns such as dots or lines are generally advisable.

12.7 CONTRAST OF PATTERN

Because many kinds of data cannot effectively be shown by tonal values alone, and because the nature of the data may dictate that other devices be used, it is common for the cartographer to rely upon various kinds of patterns. These patterns are composed of dots (stippling), lines, or combinations. The possibilities are unlimited.

Very little study has been directed toward the understanding of patterns, their effects

upon the eye, and the ability to distinguish between them. Consequently, the student can proceed only on a trial and error basis. There are, however, a few generalizations that are of assistance as guides to the use of patterns.

Patterns may be classified broadly into two groups, those composed of lines and those composed of dots. Any line anywhere has, in the eye of the viewer, a direction; that is to say, he tends to move his eyes in the direction of the line. If irregular areas are shaded by line patterns which do not vary much in value, as in Fig. 12.8, the reader's eyes will be forced to change direction frequently. Consequently, he will experience considerable difficulty in noting the positions of the boundaries.

If the line patterns of Fig. 12.8 are replaced with dot patterns, as in Fig. 12.9, the map is seen to become much more stable, the eye no longer jumps, and the boundaries are much easier to distinguish. Lettering is also easier to read against a dot background than against a line background.

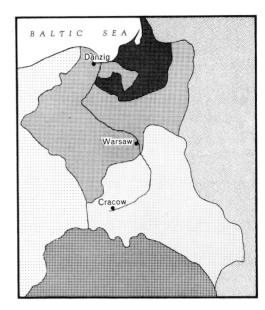

FIGURE 12.9. Same map as Fig. 12.8 but employing dot patterns.

If, however, the parallel lines are fine enough and closely enough spaced, the resulting effect is one of value only and has but a slight suggestion of direction.

Many parallel-line patterns are definitely irritating to the eye. Figure 12.10 is an example of the irritation that can occur from using parallel lines. It is probably because the eyes are unable quite to focus upon one line. The effect is somewhat reduced if the lines, whatever their width, are separated by white spaces greater than the thickness of the lines.

12.8   CHOICE OF COLOR

Colors vary in a number of ways, and the cartographer who contemplates using color is hard pressed to make a choice. Since very little experimental research has been undertaken regarding color on maps, the only course for the cartographer to follow is to base his selections on certain fundamental facts regarding the reaction of the mind and the eye to color. In addi-

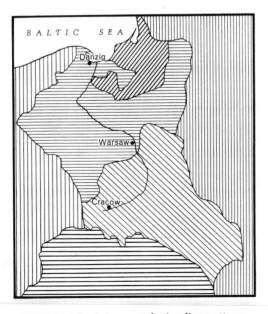

FIGURE 12.8. A map employing line patterns.

tion, he has a few well-known cartographic conventions upon which he may lean, such as blue water, green vegetation, etc. The reaction of the mind and eye to hue, and the extreme significance of value contrast, as outlined in Article 12.6, are, however, his major guides.

The eye is not particularly sensitive to hue changes, as is indicated by the relatively few words referring to hues in our language. Consequently, the farther apart, visually, that hues can be separated, the better. The eye is, moreover, definitely more sensitive to some hues than to others, that is, some are more "noticeable" than others. All observers agree that the eye is most sensitive to red, followed by green, yellow, blue, and purple, in that order. This series provides the cartographer with a partial basis for choice of color, depending upon how much emphasis is desired for the data to be represented by a color. Unfortunately, no satisfactory data seem to exist

FIGURE 12.10. Line patterns can hurt the eyes and the map on which they are used, if they are not carefully chosen.

that make it possible to grade the colors precisely according to relative degree of sensitivity.

In considering the sensitivity of the eye to hues, it is well to remember that pigment hues themselves vary in terms of their inherent value or brightness which, in turn, is of considerable significance with respect to their relative visibility and that of the data placed upon them. The relative luminosity of the spectral colors for the normal eye has been determined and is highest in the yellow-green region (555 millimicrons) and falls to approximately half its maximum within a range of 50 millimicrons each way. Disregard of the obviously significant value relationship by following simply a spectral progression of hues has led to many visual difficulties in map making. In many atlases, on the International Map, on many wall maps, and in numerous other instances where colors have been used to show altitude, the order in which colors appear in the spectrum has been taken as the basis for hypsometric shading. The lower altitudes have been shown in greens, followed by yellows for the intermediate altitudes, and then reds or near reds for the higher. Because of the relative luminosity and pigment values of the colors, by far the lightest areas, and by comparison the most visible, are therefore the areas of intermediate altitude, which are rarely the areas of great importance. Nevertheless, this progression, along with blue water, is almost a convention in cartography, and we have become so used to it that it cannot be ignored. The value of the colors used can, however, be adjusted to provide the maximum possible visibility in the significant areas. Although a spectral arrangement of hues is conventionally acceptable in the presentation of the gradations of land elevation (in spite of the fact that it has serious visual deficiencies), it probably should not be used for other kinds of gradations. Preliminary results of testing students' re-

actions to gradient colors on quantitative maps indicate that spectral gradations lead to considerable error in map interpretation.*

It is a well-known fact that some colors appear more individual than others. For example, red is red, but orange seems to be composed of both red and yellow, and purple is made up of blue and red. Many colors are named for their apparent components, such as yellowish green, greenish blue, and blue-violet. Normally only blue, green, yellow, red, white, black, and perhaps some browns appear as individual colors. The reason for this is not definitely known, but nevertheless all authorities agree that the phenomena of "pure hues" together with the "intermediate hues" are of considerable significance in color use. Their importance in cartography for showing interrelationships or mixtures of distributions is apparent.

Value is one of the three color sensations which the eye receives simultaneously, the others being hue and intensity. Its greatest significance is in the application of contrast, and the cartographer who works with hues soon finds it necessary to adjust the values of his color areas so that legibility and perceptibility will not be lost. He may do this by watering down paints or mixing white with them. He will also soon learn that he cannot gain as many distinguishable steps in a value scale of yellow as he can in one of gray. It becomes necessary, then, to mix hues to obtain more distinguishable intervals.

Intensity of colors varies, in the color-science sense, when we vary the amount of gray mixed with a color. In practical use on maps intensity may be considered loosely as brilliance. Some colors are bright—they "knock your eye out"—whereas others of the same value and hue are subdued. Undue brilliance acts as a deterrent to easy reading of a map and gen-

erally is not necessary, even for emphasis. Soft or subdued shades or tints of low intensity, such as pastels, are fully as visible as the more "aggressive" and intense colors.

The average eye and mind unconsciously assign to value and to intensity a numerical rating. Darkness and brilliance are assumed to represent "more" of something, and lightness and tints represent "less." One would not think of making a map of rainfall distribution on which the heaviest rainfall was shown by the lightest tone and the least rainfall by the darkest tone. If there is to be a gradation of amounts on a map one can approach the presentation problem by thinking in terms of a graph, on which value or brilliance is plotted as the abscissa and amount of the phenomena being presented is plotted as the ordinate, as in Fig. 12.11. This is a relatively simple problem so long as the distribution is limited to a single phenomenon, but it becomes complex when the categories to be shown are comprised of interrelated items, as, for example, on maps of climatic areas. In such maps, temperature and rainfall are usually coordinate elements, and the problem of showing an area that has both high temperature and low rainfall is difficult. The tropical areas may be shown with considerable red which is made lighter toward the savanna areas of less precipitation; but a change to another hue such as yellow at the boundary of the dry climates is likely to upset the progression owing to the necessity of using a more brilliant yellow in order to distinguish it from the white paper. It is generally desirable for the curves of value and brilliance on colored maps showing a graded scheme of things to parallel one another.

12.9   BALANCE AND LAYOUT

When the cartographer begins the designing and planning of a map he is faced with making a number of preliminary decisions. These involve problems of balance

---

* Neil Salisbury, "A Pilot Study of Visual Impressions Gained from Maps," unpublished manuscript describing tests and results carried on at the State University of Iowa, 1957.

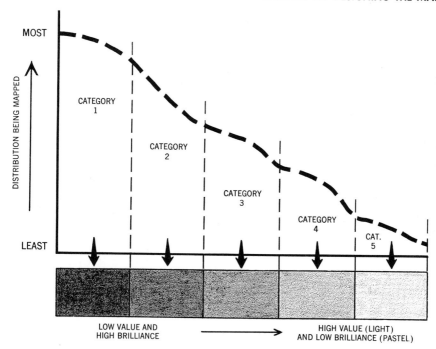

FIGURE 12.11. Theoretical graph of a graded map distribution showing the basis upon which one chooses a scale of values or brilliance. The graph could be constructed in a number of ways, but the curve of the progression of value or brilliance should correspond with the progression of the data.

and layout, such as those due to format, projection shape, land-water relations, and the general arrangement of the basic shapes of the presentation.

Balance in visual design is the positioning of the various visual components in such a way that their relationship appears logical or, in other words, so that it does not raise doubt in the reader's mind. In a well-balanced design nothing is too light or too dark, too long or too short, or too small or too large. The importance of the various components is directly related to their position and visual significance. Layout is the process of arriving at proper balance.

Visual balance depends primarily upon the relative position and visual importance of the basic parts of a map, and thus it depends upon the relation of each item to the optical center of the map and to the other items, and upon the visual weights. It may also help to think of the map as a horizontal plane; each item on a balanced map would lie in this plane. If one item is out of balance it may be prominent and lie "above" the plane visually, or if weak it will recede "below" the balance plane.

The optical center of a map is a point slightly (about 5%) above the center of the bounding shape or the map border (see Fig. 12.12). Size, value, brilliance, contrast, and, to some extent, a few other factors influence the weight of a shape. The balancing of the various items about the optical center is akin to the balance of a lever on a fulcrum. This is illustrated in Fig. 12.13, where it can be seen that a visually heavy shape near the fulcrum is balanced by a visually lighter but larger body farther from the balance point. Many other combinations will occur to the student.

The aim of the cartographer is to balance his visual items so that they "look right" or appear natural for the purpose of the map.

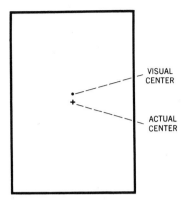

FIGURE 12.12. The visual as opposed to the actual center of a rectangle. Balancing is accomplished around the visual center.

The easiest way to accomplish this is to prepare thumbnail sketches of the main shapes, and then arrange them in various ways within the map frame until a combination is obtained that will present the items in the fashion desired. Figure 12.14 shows some thumbnail sketches of a hypothetical map in which the various shapes, that is, land, water, title, legend, and shaded area, have been arranged in various ways.

The format, or the size and shape of the paper or page on which a map is to be placed, is of considerable importance in the problem of balance and layout. Shapes of land areas vary to a surprising degree on different projections, and in many cases the necessity for the greatest possible scale within a prescribed format dictates a projection which produces an undesirable fit for the area involved. Likewise, the necessity for fitting various shapes, such as large legends, complex titles, captions, and so on, around the margins and within the border makes the format a limiting factor of more than ordinary concern. Generally speaking, a rectangle with sides having a proportion of about 3:5 is the most pleasing shape (see Fig. 12.15). Of course, when circumstances dictate otherwise, other shapes must be used.

Occasionally, the cartographer wishes to emphasize one portion of the map or a par-

ticular relationship thereon. For example, he may wish to show territories that changed hands in Europe, and he would like to make them appear above the background base data so that the eye will focus upon these areas and will only incidentally look at the locational base material "beneath" them. In cases like this the map is out of balance intentionally; that is, all elements of the map do not lie in the same plane (see Fig. 12.16). This effect is sometimes referred to as the figure-ground relationship.

The possibilities of varying balance relationships to suit the purpose of the map are legion. The cartographer will do well to analyze every visual presentation he sees, from posters to advertisements, in order to become more versatile and competent in working with this important factor of map design.

12.10   TITLES, LEGENDS, AND SCALES

The titles of maps are an important part of the design, and on different maps they serve a variety of functions. The title sometimes informs the reader of the subject or area of the map, and is therefore as im-

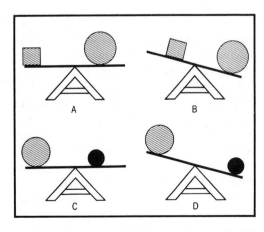

FIGURE 12.13. Visual balance. A, B, C, and D show relationships of balance. A and B are analogous to a child and an adult on a "teeter-totter"; C and D introduce relative density or visual weight.

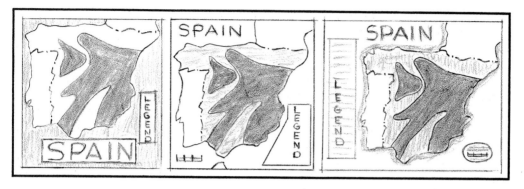

FIGURE 12.14. Thumbnail sketches of a map made in the preliminary stages to arrive at an acceptable balance.

portant as a label on a medicine bottle. But this is not always the case, for some maps are obvious in their subject matter or area and in reality need no such title. In these instances the title is often useful to the designer as a shape that he may use to help balance the composition.

It is impossible to generalize as to the form a title should take; it depends entirely upon the map, its subject, and purpose. Suppose, for example, a map had been made showing the 1959 density of population per square mile of arable land in France. The following situations might apply:

(1) If the map appeared in a textbook devoted to the general world-wide conditions at that time with respect to the subject matter, then only

FRANCE

would be appropriate, for the time and subject would be known.

(2) If the map appeared in a study of the current food situation in Europe, and if it were an important piece of evidence for some thesis, then

France

POPULATION PER SQUARE MILE ARABLE LAND

would be appropriate.

(3) If the map appeared in a publication devoted to the changes in population in France, then

POPULATION PER SQUARE MILE ARABLE LAND
1959

would be appropriate, for the area would be known but the date would be significant.

Many other combinations could be worked

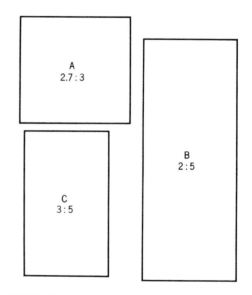

FIGURE 12.15. Various rectangles. C, with the ratio of its sides 3:5, is considered to be more stable and pleasing than the others.

out, but there is no need to belabor the fact that the title must be tailored to the occasion. Similarly, the degree of prominence and visual interest displayed by the title, through its style, size, and the blackness of the lettering employed, must be fitted into the whole design and purpose of the map.

Legends are naturally indispensable to most maps, for they provide the explanation of the various symbols used. It should be a cardinal rule of the cartographer that no symbol that is not self-explanatory should be used on a map unless it is explained in a legend. Furthermore, any symbol explained should appear in the legend *exactly* as it appears on the map, drawn in precisely the same size and manner. Legend boxes can be emphasized or subordinated by varying the shape, size, or value relationship. Figure 12.17 illustrates several variations. In the past it was the custom to enclose legends in fancy, ornate outlines which by their intricate workmanship called attention to their presence. Today it is generally conceded that the contents of the legend are more important than its outline, so the outline, if any, is usually kept simple.

The scale of a map also varies in importance from map to map. On maps showing road or rail lines, air routes, or any other phenomenon or relationship that involves distance, the scale is an important factor in making the map useful. In such cases the scale must be placed in a position of prominence, and it should be designed in such fashion that it can be easily used by the reader.

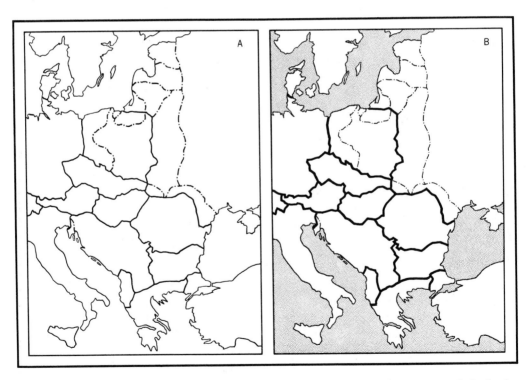

FIGURE 12.16. All elements in map A lie generally in the same visual plane. In map B the land has been made to appear above the water, and the more prominent boundaries have been made to rise above the visual plane of the land. Lines of the coordinate system on the water only, in place of the shading, would also tend to make the land appear above the water level.

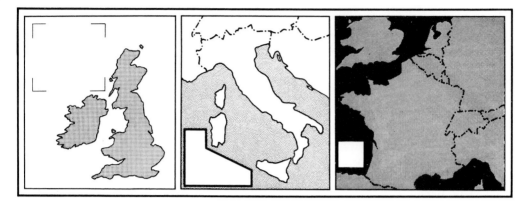

FIGURE 12.17. Variations in the prominence of legend boxes.

The method of presenting the scale may vary. For many maps, especially those of larger scale, the representative fraction, the RF, is useful for it tells the experienced map reader a great deal about the amount of generalization and selection that probably went into the preparation of the map. It should, however, be borne in mind that changing the size of a map by reduction changes the scale of the map, but does not change the printed numbers of the RF. On a map designed for reproduction the RF must be that of the final scale, not the drafting scale.

A graphic scale is much more common on small-scale maps, not only because it simplifies the user's employment of it, but because an RF in the smaller scales is not so meaningful. Graphic scales may be designed in a variety of ways. Some examples are shown in Fig. 12.18. On scales that are likely to be used precisely it is helpful to the reader if one part of the scale is subdivided in order to make finer readings possible. It is also helpful to show both an English and a metric graphic scale.

12.11 EFFECTS OF REDUCTION

It is usually the practice to draft maps at a scale larger than the reproduction scale. This is done for a variety of reasons, the most important of which is that it is often impossible to draft with the precision and detail desired at the scale of the final map. Also, reduction frequently "sharpens" the line work of the fair drawing. Drafting a map for reduction does not mean merely drawing a map that is well designed at the drafting scale. On the contrary, it requires the anticipation of the finished map and the designing of each item so that when it is reduced and reproduced it will be "right" for that scale. A map must be designed for reduction as much as for any other purpose.

The greatest problem facing the cartographer in designing for reduction is that involving line-width relationships. In gen-

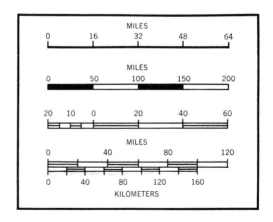

FIGURE 12.18. Kinds of graphic scales.

eral, a map on which the line relations appear correct at the drafting scale will appear "light" when it is reduced. Consequently, the map maker must make his map overly "heavy" in order to avoid its appearing too light after reduction. This applies especially to lettering and particularly to that from preprinted type impressions. It is necessary for the cartographer to "overdo" his lettering, just as it is necessary for him to make lines and symbols too large and dark on the fair drawing. Figure 12.19 illustrates these relationships. The use of a reducing glass will aid in visualizing how the map will appear when reduced.

Maps of a series should appear comparable, and since they are drawn for reproduction, they should be drafted at the same scale. This may necessitate changing the scale of base maps, which is troublesome, but which insures that the line treatment and lettering will be uniform.

Specifications for drafting and for reduction are given in terms of linear change, not

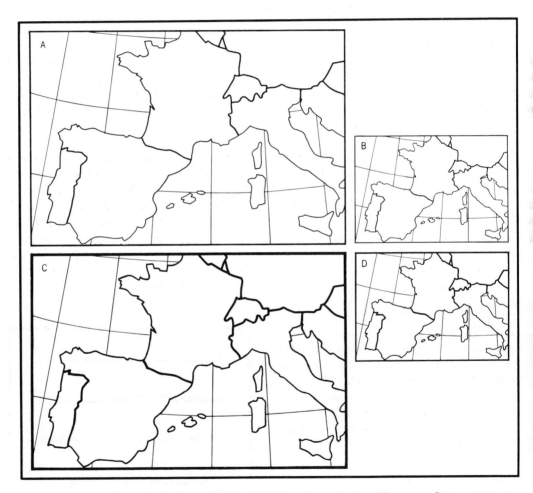

FIGURE 12.19. Effects of reduction. (A) When fair drawing is designed for proper line contrasts at drawing scale, then (B) reduction will decrease the contrasts too much. (C) When fair drawing is designed for reduction, then (D) reduction produces proper line contrast relationships.

areal relationships. It is common to speak of a fair drawing as being "50 per cent up," meaning that it is half again larger than it will be when reproduced. The same map may be referred to as being drafted for one-third reduction; that is, one-third of the linear dimensions will be lost in reduction. Figure 12.20 illustrates the relationships. Since it is common practice in large printing plants to photograph many illustrations at once, it is also desirable, for economy, to make series drawings for a common reduction.

12.12 THE WORKSHEET

The cartographer can obviate most of the troubles that beset the finishing of a map by constructing a worksheet. One of the most difficult operations in cartography is that of correcting and changing the fair drawing, for it usually is accompanied by a realization of careless and poor planning. Any such operation is bound to be an unhappy one if, with proper care, it could have been avoided.

The worksheet is the compilation and planning of the map down to the last necessary detail. It is usually done on translu-

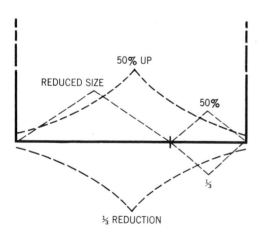

FIGURE 12.20. Relation of enlargement to reduction.

cent tracing paper or plastic. On it the lettering is planned, and all line work is done; in short, everything about which there could be any question is determined. When completed, the worksheet is comparable to the corrected, "rough draft" manuscript, for all that is necessary then is for the fair drawing to be drafted by tracing, just as the manuscript is made into good copy by the mechanical process of final typing.

The lines and other drawing on the worksheet may be done in pencil or with any satisfactory medium. Each kind of line that is to be drawn differently on the fair drawing may be put in a different color to obviate mistakes. Lettering, if the placing is no problem, may be roughly done; if the placing is important, the lettering should be laid out as to size and spacing. If the first try does not work, then it may be erased and done over. Borders and obvious line work need only be suggested by ticks.

When the worksheet and the compilation have been completed, the drafting may be done on translucent material directly over the worksheet or, if the drafting is to be done on a relatively opaque material, it may be done over a tracing table. If the drawing is to be done by the cartographer he will have in mind the character of the lines, etc.; but if it is to be drafted by someone else he must prepare a sample sheet of specifications to guide the draftsman. This is simple to do if each category is in a different color or otherwise clearly distinguished. Separation drawings for small maps may easily be made from a single worksheet and will register.

It is a common experience for the cartographer to find that many of the elements included in one map could easily be used for another. Base materials such as boundaries, hydrography, and even lettering may not vary much, if at all, from one to another in a series of maps. Consequently, the car-

tographer can save himself considerable future effort if he tries to anticipate possible subsequent use of his compilation efforts, and prepares his worksheet and drafting plan with these possibilities in mind.* Modern reproduction methods make it relatively easy to combine different separation drawings even when printing in one color (see Chapter 14).

* John C. Sherman and Waldo R. Tobler, "The Multiple Use Concept in Cartography," *The Professional Geographer*, Vol. 9, (New Series), 1957, pp. 5–7.

Lettering the Map

13.1 THE IMPORTANCE OF LETTERING

Lettering is one of the symbols used on maps to designate places and items, in the legend, in the title, and especially on the map itself. Because of the familiarity of its forms, it is not commonly considered a cartographic symbol, but in the last analysis it is difficult to draw a distinction between the lines we use to represent such concepts as the land-water boundary and the lines we use to represent the concept of name. The forms the lines assume in lettering are more commonplace, but otherwise there is little difference between this and other symbol forms.

In cartography the study of lettering as a symbol form is especially important, both because of its universal use and because it is a rather complex and, at times, bothersome element of the map. Whether we like it or not, places must be named; and the name may be small and easy to insert as, for example, "Cape Cod," which has the whole Atlantic on which to lie, or it may be long and difficult to insert in a small area, such as "Philadelphia" or "Switzerland" on small-scale maps. The problem of fitting in the lettering among the maze of other symbols is oftentimes nothing short of frustrating.

Lettering is an important element of the design of a map. Most maps have some sort of inherent design quality, such as a repeating pattern of lines, and the lettering styles may contrast with this basic characteristic or they may blend with it. Through his choice of lettering style, size, and positioning the cartographer can lead attention to, or direct it away, from the names of the elements it is to identify. Not the least important aspect of lettering is the fact that it provides one of the more noticeable indices of cartographic quality. Striving for elegance can, of course, be carried to extremes, but a well-lettered map is a pleasant thing to contemplate.

Cartographic lettering styles have changed often in the past. Before the development of printing in Europe, all lettering on maps was done freehand with a pen or brush. After printing and engraving became the accepted methods of reproduction, the lettering on maps was the task of the engraver, who cut his letters with a burin or graver in reverse on the copper plate. The great Dutch atlas makers were wont to include many pictures of animals, ships, and wondrous other things for, as Hondius explained, "adornment and for entertainment"; but their lettering was generally well planned in the classic style and well executed, as is that illustrated in Fig. 13.1.

As might have been expected, when the lettering was done by those more interested in its execution than in its use, it became

FIGURE 13.1. The Hondius map of America. This map was included in the Hondius-Mercator Atlas of 1606. The original is in the Newberry Library, Chicago. (Courtesy Rand McNally and Company.)

excessively ornate. The tendency toward poor lettering design continued well into the Victorian era, when lettering and type styles in general became so bad that there was a general revolt against them, which caused a return to the classic styles and greater simplicity. Figure 13.2 is an example of ornate lettering in the title of a nineteenth century geological map. The fancy lettering of this and earlier periods provides good examples of manual dexterity, being intricate and difficult to execute; but they are examples of poor lettering because they are difficult to read and because they call undue attention to themselves.

In the past century, and especially during the past several decades, many changes have taken place in cartographic lettering practice. No longer does the engraver do the lettering; instead, maps are "engraved" by means of photography, and it is up to the cartographer to plan and execute the lettering on the copy. More recently, techniques have been developed which make it possible, among other advantages, to apply already printed lettering to the copy, so that there is little excuse for poor style. Mechanical aids for ink lettering have also been introduced.

These developments have combined to relegate the traditional freehand lettering somewhat to the background as a part of the art of cartography. It can be stated without reservation, however, that a map well-lettered freehand will be a better lettered map than one done in any other way, because many cartographic lettering problems involving fitting, design, and positioning are

more effectively solved freehand than in any other way. For this reason, if for no other, it is well for the student of cartography to study and practice freehand lettering. Good freehand lettering is a great asset to a cartographer, and it merely involves learning principles and practicing execution. Practically anyone can learn to do an eminently satisfactory job of freehand lettering—if he will but try.

Even if the cartographer never executes freehand the ink lettering on a map, he will find the ability to letter neatly a most useful accomplishment. To be "sloppy" in almost anything usually requires more time in the long run than it does to be neat. In the cartographer's pencil compilations it is usually necessary to insert many names and to pay careful attention to positionings and spellings. If he hurries and is messy, he will make mistakes of one kind or another and these will cause trouble later.

13.2 PLANNING FOR LETTERING

Planning the lettering for a map requires careful consideration of a number of things.

The more elaborate the map, of course, the more elements must be considered; but, in general, there are at least seven major headings to the planning "check list." The complexities of the map and its purposes will add subheads to the following major elements.

(1) The style of the lettering.
(2) The form of the lettering.
(3) The size of the lettering.
(4) The color of the lettering and its background.
(5) The method of lettering.
(6) The positioning of the lettering.
(7) The relation of the lettering to reproduction.

The style refers to the appearance of the lettering, that is, its design, and it includes such elements as thickness of line and serifs. The form refers to whether it is composed of capitals, lower case, slant, upright, or combinations of these and other similar elements. The methods of lettering include freehand, mechanical aids, and preprinted letters to be used as "stick-up," a term recently introduced in cartography to include all methods of applying preprinted lettering.

FIGURE 13.2. Ornate lettering on a lithographed map of 1875. The name "Illinois" is more than 1 foot long on the original.

The positioning of the lettering involves a consideration of when and where on the map, and in the construction schedule, the lettering is applied. As is apparent from Chapter 14, different methods of reproduction require variations in parts of the above processes, and this is especially so when various effects are to be gained.

Regardless of the kind of map, the lettering is there to be seen and read. Consequently, the elements of visibility and legibility are among the major yardsticks against which the choices and possibilities are to be measured.

13.3   THE STYLE OF THE LETTERING

The cartographer is faced with a truly imposing array of possible style choices when he sets out to plan the lettering for his map. He not only has an infinite number of different alphabet designs from which to select, but he must also settle upon the wanted combinations of capital letters, lower case letters, small capitals, italic, slant, and upright forms of each alphabet. There is no other technique in cartography that provides such opportunity for individualistic treatment, and this is especially true with respect to the monochrome map. The cartographer who becomes well acquainted with styles of lettering and their uses finds that every map or map series presents an interesting challenge. When this attitude obtains, lettering the map ceases to be the mechanical chore some, whose maps reflect their disinterest, consider it to be.

Lettering and type styles have had a complex evolution since Roman times. The immediate ancestors of our present-day alphabets include such grandparents as the capital letters the Romans carved in stone and the manuscript writing of the long period prior to the discovery of printing. Subsequent to the development of printing, the types were copies of the manuscript writing, but it was not long until designers went to work to im-prove them. Using the classic Roman letters as models for the capitals and the manuscript writing for the small letters, they produced the alphabets of upper and lower case letters that it is our custom to use today.

The better designers, of course, kept much of the free-flowing, graceful appearance of freehand lettering so that their letters look as though they had been formed with a brush. The proportion of thick to thin lines is not great, and the serifs with which the strokes are ended are smooth and easily attached. Such letters are known as Classic or Old Style. They appear dignified and have about them an air of quality and good taste that they tend to impart to the maps on which they are used. The lettering or type has an appearance that is neat, but at the same time it lacks any pretense of the geometric. (See Fig. 13.3.)

A radically different kind of face was devised later, and for that reason it, unfortunately, is termed Modern. Actually, the Modern faces were tried out more than two centuries ago, although we think of them as coming into frequent use around 1800. Modern type faces, and lettering, look pre-

CHELTENHAM WIDE

Cheltenham Wide

CHELTENHAM WIDE ITALIC

Cheltenham Wide Italic

GOUDY BOLD

Goudy Bold

GOUDY BOLD ITALIC

Goudy Bold Italic

CASLON OPEN

FIGURE 13.3. Some Classic or Old Style letter forms. (Courtesy Monsen Typographers, Inc.)

BODONI BOLD

Bodoni Bold

BODONI BOLD ITALIC

Bodoni Bold Italic

FIGURE 13.4. Some Modern letter forms. (Courtesy Monsen Typographers, Inc.)

cise and geometric, as if they had been drawn with a straightedge and a compass, which they have. The difference between thick and thin lines is great and sometimes excessive. (See Fig. 13.4.)

A third type of style class includes some varieties that are definitely modern in time but not in name, as well as some of older origin. This class is called Sans Serif (without serifs), and has about it an up-to-date, clean-cut, new, and nontraditional appearance. The forms are angular or of perfect roundness. There is nothing subtle about most Sans Serif forms. (See Fig. 13.5.)

The three classes mentioned are the basic groups of the classification of printing types; there are, however, many variations. Freehand lettering generally conforms closely to the Classic and to the Sans Serif, but is ordinarily called, respectively, Roman and Gothic.

There are several other styles of type and of freehand lettering which are not common but which are occasionally used on maps. These are Text, script or italic, and Square Serif. Text, or black letter, is similar to the manuscript writing, and is dark, heavy, and difficult to read. Script and italic in type are similar to handwriting with flowing lines. They have been traditionally replaced in map work by the slant letter. Square Serif is rarely seen any more, but was popular during the last century. (See Fig. 13.6.)

This listing by no means exhausts the possibilities. There are literally hundreds of variations and modifications possible,

such as the open letter, light or heavy face, expanded or condensed, and so on. In the selection of type, or in the design of his own freehand lettering, the cartographer may be guided by certain general principles that have resulted from a considerable amount of research by the psychologist and others, as well as from the evolved artistic principles of the typographer.

Legibility depends upon the recognition of familiar forms and upon the distinctiveness of those forms from one another. For this reason "fancy" lettering or ornate letter forms are difficult to read. Flowing swash lines and excessively complex letter forms may delight the clever draftsman, but they do not make words easy to read. For this reason Text lettering is particularly difficult. Conversely, well-designed Classic, Modern, and Sans Serif forms stand at the top of the list, and apparently they rate about equally in legibility. Legibility also depends, to some extent, upon the thickness of the lines forming the lettering. The thinner the lines in relation to the size of the lettering, the harder it is to read. The cartographer is therefore called upon in his letter selection to do a bit of experimentation, for, although the bold lettering is more legible, the thicker lines may overshadow or mask other equally important data. It should also be remem-

MONSEN MEDIUM GOTHIC

Monsen Medium Gothic Italic

COPPERPLATE GOTHIC ITALIC

FUTURA MEDIUM

LYDIAN BOLD

DRAFTSMANS ITALIC

FIGURE 13.5. Some Sans Serif letter forms. (Courtesy Monsen Typographers, Inc.)

CLOISTER BLACK

Cloister Black

STYMIE MEDIUM

Stymie Medium

FIGURE 13.6. Examples of Text and Square Serif letter forms. (Courtesy Monsen Typographers, Inc.)

bered that lettering is not always the most important element in the visual outline of the map; rather it may be desirable, on occasion, that the lettering recede into the background. If so, light-line letter forms may be the effective choice.

The problem of the position of the lettering in the visual outline is one of considerable significance. For example, the title may be of great importance and the balance of the lettering of value only as a secondary reference. Size is usually more significant, in determining the relative prominence, than style, but the general pattern of the lettering may also play an important part. For example, rounded lettering may be lost along a rounded, complex coastline, whereas in the same situation angular lettering of the same size may be sufficiently prominent.

It is the convention in cartography to utilize different styles of lettering for different classes of features, but this may be easily overdone. As a general rule, the fewer the styles, the better harmony there will be. Different size combinations of capitals, small capitals, and lower case provide considerable variety, and most common type faces are available in several variants; it is better practice to utilize these as much as possible. (See Fig. 13.7.) The cartographer may, of course, do the same sort of thing freehand. If styles must be combined for emphasis or other reasons, good typographic practice allows Sans Serif to be used with either

Classic or geometric Modern. Classic and Modern should never be combined.

Whatever the choices of style and combination, the lettering should be well designed. This requires some knowledge of the development of typography and of the elements of letter design. If freehand lettering is the aim, the beginner is *not* encouraged to design his own alphabets, for the result is not likely to be fortunate. Letter design is an exacting and complex art that reflects the tradition, experience, and the distillation of centuries of effort. It is better for the beginner to spend his time copying the work of the masters of letter design until he has gained a "feel" for the simplicity and the shape and line relationships that characterize good lettering. It is particularly important,

Futura Light

Futura Light Italic

Futura Medium

Futura Medium Condensed

Futura Medium Italic

Futura Demibold

Futura Demibold Italic

Futura Bold

Futura Bold Italic

Futura Bold Condensed

Futura Bold Condensed Italic

FIGURE 13.7. Variants of a single face. This face has a larger number of variants than is usual, but the list is representative except that expanded (opposite of condensed) is missing. (Courtesy Monsen Typographers, Inc.)

whether he use type or letters freehand, that he familiarize himself with the elements of letter design by reading in the copious literature of this fascinating subject.

13.4   THE FORM OF THE LETTERING

Alphabets consist of two quite different letter forms called capitals and lower case letters. These two forms are used together in a systematic fashion in writing, but conventions as to their use are not so well established in cartography. In general, more important names and titles are usually put in capitals, and less important names and places are identified with lower case letters. Names requiring considerable separation of the letters are commonly placed in capitals.

Legibility and perceptibility tests have shown without any doubt that capitals are not so easy to recognize or read as are lower case letters, since the latter contain more clues to letter form. A greater use of well-formed lower case letters will improve the legibility of a map.

Most styles of type can be had in either upright or italic form, and, of course, freehand lettering may be rendered either upright or slanted. The tendency in cartography is for hydrography, land form, and other natural features to be labeled in slant or italic, and for cultural features (man-made) to be identified in upright forms. This can hardly be called a tradition, for departure from it is frequent, except in the case of water features. The slant or italic form seems to suggest the fluidity of water.

There is a fundamental difference between slant and italic, although the terms are sometimes used synonymously (see Fig. 13.8). True italic in the Classic or Modern faces is a cursive form similar to script or handwriting. Gothic slant and Sans Serif italic are simply upright letters tilted forward. Italic forms are considerably harder

Kennerley—an upright Classic

Kennerley in the Italic form

Monsen Medium Gothic—upright

Monsen Medium Gothic Italic

FIGURE 13.8. Differences between italic and slant forms. (Courtesy Monsen Typographers, Inc.)

to read than their upright counterparts; however, it is doubtful that there is much difference between the upright and slant letters of Gothic or Sans Serif insofar as legibility is concerned.

13.5   THE SIZE OF THE LETTERING*

Perhaps the commonest kind of decision regarding lettering, which must be made by a cartographer, concerns the sizes to be used for the great variety of items which must be named on maps. Traditionally, specifications for lettering are usually based on the size of the thing to be named or the space to be filled. Then the lettering must be graded with respect to the total design and intellectual content of the map. Much of the criticism, however, conscious or unconscious, that is leveled at map lettering is aimed specifically at size—or lack of it. There seems to be a widespread tendency among amateur (and even some professional) cartographers to overestimate the ability of the eye and to underestimate the effects of reduction.

Size of lettering or type face is designated by *points*, 1 point being nearly equal to $\frac{1}{72}$ inch. Lettering that is ¼ inch high is roughly equal to 18-point type, although not precisely since the size of type refers to the body, not the letter on it. Reduced by

* Portions of this section have been modified from Arthur H. Robinson, "The Size of Lettering for Maps and Charts," *Surveying and Mapping*, 1950, Vol. 10, pp. 37–44.

one-half, it will be nearly equivalent to 9-point lettering, although not the same as 9-point since each size in type and in free-hand lettering is designed separately for more perfect balance than would be produced by simple enlargement or reduction of one design.

There have been numerous studies during the past half century of the effect of type sizes and styles on reading habits, but most of them are somewhat limited in their application to the specific problems of cartography. Of much more significance to cartography are the variations in visibility and legibility of type faces and type sizes. Precise studies have been made by Luckiesh and Moss, based on physiologically sound determinations of the ability of the eye. Assuming no other complications (the assumption is a bit unreal), the eye reacts to size in relation to the angle the object subtends at the eye. With normal vision an object that subtends an angle of 1' can just be recognized. Letter forms are complex, however, and it has been determined that about 3-point type is the smallest, just recognizable type at usual reading distance. Normal vision is, however, a misnomer, for it certainly is not average vision. It is safer to generalize that probably 4-point or 5-point type comes closer to the lower limit of visibility for the average person.

Determinations of the relative visibility of type have significance in cartography. By means of a "visibility meter" investigators have gathered the data shown in Table 13.1. The values result from rating the tests of one font at normal reading distance with test objects of simple design which subtended known angles and had previously been rated in visibility. The table may be used as a kind of yardstick of prominence for the smaller sizes; for example, 10-point type is roughly four times more visible (or prominent) than 3-point. It should be noted that the relationship is not arithmetic but approaches logarithmic.

This relationship, of course, does not continue indefinitely. One may assume that ratings much beyond 24-point would probably have little validity, since anyone who cannot see 24-point type would be rated as blind, and visibility in the larger sizes would be more dependent upon factors other than size.

TABLE 13.1
RELATIVE VISIBILITY OF TYPE SIZE
(From Luckiesh and Moss)

Size in points	Relative visibility
3	1.10
4	1.60
5	2.11
6	2.64
8	3.64
10	4.65
12	5.66
14	6.67
18	8.67
24	11.68

Within the narrow limits prescribed by the familiar "all other factors being equal" the table provides the cartographer with a scale by means of which he can select relative sizes in accordance with intellectual significance he assigns to the different names appearing on a map. It can rarely, if ever, be exact, for in many cases it is difficult to be precise in the determination of relative significance in the map design, and because so many other factors of design are operative in producing the final "total" impression. But at least in his visual outline, or plan of using media and technique, the cartographer need not double the point size in order to make a name twice as "important."

By far the most important aspect of type size at present is indicated by the simple question "Can the observer read it at all under the circumstances?" Frequently, cartographers are called upon to prepare presentations for groups. They must face such

questions as "What is the minimum lettering size legible, under normal conditions, on a wall map or chart from the back or middle of a 40-foot room?" Or, "How large should the lettering be on a graph or map that is to be made into a slide and projected in an auditorium?" These are routine questions of considerable importance since they confront anyone who prepares or uses graphics.

Tables of equivalents are easy to use, but there are so many possibilities of changes in visibility and legibility due to other factors, such as variations of lettering design, lowering of background contrast, or confusing textural conflict, that simple tables must be used cautiously. Two types of tables are here presented, one for maps used in the original or in reduced form (Table 13.2), the other for maps enlarged by projection (Table 13.3).

Table 13.2 is based on the assumption that if a particular point size, at normal reading distance from the eye (18 inches), subtends a certain angle at the eye, then any size lettering if viewed at such a distance that it subtends the same angle is, for all practical purposes, the same size. Thus, 144-point lettering at 30 feet from the observer is the same as 8-point lettering at normal reading distance, since each circumstance results in the same angle subtended at the eye. It will be seen from the table that legibility diminishes rapidly with distance. For example, any lettering of 16-point size or smaller cannot be read even at 10 feet from the chart or map, and letters 1 inch high can be read from a distance of 40 feet only by a person with above average vision. To those with average (not normal) vision such letters are likely to be illegible from 25 feet.

TABLE 13.2

APPROXIMATE EQUIVALENT SIZES OF LETTERING VIEWED FROM VARIOUS DISTANCES
(Blank spaces indicate nonlegibility)

Point size, at 18 inches	Letter height in inches	Equivalent size in points viewed at distance (feet) from observer									
		10	20	30	40	50	60	70	80	90	100
3–16											
18	0.25	3									
24	0.33	3									
30	0.41	4–5									
36	0.50	5	3								
42	0.58	6	3								
48	0.66	7	4								
54	0.75	8	4–5	3							
60	0.83	9	4–5	3							
72	1.00	10	5	4	3						
84	1.16	12	6	4–5	3						
96	1.33	14	7	4–5	3–4	3					
108	1.50	16	8	5	4	3					
120	1.66	18	9	6	4–5	3–4	3				
132	1.83	20	10	7	5	4	3–4				
144	2.00	22	11	8	5–6	4–5	4	3			
180	2.50	28	14	9	7	5–6	4–5	4	3		
216	3.00	32	16	10	8	6	5–6	5	4	3–4	3

TABLE 13.3

LINEAR MAGNIFICATION, 9

(Blank spaces indicate nonlegibility)

Point size on original	Approximate equivalent size in points viewed at distance (feet) from screen									
	10	20	30	40	50	60	70	80	90	100
6	8	4–5	3							
8	10	5	4							
10	12	6	4–5	3–4						
12	16	8	5	4	3					
14	18	9	6	5	4	3				
16	22	11	8	5–6	4–5	4	3			
18	24	12	8	6	5	4	3–4	3		
24	32	16	10	8	6	5–6	5	4	3–4	3
30	42	21	14	11	9	7	6	5–6	5	4–5
36	48	24	16	12	10	8	7	6	5–6	5

Another type of table is required to answer the questions that arise when maps and diagrams are to be reproduced on slides and then projected. The problem in all its aspects becomes quite complicated, but the raw data concerning map size and results consequent upon magnification are helpful. It should be practicable in most cases to ascertain the actual size of a projected slide frame as well as the size of the lecture hall. With such information and Tables G.1 to G.7 in Appendix G most lens and projector characteristics may be ignored.

Tables G.1 to G.7 in Appendix G give equivalent lettering values for projected maps that are magnified from two to fifteen times their original size and viewed at various distances from the screen. An example will illustrate their use. Assume that a map is being prepared which measures *1 foot across* and is to be projected in an auditorium 70 feet long and, further, that the slide frame used in the projector equipment is *9 feet across* on the screen. From Table 13.3 (linear magnification, 9), repeated here for purposes of illustration, the following information may be derived:

(1) The smallest lettering size which can be used on the original that can be read from any place in the lecture hall by a person with normal vision is 16 point.

(2) Only the front half of the audience will be able to read 10-point type on the original drawing.

(3) Lettering to be read only by the lecturer at the front as an aid in his presentation should be no larger than 6 point on the original.

It is wise to re-emphasize the fact that the results obtained by using the tables here presented and those in Appendix G are subject to some unavoidable errors, for many other variables, in addition to size, establish relative or specific legibility. For example, if any lettering is to be on a colored background its legibility and visibility will be reduced (except if the background is yellow) roughly in proportion to the loss of value contrast. Differences in styles of type, and especially in the background patterns of shading or map data, may increase or reduce legibility. The photographic quality of the slides, the lens quality, and the amount of light from projectors frequently vary. Familiar word forms may make undersize lettering recognizable. The tables of equivalent sizes have been calculated solely on the basis of angle subtended at the eye and do not take into

account any of the less significant factors. Equivalent sizes are expressed to the nearest point in the smaller ranges with some clear intermediates noted, and in the larger they are approximate to the nearest even or common type size. Consequently, if any doubt arises as to the effect of any negative factors present, lettering sizes should be increased. Results obtained by following such a rule of thumb will rarely be unsatisfactory.

13.6 THE COLOR OF THE LETTERING AND THE BACKGROUND

Legibility and perceptibility of lettering also depend considerably upon the color of the lettering and the background upon which it stands (see Fig. 13.9). Commonly, lettering of equal importance does not appear equal in various parts of the map because of background differences. Even when the same lettering is used everywhere because of other design requirements, the cartographer should be aware of the possible effects, and perhaps, within the limits of his design, he may be able to correct or at least alleviate the situation.

Stated in general terms, the legibility and perceptibility of lettering (other effects being equal) depend upon the amount of visual contrast between the lettering and its background. Putting aside such effects as might be the result of texture of background, size of lettering, and so on, the basic variable is the degree of value contrast between the lettering and its background. Thus, black lettering on a white background would stand near the top of the scale, and as the value

of the lettering approached the value of the background, visibility would diminish. This is of concern when either large regional names are "spread" over a considerable area composed of units colored or shaded differently or when names of equal rank must be placed on areas of different values. It makes no difference whether the value contrast is the result of color or of shading. The usual lettering in cartography is either black or white (reverse lettering), but occasionally lettering will be added to one of the color plates in the flat-color method of map reproduction. Regardless of the color of the print and of the background, if the value contrast is great the lettering will be legible.

White or reversed lettering on a dark or colored background is an effective way to create contrast in the map lettering. It may be accomplished in a number of ways:

(1) Lettering in white paint or ink (this is difficult).

(2) Pasting a negative (white on black) paper print of the lettering on a black background on the map (see Article 14.6).

(3) Using a film positive as a mask (see Article 14.18).

(4) Using white preprinted lettering (see Article 13.11).

However reverse lettering is accomplished, it should be remembered that the rule of value contrast still obtains. In addition, white or open lettering appears smaller than black lettering of the same size (see Fig. 13.10). Consequently, if, for example, all names on oceans are to be white, it may

FIGURE 13.9. Perceptibility and legibility depend upon lettering-background contrast.

Kennerley—an upright Classic

Kennerley in the Italic form

Monsen Medium Gothic—upright

Monsen Medium Gothic Italic

Kennerley—an upright Classic

Kennerley in the Italic form

Monsen Medium Gothic—upright

Monsen Medium Gothic Italic

FIGURE 13.10. Reverse lettering appears slightly smaller than the opposite of the same size.

be necessary to increase their size slightly in order to bring them in balance with the other lettering.

13.7   POSITIONING THE LETTERING

The manner in which the lettering is placed on the map in relation to the other map data is an important part of the lettering technique. The map usually has a grid or pattern of lines on it, and an incongruous appearance can easily result if the orientation of the basic lettering pattern is not carefully determined. For example, the projection grid may create one pattern, and if the lettering pattern is set at an angle the entire map may appear unstable.

Generally, the convention in cartography is to place the lettering parallel to the parallels, which requires curving the lettering on many projections. This is difficult to do with lettering devices. The problem may be lessened by indicating the grid only on the water, which carries few names, or by indicating the grid only as ticks near the border, and then placing the lettering hori-

zontally. If the grid is necessary to the map purpose, then these expedients cannot be used. A particular problem is created by the "polar" and oblique forms of projections now so common. If the lettering is placed parallel to the parallels consistently, then that lettering at the side will be standing vertically; and if the lettering is oriented with north at the top, it will be upside down in the upper portion of the map. One method of preventing such predicaments is to change the orientation of the lettering at the horizontal grid line, so that it can be read with no more than a quarter turn of the head.

Names of features such as countries, mountain ranges, or oceans are usually spread so that the name includes the entire feature; but even if spread, the letters must be placed in a curve or line so that each letter follows the last normally. The letters also must be evenly spaced. This requires considerable planning in order to fit the individual letters in proper position without interfering with other lettering or lines on the map.

Names of rivers should "run" with the streams if possible. River names are normally not spread apart as are names of countries, but they should follow the curves of the adjacent portion of the stream. It is a good practice to curve them so that the upper portions of the letters are closer together. The upper part of lower case letters have more clues to letter form than the lower.

Names of lakes, islands, swamps, peninsulas, and other relatively small features should be placed so that they are either contained entirely within the feature or are entirely outside it. This is especially necessary when the color or tint of the feature is different from its surroundings.

Titles and legend lettering should be balanced around a center line and positioned carefully. This may be most easily done by first planning each line on a separate strip of paper and then shifting their position on

the map until the correct adjustment is obtained. If tracing paper or other translucent material is used, the shifting may be done beneath the paper and the final position traced on the work sheet or fair drawing.

Names of cities and other point locations should be placed to one side or the other of the symbol, and placed slightly above or below it. If put in line with the symbol, the symbol and lettering may interfere with one another.

13.8 METHODS OF LETTERING

Until two or three decades ago the lettering for most maps was done either by the draftsman or the engraver. A technique called "wax engraving" employed printing type pressed into a film of wax which was then electroplated to produce a printing plate; but the majority of lettering was either freehand in ink on the drawing or was freehand in metal by the engraver. The desire for speed, uniformity, and standardization led to the development of mechanical lettering devices and other means to escape from the admittedly slower and less uniform freehand methods. Today almost all large map-making organizations use some method other than freehand to letter their products. These methods may be grouped in three categories: (1) preprinted lettering or stickup, (2) mechanical aids for ink lettering, and (3) photo lettering.

At present (1959), photo-lettering devices are becoming more widely used, and their versatility is developing rapidly. Their potential utility for cartographic purposes is very high because variations in sizes are easily obtainable, and because the photographic black is uniform and dense, which makes it easily reproduced in the printing process.

Mechanical lettering devices of several kinds are available, and with their use acceptable, clean-cut appearing maps may be lettered. It should be emphasized, however, that the lettering produced with most of these aids appears rather mechanical and gives one the impression of looking at a building blueprint. They are most used for just this purpose—engineering drawings, wherein variations in the character and orientation of letter form are not particularly desirable. Some of the complexities of good map lettering have been detailed in previous articles, and it is not to be expected that any relatively inexpensive mechanical device can approach their attainment. Nevertheless, mechanical lettering devices will continue to find a place in cartography, especially for the production of graphs, charts, and diagrammatic maps.

Preprinted lettering is commercially available to the cartographer for a relatively low price. It is more versatile than mechanical lettering and is the accepted procedure in the majority of large map-making establishments. This technique utilizes the ordinary letters of letterpress type printed on some medium that may be made to adhere to the map. It is fast and mistakes can be easily corrected.

The most versatile of all the forms of lettering is the freehand. With this method names may be designed, inserted, oriented, and scaled as to size precisely as desired. Neither printing type faces nor many of the mechanical lettering styles have been devised particularly for map use. Although these methods are relatively rapid and under many circumstances the desirable expedient, nevertheless, the best lettering for specialized maps is the well-executed freehand. Properly designed lettering is as important to the quality of a map as any other element of design.

13.9 FREEHAND LETTERING

The learning of freehand lettering requires familiarity with and an ability to use the basic tools. It also requires a knowledge of the principles of letter formation and design.

These elements require a much more thorough treatment than can be given in a book of this sort, and the reader is referred to the bibliography for a listing of books treating these subjects.

The most important aspect for the beginner to appreciate is that lettering freehand requires planning. The planning includes, in addition to selecting the kind of letter (Gothic or Roman, slant or upright) and its sizes, the placing on the copy of guide lines which will aid in placing the letters and in making them conform to size. Guide lines may be drawn with a straightedge or a curve, but guide lines are better drawn with any of a number of patented devices designed for this purpose, such as the Ames lettering instrument or the Multi and Braddock-Rowe lettering angles. These devices have small holes in which a pencil point may be inserted. The device may then be moved along a drawing edge by moving the pencil. By placing the pencil in other holes, parallel lines may be drawn. Guide lines usually consist of three parallel lines as shown in Fig. 13.11. The bottom two determine the height of the lower case letters. As a rule of thumb for the beginner, the spacing relationship between the lines should be one-third/two-thirds, with the larger space at the bottom. This is by no means

FIGURE 13.11. Guide lines.

FIGURE 13.12. Visual compared to mechanical spacing.

a general rule, for the relationship is quite variable and depends upon the alphabet design. The upper guide line indicates the height of the capitals and the ascenders of such letters as b, d, f, etc.

After the guide lines have been placed, the lettering may be first drawn in lightly with pencil, in order that spacing and position problems may be solved. Spacing of the letters is important, for with poor spacing the words will appear ragged and uneven. Since letters are not the same shape, the distance between them must be adjusted so that the space will *appear* to be the same. The beginner will soon learn that there are different classes of letters according to their regular or irregular appearance and according to whether they are narrow, normal, or wide. They must be separated differently depending upon the combination in the word. Mechanical spacing should be avoided (see Fig. 13.12).

In order for the lettering pen or other tool to make the letter properly the letter should be stroked correctly. This depends somewhat upon the pen and the paper, but most pens cannot be moved up against the paper, for they will dig into the surface and then

spatter. In general, strokes should be down or to the side (see Fig. 13.13).

The greatest difficulty for the beginner to overcome is his probable mental attitude toward freehand lettering, for the chances are that he will approach the operation with trembling, which will be reflected in his lettering. He no doubt feels that the "pressure is on" when he puts ink to paper, and he is likely to complain that he can do much better with pencil. He probably can—because he is more relaxed. Smooth, easy lettering with a loose hand is not difficult, if the beginner will give himself a chance.

As soon as the beginner has mastered the use of guide lines and the "feel" of his lettering pens, he is ready to learn the common alphabets. It is important for him to realize that the design of lettering and its spacing are far more important than precise execution. There is, of course, no limit to the number of lettering designs for freehand execution. Books on lettering are inexpensive and widely available in most book and art supply stores.* The beginner should not attempt his own designs at first, but should carefully copy styles that have been worked out by more experienced designers.

The freehand lettering on maps is usually confined to either the Roman or Gothic and the upright or slanted forms. Roman lettering consists of thick and thin strokes usually made with a square-tipped pen such as the Speedball Style C or the N or Z style of Graphos nibs (see Figs. 3.10 and 3.11). Gothic lettering is made with round or tubular nibs so that whichever way the nib moves the line thickness remains the same. Figure 13.14 shows an example of each style. Careful examination of well-executed freehand lettered maps, such as those in the *Geographical Journal* of the Royal Geographical Society, will aid the the beginner to develop a sense of letter design.

13.10 MECHANICAL LETTERING

The best-known devices require a special pen, feeding through a small tube, while the pen is guided either mechanically or by hand with the aid of a template.

Leroy is the patented name of a lettering system involving templates, a scriber, and special Leroy pens (see Fig. 13.15). A different template is necessary for each size lettering. The template is moved along the T-square or steel straightedge, and the scriber traces the depressed letters of the template and reproduces them with the pen beyond the template. Spacing is usually done by eye. A variety of letter weights and sizes in capitals and lower case is possible by interchanging templates and pens

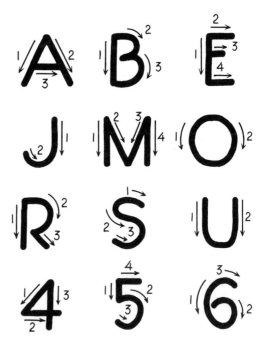

FIGURE 13.13. Examples of proper letter stroking in some of the letters and numbers of a simple Gothic alphabet. (By Randall D. Sale.)

---

* One of the best and most helpful to beginners is Ross F. George, *Speedball Textbook*, 17th Ed., Hunt Pen Co., Camden, New Jersey, 1956. The cost is approximately seventy-five cents.

ABCDEFGHIJKL
MNOPQRSTUV
WXYZ
abcdefghijklmnop
qrstuvwxyz
1234567890

ABCDEFGHIJKLM
NOPQRSTUVW
XYZ
abcdefghijklmnopqr
stuvwxyz
1234567890

FIGURE 13.14. Two simple freehand alphabets. The left-hand alphabet is classed as upright Roman; the right-hand as slanted or inclined Gothic. (By Randall D. Sale.)

(see Fig. 13.16). In addition, templates with geological and mathematical symbols are available. The normal template of the Leroy is a simple Sans Serif or Gothic, but extended, condensed, and outline forms are also available. A template carrying Cheltenham letters has been added to those available.

Varigraph is the patented name of a versatile lettering device also involving a template with depressed letters and a stylus (see Fig. 13.17). The device is actually a sort of small, adjustable pantograph which fits over a template. The letters are traced from the template and are scribed with a pen at the other end of the pantograph-like assembly. Adjustments may be made to make large or small, extended or condensed

lettering from a single template. Templates of a variety of letter styles are available, ranging from a simple Gothic to a Sans Serif, and from a Cartographic Roman (see Fig. 13.18) to Old English Text.

Wrico is the patented name of a lettering system involving perforated templates or guides and special pens (see Fig. 13.19). The lettering guides are placed directly over the area to be lettered and are moved back and forth to form the various parts of a letter. The pen is held in the hand and is moved around the stencil cut in the guide. The guide rests on small blocks which hold it above the paper surface to prevent smearing. A considerable variety of letter forms are possible including condensed and extended. A different guide is necessary for

FIGURE 13.15. The Leroy Scriber and one template. (Courtesy Keuffel and Esser Company.)

TEMPLATE NO.	PEN NO.									
	00	0	1	2	3	4	5	6	7N	8N
80	A	B	C							
100	A	B	C	D						
120	A	B	C	D	E					
140	A	B	C	D	E	F				
175	A	B	C	D	E	F	G			
200	A	B	C	D	E	F	G	H		
240	A	B	C	D	E	F	G	H		
290	A	B	C	D	E	F	G	H	K	
350	A	B	C	D	E	F	G	H	K	L
425	A	B	C	D	E	F	G	H	K	L
500	A	B	C	D	E	F	G	H	K	L

FIGURE 13.16. Sample of Leroy lettering. (Courtesy Keuffel and Esser Company.)

each size, although width of line may be varied by changing the pen size.

Another method of applying lettering to the map mechanically is by means of an imprinter. This is a small form of a typographer's composing stick in which type may be placed and locked in position. It is then inked and pressed in place on the map. The type must then be cleaned and distributed before another name can be applied. Curved lettering is, of course, difficult to apply. The use of an imprinter is relatively slow compared to other methods. Essentially the same technique was formerly used in the wax-engraving process. The lettering on wax-engraved maps appears more mechanical than any other type of lettering, partly because of the poor letter forms and partly because of the tendency to overcrowd.

13.11   PREPRINTED LETTERING

Stick-up lettering has a number of advantages over other methods of lettering which require the use of ink on the copy. Any of the thousands of type styles and sizes used in printing can be selected. The letters may be used as composed in a straight unit, or they may be cut apart and applied sepa-

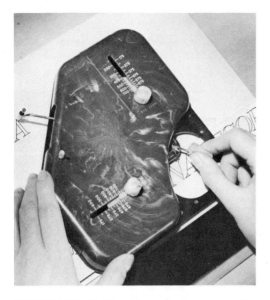

FIGURE 13.17. Varigraph lettering instrument. The scales are for adjusting the height and width of the letter. (Courtesy The Varigraph Company, Madison, Wisconsin.)

obtained. Type style and point size must be designated for all lettering. The printer will compose the names as listed, and since possibilities of inadvertent omission are relatively high, it is good practice to include a request for alphabets of the styles and sizes being used. Prices vary considerably, depending upon whether the type to be used must be hand set or machine set, so careful planning is desirable.

One disadvantage of stick-up is that, at present, it is necessary to use type faces originally designed for printing books. Such type faces have not been designed for any position except horizontal, neither have they been designed for any reduction. When such type is put in a curved position it is not so well designed as is good freehand lettering. Each size of a type style has been designed separately for use at that size. Consequently, when used on maps planned for reduction there is a tendency for the lettering to appear somewhat light, since 18-point lettering reduced one-half has thinner strokes than the 9-point size of the same style. It is generally necessary, when using stick-up lettering, to choose a somewhat larger point size than would ordinarily be warranted.

rately to fit curves. If the position first selected for the name is not suitable, the name may be relocated with no attendant problem of erasing.

The cartographer must make for the printer a complete list of all names and lettering that are to appear on the map or series of maps for which he plans to use stick-up. Spellings must, of course, be reviewed carefully. Since the printer supplies a number of copies of the composition it is only necessary to repeat names, such as "river" or "lake," as many times as the total number of map occurrences divided by the number of copies of the composition to be

The preprinting may be done on a variety of surfaces, depending upon the printer's materials, such as gummed stock requiring only wetting, or thin tissue which can be "floated" into place with a thin adhesive or solvent, or Cellophane with an adhesive on the back. The last system combines the advantages of transparent backing and easy changing. The foremost commercial pro-

FIGURE 13.18. Sample of Varigraph lettering (Cartographic Roman) showing a few of the possible variations from a single template.

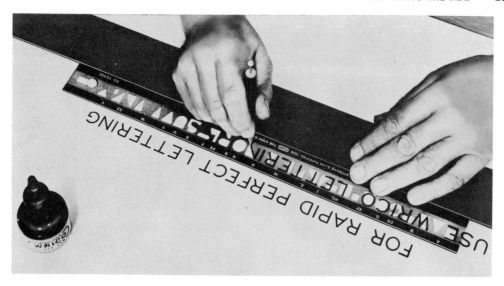

FIGURE 13.19. Wrico pen and guide in operation. (Courtesy Wood-Regan Instrument Company.)

duction of this kind of lettering for map use is by Monsen Typographers, Inc., which uses the same technique that is used for pre-printed symbols, that is, wax-backed cellophane.* Their Trans-Adhesive impressions are available on glossy acetate, matte-finish acetate, and flexible film (Vinylite) for slight curves without cutting apart; and all have a wax backing. The same sort of material is available also in black ink on a white backing, which automatically masks the area around the letters, or in white ink for use over solid black to provide open or reverse lettering.

In use, wax-backed stick-up lettering is merely cut from the printed sheet with a sharp, thin knife or needle and placed in position (see Fig. 13.20). It is then burnished tight.

13.12 GEOGRAPHICAL NAMES

The cartographer frequently finds that the selection of styles and the application of the

* Monsen Typographers, Inc., 22 East Illinois Street, Chicago II, Illinois, and 960 West 12th Street, Los Angeles 15, California.

lettering are not nearly so knotty as problems as is the selection of the proper or appropriate spelling of the names he wishes to use. For example, does one name an important river in Europe *Donau* (German and Austrian), *Duna* (Hungarian), *Dunav* (Yugoslavian and Bulgarian), *Dunărea* (Rumanian), or does one spell it *Danube,* a form not used by any country through which it flows! Is it *Florence* or *Firenze, Rome* or *Roma, Wien* or *Vienna, Thessalonikē* or *Thessoloniki,* or *Salonika* or *Saloniki,* or any of a number of other variants? The problem is made even more difficult by the fact that names change because official languages change or because internal administrative changes occur. The problem of spelling is difficult indeed.

The problem is of sufficient moment that governments that produce many maps have established agencies whose sole job it is to formulate policy and to specify the spelling to be used for names on maps and in official documents. Such are the British Permanent Committee on Geographical Names (PCGN) and the United States Board on Geographical Names (BGN) of the Department of the

FIGURE 13.20. Preparing stick-up copy for the name plate of a map. Names are being cut from the preprinted lists on each side of the fair drawing, or copy, on which the draftsman is working. Note the use of the preprinted symbols in the lower portion of the illustration. (Courtesy Rand Mc-Nally and Company.)

Interior. The majority of such governmental agencies concern themselves only with domestic problems, but the two named above include the spelling of all geographical names as part of their function.

One of the major tasks of such an agency (and of every cartographer) is the determination of how a name that exists in its original form in a non-Latin alphabet shall be rendered in the Latin alphabet. Various systems of transliteration from one alphabet to another have been devised by experts, and the agencies have published the approved systems. The Board on Geographic Names has published numerous bulletins of place-name decisions and guides recommending treatment and sources of information for many foreign areas. These are available upon application. It is well for the cartographer to acquire, or at least to

have available, such bulletins for he is frequently required to make decisions on matters of transliteration. Even more frequently he will find himself using map sources that contain other alphabets, characters, and ideographs.

The general rule is to use the conventional English form whenever such exists. Thus, *Finland* (instead of *Suomi*) and *Danube River* would be preferred. Names of places and features in countries using the Latin alphabet may, of course, be used in their local official form if the purpose of the map makes such treatment desirable or if there is no conventional English form.

The problem is much too complex to be treated in any detail in this book, but it is well for the student to be aware of it. His main worry, as a student, will be that of consistency in whatever general system he chooses. Above all, he must not let himself fall into toponymic blunders by placing on maps such names as *Rio Grande River, Lake Windermere,* or *Sierra Nevada Mountains.*

Map Reproduction: Processes and Preparation of Drawings

14.1 MAP REPRODUCTION

Most drafted maps are made to be reproduced by some kind of mechanical process in order to obtain multiple copies. This has not always been the case, for prior to the use of printing all copies were prepared by exactly the same drafting method that was used on the original drawing. Manuscripts were "reproduced" by copyists who laboriously and slowly duplicated the lettering of the original text, and maps were just another kind of manuscript. Although hand carved printing blocks were used at an early date the general introduction of printing in the middle of the fifteenth century changed all this. There were several important consequences, chief among which was the explosive cultural effect of the wide dissemination of textual and graphic material. Of quite another order of relative importance were the rather fundamental effects printing had upon the graphic characteristics of lettering and map delineation.

For nearly four hundred years after about 1450 the requirements of a mechanical system placed more or less stringent controls on the author and graphic artist. No matter what style and form of lettering seemed desirable for a book, or what types of lines, symbols, and colors might best convey the concept of a map, only those available to the printer and engraver could be used. Because of the overwhelming importance of the technicians in the mechanics of the publication process their influence was widely felt. The development of letter styles and map symbolism during this period clearly bears the imprint of this mechanistic effect. To be sure, this was not always undesirable, for many engravers were accomplished artists in the true sense of the word; nevertheless, any limitation on the media of expression, be it mechanical or otherwise, obviously can have only a retarding effect and further the tendency toward convention and mediocrity. Fortunately for cartography, however, several inventions during the nineteenth century effectively neutralized these damaging consequences, and the requirements of modern-day production printing have comparatively little general effect upon the choice of graphic techniques.

This relatively happy state of affairs applies to the field of cartography in general, but usually not to the individual cartographer. Although it is mechanically possible to reproduce virtually anything and to obtain whatever results are desired, neverthe-

less a variety of economic and other practical considerations usually restricts the choice of methods open to the cartographer for each map-making effort. Only the large government agencies and map publishing houses have sufficiently large resources to enable them to come close to selecting the ideal methods for each kind of map.

14.2 PLANNING FOR MAP REPRODUCTION

Whenever a map is being contemplated, whether it be a single sheet, or for a book illustration, an atlas, a dissertation, or even a term paper the first step is to give careful consideration to the reproduction possibilities. The cartographer must learn what choice there is as to method of reproduction, and he must choose the most appropriate one in terms of cost, number of copies required, future use of the map, as well as a number of other elements. Even after the process has been decided there is still considerable choice regarding the method of preparing copy for some kinds of maps, especially colored maps. He will find that the designing of his map and the drafting operations are closely related to the reproduction requirements.

The designing of a map for reproduction involves a number of important decisions and techniques. One of the more important considerations is of the relation between the size of the copy (fair drawing prepared for reproduction) and the printed or reproduced size in terms of the degree of detail, line widths, and lettering sizes. Many maps that appear correct in these aspects in copy form appear crowded and heavy, or the opposite, light and weak, when reduced and printed. This may be a result of poor design, treated elsewhere in this book, or the result of a lighter printing ink on an absorbent paper or some other similar circumstance. In addition, if the map is to be reproduced in color it must be kept in register as the separate plates are drawn. Also, the line work

of a drawing must be more carefully drafted on copy that is to be reproduced by the camera, for sensitized paper or film is much more sensitive to differences in blackness than is the human eye. The copy must be appropriate to the process; that is, it must not ask too much of the particular duplicating technique. Very fine lines can be reproduced in only a few copies by some processes, and in many copies by others.

A thorough knowledge of reproduction processes is desirable for still another reason. In the printing process, and in some other methods of reproduction, photography is an important step. Much of the photography results in film on which there are only two kinds of areas, opaque and transparent. This fact can be utilized in the construction of a map in a number of ways which will effect great savings of time for the cartographer. Masking of unwanted areas, application of tints and screen patterns, and so on, can often be most expeditiously done during this part of the printing process. The cartographer who is versed in "reproduction cartography" can save himself considerable effort at the same time that he is producing a finer product.

The contemplation of his first reproduced map is likely to be one of the great events in a cartographer's professional life. Sometimes the event generates sorrow. Of certain results it might be said, "Any resemblance between this printed map and the fair drawing is purely coincidental," for what happens to a neophyte's map when reproduced is sometimes startling. It need not be, however, if the cartographer will but bear in mind that any map to be reproduced must be designed and drafted for some particular process of reproduction.

14.3 CLASSIFICATION OF DUPLICATING METHODS

It is difficult to classify reproduction methods in a satisfactory manner, because

many processes require more than one technique, and the intermediate techniques in one may be an end in themselves in another, or they may be intermediate in several different processes. For example, photography is a step in the printing process but it can also be considered a separate reproduction process. Perhaps the most practical manner of classification is to group the reproduction methods on the basis of whether or not they involve a decreasing unit cost with increasing numbers of copies. It so happens that segregation on this basis also separates the common processes according to whether or not they require printing plates and printing ink, that is, whether they are printing processes or nonprinting processes.

In the following descriptions only the widely used and generally available processes are considered. It should, however, be pointed out that there are a number of other processes which produce excellent results in specific "requirement situations," ranging from stencil reproduction and silk screen to gravure and collotype. These and others of the same category (not widely used in cartography) are not considered here, but the interested student can find abundant information about them in the graphic arts literature.

The nonprinting processes are distinguished by providing low-cost, one-color copies at a unit cost that ordinarily does not vary much with the "run," or number of copies. They are therefore ideal for short runs but are not appropriate for large runs. The printing processes, on the other hand, provide low-cost, monochrome, or multi-color copies at a unit cost that decreases with the number of copies run. The initial cost is high compared to the nonprinting methods. The printing processes are therefore not appropriate for very small runs.

The widely used nonprinting processes are: (1) direct contact positive or diazo, for example, Ozalid, (2) direct contact negative, for example, blueprint, (3) photo copy,

for example, Photostat, and (4) film photograph. This is an unsystematic listing in several respects as there are many similarities and differences among the processes that would enable them to be grouped differently. On the other hand these are the categories usually used in "the trade," so it is convenient not to deviate. The widely used printing processes are: (1) letterpress, and (2) lithography.

A source of considerable confusion for the beginner is the terminology employed in the printing and duplicating businesses. Context will often supply a guide to the meanings of the words, but a few commonly used terms are defined below.

Copy is a term applied to either the original drawing or the duplicate obtained from it by a reproduction process. *The* copy refers to the original; *a* copy to the duplicate. The term *positive* is applied to any duplicate in which the relation between the lines and the background is the same as that of the original drawing, for example, dark lines on a light background. A *negative* is any duplicate where this relationship has been reversed, whether on film or paper. *To reverse* a drawing means to change the relationship. *Fair drawing, original, original drawing, art work,* and *the copy* are all synonymous, and refer to that which the cartographer or draftsman has prepared, that is, that which is to be reproduced.

14.4   DIRECT CONTACT POSITIVES

Direct contact positives are made by exposing a translucent drawing in contact with a printing paper sensitized with light-sensitive diazo compounds. The exposed paper is then ordinarily developed with ammonia fumes, but it may be treated with an aqueous solution. The resulting print is a positive reading print the same size as the original drawing. The trade name Ozalid applies to this type of process.

It is not possible when making direct con-

tact diazo prints to enlarge or reduce. Consequently, the copy must be designed for "same-size" reproduction. The process depends upon the translucence of the drawing; and therefore painting out imperfections is impossible, for paint is as opaque as the ink and would appear as a dark spot in the print. Creases on the tracing paper or cloth and heavy erasures which affect the translucence are also frequently visible on the print. Prints are commonly obtained by feeding the original drawing into a machine against a roll of the diazo sensitized paper; the exposure and dry developing take place rapidly within the machine. The drawing is returned and may be immediately reinserted for another exposure and copy.

Diazo paper has an acceptable drafting surface, so this process is also useful for obtaining copies of base maps. The image is not absolutely permanent, however, and may not be acceptable in those circumstances where permanence is required as, for example, for the library copy of a dissertation.

Zip-A-Tone, ordinary stick-up, and similar products on drawings do not produce very good results in the direct contact process because of "shadowing" which takes place when exposure is made through the translucent drafting medium. An additional hazard with the standard forms of these materials is present in the Ozalid diazo process, because the drawing must be fed around a roller, and such materials tend to curl off the paper if it is heated and rolled. New types of preprinted sheets and stick-up lettering are available to obviate this difficulty. Another way of circumventing this problem is to have a film or paper "intermediate" made by a photographer. If the photographer prepares the intermediate on translucent paper or prints his ordinary film negative on another piece of film, the result is a direct reading translucent positive. It is called an intermediate because it is to be used to make the subsequent contact positives in place of the original drawing. When on film it is called a film positive, or sometimes a diapositive. If the photographer can arrange the printing of the film positive so that the emulsion side is on the bottom when the film positive "reads" correctly, then it may be fed onto the drum of an Ozalid machine with good results. It is not absolutely necessary to have the emulsion arranged as suggested, but the result will be more satisfactory.

Another use of intermediates is occasionally very helpful. If the cartographer or researcher has available a base map which he wishes to use as a compilation base for a series of maps but on which he does not wish to draw, he can proceed as follows. First, an intermediate may be prepared from the original; then he may add data to the intermediate; and finally, the corrected or modified intermediate becomes the copy for subsequent direct contact positives.

14.5   DIRECT CONTACT NEGATIVES

The direct contact negative process is here used as a collective term to include several processes that produce results by similar techniques. A commonly employed variety is the standard blueprint process. In this process the copy is laid next to iron-sensitized paper and is then exposed to special lights. The exposed print is wet developed and is, consequently, subject to some distortion. The print appears as a right-reading negative, that is, the darks and lights are the reverse of the original copy. If a positive copy is desired, a special "negative" can be made from the original, which is then used as copy, and the prints are then produced as dark lines on a white background. Another variety (B-W) using special papers produces positive copies directly. Whatever the variety, the prints will be the same size as the original.

The major use of these direct contact positive or negative processes in cartography is

to obtain a few relatively inexpensive copies on thin paper. They are also useful for obtaining "same-size" copies of base maps so that a variety of other maps requiring the same base data may be made, without the necessity of redrawing the base data for each map. Papers used for contact positives and negatives have a relatively good drafting surface, but the combination of drawing ink lines and the blue, "black," red, or brown lines of the print are not particularly satisfactory for subsequent printing reproduction, although the results are not unusable.

14.6   PHOTOCOPY PROCESS

This process provides prints in reverse or negative form on sensitized paper, without the necessity of any intermediate film step. It involves the exposure of the original drawing through a lens directly to the sensitized paper, which is then wet developed. The developing process and the subsequent drying frequently cause unequal shrinkage, so that some distortion of dimensions and directions is often present in a photocopy. Photostat is a term commonly used synonymously with photocopy, but it is a trade name referring to a specific machine and the paper used in it for photocopying.

The prints are reversed each time through the photocopy process. If a drawing of black lines on a white background is photocopied, the result will be a paper negative, that is, a reproduction with white lines on a black background. To gain positive copies (same as original copy), it is necessary to repeat the process using the negative as the copy.

Maps may be enlarged or reduced in the photocopy process, and the only limitation is the size of the paper and the quality of the lens. Photocopy paper is usually limited to 18 × 24 inch sheets, but the edges are commonly rather badly distorted so that the effective size is somewhat smaller.

Many time-saving and useful results can be obtained by using the photocopy process in cartography. For example, if one wishes to have white lettering on a solid background (reverse lettering) on a printed map, it is a simple matter to do the lettering in black ink on white paper and then to obtain a negative photocopy. This may then be pasted on the drawing. It is much easier than attempting to letter with white paint on a black background. Other cases where reversing a drawing by photocopy methods, intermediate in the drafting process, is advantageous will occur to the reader.

The primary use of photocopies, however, is for obtaining a few relatively inexpensive duplicates of a black and white map that has been drawn on opaque or translucent paper. Mistakes can be corrected either on the original (by painting over, etc.) or on the photocopy negative if positives are to be used.

14.7   FILM PHOTOGRAPH PROCESS

This is the standard process of photography involving camera, film negative, and paper prints. Although the cost of photography per square foot is about the same as photocopy, there are certain cases where photography is desirable. Grays and tones may be somewhat better controlled and are available in greater variety photographically. Enlargement or reductions not in simple proportion are easier to make photographically than in the photocopy process, and photographic enlargements on one sheet are available at a larger size through the use of an enlarger.

To make corrections on the negative is costly and difficult in the photographic process, so that for ordinary work where only a few prints are required the original drawing must be "ready to go."

14.8   PRINTING PROCESSES

The earliest printing or duplicating process was undoubtedly that involving a raised surface which could be pressed into a soft

medium, such as clay, in order to leave a mark therein. There is evidence that this was done several thousand years ago. At a very early time, the Chinese carved block characters, inked the raised portion, and transferred the impression to paper. This is the kind of printing from movable type that subsequently was "invented" in the Western world and grew rapidly after the middle of the fifteenth century. Today printed material from a plate on which the printing surfaces stand in relief is known as *letterpress;* it is a standard form of printing (see Fig. 14.1).

Another method of reproduction, *engraving,* involving ink and an uneven surface was also developed at about the same time that movable type was first used in Europe. Someone conceived the idea of cutting or engraving grooves in a metal plate and filling them with ink. The flat surface of the plate was then cleaned off and the plate with its ink-filled grooves was squeezed against a sheet of paper. The paper "took hold" of the ink and when removed from the metal plate the pattern of grooves appeared as ink lines. In a sense this process of engraving from an *intaglio* surface is just the opposite of letterpress printing, for the inking area is "down" instead of "up." Until the end of the nineteenth century most printed maps were reproduced by some form of the engraving process.

About a century and a half ago it was discovered that a drawing could be made on the smooth surface of a particular kind of limestone with oily ink or greasy crayon. The fats combined chemically with the elements in the stone to form a calcium oleate which had the property of repelling water. The unmarked portion of the surface could then be dampened, and when a greasy printing ink, which was repelled by the water, was rolled across the surface, the ink would adhere to the oily marked areas but not to the clean dampened areas. Paper pressed against the stone would pick up the ink. Because of the use of stone in the original form, the process was named *lithography.* Today stone is no longer used, except in rare instances. Although thin metal plates have been substituted, it is still known as lithography. It is also frequently called offset, because the image is offset by the press to a rubber roller, which in turn prints it on the paper. Whatever printing surface prints directly to the paper, the printing surface will be "backwards." By offsetting to an intermediate roller, which then prints to the paper, the printing plate will "read correctly." This is advantageous in its processing, and it also allows delicate printing plates to have a longer life on the press, since rubber is softer than paper. In any case it is a *planographic* process, that is, the surface of the lithographic printing plate is a plane, having no significant difference in "elevation" between the inked and the non-inked areas.

The three kinds of printing and printing surfaces, relief, intaglio, and planographic, are still used, but most maps are printed by either letterpress or lithography. Larger maps are usually done by lithography and the smaller, such as book "cuts," by letterpress.

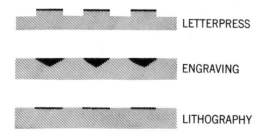

LETTERPRESS

ENGRAVING

LITHOGRAPHY

FIGURE 14.1. The basic processes of letterpress, engraving, and lithography operate in different ways to produce a surface from which ink may be transferred to paper.

14.9   TRANSFERRING THE DRAWING TO THE PRINTING PLATE

Until the latter part of the nineteenth century the major problem in all three print-

ing processes was that of obtaining the image (of the drawing which was to be printed) on the printing plate. There was no mechanical way to accomplish this; and as a consequence, arts such as engraving with a burin or graver directly in the metal, or drawing directly on the lithographic stone, were highly developed, and few possessed the necessary skills. Some idea of the problems involved may be gained by the student from the simple fact that everything on the printing plate had to be backward, including, of course, the lettering! The development of the specialized skills of the engraver or the lithographic artist had several effects on the development of cartography, the most important of which was that much of the detail of letter forms and other elements of the map design were delegated to the technician rather than being the responsibility of the cartographer.

With the rapid development of photography after approximately 1850, a fundamental change took place in the printing, industry and, naturally, also in cartography. It was discovered that the image of the drawing could be transferred to a photographic emulsion, which when developed resulted in a film or glass negative. This consisted of opaque and transparent sections, the transparent corresponding to the lines on the original drawing. By a variety of ingenious processes involving special emulsions and etching compounds, a printing plate could be prepared directly by mechanical means.

Today all ordinary printing plate preparation involves exposing a "negative" or "positive" on a light-sensitive printing plate which is then made ready for printing. This has freed the cartographer from depending upon others for the actual delineation of the map; he can do it himself (or direct the draftsman) and he is responsible for the result.

The introduction of the photographic process of producing the negative from which the printing plate is produced itself introduced a new set of problems, chief among which are (1) the maintenance of exact size and fit with other drawings for multicolor maps (register), and (2) the cost in time and money of the necessary photography. Particularly because of the problem of register, a relatively new process called *scribing* has been developed by which "negatives" are prepared for plate making without the use of the camera. Scribing is also useful in some other connections in cartography and the description follows (see Article 14.13). Nevertheless, a large proportion of the smaller-scale cartography done by individual cartographers, as well as that done by many map-making companies and agencies, is still processed by means of a photographically made negative as an integral part of the entire printing operation.

14.10 STEPS IN THE PRINTING PROCESS

The basic steps in the printing process, from the time the printer receives the copy until he delivers the printed maps, are much the same whether the process is letterpress or lithography. For a normal piece of copy involving no complications the process consists, in the main, of the following operations:

(1) Photographing the original drawing.
(2) Processing the negative.
(3) Making the plate.
(4) Presswork.

The cartographer is concerned with one or all of the first three. Beyond understanding the problems of the pressman he is little concerned with the fourth stage.

Perhaps the major difference between letterpress and lithography, insofar as the cartographer is concerned, results from the fact that commonly the lithographer handles all four operations in his establishment and is therefore a somewhat more satisfactory person with whom to deal. In letterpress, on the other hand, it is not unusual for the first two or three steps, as listed above, to be accomplished by a photoengraver who

does no presswork. This means, so to speak, that one more cook is concerned with the broth making, and the danger of spoilage due to inadequate planning is thereby increased.

Photographing the original drawing or copy is an exacting process requiring the use of what is called a copy camera, which is a large, rigidly mounted camera capable of making large or small exposures. The copy is first placed in a vacuum frame with a glass cover, which holds it perfectly flat, and is exposed for several seconds under illumination by arc lights. Relatively slow film is used in order to give the photographer greater control over the quality of the negative. For the printing processes (lithography and letterpress), the resulting negative must be composed of either opaque areas or transparent areas and nothing intermediate. Grays are not permitted on the negative as they, of course, are in ordinary photography. The printing plate, to be made subsequently from the negative, must be entirely divided into two kinds of surfaces, one which takes ink and one which does not. For this reason all drawings should be drafted with marks of uniform blackness. Lack of dense, uniform blackness of the marks on the copy makes it very difficult if not impossible for the photographer to produce a satisfactory negative.

Any reduction that is to be made is done at this stage. The photographer can adjust the camera precisely either by calculating the ratio of reduction or by actually measuring the image in the camera before the exposure.

It is important that the nature of the emulsion normally used be fully understood. This emulsion is orthochromatic, that is, sensitive to black and to the red end of the spectrum, but not particularly sensitive to the blue end. Consequently, red photographs black, but light blue (and some similar colors) do not photograph at all. For this reason the cartographer should, as far as possible, draw any guide lines with a light blue pencil. Filters may be used in special circumstances.

After exposure the negative is developed, washed, and dried and is then ready for the next step. The emulsions are on film or glass backing, and for some plate making it is necessary for the photographer to make a film positive which then is treated as the "negative." There are two lithographic printing processes normally in use, albumin or ordinary lithography and deep-etch lithography. The first employs a true negative to make the printing plate, whereas the deep-etch process employs a film positive made from the original negative. In the deep-etch process the printing surfaces on the plate are relatively thick and are "sunk" into the metal slightly. The printing surface, on a fresh plate, stands very slightly above the nonprinting surface. The combination produces sharper detail on the printed copy and the plate does not wear out so quickly, making deep etch desirable for longer "press runs."

The manner in which a deep-etch printing plate is processed to produce the printing image from a film positive is of no concern to the cartographer, but the fact that a film positive is required instead of a negative makes a difference. There are a number of techniques which are cartographically useful that may be utilized in the negative or film positive processing stage. If a film positive is to be used to make the plate, these techniques may need to be planned as the opposite of those that would be employed if a negative were the end result. Because it is confusing to jump back and forth between negative and film positive in discussing the processing necessary and possible, the subsequent description will refer only to a negative.

14.11 PROCESSING THE NEGATIVE

Processing the negative is one of the more important steps in the cartographic technique, for it is in this stage that some results

can be obtained better than in the drafting stage. No matter what processing or modification is to take place, however, the negative must be brought to perfection by removing all "pinholes" and blemishes in the emulsion so that the image is left sharp and clear. This is done by placing the negative on a light-table and opaquing with paint or scraping clean those spots and areas requiring repair or change (see Fig. 14.2). If film positives are required for deep etch they are made from the perfected negative at this stage.

In addition to the process of perfecting the negative, called by the general term "opaquing," other operations can be performed or initiated during the "negative stage" in the printing process such as (1) adding or subtracting material, (2) screening of all or a portion of the negative, (3) opaquing of identical negatives for color separation, and (4) masking of one negative with another.

Depending upon the circumstances, it is sometimes possible at this stage to add or subtract names and lines. If an important piece of information has been omitted or a word misspelled, a new piece of emulsion or emulsion-like material may be "stripped" into place on the negative. If material has been omitted it can sometimes be added by "engraving" it in the emulsion or, in the case of a film positive, added by painting. Since these operations are costly and time consuming, it is better if the cartographer prepares his copy correctly in the beginning.

Screening of the negative involves the positioning of thin transparent sheets containing patterns of lines or dots (called screens) over particular areas of the negative. This accomplishes the same end result on the printing plate as applying Zip-A-Tone or similar shading film to, or drafting such shading on, the original drawing. Better results are obtained with extra fine patterns of lines or dots by applying them at this stage, after photography, than by making them "stand up" through the photographic process. Furthermore, opaquing can be done first and screening second, which is desirable because the negative is more difficult to opaque if the emulsion already contains a fine pattern of lines or dots in addition to the other data.

If a map is to be printed with two or more colored inks, it is necessary that there be a negative and printing plate for each color ink. Copy for separate plates may either be drafted by the cartographer, or he may draft all colors in black on one drawing. If the latter is done the photographer supplies as many identical negatives as there are colors-to-be. The negatives are then opaqued so that only those items which are to be printed in a single color are left transparent on each negative. They are then treated as different negatives. In many instances this insures better registry as well as saving time for the cartographer. It is obvious, however, that on some complicated maps this would not be feasible. This process of producing separation negatives

FIGURE 14.2. Opaquing a negative. (Courtesy Rand McNally and Company.)

for color reproduction is only one of a number of ways the cartographer and photographer can produce a separate negative for each color (see Article 14.16).

It may be convenient for the cartographer to have the photographer prepare masking negatives or film positives at this stage. The cartographer can, of course, draft such drawings. Masks are used to "block out" areas on a negative when the plate is being made, and is accomplished by exposing two negatives at once to the plate. A simple application of this technique is illustrated in Article 14.18.

After a negative has been processed it is marked for position on the plate and in general made ready for plate making.

14.12 PLATE MAKING

Printing plates for both lithography and letterpress are made of various metals and for smaller lithographic presses, even of plastic or composition material. The ingenious methods by which plates are prepared so that they will "hold" an emulsion and a printing ink vary considerably and do not concern the cartographer. Whatever their composition and method of preparation the printing surface is made light sensitive (see Fig. 14.3). The negative or film positive is placed on the surface of the plate, and the two are put in a vacuum frame and exposed to arc light long enough so that the light may effect a change in the sensitive surface. Whether the plate is to be etched deeply for letterpress, lightly for deep-etch lithography, or practically not at all for standard lithography makes no difference to the cartographer. By the time this stage of the printing process has been reached the "die is almost cast," for that map. It is possible, however, to take advantage of one opportunity at this stage—multiple exposing of the plate. Separate negatives may be "burned" on the plate one after the other, in perfect register, so that the resulting

FIGURE 14.3. Sensitizing the printing plate. The printing plate is here shown in a "whirler," which rotates it to spread smoothly the emulsion being poured on it. (Courtesy Rand McNally and Company.)

printing plate is a composite. The advantage of this will be described in Article 14.18. It is also possible at this stage to apply screens directly to the printing plate. These are called Ben Day patterns and may also be added during the negative stage as previously described.

Presswork involves placing the completed plate in exact position on the press, inking the press so that just the right amount is applied to each part of the plate, and feeding the paper through the press (see Fig. 14.4). Except for the fact that rough changes, such as removing a mark, can be made on the plate after it has been made ready for the press, the cartographer has no further part in the printing process. He must depend at this stage on the skill of the pressman for such things as an even impression, proper inking, and maintenance of correct registry.

Although the principles of the process are straightforward, the details may vary con-

siderably because of the different methods, letterpress and lithography, and because of variations resulting from different metals, emulsions, and the like. Consequently the student should take the opportunity to visit printing establishments in order to observe this fascinating process which is so important in present-day cartography.

14.13   SCRIBING

The technical production phases of cartography have continually undergone change since the invention of printing. The development of etching techniques, lithography, color printing, offset processes, photography in all its applications, and many other innovations exemplify the steady development of the processes by which a map is prepared for printing. Almost the equal of photography in its potential effect is the scribing process, which has come into use since 1940.*

Scribing is a technique almost the opposite of drafting with pen and ink. In drafting, the desired lines and marks are applied by the draftsman; in scribing, the desired marks are obtained by the draftsman removing material. The draftsman starts with a sheet of plastic film to which a translucent coating has been applied. Then working over a light-table, he removes the coating by cutting and scraping to produce the lines and symbols. When he is finished, the sheet has the same general appearance as a negative made photographically. The scribe coating is compounded so that, among other properties, it is visually translucent but actinically opaque, that is, opaque to those wavelengths of light by which light sensitive emulsions are especially affected. This

FIGURE 14.4. A modern printing press. This is a two-color offset press. (Courtesy Rand McNally and Company.)

makes it possible to use the scribed sheet in place of the negative in the plate-making operation. Since the photographic step is unnecessary there is considerable cost saving.

Scribing also lends itself to many other advantageous methods of map preparation, only a few of which can be suggested in this book. For example, a map may be scribed on a sheet with a white coating. When backed with black paper in the copy frame a normal negative can be made. Standard positive stickup may be used on the scribe sheet.

Scribing is a direct substitute for pen and ink drafting. It has been found that, for many kinds of maps, it generally results in better quality line and symbol work with less effort and experience on the draftsman's part, all in a shorter period of time. It has been adopted as the standard "drafting" technique by most federal mapping agencies. It also has considerable application to small-scale cartography where printing is the end process, especially when color reproduction is involved. On the other hand, it should

---

* For a concise description of the scribing process and its applications (with bibliography) see the *Report on Scribing*, Part I, by the Inter-Agency Committee on Negative Scribing, Washington, D.C., 1957. Parts II and III are scheduled for publication. Available from the Map Information Office, U. S. Geological Survey, Washington 25, D.C.

be pointed out that ordinary "pen and ink" drafting procedures are still standard methods for much of small-scale and special cartography; they are likely to remain so for some time to come. As the base materials, the scribe coatings, and the scribing tools become steadily better, as their costs decrease, and as the process becomes more widely known it will be used more and more as a drafting technique. It is, as yet, relatively new, and vigorous research is being pushed to develop its obvious potentialities.

14.14   SCRIBE BASE MATERIALS, COATINGS, AND INSTRUMENTS

The base material used for most scribing is either of two commercially developed translucent plastics, Vinylite and Mylar "D." Glass can also be employed, but because it is breakable, heavy, and dangerous it is not widely used. Either of the plastics is sufficiently hard so that the tools can cut through the coating and glide across the surface without gouging. In general, Vinylite is easier to use. These two plastics are also nearly dimensionally stable, the difference being of significance only in unusual circumstances. Dimensional stability is extremely important in connection with color printing and also when a single base map is to be used for a variety of subsequent special maps. The sheets are commonly used in thicknesses of 0.0075 inch (Mylar), 0.010 inch (either Mylar or Vinylite), or 0.015 inch (Vinylite). The first two are recommended for most cartographic work, with 0.010 inch for general use and 0.0075 inch for especially precise effects. It is not advisable to use the two plastics on the same operation because they do not have quite the same coefficients of expansion.

The requirements of a scribe coating are many and include such qualities as: sufficient translucency to enable its use as a tracing medium, actinically opaque, non-

abrasive to the instruments, tight adherence to the base material, easy removal of the coating with graver points, and a number of others of more particular importance in special operations. Commercial outlets now supply precoated sheets. An important advantage of the scribing technique is the fact that it is possible to apply an image to the coating which then acts as a guide for the scribing of separation "negatives" in register. Commercial water-based sensitizers are available which can be applied to the coated sheet and, after exposure, developed with a weak ammonia solution.

A large variety of instruments has been developed for scribing. They range from gravers which make lines and dots in the coating to templates of various kinds with which the graver can be guided to produce symbols; they also include the special sharpening tools needed to maintain the conical or wedge-shaped graver points. Most gravers are held in a rigid position by an assembly which glides easily over the scribe coating. Some of these are illustrated in Fig. 14.5.

14.15   LINE AND HALFTONE

All copy, that is, original drawings or anything else to be printed, belongs to either of two classes, line copy and halftone copy. The distinguishing characteristic that places a drawing in one or the other class is whether or not it contains any color shading or gray tones. If it does, it is halftone copy and must be dealt with in the reproduction process by a different (and more costly) procedure. The significance of this division results from the fact that the ordinary printing processes depend upon printing from a surface that is either inked or is not inked. There is no such thing in lithography and letterpress as "halfway inking."

It is possible, however, to make a printed area appear gray, or shade from light to dark (continuous tone), as if the surface had

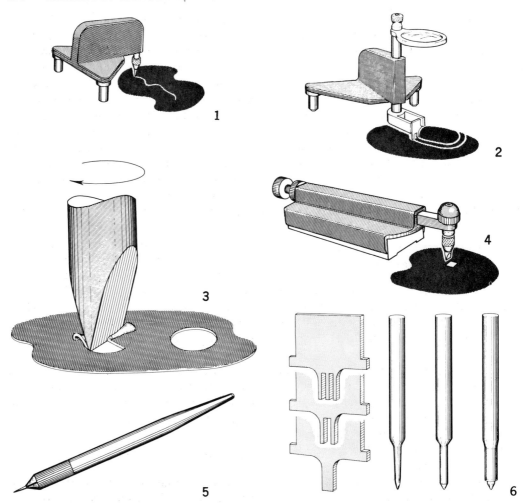

FIGURE 14.5. Some of the kinds of scribing instruments used to remove the scribe coating. At the top are shown a rigid graver (1) and a swivel graver (2), both of which are used for line work. The dot graver (3) and the "building" graver (4) are used to make small circular or square openings in the coating, such as for dots or buildings on a topographic map. The pen-type graver (5) is used for freehand work, and at the right (6) are shown some of the types of graver points, such as the single or multiple chisel-edged points and needle points. (Courtesy the U. S. Geological Survey.)

more or less ink on it. The process, half-toning, is accomplished by transforming the tone area into a large number of small dots of different sizes, depending upon whether it is to be dark or light. The dots print ink, and the spaces between do not. The dots are so close together that the eye is unable to distinguish them easily, so that the com-bination of inked spots and white spaces blends and appears as a tone.

The tone area is broken up by inserting a special screen directly in front of the emul-sion. This screen is either on film or is made of two circular sheets of glass on which fine, parallel, closely spaced grooves have been cut. The grooves are filled with

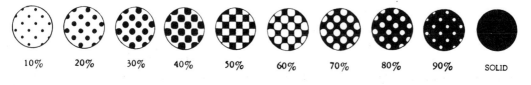

10%   20%   30%   40%   50%   60%   70%   80%   90%   SOLID

FIGURE 14.6. How tonal values are recorded by halftone dots. The circles above the percentage figures show how the dots would appear if greatly magnified. Compare with Fig. 14.7. These also show the dot formation (magnified) of screening media such as Artype when it is used directly on the drawing. The band at the bottom shows the range of dot formations from about 20% to 80%. (Courtesy of the Chicago Lithographic Institute, Inc.)

opaque paint, and the two sheets are cemented together so that the grooves are at right angles to one another. The light that passes through the screen is rendered as dots on the emulsion. All other things being equal, the closer the grooves the smaller and closer together the dots will be. The closer together they are, the more difficult it is for the eye to see them individually and the smoother and more natural the result will appear. Screens range from 40 or 50 to more than 200 lines per inch. A screen of 120 lines to the inch provides more than 14,000 dots per square inch!

The size of the printing dots relative to the white spaces between is dependent upon the darkness or lightness of the tones on the copy. It should be remembered, however, that unless special additional processing takes place, no part of a halftone will be without dots. All lines and lettering will therefore have fuzzy edges. Pure whites on the original drawing, in ordinary halftoning, be printed with a covering of very small dots and therefore a light tone, whereas solid areas will reproduce with small white spaces rather than being completely solid. These effects can be removed by

opaquing or scraping on the halftone negative, but this is difficult if the areas involved are complex. One of the reasons why halftoning is so expensive is that just the right distribution of the dot sizes is rarely obtained by photography alone. It is frequently necessary for a skilled operator to adjust

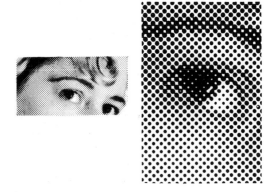

FIGURE 14.7. How a halftone looks under magnification. The right-hand illustration shows clearly that the *number* of dots per unit area remains uniform; only their sizes vary. Compare with any photograph in this book, for example, Fig. 14.4, under a strong magnifying glass. (Courtesy of the Chicago Lithographic Institute, Inc.)

the sizes of the dots after photography. This is a delicate operation, to say the least.

Since ordinary halftoning at least doubles the cost of reproduction, there is considerable saving if the cartographer can gain a similar effect with line copy. This can be done by

(1) Shading either uniformly or for continuous-tone effect by hatching or stippling with pen and ink, "spatter painting" with an air brush, or shading on a coarse, rough surface.

(2) Using preprinted symbols on the drawing.

(3) Screening portions of the negative by covering them with shading film.

(4) Using Ross or Coquille board for continuous-tone effect.

(5) Using Ben Day screens on the negative or on the printing plate for uniform shading.

(6) Using specially prepared drawing papers, such as Craftint Singletone or Doubletone.

The variety of methods available and the commercial materials that have been developed to simulate continuous tone by line methods are ample evidence, of the significant savings that can be accomplished if copy does not require halftoning.

14.16   COLOR REPRODUCTION

The reproduction of maps in color does not differ from black reproduction except that different colored inks are used. Each separate ink requires, of course, a separate printing plate, and thus a complete duplication of the steps in the whole process. Thus, generally speaking, the costs of color reproduction are many times that of the single color (usually black) reproduction. There are, however, two basically different color reproduction processes, and it is unwise to generalize further about relative costs. The two processes are called "flat color" and "process color." The major difference between them is that the color copy for process color is prepared as a single color drawing, whereas that for flat color is prepared in black and white and usually requires a different drawing for each ink.

Flat color is the method most often used for maps and involves a straightforward procedure that varies little from the procedure described previously. For the flat color procedure the map is planned for a certain number of colored printing inks, and a separate drawing is prepared for each ink. Of course, many combinations of line and halftone effects are possible.

Process color, or more properly four-color process, is the name applied to an essentially different procedure. This method is based on the fact that almost all color combinations can be obtained by varying mixtures of red, yellow, blue, white, and black. The copy consists usually of two pieces, the color drawing and a black line plate. The black plate usually contains the border (if any), lettering, grid, outlines, etc., and is the base for a blue-line board (see Article 14.17). On the blue line all color work is done by painting, airbrush, etc. The color copy is photographed three times, each time through an appropriate color filter and a halftone screen, so that the three printing plates are halftones of the varying amounts of the primary colors. The black plate is treated as a line drawing. When printed together again the halftone dots and transparent inks merge and recreate the colors of the original drawing. The process is expensive because it is exacting. Much work by highly skilled persons is necessary on the halftone negatives, and the combination of halftone negatives, their modification, and careful processing throughout the printing process is time consuming.

Process color allows smooth gradations of hues and tints composed of mixtures of hues. The reproduction of color photographs and painted art work in popular magazines is

done by process color. Extremely careful manipulation of prepared screens can produce similar hue combinations by the flat color process, although the colors produced must necessarily be uniform over their map extent, that is, no gradations or continuous hue changes are ordinarily possible. Soil maps, altitude tint maps in atlases, and other maps containing many hue combinations are examples. Such hue combinations are not usually prepared by the cartographer for photography. Instead he tapes tracing paper or tissue "overlays" or "flaps" on his drawings, outlines and identifies the areas to be colored, and specifies for the printer the color combinations he desires. He must always consult with the printer before proceeding.

The preceding explanation of the principal color processes used in reproducing maps is greatly abbreviated and simplified, but it is included in order that the student may have an idea of the basic procedures. If the student is interested in color reproduction he may investigate these interesting processes more carefully through reading (see bibliography) and especially by visits to printing plants where this type of work is done.

14.17   REGISTER

The basic mechanical problem of multicolor map preparation and double printing of photographic negatives or scribe negatives is register. Register involves (1) preparing the individual drawings so that they fit one another exactly in all respects, and (2) maintaining this perfect fit through the processing which results in the printed maps. The first involves knowing precisely where to draft the lines, symbols, lettering, etc., on the different drawings which are to be combined, and the second requires that the materials maintain their size and shape while being processed. Ever since color map reproduction was first begun more than a century ago register has been a problem of first

magnitude. Register may be maintained in a number of ways:

(1) by using a dimensionally stable drawing surface, (2) by using blue-line boards, and (3) by negative separation. Whatever the method employed, great care must be expended to maintain as perfect registry as possible.

To facilitate register during the drafting and processing of the map, small crosses, called register marks, are placed on the four margins of every plate (drawing) of the copy in exactly the same place on each (see Fig. 14.8). The marks are retained on the negatives and on the printing plate. As soon as the plate has been properly adjusted on the press they are removed. When drafting with ink or using scribe sheets it is also common practice to punch precisely matched holes in the various sheets. Pegs or studs can be inserted in the holes, and the various overlays will register perfectly. Register marks are also necessary so that they will appear on the press plates.

The larger the drawing and the reproduction the more important is the use of dimen-

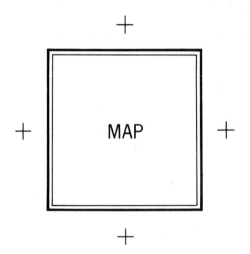

FIGURE 14.8. Register marks showing their usual position. They are placed close to the margins and are made with very thin lines.

sionally stable materials. Plastics (Vinylite and Mylar) are stable, and some drawing papers and tracing papers can be used in the smaller sizes. If drawing papers or tracing papers are used, care must be taken that the grain of the paper runs in the same direction on each overlay or drawing, so that if expansion or contraction does take place it will be more nearly uniform on each.

The blue-line board, if carefully used, is an excellent method of maintaining register for relatively complex color maps. In this process the original copy for the black plate is drafted and all boundaries of color areas are included. The printer can supply from this drawing any number of same-size reproductions in light blue on a white drawing surface. The common blue lines are on heavy paper or illustration board. The light blue is nonphotographic and serves as a guide for further drafting. All areas and lines (including register marks) to be printed in red, for example, are drafted in black, screened, etc., on one board; all areas in blue, or whatever the color may be, are drafted on another, and so on. The lines used only for color guides on the original black plate drawing may be removed from the drawing, or opaqued on the negative later. The cartographer then delivers a series of black and white "separation drawings," properly labeled, to the printer who treats them as single pieces of copy through the entire process. The pressman prints them on top of one another in the appropriate inks, and a multicolor map results.

Another method of insuring register, which is appropriate under some circumstances, is for the cartographer to draft all lines of all colors on the same drawing. This is photographed, and as many duplicate negatives are made as there are colors-to-be. These may then be opaqued in such a way as to leave on each negative only that which is to be printed in a particular color. Screens, etc., may be added as usual to the negatives, and the final separation negatives are the same as would have resulted from separation drawings.

Translucence of the drawing media is extremely desirable in the preparation of the separation drawings for multicolor maps. Regardless of the care that may be taken to anticipate registry and drafting details, there are always a series of subsequent decisions that must be made, such as where exactly to start or stop a line or where to place a symbol. Until recently translucence and drafting qualities have been combined only in drawing and tracing papers which are not dimensionally stable. This is one reason why drafting on stable translucent plastics has gained so much favor. The ability to sensitize the scribe coating and thereby to obtain the guide image mechanically on an optically translucent, dimensionally stable drafting medium is an important reason for the growing popularity of the scribing process. In addition to its other potentialities, it therefore combines the advantages of the image on a blue-line board with the desirable quality of an optically translucent "drawing" surface.

There are many ways to proceed toward the same end result in preparing multiple drawings for reproduction, and each engraver and printer has his "standard operating procedure." It is always wise to confer with the printer in order to plan in detail the exact drafting operations to be followed.

14.18 MULTIPLE USE OF FILM NEGATIVES AND POSITIVES

It has perhaps already occurred to the student that the negatives and positives used to prepare the printing plates lend themselves to various combinations. For example, it is possible to expose two negatives simultaneously, one a halftone and the other a line negative, on the same printing plate; or part of the negative used for one plate may be reversed and used as a film positive and be the basis for another printing plate.

The following example will illustrate some of the short-cuts possible, which not only save drafting time but result in a better final product as well. Suppose a map of North America is to be made, and on the printed final map it is desired that the oceans be a blue tint (screened) with white (reverse) lettering, the land be a brown tint (screened) and the line work (boundaries, etc.) on the land be black. This will require three printing plates, one for each color. Yet only two drawings need be prepared and one of them is very simple (see Fig. 14.9).

The two drawings are:

I. All line work drafted in black including
    a. Grid on oceans.
    b. Boundaries and coastline.
    c. All lettering in black.
II. A masking drawing consisting of
    a. Black oceans (most easily done with red Zip-A-Tone or some other stripping material).

The processing of these two drawings is as follows:

A. One negative of the line drawing is made (transparent lines on opaque background).
B. One film positive of the line drawing is made (opaque lines on transparent background).
C. One negative of the masking drawing is made (opaque land on transparent ocean).
D. One film positive of the masking drawing is made (opaque ocean on transparent land).

The printing plates are made as follows:

(1) Negative A is combined with film positive D to provide a black printing plate with coastline, boundaries, and lettering on the land.
(2) Film positive D is screened and provides a brown printing plate with a tint on all the land.
(3) Film positive B is combined with screened negative C which provides a blue-tint ocean with white (reversed) lettering and white grid ending at the land.

There is an unlimited number of possibilities of producing interesting effects by combining various negatives and film positives, and by using various kinds of screens in combination with negatives. An interesting and instructive exercise for the student of cartography is to try to analyze the methods by which the color or black and white maps that are available to him have been reproduced, and to suggest alternative ways of arriving at the same or better results.

DRAWINGS

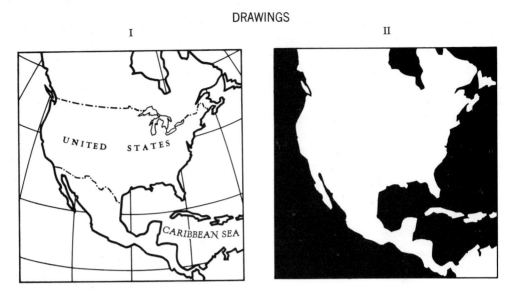

NEGATIVES AND FILM POSITIVES

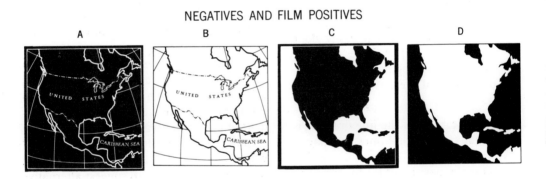

PRINTING PLATES PRODUCED BY:

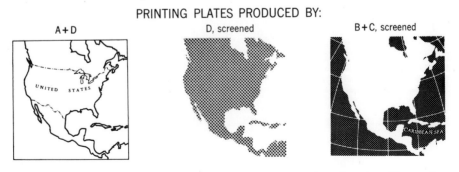

FIGURE 14.9. An example of possible negative manipulation and combination. The numbers and letters are keyed to the explanation in Article 14.18. The coarseness of the screens is, of course, exaggerated.

Common Logarithms

The common logarithm of a number is the power to which 10 must be raised to equal that number. For example, the number $356 = 10^{2.55145}$; therefore, the logarithm of 356 is 2.55145. The integer to the left of the decimal point in a logarithm is called the *characteristic.* The decimal fractional part of the logarithm (the numbers to the right of the decimal point) is called the *mantissa.* The logarithm of any number in which the same integers are in the same order, for example, 35,600, or 35.60, or 0.03560, has the same mantissa but a different characteristic. Characteristics are easy to determine; hence tables of logarithms show only the mantissas.

When any number is equal to or greater than 1, then the characteristic of its logarithm is positive, and it is numerically *one less* than the number of places to the left of the decimal point in the original number. When any number is less than one, then the characteristic of its logarithm is negative, and it is numerically *one more* than the number of zeros immediately to the right of the decimal point. For example:

Number		Logarithm
	Etc.	
35,600.0		4.55145
3,560.0		3.55145
356.0		2.55145
35.60		1.55145

3.560	0.55145
0.3560	-1.55145 or $9.55145 - 10$
0.03560	-2.55145 or $8.55145 - 10$
0.003560	-3.55145 or $7.55145 - 10$
Etc.	

When one adds or subtracts logarithms that have negative characteristics, it is usually convenient to use the method of notation shown at the far right in the preceding table.

Logarithms are used for the multiplication and division of large or complex numbers. When the logarithm of any number is *added* to the logarithm of any other number, for example, $\log x + \log y$, the sum of the two logarithms is the logarithm of the *product* of the two numbers, that is, $\log x + \log y = \log$ of xy. The numerical value of the product of xy is obtained by finding the mantissa of the sum in the table, noting the number to which it refers (called the *antilogarithm*), and then placing the decimal point according to the value of the characteristic. Similarly, $\log x - \log y = \log$ of $x \div y$. Consequently, multiplication and division of large or complex numbers are enormously simplified by using logarithms.

Powers and roots of numbers may be easily obtained with the aid of logarithms, as illustrated below. The logarithm of any number, when *directly multiplied* by a number, provides the logarithm of that power of

the original number. For example, 356 × 356 = 356² = 126,736; the logarithm of 356 is 2.55145; 2.55145 × 2 = 5.10290, which is the logarithm of 126,736. Note that the logarithm is directly multiplied by the numerical value of the power, 2 in this example. Similarly, any root of any num-ber may be obtained by *directly dividing* the logarithm of the number by the numerical value of the root desired. For example, the logarithm 2.55145 divided by 2 = 1.275725, which is the logarithm of 18.86, which is the approximate square root of 356.

USEFUL FORMULAS AND RELATIONSHIPS AND THEIR LOGARITHMS

Relationship	Number or formula	Logarithm
Area of a circle	πr^2	
Area of a sphere	$4\pi r^2$	
Area of an ellipse	πab	
The circumference to the diameter of a circle (π)	3.141593	0.49715
Statute miles in equatorial circumference	24 899	4.39618
Kilometers in equatorial circumference	40 075	4.60286
Miles in radius of sphere of equal area	3 958.5	3.59753
Kilometers in radius of sphere of equal area	6 371	3.80418
Square miles in area of earth	197 260 000 (approx.)	8.29504
Square kilometers in area of earth	510 900 000 (approx.)	8.70834
Inches in one foot	12.0	1.07918
Feet in one statute mile	5 280.0	3.72263
Inches in one statute mile	63 360.0	4.80182
Statute miles in one nautical mile (Int.)	1.1508	0.06099
Inches in one centimeter	0.3937	9.59517–10
Centimeters in one inch	2.540	0.40483
Statute miles in one kilometer	0.62137	9.79335–10
Kilometers in one statute mile	1.60935	0.20665
Feet in one kilometer	3 280.83	3.51598
Square statute miles in one square kilometer	0.3861	9.58670–10
Square kilometers in one square statute mile	2.590	0.41330

Note: Because of rounding of numbers and differences in definitions some internal inconsistencies appear in the above table.

TRIGONOMETRIC FUNCTIONS OF AN ACUTE ANGLE IN A RIGHT TRIANGLE

$$\text{sine} = \frac{\text{opposite side}}{\text{hypotenuse}}$$

$$\text{cosine} = \frac{\text{adjacent side}}{\text{hypotenuse}}$$

$$\text{tangent} = \frac{\text{opposite side}}{\text{adjacent side}}$$

$$\text{cotangent} = \frac{\text{adjacent side}}{\text{opposite side}}$$

$$\text{secant} = \frac{\text{hypotenuse}}{\text{adjacent side}}$$

$$\text{cosecant} = \frac{\text{hypotenuse}}{\text{opposite side}}$$

TABLE A.1 FIVE-PLACE LOGARITHMS: 100—150

N	0	1	2	3	4	5	6	7	8	9
100	00 000	043	087	130	173	217	260	303	346	389
01	432	475	518	561	604	647	689	732	775	817
02	00 860	903	945	988	*030	*072	*115	*157	*199	*242
03	01 284	326	368	410	452	494	536	578	620	662
04	01 703	745	787	828	870	912	953	995	*036	*078
05	02 119	160	202	243	284	325	366	407	449	490
06	531	572	612	653	694	735	776	816	857	898
07	02 938	979	*019	*060	*100	*141	*181	*222	*262	*302
08	03 342	383	423	463	503	543	583	623	663	703
09	03 743	782	822	862	902	941	981	*021	*060	*100
110	04 139	179	218	258	297	336	376	415	454	493
11	532	571	610	650	689	727	766	805	844	883
12	04 922	961	999	*038	*077	*115	*154	*192	*231	*269
13	05 308	346	385	423	461	500	538	576	614	652
14	05 690	729	767	805	843	881	918	956	994	*032
15	06 070	108	145	183	221	258	296	333	371	408
16	446	483	521	558	595	633	670	707	744	781
17	06 819	856	893	930	967	*004	*041	*078	*115	*151
18	07 188	225	262	298	335	372	408	445	482	518
19	555	591	628	664	700	737	773	809	846	882
120	07 918	954	990	*027	*063	*099	*135	*171	*207	*243
21	08 279	314	350	386	422	458	493	529	565	600
22	636	672	707	743	778	814	849	884	920	955
23	08 991	*026	*061	*096	*132	*167	*202	*237	*272	*307
24	09 342	377	412	447	482	517	552	587	621	656
25	09 691	726	760	795	830	864	899	934	968	*003
26	10 037	072	106	140	175	209	243	278	312	346
27	380	415	449	483	517	551	585	619	653	687
28	10 721	755	789	823	857	890	924	958	992	*025
29	11 059	093	126	160	193	227	261	294	327	361
130	394	428	461	494	528	561	594	628	661	694
31	11 727	760	793	826	860	893	926	959	992	*024
32	12 057	090	123	156	189	222	254	287	320	352
33	385	418	450	483	516	548	581	613	646	678
34	12 710	743	775	808	840	872	905	937	969	*001
35	13 033	066	098	130	162	194	226	258	290	322
36	354	386	418	450	481	513	545	577	609	640
37	672	704	735	767	799	830	862	893	925	956
38	13 988	*019	*051	*082	*114	*145	*176	*208	*239	*270
39	14 301	333	364	395	426	457	489	520	551	582
140	613	644	675	706	737	768	799	829	860	891
41	14 922	953	983	*014	*045	*076	*106	*137	*168	*198
42	15 229	259	290	320	351	381	412	442	473	503
43	534	564	594	625	655	685	715	746	776	806
44	15 836	866	897	927	957	987	*017	*047	*077	*107
45	16 137	167	197	227	256	286	316	346	376	406
46	435	465	495	524	554	584	613	643	673	702
47	16 732	761	791	820	850	879	909	938	967	997
48	17 026	056	085	114	143	173	202	231	260	289
49	319	348	377	406	435	464	493	522	551	580
150	17 609	638	667	696	725	754	782	811	840	869
N	0	1	2	3	4	5	6	7	8	9

Prop. Parts

	44	43	42
1	4.4	4.3	4.2
2	8.8	8.6	8.4
3	13.2	12.9	12.6
4	17.6	17.2	16.8
5	22.0	21.5	21.0
6	26.4	25.8	25.2
7	30.8	30.1	29.4
8	35.2	34.4	33.6
9	39.6	38.7	37.8

	41	40	39
1	4.1	4	3.9
2	8.2	8	7.8
3	12.3	12	11.7
4	16.4	16	15.6
5	20.5	20	19.5
6	24.6	24	23.4
7	28.7	28	27.3
8	32.8	32	31.2
9	36.9	36	35.1

	38	37	36
1	3.8	3.7	3.6
2	7.6	7.4	7.2
3	11.4	11.1	10.8
4	15.2	14.8	14.4
5	19.0	18.5	18.0
6	22.8	22.2	21.6
7	26.6	25.9	25.2
8	30.4	29.6	28.8
9	34.2	33.3	32.4

	35	34	33
1	3.5	3.4	3.3
2	7.0	6.8	6.6
3	10.5	10.2	9.9
4	14.0	13.6	13.2
5	17.5	17.0	16.5
6	21.0	20.4	19.8
7	24.5	23.8	23.1
8	28.0	27.2	26.4
9	31.5	30.6	29.7

	32	31	30
1	3.2	3.1	3
2	6.4	6.2	6
3	9.6	9.3	9
4	12.8	12.4	12
5	16.0	15.5	15
6	19.2	18.6	18
7	22.4	21.7	21
8	25.6	24.8	24
9	28.8	27.9	27

TABLE A.1   FIVE-PLACE LOGARITHMS: 150—200

Proportional Parts:

	29	28
1	2.9	2.8
2	5.8	5.6
3	8.7	8.4
4	11.6	11.2
5	14.5	14.0
6	17.4	16.8
7	20.3	19.6
8	23.2	22.4
9	26.1	25.2

	27	26
1	2.7	2.6
2	5.4	5.2
3	8.1	7.8
4	10.8	10.4
5	13.5	13.0
6	16.2	15.6
7	18.9	18.2
8	21.6	20.8
9	24.3	23.4

	25
1	2.5
2	5.0
3	7.5
4	10.0
5	12.5
6	15.0
7	17.5
8	20.0
9	22.5

	24	23
1	2.4	2.3
2	4.8	4.6
3	7.2	6.9
4	9.6	9.2
5	12.0	11.5
6	14.4	13.8
7	16.8	16.1
8	19.2	18.4
9	21.6	20.7

	22	21
1	2.2	2.1
2	4.4	4.2
3	6.6	6.3
4	8.8	8.4
5	11.0	10.5
6	13.2	12.6
7	15.4	14.7
8	17.6	16.8
9	19.8	18.9

N	0	1	2	3	4	5	6	7	8	9
150	17 609	638	667	696	725	754	782	811	840	869
51	17 898	926	955	984	*013	*041	*070	*099	*127	*156
52	18 184	213	241	270	298	327	355	384	412	441
53	469	498	526	554	583	611	639	667	696	724
54	18 752	780	808	837	865	893	921	949	977	*005
55	19 033	061	089	117	145	173	201	229	257	285
56	312	340	368	396	424	451	479	507	535	562
57	590	618	645	673	700	728	756	783	811	838
58	19 866	893	921	948	976	*003	*030	*058	*085	*112
59	20 140	167	194	222	249	276	303	330	358	385
160	412	439	466	493	520	548	575	602	629	656
61	683	710	737	763	790	817	844	871	898	925
62	20 952	978	*005	*032	*059	*085	*112	*139	*165	*192
63	21 219	245	272	299	325	352	378	405	431	458
64	484	511	537	564	590	617	643	669	696	722
65	21 748	775	801	827	854	880	906	932	958	985
66	22 011	037	063	089	115	141	167	194	220	246
67	272	298	324	350	376	401	427	453	479	505
68	531	557	583	608	634	660	686	712	737	763
69	22 789	814	840	866	891	917	943	968	994	*019
170	23 045	070	096	121	147	172	198	223	249	274
71	300	325	350	376	401	426	452	477	502	528
72	553	578	603	629	654	679	704	729	754	779
73	23 805	830	855	880	905	930	955	980	*005	*030
74	24 055	080	105	130	155	180	204	229	254	279
75	304	329	353	378	403	428	452	477	502	527
76	551	576	601	625	650	674	699	724	748	773
77	24 797	822	846	871	895	920	944	969	993	*018
78	25 042	066	091	115	139	164	188	212	237	261
79	285	310	334	358	382	406	431	455	479	503
180	527	551	575	600	624	648	672	696	720	744
81	25 768	792	816	840	864	888	912	935	959	983
82	26 007	031	055	079	102	126	150	174	198	221
83	245	269	293	316	340	364	387	411	435	458
84	482	505	529	553	576	600	623	647	670	694
85	717	741	764	788	811	834	858	881	905	928
86	26 951	975	998	*021	*045	*068	*091	*114	*138	*161
87	27 184	207	231	254	277	300	323	346	370	393
88	416	439	462	485	508	531	554	577	600	623
89	646	669	692	715	738	761	784	807	830	852
190	27 875	898	921	944	967	989	*012	*035	*058	*081
91	28 103	126	149	171	194	217	240	262	285	307
92	330	353	375	398	421	443	466	488	511	533
93	556	578	601	623	646	668	691	713	735	758
94	28 780	803	825	847	870	892	914	937	959	981
95	29 003	026	048	070	092	115	137	159	181	203
96	226	248	270	292	314	336	358	380	403	425
97	447	469	491	513	535	557	579	601	623	645
98	667	688	710	732	754	776	798	820	842	863
99	29 885	907	929	951	973	994	*016	*038	*060	*081
200	30 103	125	146	168	190	211	233	255	276	298

TABLE A.1   FIVE-PLACE LOGARITHMS: 200—250

N	0	1	2	3	4	5	6	7	8	9	Prop. Parts
200	30 103	125	146	168	190	211	233	255	276	298	
01	320	341	363	384	406	428	449	471	492	514	
02	535	557	578	600	621	643	664	685	707	728	
03	750	771	792	814	835	856	878	899	920	942	
04	30 963	984	*006	*027	*048	*069	*091	*112	*133	*154	
05	31 175	197	218	239	260	281	302	323	345	366	
06	387	408	429	450	471	492	513	534	555	576	
07	597	618	639	660	681	702	723	744	765	785	
08	31 806	827	848	869	890	911	931	952	973	994	
09	32 015	035	056	077	098	118	139	160	181	201	
210	222	243	263	284	305	325	346	366	387	408	
11	428	449	469	490	510	531	552	572	593	613	
12	634	654	675	695	715	736	756	777	797	818	
13	32 838	858	879	899	919	940	960	980	*001	*021	
14	33 041	062	082	102	122	143	163	183	203	224	
15	244	264	284	304	325	345	365	385	405	425	
16	445	465	486	506	526	546	566	586	606	626	
17	646	666	686	706	726	746	766	786	806	826	
18	33 846	866	885	905	925	945	965	985	*005	*025	
19	34 044	064	084	104	124	143	163	183	203	223	
220	242	262	282	301	321	341	361	380	400	420	
21	439	459	479	498	518	537	557	577	596	616	
22	635	655	674	694	713	733	753	772	792	811	
23	34 830	850	869	889	908	928	947	967	986	*005	
24	35 025	044	064	083	102	122	141	160	180	199	
25	218	238	257	276	295	315	334	353	372	392	
26	411	430	449	468	488	507	526	545	564	583	
27	603	622	641	660	679	698	717	736	755	774	
28	793	813	832	851	870	889	908	927	946	965	
29	35 984	*003	*021	*040	*059	*078	*097	*116	*135	*154	
230	36 173	192	211	229	248	267	286	305	324	342	
31	361	380	399	418	436	455	474	493	511	530	
32	549	568	586	605	624	642	661	680	698	717	
33	736	754	773	791	810	829	847	866	884	903	
34	36 922	940	959	977	996	*014	*033	*051	*070	*088	
35	37 107	125	144	162	181	199	218	236	254	273	
36	291	310	328	346	365	383	420	420	438	457	
37	475	493	511	530	548	566	585	603	621	639	
38	658	676	694	712	731	749	767	785	803	822	
39	37 840	858	876	894	912	931	949	967	985	*003	
240	38 021	039	057	075	093	112	130	148	166	184	
41	202	220	238	256	274	292	310	328	346	364	
42	382	399	417	435	453	471	489	507	525	543	
43	561	578	596	614	632	650	668	686	703	721	
44	739	757	775	792	810	828	846	863	881	899	
45	38 917	934	952	970	987	*005	*023	*041	*058	*076	
46	39 094	111	129	146	164	182	199	217	235	252	
47	270	287	305	322	340	358	375	393	410	428	
48	445	463	480	498	515	533	550	568	585	602	
49	620	637	655	672	690	707	724	742	759	777	
250	39 794	811	829	846	863	881	898	915	933	950	
N	**0**	**1**	**2**	**3**	**4**	**5**	**6**	**7**	**8**	**9**	Prop. Parts

Prop. Parts

	22	21
1	2.2	2.1
2	4.4	4.2
3	6.6	6.3
4	8.8	8.4
5	11.0	10.5
6	13.2	12.6
7	15.4	14.7
8	17.6	16.8
9	19.8	18.9

	20
1	2
2	4
3	6
4	8
5	10
6	12
7	14
8	16
9	18

	19
1	1.9
2	3.8
3	5.7
4	7.6
5	9.5
6	11.4
7	13.3
8	15.2
9	17.1

	18
1	1.8
2	3.6
3	5.4
4	7.2
5	9.0
6	10.8
7	12.6
8	14.4
9	16.2

	17
1	1.7
2	3.4
3	5.1
4	6.8
5	8.5
6	10.2
7	11.9
8	13.6
9	15.3

TABLE A.1   FIVE-PLACE LOGARITHMS: 250—300

N	0	1	2	3	4	5	6	7	8	9
250	39 794	811	829	846	863	881	898	915	933	950
51	39 967	985	*002	*019	*037	*054	*071	*088	*106	*123
52	40 140	157	175	192	209	226	243	261	278	295
53	312	329	346	364	381	398	415	432	449	466
54	483	500	518	535	552	569	586	603	620	637
55	654	671	688	705	722	739	756	773	790	807
56	824	841	858	875	892	909	926	943	960	976
57	40 993	*010	*027	*044	*061	*078	*095	*111	*128	*145
58	41 162	179	196	212	229	246	263	280	296	313
59	330	347	363	380	397	414	430	447	464	481
260	497	514	531	547	564	581	597	614	631	647
61	664	681	697	714	731	747	764	780	797	814
62	830	847	863	880	896	913	929	946	963	979
63	41 996	*012	*029	*045	*062	*078	*095	*111	*127	*144
64	42 160	177	193	210	226	243	259	275	292	308
65	325	341	357	374	390	406	423	439	455	472
66	488	504	521	537	553	570	586	602	619	635
67	651	667	684	700	716	732	749	765	781	797
68	813	830	846	862	878	894	911	927	943	959
69	42 975	991	*008	*024	*040	*056	*072	*088	*104	*120
270	43 136	152	169	185	201	217	233	249	265	281
71	297	313	329	345	361	377	393	409	425	441
72	457	473	489	505	521	537	553	569	584	600
73	616	632	648	664	680	696	712	727	743	759
74	775	791	807	823	838	854	870	886	902	917
75	43 933	949	965	981	996	*012	*028	*044	*059	*075
76	44 091	107	122	138	154	170	185	201	217	232
77	248	264	279	295	311	326	342	358	373	389
78	404	420	436	451	467	483	498	514	529	545
79	560	576	592	607	623	638	654	669	685	700
280	716	731	747	762	778	793	809	824	840	855
81	44 871	886	902	917	932	948	963	979	994	*010
82	45 025	040	056	071	086	102	117	133	148	163
83	179	194	209	225	240	255	271	286	301	317
84	332	347	362	378	393	408	423	439	454	469
85	484	500	515	530	545	561	576	591	606	621
86	637	652	667	682	697	712	728	743	758	773
87	788	803	818	834	849	864	879	894	909	924
88	45 939	954	969	984	*000	*015	*030	*045	*060	*075
89	46 090	105	120	135	150	165	180	195	21C	225
290	240	255	270	285	300	315	330	345	359	374
91	389	404	419	434	449	464	479	494	509	523
92	538	553	568	583	598	613	627	642	657	672
93	687	702	716	731	746	761	776	790	805	820
94	835	850	864	879	894	909	923	938	953	967
95	46 982	997	*012	*026	*041	*056	*070	*085	*100	*114
96	47 129	144	159	173	188	202	217	232	246	261
97	276	290	305	319	334	349	363	378	392	407
98	422	436	451	465	480	494	509	524	538	553
99	567	582	596	611	625	640	654	669	683	698
300	47 712	727	741	756	770	784	799	813	828	842

Prop. Parts

	18	17	16	15	14
1	1.8	1.7	1.6	1.5	1.4
2	3.6	3.4	3.2	3.0	2.8
3	5.4	5.1	4.8	4.5	4.2
4	7.2	6.8	6.4	6.0	5.6
5	9.0	8.5	8.0	7.5	7.0
6	10.8	10.2	9.6	9.0	8.4
7	12.6	11.9	11.2	10.5	9.8
8	14.4	13.6	12.8	12.0	11.2
9	16.2	15.3	14.4	13.5	12.6

TABLE A.1   FIVE-PLACE LOGARITHMS: 300—350

N	0	1	2	3	4	5	6	7	8	9	Prop. Parts	
300	47 712	727	741	756	770	784	799	813	828	842		
01	47 857	871	885	900	914	929	943	958	972	986		
02	48 001	015	029	044	058	073	087	101	116	130		
03	144	159	173	187	202	216	230	244	259	273		**15**
04	287	302	316	330	344	359	373	387	401	416	1	1.5
05	430	444	458	473	487	501	515	530	544	558	2	3.0
06	572	586	601	615	629	643	657	671	686	700	3	4.5
											4	6.0
07	714	728	742	756	770	785	799	813	827	841	5	7.5
08	855	869	883	897	911	926	940	954	968	982	6	9.0
09	48 996	*010	*024	*038	*052	*066	*080	*094	*108	*122	7	10.5
											8	12.0
310	49 136	150	164	178	192	206	220	234	248	262	9	13.5
11	276	290	304	318	332	346	360	374	388	402		
12	415	429	443	457	471	485	499	513	527	541		
13	554	568	582	596	610	624	638	651	665	679		
14	693	707	721	734	748	762	776	790	803	817		
15	831	845	859	872	886	900	914	927	941	955		
16	49 969	982	996	*010	*024	*037	*051	*065	*079	*092		**14**
17	50 106	120	133	147	161	174	188	202	215	229	1	1.4
18	243	256	270	284	297	311	325	338	352	365	2	2.8
19	379	393	406	420	433	447	461	474	488	501	3	4.2
											4	5.6
320	515	529	542	556	569	583	596	610	623	637	5	7.0
21	651	664	678	691	705	718	732	745	759	772	6	8.4
22	786	799	813	826	840	853	866	880	893	907	7	9.8
23	50 920	934	947	961	974	987	*001	*014	*028	*041	8	11.2
											9	12.6
24	51 055	068	081	095	108	121	135	148	162	175		
25	188	202	215	228	242	255	268	282	295	308		
26	322	335	348	362	375	388	402	415	428	441		
27	455	468	481	495	508	521	534	548	561	574		
28	587	601	614	627	640	654	667	680	693	706		
29	720	733	746	759	772	786	799	812	825	838		**13**
330	851	865	878	891	904	917	930	943	957	970	1	1.3
											2	2.6
31	51 983	996	*009	*022	*035	*048	*061	*075	*088	*101	3	3.9
32	52 114	127	140	153	166	179	192	205	218	231	4	5.2
33	244	257	270	284	297	310	323	336	349	362	5	6.5
											6	7.8
34	375	388	401	414	427	440	453	466	479	492	7	9.1
35	504	517	530	543	556	569	582	595	608	621	8	10.4
36	634	647	660	673	686	699	711	724	737	750	9	11.7
37	763	776	789	802	815	827	840	853	866	879		
38	52 892	905	917	930	943	956	969	982	994	*007		
39	53 020	033	046	058	071	084	097	110	122	135		
340	148	161	173	186	199	212	224	237	250	263		
41	275	288	301	314	326	339	352	364	377	390		**12**
42	403	415	428	441	453	466	479	491	504	517	1	1.2
43	529	542	555	567	580	593	605	618	631	643	2	2.4
											3	3.6
44	656	668	681	694	706	719	732	744	757	769	4	4.8
45	782	794	807	820	832	845	857	870	882	895	5	6.0
46	53 908	920	933	945	958	970	983	995	*008	*020	6	7.2
											7	8.4
47	54 033	045	058	070	083	095	108	120	133	145	8	9.6
48	158	170	183	195	208	220	233	245	258	270	9	10.8
49	283	295	307	320	332	345	357	370	382	394		
350	54 407	419	432	444	456	469	481	494	506	518		
N	0	1	2	3	4	5	6	7	8	9	Prop. Parts	

TABLE A.1   FIVE-PLACE LOGARITHMS: 350—400

N	0	1	2	3	4	5	6	7	8	9
350	54 407	419	432	444	456	469	481	494	506	518
51	531	543	555	568	580	593	605	617	630	642
52	654	667	679	691	704	716	728	741	753	765
53	777	790	802	814	827	839	851	864	876	888
54	54 900	913	925	937	949	962	974	986	998	*011
55	55 023	035	047	060	072	084	096	108	121	133
56	145	157	169	182	194	206	218	230	242	255
57	267	279	291	303	315	328	340	352	364	376
58	388	400	413	425	437	449	461	473	485	497
59	509	522	534	546	558	570	582	594	606	618
360	630	642	654	666	678	691	703	715	727	739
61	751	763	775	787	799	811	823	835	847	859
62	871	883	895	907	919	931	943	955	967	979
63	55 991	*003	*015	*027	*038	*050	*062	*074	*086	*098
64	56 110	122	134	146	158	170	182	194	205	217
65	229	241	253	265	277	289	301	312	324	336
66	348	360	372	384	396	407	419	431	443	455
67	467	478	490	502	514	526	538	549	561	573
68	585	597	608	620	632	644	656	667	679	691
69	703	714	726	738	750	761	773	785	797	808
370	820	832	844	855	867	879	891	902	914	926
71	56 937	949	961	972	984	996	*008	*019	*031	*043
72	57 054	066	078	089	101	113	124	136	148	159
73	171	183	194	206	217	229	241	252	264	276
74	287	299	310	322	334	345	357	368	380	392
75	403	415	426	438	449	461	473	484	496	507
76	519	530	542	553	565	576	588	600	611	623
77	634	646	657	669	680	692	703	715	726	738
78	749	761	772	784	795	807	818	830	841	852
79	864	875	887	898	910	921	933	944	955	967
380	57 978	990	*001	*013	*024	*035	*047	*058	*070	*081
81	58 092	104	115	127	138	149	161	172	184	195
82	206	218	229	240	252	263	274	286	297	309
83	320	331	343	354	365	377	388	399	410	422
84	433	444	456	467	478	490	501	512	524	535
85	546	557	569	580	591	602	614	625	636	647
86	659	670	681	692	704	715	726	737	749	760
87	771	782	794	805	816	827	838	850	861	872
88	883	894	906	917	928	939	950	961	973	984
89	58 995	*006	*017	*028	*040	*051	*062	*073	*084	*095
390	59 106	118	129	140	151	162	173	184	195	207
91	218	229	240	251	262	273	284	295	306	318
92	329	340	351	362	373	384	395	406	417	428
93	439	450	461	472	483	494	506	517	528	539
94	550	561	572	583	594	605	616	627	638	649
95	660	671	682	693	704	715	726	737	748	759
96	770	780	791	802	813	824	835	846	857	868
97	879	890	901	912	923	934	945	956	966	977
98	59 988	999	*010	*021	*032	*043	*054	*065	*076	*086
99	60 097	108	119	130	141	152	163	173	184	195
400	60 206	217	228	239	249	260	271	282	293	304

Prop. Parts

13	12	11	10
1 1.3	1 1.2	1 1.1	1 1.0
2 2.6	2 2.4	2 2.2	2 2.0
3 3.9	3 3.6	3 3.3	3 3.0
4 5.2	4 4.8	4 4.4	4 4.0
5 6.5	5 6.0	5 5.5	5 5.0
6 7.8	6 7.2	6 6.6	6 6.0
7 9.1	7 8.4	7 7.7	7 7.0
8 10.4	8 9.6	8 8.8	8 8.0
9 11.7	9 10.8	9 9.9	9 9.0

TABLE A.1   FIVE-PLACE LOGARITHMS: 400—450

N	0	1	2	3	4	5	6	7	8	9	Prop. Parts	
400	60 206	217	228	239	249	260	271	282	293	304		
01	314	325	336	347	358	369	379	390	401	412		
02	423	433	444	455	466	477	487	498	509	520		
03	531	541	552	563	574	584	595	606	617	627		
04	638	649	660	670	681	692	703	713	724	735		
05	746	756	767	778	788	799	810	821	831	842		
06	853	863	874	885	895	906	917	927	938	949		
07	60 959	970	981	991	*002	*013	*023	*034	*045	*055	1	11
08	61 066	077	087	098	109	119	130	140	151	162	2	1.1
09	172	183	194	204	215	225	236	247	257	268	3	2.2
410	278	289	300	310	321	331	342	352	363	374	4	3.3
11	384	395	405	416	426	437	448	458	469	479	5	4.4
12	490	500	511	521	532	542	553	563	574	584	6	5.5
13	595	606	616	627	637	648	658	669	679	690	7	6.6
14	700	711	721	731	742	752	763	773	784	794	8	7.7
15	805	815	826	836	847	857	868	878	888	899	9	8.8
16	61 909	920	930	941	951	962	972	982	993	*003		9.9
17	62 014	024	034	045	055	066	076	086	097	107		
18	118	128	138	149	159	170	180	190	201	211		
19	221	232	242	252	263	273	284	294	304	315		
420	325	335	346	356	366	377	387	397	408	418		
21	428	439	449	459	469	480	490	500	511	521		
22	531	542	552	562	572	583	593	603	613	624		
23	634	644	655	665	675	685	696	706	716	726	1	10
24	737	747	757	767	778	788	798	808	818	829	2	1.0
25	839	849	859	870	880	890	900	910	921	931	3	2.0
26	62 941	951	961	972	982	992	*002	*012	*022	*033	4	3.0
27	63 043	053	063	073	083	094	104	114	124	134	5	4.0
28	144	155	165	175	185	195	205	215	225	236	6	5.0
29	246	256	266	276	286	296	306	317	327	337	7	6.0
430	347	357	367	377	387	397	407	417	428	438	8	7.0
31	448	458	468	478	488	498	508	518	528	538	9	8.0
32	548	558	568	579	589	599	609	619	629	639		9.0
33	649	659	669	679	689	699	709	719	729	739		
34	749	759	769	779	789	799	809	819	829	839		
35	849	859	869	879	889	899	909	919	929	939		
36	63 949	959	969	979	988	998	*008	*018	*028	*038		
37	64 048	058	068	078	088	098	108	118	128	137		
38	147	157	167	177	187	197	207	217	227	237	1	9
39	246	256	266	276	286	296	306	316	326	335	2	0.9
440	345	355	365	375	385	395	404	414	424	434	3	1.8
41	444	454	464	473	483	493	503	513	523	532	4	2.7
42	542	552	562	572	582	591	601	611	621	631	5	3.6
43	640	650	660	670	680	689	699	709	719	729	6	4.5
44	738	748	758	768	777	787	797	807	816	826	7	5.4
45	836	846	856	865	875	885	895	904	914	924	8	6.3
46	64 933	943	953	963	972	982	992	*002	*011	*021	9	7.2
47	65 031	040	050	060	070	079	089	099	108	118		8.1
48	128	137	147	157	167	176	186	196	205	215		
49	225	234	244	254	263	273	283	292	302	312		
450	65 321	331	341	350	360	369	379	389	398	408		
N	0	1	2	3	4	5	6	7	8	9	Prop. Parts	

TABLE A.1   FIVE-PLACE LOGARITHMS: 450—500

N	0	1	2	3	4	5	6	7	8	9
450	65 321	331	341	350	360	369	379	389	398	408
51	418	427	437	447	456	466	475	485	495	504
52	514	523	533	543	552	562	571	581	591	600
53	610	619	629	639	648	658	667	677	686	696
54	706	715	725	734	744	753	763	772	782	792
55	801	811	820	830	839	849	858	868	877	887
56	896	906	916	925	935	944	954	963	973	982
57	65 992	*001	*011	*020	*030	*039	*049	*058	*068	*077
58	66 087	096	106	115	124	134	143	153	162	172
59	181	191	200	210	219	229	238	247	257	266
460	276	285	295	304	314	323	332	342	351	361
61	370	380	389	398	408	417	427	436	445	455
62	464	474	483	492	502	511	521	530	539	549
63	558	567	577	586	596	605	614	624	633	642
64	652	661	671	680	689	699	708	717	727	736
65	745	755	764	773	783	792	801	811	820	829
66	839	848	857	867	876	885	894	904	913	922
67	66 932	941	950	960	969	978	987	997	*006	*015
68	67 025	034	043	052	062	071	080	089	099	108
69	117	127	136	145	154	164	173	182	191	201
470	210	219	228	237	247	256	265	274	284	293
71	302	311	321	330	339	348	357	367	376	385
72	394	403	413	422	431	440	449	459	468	477
73	486	495	504	514	523	532	541	550	560	569
74	578	587	596	605	614	624	633	642	651	660
75	669	679	688	697	706	715	724	733	742	752
76	761	770	779	788	797	806	815	825	834	843
77	852	861	870	879	888	897	906	916	925	934
78	67 943	952	961	970	979	988	997	*006	*015	*024
79	68 034	043	052	061	070	079	088	097	106	115
480	124	133	142	151	160	169	178	187	196	205
81	215	224	233	242	251	260	269	278	287	296
82	305	314	323	332	341	350	359	368	377	386
83	395	404	413	422	431	440	449	458	467	476
84	485	494	502	511	520	529	538	547	556	565
85	574	583	592	601	610	619	628	637	646	655
86	664	673	681	690	699	708	717	726	735	744
87	753	762	771	780	789	797	806	815	824	833
88	842	851	860	869	878	886	895	904	913	922
89	68 931	940	949	958	966	975	984	993	*002	*011
490	69 020	028	037	046	055	064	073	082	090	099
91	108	117	126	135	144	152	161	170	179	188
92	197	205	214	223	232	241	249	258	267	276
93	285	294	302	311	320	329	338	346	355	364
94	373	381	390	399	408	417	425	434	443	452
95	461	469	478	487	496	504	513	522	531	539
96	548	557	566	574	583	592	601	609	618	627
97	636	644	653	662	671	679	688	697	705	714
98	723	732	740	749	758	767	775	784	793	801
99	810	819	827	836	845	854	862	871	880	888
500	69 897	906	914	923	932	940	949	958	966	975

Prop. Parts

10		9		8	
1	1.0	1	0.9	1	0.8
2	2.0	2	1.8	2	1.6
3	3.0	3	2.7	3	2.4
4	4.0	4	3.6	4	3.2
5	5.0	5	4.5	5	4.0
6	6.0	6	5.4	6	4.8
7	7.0	7	6.3	7	5.6
8	8.0	8	7.2	8	6.4
9	9.0	9	8.1	9	7.2

TABLE A.1   FIVE-PLACE LOGARITHMS: 500—550

N	0	1	2	3	4	5	6	7	8	9	Prop. Parts
500	69 897	906	914	923	932	940	949	958	966	975	
01	69 984	992	*001	*010	*018	*027	*036	*044	*053	*062	
02	70 070	079	088	096	105	114	122	131	140	148	
03	157	165	174	183	191	200	209	217	226	234	
04	243	252	260	269	278	286	295	303	312	321	
05	329	338	346	355	364	372	381	389	398	406	
06	415	424	432	441	449	458	467	475	484	492	
07	501	509	518	526	535	544	552	561	569	578	
08	586	595	603	612	621	629	638	646	655	663	
09	672	680	689	697	706	714	723	731	740	749	
510	757	766	774	783	791	800	808	817	825	834	
11	842	851	859	868	876	885	893	902	910	919	
12	70 927	935	944	952	961	969	978	986	995	*003	
13	71 012	020	029	037	046	054	063	071	079	088	
14	096	105	113	122	130	139	147	155	164	172	
15	181	189	198	206	214	223	231	240	248	257	
16	265	273	282	290	299	307	315	324	332	341	
17	349	357	366	374	383	391	399	408	416	425	
18	433	441	450	458	466	475	483	492	500	508	
19	517	525	533	542	550	559	567	575	584	592	
520	600	609	617	625	634	642	650	659	667	675	
21	684	692	700	709	717	725	734	742	750	759	
22	767	775	784	792	800	809	817	825	834	842	
23	850	858	867	875	883	892	900	908	917	925	
24	71 933	941	950	958	966	975	983	991	999	*008	
25	72 016	024	032	041	049	057	066	074	082	090	
26	099	107	115	123	132	140	148	156	165	173	
27	181	189	198	206	214	222	230	239	247	255	
28	263	272	280	288	296	304	313	321	329	337	
29	346	354	362	370	378	387	395	403	411	419	
530	428	436	444	452	460	469	477	485	493	501	
31	509	518	526	534	542	550	558	567	575	583	
32	591	599	607	616	624	632	640	648	656	665	
33	673	681	689	697	705	713	722	730	738	746	
34	754	762	770	779	787	795	803	811	819	827	
35	835	843	852	860	868	876	884	892	900	908	
36	916	925	933	941	949	957	965	973	981	989	
37	72 997	*006	*014	*022	*030	*038	*046	*054	*062	*070	
38	73 078	086	094	102	111	119	127	135	143	151	
39	159	167	175	183	191	199	207	215	223	231	
540	239	247	255	263	272	280	288	296	304	312	
41	320	328	336	344	352	360	368	376	384	392	
42	400	408	416	424	432	440	448	456	464	472	
43	480	488	496	504	512	520	528	536	544	552	
44	560	568	576	584	592	600	608	616	624	632	
45	640	648	656	664	672	679	687	695	703	711	
46	719	727	735	743	751	759	767	775	783	791	
47	799	807	815	823	830	838	846	854	862	870	
48	878	886	894	902	910	918	926	933	941	949	
49	73 957	965	973	981	989	997	*005	*013	*020	*028	
550	74 036	044	052	060	068	076	084	092	099	107	
N	0	1	2	3	4	5	6	7	8	9	Prop. Parts

Proportional Parts:

	9
1	0.9
2	1.8
3	2.7
4	3.6
5	4.5
6	5.4
7	6.3
8	7.2
9	8.1

	8
1	0.8
2	1.6
3	2.4
4	3.2
5	4.0
6	4.8
7	5.6
8	6.4
9	7.2

	7
1	0.7
2	1.4
3	2.1
4	2.8
5	3.5
6	4.2
7	4.9
8	5.6
9	6.3

TABLE A.1   FIVE-PLACE LOGARITHMS: 550—600

Prop. Parts	N	0	1	2	3	4	5	6	7	8	9
	550	74 036	044	052	060	068	076	084	092	099	107
	51	115	123	131	139	147	155	162	170	178	186
	52	194	202	210	218	225	233	241	249	257	265
	53	273	280	288	296	304	312	320	327	335	343
	54	351	359	367	374	382	390	398	406	414	421
	55	429	437	445	453	461	468	476	484	492	500
	56	507	515	523	531	539	547	554	562	570	578
	57	586	593	601	609	617	624	632	640	648	656
	58	663	671	679	687	695	702	710	718	726	733
	59	741	749	757	764	772	780	788	796	803	811
	560	819	827	834	842	850	858	865	873	881	889
	61	896	904	912	920	927	935	943	950	958	966
	62	74 974	981	989	997	*005	*012	*020	*028	*035	*043
	63	75 051	059	066	074	082	089	097	105	113	120
	64	128	136	143	151	159	166	174	182	189	197
	65	205	213	220	228	236	243	251	259	266	274
	66	282	289	297	305	312	320	328	335	343	351
	67	358	366	374	381	389	397	404	412	420	427
	68	435	442	450	458	465	473	481	488	496	504
	69	511	519	526	534	542	549	557	565	572	580
	570	587	595	603	610	618	626	633	641	648	656
	71	664	671	679	686	694	702	709	717	724	732
	72	740	747	755	762	770	778	785	793	800	808
	73	815	823	831	838	846	853	861	868	876	884
	74	891	899	906	914	921	929	937	944	952	959
	75	75 967	974	982	989	997	*005	*012	*020	*027	*035
	76	76 042	050	057	065	072	080	087	095	103	110
	77	118	125	133	140	148	155	163	170	178	185
	78	193	200	208	215	223	230	238	245	253	260
	79	268	275	283	290	298	305	313	320	328	335
	580	343	350	358	365	373	380	388	395	403	410
	81	418	425	433	440	448	455	462	470	477	485
	82	492	500	507	515	522	530	537	545	552	559
	83	567	574	582	589	597	604	612	619	626	634
	84	641	649	656	664	671	678	686	693	701	708
	85	716	723	730	738	745	753	760	768	775	782
	86	790	797	805	812	819	827	834	842	849	856
	87	864	871	879	886	893	901	908	916	923	930
	88	76 938	945	953	960	967	975	982	989	997	*004
	89	77 012	019	026	034	041	048	056	063	070	078
	590	085	093	100	107	115	122	129	137	144	151
	91	159	166	173	181	188	195	203	210	217	225
	92	232	240	247	254	262	269	276	283	291	298
	93	305	313	320	327	335	342	349	357	364	371
	94	379	386	393	401	408	415	422	430	437	444
	95	452	459	466	474	481	488	495	503	510	517
	96	525	532	539	546	554	561	568	576	583	590
	97	597	605	612	619	627	634	641	648	656	663
	98	670	677	685	692	699	706	714	721	728	735
	99	743	750	757	764	772	779	786	793	801	808
	600	77 815	822	830	837	844	851	859	866	873	880
Prop. Parts	N	0	1	2	3	4	5	6	7	8	9

Prop. Parts (between rows 62–69):

	8
1	0.8
2	1.6
3	2.4
4	3.2
5	4.0
6	4.8
7	5.6
8	6.4
9	7.2

Prop. Parts (between rows 81–88):

	7
1	0.7
2	1.4
3	2.1
4	2.8
5	3.5
6	4.2
7	4.9
8	5.6
9	6.3

TABLE A.1   FIVE-PLACE LOGARITHMS: 600—650

N	0	1	2	3	4	5	6	7	8	9	Prop. Parts
600	77 815	822	830	837	844	851	859	866	873	880	
01	887	895	902	909	916	924	931	938	945	952	
02	77 960	967	974	981	988	996	*003	*010	*017	*025	
03	78 032	039	046	053	061	068	075	082	089	097	
04	104	111	118	125	132	140	147	154	161	168	
05	176	183	190	197	204	211	219	226	233	240	
06	247	254	262	269	276	283	290	297	305	312	
07	319	326	333	340	347	355	362	369	376	383	**8**
08	390	398	405	412	419	426	433	440	447	455	**1** 0.8
09	462	469	476	483	490	497	504	512	519	526	**2** 1.6
610	533	540	547	554	561	569	576	583	590	597	**3** 2.4 **4** 3.2 **5** 4.0 **6** 4.8
11	604	611	618	625	633	640	647	654	661	668	**7** 5.6
12	675	682	689	696	704	711	718	725	732	739	**8** 6.4
13	746	753	760	767	774	781	789	796	803	810	**9** 7.2
14	817	824	831	838	845	852	859	866	873	880	
15	888	895	902	909	916	923	930	937	944	951	
16	78 958	965	972	979	986	993	*000	*007	*014	*021	
17	79 029	036	043	050	057	064	071	078	085	092	
18	099	106	113	120	127	134	141	148	155	162	
19	169	176	183	190	197	204	211	218	225	232	
620	239	246	253	260	267	274	281	288	295	302	
21	309	316	323	330	337	344	351	358	365	372	
22	379	386	393	400	407	414	421	428	435	442	**7**
23	449	456	463	470	477	484	491	498	505	511	**1** 0.7
24	518	525	532	539	546	553	560	567	574	581	**2** 1.4 **3** 2.1
25	588	595	602	609	616	623	630	637	644	650	**4** 2.8 **5** 3.5
26	657	664	671	678	685	692	699	706	713	720	**6** 4.2
27	727	734	741	748	754	761	768	775	782	789	**7** 4.9
28	796	803	810	817	824	831	837	844	851	858	**8** 5.6
29	865	872	879	886	893	900	906	913	920	927	**9** 6.3
630	79 934	941	948	955	962	969	975	982	989	996	
31	80 003	010	017	024	030	037	044	051	058	065	
32	072	079	085	092	099	106	113	120	127	134	
33	140	147	154	161	168	175	182	188	195	202	
34	209	216	223	229	236	243	250	257	264	271	
35	277	284	291	298	305	312	318	325	332	339	
36	346	353	359	366	373	380	387	393	400	407	
37	414	421	428	434	441	448	455	462	468	475	**6**
38	482	489	496	502	509	516	523	530	536	543	**1** 0.6
39	550	557	564	570	577	584	591	598	604	611	**2** 1.2 **3** 1.8
640	618	625	632	638	645	652	659	665	672	679	**4** 2.4 **5** 3.0
41	686	693	699	706	713	720	726	733	740	747	**6** 3.6
42	754	760	767	774	781	787	794	801	808	814	**7** 4.2
43	821	828	835	841	848	855	862	868	875	882	**8** 4.8
44	889	895	902	909	916	922	929	936	943	949	**9** 5.4
45	80 956	963	969	976	983	990	996	*003	*010	*017	
46	81 023	030	037	043	050	057	064	070	077	084	
47	090	097	104	111	117	124	131	137	144	151	
48	158	164	171	178	184	191	198	204	211	218	
49	224	231	238	245	251	258	265	271	278	285	
650	81 291	298	305	311	318	325	331	338	345	351	
N	0	1	2	3	4	5	6	7	8	9	Prop. Parts

TABLE A.1 FIVE-PLACE LOGARITHMS: 650—700

Prop. Parts	N	0	1	2	3	4	5	6	7	8	9
	650	81 291	298	305	311	318	325	331	338	345	351
	51	358	365	371	378	385	391	398	405	411	418
	52	425	431	438	445	451	458	465	471	478	485
	53	491	498	505	511	518	525	531	538	544	551
	54	558	564	571	578	584	591	598	604	611	617
	55	624	631	637	644	651	657	664	671	677	684
	56	690	697	704	710	717	723	730	737	743	750
	57	757	763	770	776	783	790	796	803	809	816
	58	823	829	836	842	849	856	862	869	875	882
	59	889	895	902	908	915	921	928	935	941	948
	660	81 954	961	968	974	981	987	994	*000	*007	*014
	61	82 020	027	033	040	046	053	060	066	073	079
7	62	086	092	099	105	112	119	125	132	138	145
1 0.7	63	151	158	164	171	178	184	191	197	204	210
2 1.4	64	217	223	230	236	243	249	256	263	269	276
3 2.1	65	282	289	295	302	308	315	321	328	334	341
4 2.8	66	347	354	360	367	373	380	387	393	400	406
5 3.5	67	413	419	426	432	439	445	452	458	465	471
6 4.2	68	478	484	491	497	504	510	517	523	530	536
7 4.9	69	543	549	556	562	569	575	582	588	595	601
8 5.6	**670**	607	614	620	627	633	640	646	653	659	666
9 6.3	71	672	679	685	692	698	705	711	718	724	730
	72	737	743	750	756	763	769	776	782	789	795
	73	802	808	814	821	827	834	840	847	853	860
	74	866	872	879	885	892	898	905	911	918	924
	75	930	937	943	950	956	963	969	975	982	988
	76	82 995	*001	*008	*014	*020	*027	*033	*040	*046	*052
	77	83 059	065	072	078	085	091	097	104	110	117
	78	123	129	136	142	149	155	161	168	174	181
	79	187	193	200	206	213	219	225	232	238	245
	680	251	257	264	270	276	283	289	296	302	308
	81	315	321	327	334	340	347	353	359	366	372
6	82	378	385	391	398	404	410	417	423	429	436
1 0.6	83	442	448	455	461	467	474	480	487	493	499
2 1.2	84	506	512	518	525	531	537	544	550	556	563
3 1.8	85	569	575	582	588	594	601	607	613	620	626
4 2.4	86	632	639	645	651	658	664	670	677	683	689
5 3.0	87	696	702	708	715	721	727	734	740	746	753
6 3.6	88	759	765	771	778	784	790	797	803	809	816
7 4.2	89	822	828	835	841	847	853	860	866	872	879
8 4.8	**690**	885	891	897	904	910	916	923	929	935	942
9 5.4	91	83 948	954	960	967	973	979	985	992	998	*004
	92	84 011	017	023	029	036	042	048	055	061	067
	93	073	080	086	092	098	105	111	117	123	130
	94	136	142	148	155	161	167	173	180	186	192
	95	198	205	211	217	223	230	236	242	248	255
	96	261	267	273	280	286	292	298	305	311	317
	97	323	330	336	342	348	354	361	367	373	379
	98	386	392	398	404	410	417	423	429	435	442
	99	448	454	460	466	473	479	485	491	497	504
	700	84 510	516	522	528	535	541	547	553	559	566
Prop. Parts	N	0	1	2	3	4	5	6	7	8	9

TABLE A.1   FIVE-PLACE LOGARITHMS: 700—750

N	0	1	2	3	4	5	6	7	8	9
700	84 510	516	522	528	535	541	547	553	559	566
01	572	578	584	590	597	603	609	615	621	628
02	634	640	646	652	658	665	671	677	683	689
03	696	702	708	714	720	726	733	739	745	751
04	757	763	770	776	782	788	794	800	807	813
05	819	825	831	837	844	850	856	862	868	874
06	880	887	893	899	905	911	917	924	930	936
07	84 942	948	954	960	967	973	979	985	991	997
08	85 003	009	016	022	028	034	040	046	052	058
09	065	071	077	083	089	095	101	107	114	120
710	126	132	138	144	150	156	163	169	175	181
11	187	193	199	205	211	217	224	230	236	242
12	248	254	260	266	272	278	285	291	297	303
13	309	315	321	327	333	339	345	352	358	364
14	370	376	382	388	394	400	406	412	418	425
15	431	437	443	449	455	461	467	473	479	485
16	491	497	503	509	516	522	528	534	540	546
17	552	558	564	570	576	582	588	594	600	606
18	612	618	625	631	637	643	649	655	661	667
19	673	679	685	691	697	703	709	715	721	727
720	733	739	745	751	757	763	769	775	781	788
21	794	800	806	812	818	824	830	836	842	848
22	854	860	866	872	878	884	890	896	902	908
23	914	920	926	932	938	944	950	956	962	968
24	85 974	980	986	992	998	*004	*010	*016	*022	*028
25	86 034	040	046	052	058	064	070	076	082	088
26	094	100	106	112	118	124	130	136	141	147
27	153	159	165	171	177	183	189	195	201	207
28	213	219	225	231	237	243	249	255	261	267
29	273	279	285	291	297	303	308	314	320	326
730	332	338	344	350	356	362	368	374	380	386
31	392	398	404	410	415	421	427	433	439	445
32	451	457	463	469	475	481	487	493	499	504
33	510	516	522	528	534	540	546	552	558	564
34	570	576	581	587	593	599	605	611	617	623
35	629	635	641	646	652	658	664	670	676	682
36	688	694	700	705	711	717	723	729	735	741
37	747	753	759	764	770	776	782	788	794	800
38	806	812	817	823	829	835	841	847	853	859
39	864	870	876	882	888	894	900	906	911	917
740	923	929	935	941	947	953	958	964	970	976
41	86 982	988	994	999	*005	*011	*017	*023	*029	*035
42	87 040	046	052	058	064	070	075	081	087	093
43	099	105	111	116	122	128	134	140	146	151
44	157	163	169	175	181	186	192	198	204	210
45	216	221	227	233	239	245	251	256	262	268
46	274	280	286	291	297	303	309	315	320	326
47	332	338	344	349	355	361	367	373	379	384
48	390	396	402	408	413	419	425	431	437	442
49	448	454	460	466	471	477	483	489	495	500
750	87 506	512	518	523	529	535	541	547	552	558
N	0	1	2	3	4	5	6	7	8	9

Prop. Parts

	7		6		5
1	0.7	1	0.6	1	0.5
2	1.4	2	1.2	2	1.0
3	2.1	3	1.8	3	1.5
4	2.8	4	2.4	4	2.0
5	3.5	5	3.0	5	2.5
6	4.2	6	3.6	6	3.0
7	4.9	7	4.2	7	3.5
8	5.6	8	4.8	8	4.0
9	6.3	9	5.4	9	4.5

TABLE A.1   FIVE-PLACE LOGARITHMS: 750—800

Prop. Parts	N	0	1	2	3	4	5	6	7	8	9
	750	87 506	512	518	523	529	535	541	547	552	558
	51	564	570	576	581	587	593	599	604	610	616
	52	622	628	633	639	645	651	656	662	668	674
	53	679	685	691	697	703	708	714	720	726	731
	54	737	743	749	754	760	766	772	777	783	789
	55	795	800	806	812	818	823	829	835	841	846
	56	852	858	864	869	875	881	887	892	898	904
	57	910	915	921	927	933	938	944	950	955	961
	58	87 967	973	978	984	990	996	*001	*007	*013	*018
	59	88 024	030	036	041	047	053	058	064	070	076
	760	081	087	093	098	104	110	116	121	127	133
	61	138	144	150	156	161	167	173	178	184	190
	62	195	201	207	213	218	224	230	235	241	247
	63	252	258	264	270	275	281	287	292	298	304
	64	309	315	321	326	332	338	343	349	355	360
	65	366	372	377	383	389	395	400	406	412	417
	66	423	429	434	440	446	451	457	463	468	474
	67	480	485	491	497	502	508	513	519	525	530
	68	536	542	547	553	559	564	570	576	581	587
	69	593	598	604	610	615	621	627	632	638	643
	770	649	655	660	666	672	677	683	689	694	700
	71	705	711	717	722	728	734	739	745	750	756
	72	762	767	773	779	784	790	795	801	807	812
	73	818	824	829	835	840	846	852	857	863	868
	74	874	880	885	891	897	902	908	913	919	925
	75	930	936	941	947	953	958	964	969	975	981
	76	88 986	992	997	*003	*009	*014	*020	*025	*031	*037
	77	89 042	048	053	059	064	070	076	081	087	092
	78	098	104	109	115	120	126	131	137	143	148
	79	154	159	165	170	176	182	187	193	198	204
	780	209	215	221	226	232	237	243	248	254	260
	81	265	271	276	282	287	293	298	304	310	315
	82	321	326	332	337	343	348	354	360	365	371
	83	376	382	387	393	398	404	409	415	421	426
	84	432	437	443	448	454	459	465	470	476	481
	85	487	492	498	504	509	515	520	526	531	537
	86	542	548	553	559	564	570	575	581	586	592
	87	597	603	609	614	620	625	631	636	642	647
	88	653	658	664	669	675	680	686	691	697	702
	89	708	713	719	724	730	735	741	746	752	757
	790	763	768	774	779	785	790	796	801	807	812
	91	818	823	829	834	840	845	851	856	862	867
	92	873	878	883	889	894	900	905	911	916	922
	93	927	933	938	944	949	955	960	966	971	977
	94	89 982	988	993	998	*004	*009	*015	*020	*026	*031
	95	90 037	042	048	053	059	064	069	075	080	086
	96	091	097	102	108	113	119	124	129	135	140
	97	146	151	157	162	168	173	179	184	189	195
	98	200	206	211	217	222	227	233	238	244	249
	99	255	260	266	271	276	282	287	293	298	304
	800	90 309	314	320	325	331	336	342	347	352	358
Prop. Parts	N	0	1	2	3	4	5	6	7	8	9

Prop. Parts

6
1	0.6
2	1.2
3	1.8
4	2.4
5	3.0
6	3.6
7	4.2
8	4.8
9	5.4

5
1	0.5
2	1.0
3	1.5
4	2.0
5	2.5
6	3.0
7	3.5
8	4.0
9	4.5

TABLE A.1 FIVE-PLACE LOGARITHMS: 800—850

N	0	1	2	3	4	5	6	7	8	9	Prop. Parts
800	90 309	314	320	325	331	336	342	347	352	358	
01	363	369	374	380	385	390	396	401	407	412	
02	417	423	428	434	439	445	450	455	461	466	
03	472	477	482	488	493	499	504	509	515	520	
04	526	531	536	542	547	553	558	563	569	574	
05	580	585	590	596	601	607	612	617	623	628	
06	634	639	644	650	655	660	666	671	677	682	
07	687	693	698	703	709	714	720	725	730	736	
08	741	747	752	757	763	768	773	779	784	789	
09	795	800	806	811	816	822	827	832	838	843	
810	849	854	859	865	870	875	881	886	891	897	
11	902	907	913	918	924	929	934	940	945	950	
12	90 956	961	966	972	977	982	988	993	998	*004	**6**
13	91 009	014	020	025	030	036	041	046	052	057	1 0.6
14	062	068	073	078	084	089	094	100	105	110	2 1.2 3 1.8
15	116	121	126	132	137	142	148	153	158	164	4 2.4 5 3.0
16	169	174	180	185	190	196	201	206	212	217	6 3.6
17	222	228	233	238	243	249	254	259	265	270	7 4.2
18	275	281	286	291	297	302	307	312	318	323	8 4.8
19	328	334	339	344	350	355	360	365	371	376	9 5.4
820	381	387	392	397	403	408	413	418	424	429	
21	434	440	445	450	455	461	466	471	477	482	
22	487	492	498	503	508	514	519	524	529	535	
23	540	545	551	556	561	566	572	577	582	587	
24	593	598	603	609	614	619	624	630	635	640	
25	645	651	656	661	666	672	677	682	687	693	
26	698	703	709	714	719	724	730	735	740	745	
27	751	756	761	766	772	777	782	787	793	798	
28	803	808	814	819	824	829	834	840	845	850	
29	855	861	866	871	876	882	887	892	897	903	
830	908	913	918	924	929	934	939	944	950	955	
31	91 960	965	971	976	981	986	991	997	*002	*007	**5**
32	92 012	018	023	028	033	038	044	049	054	059	1 0.5
33	065	070	075	080	085	091	096	101	106	111	2 1.0 3 1.5
34	117	122	127	132	137	143	148	153	158	163	4 2.0
35	169	174	179	184	189	195	200	205	210	215	5 2.5 6 3.0
36	221	226	231	236	241	247	252	257	262	267	7 3.5
37	273	278	283	288	293	298	304	309	314	319	8 4.0
38	324	330	335	340	345	350	355	361	366	371	9 4.5
39	376	381	387	392	397	402	407	412	418	423	
840	428	433	438	443	449	454	459	464	469	474	
41	480	485	490	495	500	505	511	516	521	526	
42	531	536	542	547	552	557	562	567	572	578	
43	583	588	593	598	603	609	614	619	624	629	
44	634	639	645	650	655	660	665	670	675	681	
45	686	691	696	701	706	711	716	722	727	732	
46	737	742	747	752	758	763	768	773	778	783	
47	788	793	799	804	809	814	819	824	829	834	
48	840	845	850	855	860	865	870	875	881	886	
49	891	896	901	906	911	916	921	927	932	937	
850	92 942	947	952	957	962	967	973	978	983	988	
N	0	1	2	3	4	5	6	7	8	9	Prop. Parts

TABLE A.1   FIVE-PLACE LOGARITHMS: 850—900

Prop. Parts

6	
1	0.6
2	1.2
3	1.8
4	2.4
5	3.0
6	3.6
7	4.2
8	4.8
9	5.4

5	
1	0.5
2	1.0
3	1.5
4	2.0
5	2.5
6	3.0
7	3.5
8	4.0
9	4.5

4	
1	0.4
2	0.8
3	1.2
4	1.6
5	2.0
6	2.4
7	2.8
8	3.2
9	3.6

N	0	1	2	3	4	5	6	7	8	9
850	92 942	947	952	957	962	967	973	978	983	988
51	92 993	998	*003	*008	*013	*018	*024	*029	*034	*039
52	93 044	049	054	059	064	069	075	080	085	090
53	095	100	105	110	115	120	125	131	136	141
54	146	151	156	161	166	171	176	181	186	192
55	197	202	207	212	217	222	227	232	237	242
56	247	252	258	263	268	273	278	283	288	293
57	298	303	308	313	318	323	328	334	339	344
58	349	354	359	364	369	374	379	384	389	394
59	399	404	409	414	420	425	430	435	440	445
860	450	455	460	465	470	475	480	485	490	495
61	500	505	510	515	520	526	531	536	541	546
62	551	556	561	566	571	576	581	586	591	596
63	601	606	611	616	621	626	631	636	641	646
64	651	656	661	666	671	676	682	687	692	697
65	702	707	712	717	722	727	732	737	742	747
66	752	757	762	767	772	777	782	787	792	797
67	802	807	812	817	822	827	832	837	842	847
68	852	857	862	867	872	877	882	887	892	897
69	902	907	912	917	922	927	932	937	942	947
870	93 952	957	962	967	972	977	982	987	992	997
71	94 002	007	012	017	022	027	032	037	042	047
72	052	057	062	067	072	077	082	086	091	096
73	101	106	111	116	121	126	131	136	141	146
74	151	156	161	166	171	176	181	186	191	196
75	201	206	211	216	221	226	231	236	240	245
76	250	255	260	265	270	275	280	285	290	295
77	300	305	310	315	320	325	330	335	340	345
78	349	354	359	364	369	374	379	384	389	394
79	399	404	409	414	419	424	429	433	438	443
880	448	453	458	463	468	473	478	483	488	493
81	498	503	507	512	517	522	527	532	537	542
82	547	552	557	562	567	571	576	581	586	591
83	596	601	606	611	616	621	626	630	635	640
84	645	650	655	660	665	670	675	680	685	689
85	694	699	704	709	714	719	724	729	734	738
86	743	748	753	758	763	768	773	778	783	787
87	792	797	802	807	812	817	822	827	832	836
88	841	846	851	856	861	866	871	876	880	885
89	890	895	900	905	910	915	919	924	929	934
890	939	944	949	954	959	963	968	973	978	983
91	94 988	993	998	*002	*007	*012	*017	*022	*027	*032
92	95 036	041	046	051	056	061	066	071	075	080
93	085	090	095	100	105	109	114	119	124	129
94	134	139	143	148	153	158	163	168	173	177
95	182	187	192	197	202	207	211	216	221	226
96	231	236	240	245	250	255	260	265	270	274
97	279	284	289	294	299	303	308	313	318	323
98	328	332	337	342	347	352	357	361	366	371
99	376	381	386	390	395	400	405	410	415	419
900	95 424	429	434	439	444	448	453	458	463	468

Prop. Parts | N | 0 | 1 | 2 | 3 | 4 | 5 | 6 | 7 | 8 | 9 |

TABLE A.1 FIVE-PLACE LOGARITHMS: 900—950

N	0	1	2	3	4	5	6	7	8	9	Prop. Parts
900	95 424	429	434	439	444	448	453	458	463	468	
01	472	477	482	487	492	497	501	506	511	516	
02	521	525	530	535	540	545	550	554	559	564	
03	569	574	578	583	588	593	598	602	607	612	
04	617	622	626	631	636	641	646	650	655	660	
05	665	670	674	679	684	689	694	698	703	708	
06	713	718	722	727	732	737	742	746	751	756	
07	761	766	770	775	780	785	789	794	799	804	
08	809	813	818	823	828	832	837	842	847	852	
09	856	861	866	871	875	880	885	890	895	899	
910	904	909	914	918	923	928	933	938	942	947	
11	952	957	961	966	971	976	980	985	990	995	
12	95 999	*004	*009	*014	*019	*023	*028	*033	*038	*042	5
13	96 047	052	057	061	066	071	076	080	085	090	1 0.5
14	095	099	104	109	114	118	123	128	133	137	2 1.0 · 3 1.5
15	142	147	152	156	161	166	171	175	180	185	4 2.0 · 5 2.5
16	190	194	199	204	209	213	218	223	227	232	6 3.0
17	237	242	246	251	256	261	265	270	275	280	7 3.5
18	284	289	294	298	303	308	313	317	322	327	8 4.0
19	332	336	341	346	350	355	360	365	369	374	9 4.5
920	379	384	388	393	398	402	407	412	417	421	
21	426	431	435	440	445	450	454	459	464	468	
22	473	478	483	487	492	497	501	506	511	515	
23	520	525	530	534	539	544	548	553	558	562	
24	567	572	577	581	586	591	595	600	605	609	
25	614	619	624	628	633	638	642	647	652	656	
26	661	666	670	675	680	685	689	694	699	703	
27	708	713	717	722	727	731	736	741	745	750	
28	755	759	764	769	774	778	783	788	792	797	
29	802	806	811	816	820	825	830	834	839	844	
930	848	853	858	862	867	872	876	881	886	890	
31	895	900	904	909	914	918	923	928	932	937	
32	942	946	951	956	960	965	970	974	979	984	4
33	96 988	993	997	*002	*007	*011	*016	*021	*025	*030	1 0.4
34	97 035	039	044	049	053	058	063	067	072	077	2 0.8 · 3 1.2
35	081	086	090	095	100	104	109	114	118	123	4 1.6 · 5 2.0
36	128	132	137	142	146	151	155	160	165	169	6 2.4
37	174	179	183	188	192	197	202	206	211	216	7 2.8
38	220	225	230	234	239	243	248	253	257	262	8 3.2
39	267	271	276	280	285	290	294	299	304	308	9 3.6
940	313	317	322	327	331	336	340	345	350	354	
41	359	364	368	373	377	382	387	391	396	400	
42	405	410	414	419	424	428	433	437	442	447	
43	451	456	460	465	470	474	479	483	488	493	
44	497	502	506	511	516	520	525	529	534	539	
45	543	548	552	557	562	566	571	575	580	585	
46	589	594	598	603	607	612	617	621	626	630	
47	635	640	644	649	653	658	663	667	672	676	
48	681	685	690	695	699	704	708	713	717	722	
49	727	731	736	740	745	749	754	759	763	768	
950	97 772	777	782	786	791	795	800	804	809	813	
N	0	1	2	3	4	5	6	7	8	9	Prop. Parts

TABLE A.1   FIVE-PLACE LOGARITHMS: 950—1000

Prop. Parts	N	0	1	2	3	4	5	6	7	8	9
	950	97 772	777	782	786	791	795	800	804	809	813
	51	818	823	827	832	836	841	845	850	855	859
	52	864	868	873	877	882	886	891	896	900	905
	53	909	914	918	923	928	932	937	941	946	950
	54	97 955	959	964	968	973	978	982	987	991	996
	55	98 000	005	009	014	019	023	028	032	037	041
	56	046	050	055	059	064	068	073	078	082	087
	57	091	096	100	105	109	114	118	123	127	132
	58	137	141	146	150	155	159	164	168	173	177
	59	182	186	191	195	200	204	209	214	218	223
	960	227	232	236	241	245	250	254	259	263	268
	61	272	277	281	286	290	295	299	304	308	313
5	62	318	322	327	331	336	340	345	349	354	358
1 0.5	63	363	367	372	376	381	385	390	394	399	403
2 1.0											
3 1.5	64	408	412	417	421	426	430	435	439	444	448
4 2.0	65	453	457	462	466	471	475	480	484	489	493
5 2.5	66	498	502	507	511	516	520	525	529	534	538
6 3.0											
7 3.5	67	543	547	552	556	561	565	570	574	579	583
8 4.0	68	588	592	597	601	605	610	614	619	623	628
9 4.5	69	632	637	641	646	650	655	659	664	668	673
	970	677	682	686	691	695	700	704	709	713	717
	71	722	726	731	735	740	744	749	753	758	762
	72	767	771	776	780	784	789	793	798	802	807
	73	811	816	820	825	829	834	838	843	847	851
	74	856	860	865	869	874	878	883	887	892	896
	75	900	905	909	914	918	923	927	932	936	941
	76	945	949	954	958	963	967	972	976	981	985
	77	98 989	994	998	*003	*007	*012	*016	*021	*025	*029
	78	99 034	038	043	047	052	056	061	065	069	074
	79	078	083	087	092	096	100	105	109	114	118
	980	123	127	131	136	140	145	149	154	158	162
	81	167	171	176	180	185	189	193	198	202	207
4	82	211	216	220	224	229	233	238	242	247	251
1 0.4	83	255	260	264	269	273	277	282	286	291	295
2 0.8											
3 1.2	84	300	304	308	313	317	322	326	330	335	339
4 1.6	85	344	348	352	357	361	366	370	374	379	383
5 2.0	86	388	392	396	401	405	410	414	419	423	427
6 2.4											
7 2.8	87	432	436	441	445	449	454	458	463	467	471
8 3.2	88	476	480	484	489	493	498	502	506	511	515
9 3.6	89	520	524	528	533	537	542	546	550	555	559
	990	564	568	572	577	581	585	590	594	599	603
	91	607	612	616	621	625	629	634	638	642	647
	92	651	656	660	664	669	673	677	682	686	691
	93	695	699	704	708	712	717	721	726	730	734
	94	739	743	747	752	756	760	765	769	774	778
	95	782	787	791	795	800	804	808	813	817	822
	96	826	830	835	839	843	848	852	856	861	865
	97	870	874	878	883	887	891	896	900	904	909
	98	913	917	922	926	930	935	939	944	948	952
	99	99 957	961	965	970	974	978	983	987	991	996
	1000	00 000	004	009	013	017	022	026	030	035	039
Prop. Parts	N	0	1	2	3	4	5	6	7	8	9

Natural Trigonometric Functions

The following table gives the values of the *sine, cosine, tangent,* and *cotangent* of degrees from 0° to 90°. For degrees at the left use the column headings at the top; for degrees at the right use column headings at the bottom.

For fractions of degrees an appropriate amount of the difference between adjacent values may be used. For precise calculations, however, one should employ a more complete table and especially one showing the logarithms of the trigonometric functions.

The values of the *secant* and *cosecant* may be derived as follows: secant = 1 ÷ cos; cosecant = 1 ÷ sin.

TABLE B.1

NATURAL TRIGONOMETRIC FUNCTIONS

°	Sin	Tan	Cot	Cos	°	°	Sin	Tan	Cot	Cos	°
0	.0000	.0000	—	1.0000	90	23	.3907	.4245	2.356	.9205	67
1	.0174	.0175	57.290	.9998	89	24	.4067	.4452	2.246	.9135	66
2	.0349	.0349	28.636	.9994	88	25	.4226	.4663	2.144	.9063	65
3	.0523	.0524	19.081	.9986	87	26	.4384	.4877	2.050	.8988	64
4	.0698	.0699	14.301	.9976	86	27	.4540	.5095	1.963	.8910	63
5	.0872	.0875	11.430	.9962	85	28	.4695	.5317	1.881	.8829	62
6	.1045	.1051	9.514	.9945	84	29	.4848	.5543	1.804	.8746	61
7	.1219	.1228	8.144	.9925	83						
8	.1392	.1405	7.115	.9903	82	30	.5000	.5773	1.732	.8660	60
9	.1564	.1584	6.314	.9877	81	31	.5150	.6009	1.664	.8572	59
						32	.5299	.6249	1.600	.8480	58
10	.1736	.1763	5.671	.9848	80	33	.5446	.6494	1.540	.8387	57
11	.1908	.1944	5.145	.9816	79	34	.5592	.6745	1.483	.8290	56
12	.2079	.2126	4.705	.9781	78	35	.5736	.7002	1.428	.8191	55
13	.2249	.2309	4.331	.9744	77	36	.5878	.7265	1.376	.8090	54
14	.2419	.2493	4.011	.9703	76	37	.6018	.7535	1.327	.7986	53
15	.2588	.2679	3.732	.9659	75	38	.6157	.7813	1.280	.7880	52
16	.2756	.2867	3.487	.9613	74	39	.6293	.8098	1.235	.7771	51
17	.2924	.3057	3.271	.9563	73						
18	.3090	.3249	3.078	.9511	72	40	.6428	.8391	1.192	.7660	50
19	.3256	.3443	2.904	.9455	71	41	.6561	.8693	1.150	.7547	49
						42	.6691	.9004	1.111	.7431	48
20	.3420	.3640	2.747	.9397	70	43	.6820	.9325	1.072	.7313	47
21	.3584	.3839	2.605	.9336	69	44	.6947	.9657	1.035	.7193	46
22	.3746	.4040	2.475	.9272	68	45	.7071	1.0000	1.000	.7071	45
°	Cos	Cot	Tan	Sin	°	°	Cos	Cot	Tan	Sin	°

Squares, Cubes, and Roots

TABLE C.1
SQUARES, CUBES, AND ROOTS

n	n^2	$\sqrt{n}$	$\sqrt{10n}$	n^3	$\sqrt[3]{n}$	$\sqrt[3]{10n}$
1	1	1.000	3.162	1	1.000	2.154
2	4	1.414	4.472	8	1.260	2.714
3	9	1.732	5.477	27	1.442	3.107
4	16	2.000	6.325	64	1.587	3.420
5	25	2.236	7.071	125	1.710	3.684
6	36	2.449	7.746	216	1.817	3.915
7	49	2.646	8.367	343	1.913	4.121
8	64	2.828	8.944	512	2.000	4.309
9	81	3.000	9.487	729	2.080	4.481
10	100	3.162	10.000	1 000	2.154	4.642
11	121	3.317	10.488	1 331	2.224	4.791
12	144	3.464	10.954	1 728	2.289	4.932
13	169	3.606	11.402	2 197	2.351	5.066
14	196	3.742	11.832	2 744	2.410	5.192
15	225	3.873	12.247	3 375	2.466	5.313
16	256	4.000	12.649	4 096	2.520	5.429
17	289	4.123	13.038	4 913	2.571	5.540
18	324	4.243	13.416	5 832	2.621	5.646
19	361	4.359	13.784	6 859	2.668	5.749
20	400	4.472	14.142	8 000	2.714	5.848
21	441	4.583	14.491	9 261	2.759	5.944
22	484	4.690	14.832	10 648	2.802	6.037
23	529	4.796	15.166	12 167	2.844	6.127
24	576	4.899	15.492	13 824	2.884	6.214
25	625	5.000	15.811	15 625	2.924	6.300
26	676	5.099	16.125	17 576	2.962	6.383
27	729	5.196	16.432	19 683	3.000	6.463
28	784	5.292	16.733	21 952	3.037	6.542
29	841	5.385	17.029	24 389	3.072	6.619
30	900	5.477	17.321	27 000	3.107	6.694
31	961	5.568	17.607	29 791	3.141	6.768
32	1 024	5.657	17.889	32 768	3.175	6.840
33	1 089	5.745	18.166	35 937	3.208	6.910
34	1 156	5.831	18.439	39 304	3.240	6.980
35	1 225	5.916	18.708	42 875	3.271	7.047
36	1 296	6.000	18.974	46 656	3.302	7.114

TABLE C.1

SQUARES, CUBES, AND ROOTS (Continued)

n	n^2	$\sqrt{n}$	$\sqrt{10n}$	n^3	$\sqrt[3]{n}$	$\sqrt[3]{10n}$
37	1 369	6.083	19.235	50 653	3.332	7.179
38	1 444	6.164	19.494	54 872	3.362	7.243
39	1 521	6.245	19.748	59 319	3.391	7.306
40	1 600	6.325	20.000	64 000	3.420	7.368
41	1 681	6.403	20.248	68 921	3.448	7.429
42	1 764	6.481	20.494	74 088	3.476	7.489
43	1 849	6.557	20.736	79 507	3.503	7.548
44	1 936	6.633	20.976	85 184	3.530	7.606
45	2 025	6.708	21.213	91 125	3.557	7.663
46	2 116	6.782	21.448	97 336	3.583	7.719
47	2 209	6.856	21.679	103 823	3.609	7.775
48	2 304	6.928	21.909	110 592	3.634	7.830
49	2 401	7.000	22.136	117 649	3.659	7.884
50	2 500	7.071	22.361	125 000	3.684	7.937
51	2 601	7.141	22.583	132 651	3.708	7.990
52	2 704	7.211	22.804	140 608	3.733	8.041
53	2 809	7.280	23.022	148 877	3.756	8.093
54	2 916	7.348	23.238	157 464	3.780	8.143
55	3 025	7.416	23.452	166 375	3.803	8.193
56	3 136	7.483	23.664	175 616	3.826	8.243
57	3 249	7.550	23.875	185 193	3.849	8.291
58	3 364	7.616	24.083	195 112	3.871	8.340
59	3 481	7.681	24.290	205 379	3.893	8.387
60	3 600	7.746	24.495	216 000	3.915	8.434
61	3 721	7.810	24.698	226 981	3.936	8.481
62	3 844	7.874	24.900	238 328	3.958	8.527
63	3 969	7.937	25.100	250 047	3.979	8.573
64	4 096	8.000	25.298	262 144	4.000	8.618
65	4 225	8.062	25.495	274 625	4.021	8.662
66	4 356	8.124	25.690	287 496	4.041	8.707
67	4 489	8.185	25.884	300 763	4.062	8.750
68	4 624	8.246	26.077	314 432	4.082	8.794
69	4 761	8.307	26.268	328 509	4.102	8.837
70	4 900	8.367	26.458	343 000	4.121	8.879
71	5 041	8.426	26.646	357 911	4.141	8.921
72	5 184	8.485	26.833	373 248	4.160	8.963
73	5 329	8.544	27.019	389 017	4.179	9.004
74	5 476	8.602	27.203	405 224	4.198	9.045
75	5 625	8.660	27.386	421 875	4.217	9.086
76	5 776	8.718	27.568	438 976	4.236	9.126
77	5 929	8.775	27.749	456 533	4.254	9.166
78	6 084	8.832	27.928	474 552	4.273	9.205
79	6 241	8.888	28.107	493 039	4.291	9.244
80	6 400	8.944	28.284	512 000	4.309	9.283

TABLE C.1

SQUARES, CUBES, AND ROOTS (Continued)

n	n^2	$\sqrt{n}$	$\sqrt{10n}$	n^3	$\sqrt[3]{n}$	$\sqrt[3]{10n}$
81	6 561	9.000	28.461	531 441	4.327	9.322
82	6 724	9.055	28.636	551 368	4.344	9.360
83	6 889	9.110	28.810	571 787	4.362	9.398
84	7 056	9.165	28.983	592 704	4.380	9.435
85	7 225	9.220	29.155	614 125	4.397	9.473
86	7 396	9.274	29.326	636 056	4.414	9.510
87	7 569	9.327	29.496	658 503	4.431	9.546
88	7 744	9.381	29.665	681 472	4.448	9.583
89	7 921	9.434	29.833	704 969	4.465	9.619
90	8 100	9.487	30.000	729 000	4.481	9.655
91	8 281	9.539	30.166	753 571	4.498	9.691
92	8 464	9.592	30.332	778 688	4.514	9.726
93	8 649	9.644	30.496	804 357	4.531	9.761
94	8 836	9.695	30.659	830 584	4.547	9.796
95	9 025	9.747	30.822	857 375	4.563	9.830
96	9 216	9.798	30.984	884 736	4.579	9.865
97	9 409	9.849	31.145	912 673	4.595	9.899
98	9 604	9.899	31.305	941 192	4.610	9.933
99	9 801	9.950	31.464	970 299	4.626	9.967
100	10 000	10.000	31.623	1 000 000	4.642	10.000

Geographical Tables *

TABLE D.1

LENGTHS OF DEGREES OF THE PARALLEL

Lat.	Meters	Statute miles	Lat.	Meters	Statute miles	Lat.	Meters	Statute miles
° ′			° ′			° ′		
0 00	111 321	69.172	30 00	96 488	59.956	60 00	55 802	34.674
1 00	111 304	69.162	31 00	95 506	59.345	61 00	54 110	33.623
2 00	111 253	69.130	32 00	94 495	58.716	62 00	52 400	32.560
3 00	111 169	69.078	33 00	93 455	58.071	63 00	50 675	31.488
4 00	111 051	69.005	34 00	92 387	57.407	64 00	48 934	30.406
5 00	110 900	68.911	35 00	91 290	56.725	65 00	47 177	29.315
6 00	110 715	68.795	36 00	90 166	56.027	66 00	45 407	28.215
7 00	110 497	68.660	37 00	89 014	55.311	67 00	43 622	27.106
8 00	110 245	68.504	38 00	87 835	54.579	68 00	41 823	25.988
9 00	109 959	68.326	39 00	86 629	53.829	69 00	40 012	24.862
10 00	109 641	68.129	40 00	85 396	53.063	70 00	38 188	23.729
11 00	109 289	67.910	41 00	84 137	52.281	71 00	36 353	22.589
12 00	108 904	67.670	42 00	82 853	51.483	72 00	34 506	21.441
13 00	108 486	67.410	43 00	81 543	50.669	73 00	32 648	20.287
14 00	108 036	67.131	44 00	80 208	49.840	74 00	30 781	19.127
15 00	107 553	66.830	45 00	78 849	48.995	75 00	28 903	17.960
16 00	107 036	66.510	46 00	77 466	48.136	76 00	27 017	16.788
17 00	106 487	66.169	47 00	76 058	47.261	77 00	25 123	15.611
18 00	105 906	65.808	48 00	74 628	46.372	78 00	23 220	14.428
19 00	105 294	65.427	49 00	73 174	45.469	79 00	21 311	13.242
20 00	104 649	65.026	50 00	71 698	44.552	80 00	19 394	12.051
21 00	103 972	64.606	51 00	70 200	43.621	81 00	17 472	10.857
22 00	103 264	64.166	52 00	68 680	42.676	82 00	15 545	9.659
23 00	102 524	63.706	53 00	67 140	41.719	83 00	13 612	8.458
24 00	101 754	63.228	54 00	65 578	40.749	84 00	11 675	7.255
25 00	100 952	62.729	55 00	63 996	39.766	85 00	9 735	6.049
26 00	100 119	62.212	56 00	62 395	38.771	86 00	7 792	4.842
27 00	99 257	61.676	57 00	60 774	37.764	87 00	5 846	3.632
28 00	98 364	61.122	58 00	59 135	36.745	88 00	3 898	2.422
29 00	97 441	60.548	59 00	57 478	35.716	89 00	1 949	1.211
						90 00	0	0

* Tables D.1 and D.2 are from U.S. Coast and Geodetic Survey; Table D.3 is from *Smithsonian Geographical Tables.*

TABLE D.2

LENGTHS OF DEGREES OF THE MERIDIAN

Lat.	Meters	Statute miles	Lat.	Meters	Statute miles	Lat.	Meters	Statute miles
°			°			°		
0–1	110 567.3	68.703	30–31	110 857.0	68.883	60–61	111 423.1	69.235
1–2	110 568.0	68.704	31–32	110 874.4	68.894	61–62	111 439.9	69.246
2–3	110 569.4	68.705	32–33	110 892.1	68.905	62–63	111 456.4	69.256
3–4	110 571.4	68.706	33–34	110 910.1	68.916	63–64	111 472.4	69.266
4–5	110 574.1	68.707	34–35	110 928.3	68.928	64–65	111 488.1	69.275
5–6	110 577.6	68.710	35–36	110 946.9	68.939	65–66	111 503.3	69.285
6–7	110 581.6	68.712	36–37	110 965.6	68.951	66–67	111 518.0	69.294
7–8	110 586.4	68.715	37–38	110 984.5	68.962	67–68	111 532.3	69.303
8–9	110 591.8	68.718	38–39	111 003.7	68.974	68–69	111 546.2	69.311
9–10	110 597.8	68.722	39–40	111 023.0	68.986	69–70	111 559.5	69.320
10–11	110 604.5	68.726	40–41	111 042.4	68.998	70–71	111 572.2	69.328
11–12	110 611.9	68.731	41–42	111 061.9	69.011	71–72	111 584.5	69.335
12–13	110 619.8	68.736	42–43	111 081.6	69.023	72–73	111 596.2	69.343
13–14	110 628.4	68.741	43–44	111 101.3	69.035	73–74	111 607.3	69.349
14–15	110 637.6	68.747	44–45	111 121.0	69.047	74–75	111 617.9	69.356
15–16	110 647.5	68.753	45–46	111 140.8	69.060	75–76	111 627.8	69.362
16–17	110 657.8	68.759	46–47	111 160.5	69.072	76–77	111 637.1	69.368
17–18	110 668.8	68.766	47–48	111 180.2	69.084	77–78	111 645.9	69.373
18–19	110 680.4	68.773	48–49	111 199.9	69.096	78–79	111 653.9	69.378
19–20	110 692.4	68.781	49–50	111 219.5	69.108	79–80	111 661.4	69.383
20–21	110 705.1	68.789	50–51	111 239.0	69.121	80–81	111 668.2	69.387
21–22	110 718.2	68.797	51–52	111 258.3	69.133	81–82	111 674.4	69.391
22–23	110 731.8	68.805	52–53	111 277.6	69.145	82–83	111 679.9	69.395
23–24	110 746.0	68.814	53–54	111 296.6	69.156	83–84	111 684.7	69.398
24–25	110 760.6	68.823	54–55	111 315.4	69.168	84–85	111 688.9	69.400
25–26	110 775.6	68.833	55–56	111 334.0	69.180	85–86	111 692.3	69.402
26–27	110 791.1	68.842	56–57	111 352.4	69.191	86–87	111 695.1	69.404
27–28	110 807.0	68.852	57–58	111 370.5	69.202	87–88	111 697.2	69.405
28–29	110 823.3	68.862	58–59	111 388.4	69.213	88–89	111 698.6	69.406
29–30	110 840.0	68.873	59–60	111 405.9	69.224	89–90	111 699.3	69.407

TABLE D.3

AREAS OF QUADRILATERALS OF EARTH'S SURFACE OF 1° EXTENT IN LATITUDE AND LONGITUDE

Lower latitude of quadrilateral °	Area in square miles	Lower latitude of quadrilateral °	Area in square miles
0	4 752.16	45	3 354.01
1	4 750.75	46	3 294.71
2	4 747.93	47	3 234.39
3	4 743.71	48	3 173.04
4	4 738.08	49	3 110.69
5	4 731.04		
6	4 722.61	50	3 047.37
7	4 712.76	51	2 983.08
8	4 701.52	52	2 917.85
9	4 688.89	53	2 851.68
		54	2 784.62
10	4 674.86	55	2 716.67
11	4 659.43	56	2 647.85
12	4 642.63	57	2 578.19
13	4 624.44	58	2 507.70
14	4 604.87	59	2 436.42
15	4 583.92		
16	4 561.61	60	2 364.34
17	4 537.93	61	2 291.51
18	4 512.90	62	2 217.94
19	4 486.51	63	2 143.66
		64	2 068.68
20	4 458.78	65	1 993.04
21	4 429.71	66	1 916.75
22	4 399.30	67	1 839.84
23	4 367.57	68	1 762.33
24	4 334.52	69	1 684.24
25	4 300.17		
26	4 264.51	70	1 605.62
27	4 227.56	71	1 526.46
28	4 189.33	72	1 446.81
29	4 149.83	73	1 366.69
		74	1 286.12
30	4 109.06	75	1 205.13
31	4 067.05	76	1 123.75
32	4 023.79	77	1 041.99
33	3 979.30	78	959.90
34	3 933.59	79	877.49
35	3 886.67		
36	3 838.56	80	794.79
37	3 789.26	81	711.83
38	3 738.80	82	628.64
39	3 687.18	83	545.24
		84	461.66
40	3 634.42	85	377.93
41	3 580.54	86	294.08
42	3 525.54	87	210.12
43	3 469.44	88	126.10
44	3 412.26	89	42.04

Lambert Projection Tables

TABLE E.1

TABLE FOR THE CONSTRUCTION OF A LAMBERT AZIMUTHAL EQUAL-AREA PROJECTION CENTERED ON THE EQUATOR. COORDINATES IN UNITS OF THE EARTH'S RADIUS ($R = 1$) (From Deetz and Adams)

Lat.	Long. 0°		Long. 10°		Long. 20°		Long. 30°		Long. 40°	
	x	y	x	y	x	y	x	y	x	y
0°	0	0.000	0.174	0.000	0.347	0.000	0.518	0.000	0.684	0.000
10°	0	0.174	0.172	0.175	0.343	0.177	0.512	0.180	0.676	0.185
20°	0	0.347	0.166	0.349	0.331	0.352	0.493	0.359	0.651	0.369
30°	0	0.518	0.156	0.519	0.311	0.525	0.463	0.535	0.610	0.548
40°	0	0.684	0.142	0.686	0.283	0.693	0.420	0.705	0.553	0.722
50°	0	0.845	0.124	0.848	0.245	0.855	0.364	0.868	0.478	0.887
60°	0	1.000	0.101	1.003	0.199	1.010	0.295	1.023	0.386	1.041
70°	0	1.147	0.073	1.149	0.144	1.156	0.212	1.167	0.277	1.183
80°	0	1.286	0.039	1.287	0.078	1.291	0.114	1.299	0.148	1.308
90°	0	1.414	0.000	1.414	0.000	1.414	0.000	1.414	0.000	1.414

Lat.	Long. 50°		Long. 60°		Long. 70°		Long. 80°		Long. 90°	
	x	y	x	y	x	y	x	y	x	y
0°	0.845	0.000	1.000	0.000	1.147	0.000	1.286	0.000	1.414	0.000
10°	0.835	0.192	0.987	0.201	1.132	0.212	1.267	0.227	1.393	0.246
20°	0.804	0.382	0.949	0.399	1.086	0.421	1.213	0.448	1.329	0.484
30°	0.752	0.567	0.886	0.591	1.011	0.621	1.125	0.659	1.225	0.707
40°	0.679	0.744	0.798	0.773	0.906	0.809	1.002	0.854	1.083	0.909
50°	0.586	0.911	0.685	0.942	0.773	0.981	0.849	1.028	0.909	1.083
60°	0.471	1.065	0.548	1.095	0.614	1.132	0.668	1.175	0.707	1.225
70°	0.335	1.203	0.387	1.228	0.430	1.257	0.463	1.291	0.484	1.329
80°	0.178	1.321	0.204	1.336	0.224	1.353	0.238	1.372	0.246	1.393
90°	0.000	1.414	0.000	1.414	0.000	1.414	0.000	1.414	0.000	1.414

TABLE E.2

TABLE FOR THE CONSTRUCTION OF A LAMBERT EQUAL-AREA PROJECTION CENTERED AT LATITUDE 40°. CO-ORDINATES IN UNITS OF THE EARTH'S RADIUS ($R = 1$) (Adapted from Deetz and Adams)

Lat.	Long. 0°		Long. 10°		Long. 20°		Long. 30°		Long. 40°	
	x	y	x	y	x	y	x	y	x	y
90°	0	+0.845	0.000	+0.845	0.000	+0.845	0.000	+0.845	0.000	+0.845
80°	0	+0.684	0.032	+0.686	0.063	+0.692	0.093	+0.704	0.120	+0.718
70°	0	+0.518	0.062	+0.521	0.121	+0.533	0.175	+0.553	0.231	+0.580
60°	0	+0.347	0.088	+0.352	0.174	+0.369	0.257	+0.396	0.334	+0.434
50°	0	+0.174	0.112	+0.181	0.222	+0.200	0.328	+0.234	0.427	+0.280
40°	0	0.000	0.133	+0.007	0.264	+0.029	0.391	+0.067	0.510	+0.120
30°	0	−0.174	0.151	−0.166	0.300	−0.142	0.445	−0.102	0.582	−0.045
20°	0	−0.347	0.166	−0.338	0.331	−0.314	0.489	−0.272	0.642	−0.214
10°	0	−0.518	0.177	−0.509	0.353	−0.484	0.524	−0.442	0.689	−0.383
0°	0	−0.684	0.185	−0.675	0.369	−0.651	0.548	−0.610	0.722	−0.553
−10°	0	−0.845	—	—	—	—	—	—	—	—

Lat.	Long. 50°		Long. 60°		Long. 70°		Long. 80°		Long. 90°		Long. 100°	
	x	y	x	y	x	y	x	y	x	y	x	y
90°	0.000	+0.845	0.000	+0.845	0.000	+0.845	0.000	+0.845	0.000	+0.845	0.000	+0.845
80°	0.143	+0.736	0.163	+0.758	0.178	+0.782	0.188	+0.808	0.192	+0.834	—	—
70°	0.278	+0.613	0.318	+0.646	0.349	+0.701	0.371	+0.751	0.382	+0.804	—	—
60°	0.403	+0.481	0.463	+0.538	0.511	+0.602	0.547	+0.674	0.567	+0.752	0.570	+0.833
50°	0.518	+0.338	0.583	+0.408	0.663	+0.489	0.713	+0.580	0.744	+0.679	0.755	+0.785
40°	0.620	+0.186	0.702	+0.267	0.801	+0.361	—	—	—	—	—	—
30°	0.710	+0.027	0.825	+0.115	—	—	—	—	—	—	—	—
20°	0.785	−0.138	—	—	—	—	—	—	—	—	—	—
10°	0.844	−0.307	—	—	—	—	—	—	—	—	—	—
0°	0.887	−0.478	—	—	—	—	—	—	—	—	—	—

Stereographic Projection Tables

Professor James A. Barnes has worked out a simplified method of calculating tables for constructing the stereographic projection. Anyone who can read values from a table of logarithms of the trigonometric functions can compute values for a projection centered on any point on the sphere. The formulas originally appeared in *Surveying and Mapping*. The symbols are:

α = angle of tilt (position of center).
ϕ = latitude.
λ = longitude.
U = upper intersection of parallel with central meridian.
L = lower intersection of parallel with central meridian.
Q = intersection of homolatitude of center point and central meridian.
N = intersection of meridian and homolatitude.
M = center of meridian arc on homolatitude.

Calculation of the position of the parallels:

For north latitudes and equator: $U = + \tan \frac{1}{2}(180° - \phi - \alpha)$.
For south latitudes less than α: $U = + \tan \frac{1}{2}(180° + \phi - \alpha)$.
For south latitudes greater than α: $U = - \tan \frac{1}{2}(\phi + \alpha)$.

For north latitudes greater than α: $L = + \tan \frac{1}{2}(\phi - \alpha)$.
For north latitudes less than α and equator: $L = - \tan \frac{1}{2}(\alpha - \phi)$.
For south latitudes less than α: $L = - \tan \frac{1}{2}(\phi + \alpha)$.
For south latitudes greater than α: $L = - \tan \frac{1}{2}(180° + \alpha - \phi)$.

Note: Plus and minus signs indicate whether the value is above or below the center of the projection. The center of any parallel is midway between U and L.

Calculation of the position of the meridians:

$Q = - \tan \alpha$.
$N = \sec \alpha \cdot \tan \frac{1}{2}\lambda$.
$M = \sec \alpha \cdot \cot \lambda$.

Note: N and M correspond to *Bow* and *Center* values in the following tables.

The following tables have been computed (by J. A. Barnes) for projections centered at 10°-latitude intervals (the table for 40° appears in Article 6.20), and will be sufficient for most purposes of small-scale maps, where the stereographic is desired as an end, or as a means to an end as suggested in Articles 6.23 and 6.24. For large-scale and precision work the formulas above should be used to compute values for the exact center.

Values in the tables and those resulting from the above formulas are for a globe with a diameter of unity ($D = 1$). To determine figures to scale multiply each calculation by the diameter of the generating globe of chosen scale.

Directions for the use of the tables appear in Article 6.20.

TABLE F.1

TABLE FOR CONSTRUCTING THE STEREOGRAPHIC PROJECTION CENTERED ON 0°

(D = 1)

Parallels	Upper		Lower
North pole		1.00000	
80°	1.19175		0.83910
70°	1.42815		0.70021
60°	1.73205		0.57735
50°	2.14451		0.46631
40°	2.74748		0.36397
30°	3.73205		0.26795
20°	5.67128		0.17633
10°	11.43005		0.08749
0°	0.00000	0.00000	0.00000
10°	−0.08749		−11.43005
20°	−0.17633		−5.67128
30°	−0.26795		−3.73205
40°	−0.36397		−2.74748
50°	−0.46631		−2.14451
60°	−0.57735		−1.73205
70°	−0.70021		−1.42815
80°	−0.83910		−1.19175
South pole		−1.00000	

$$H = 0.00000$$

Meridians	Bow	Center
10°	0.08749	5.67128
20°	0.17633	2.74748
30°	0.26795	1.73205
40°	0.36397	1.19175
50°	0.46631	0.83910
60°	0.57735	0.57735
70°	0.70021	0.36397
80°	0.83910	0.17633
90°	1.00000	0.00000

TABLE F.2

TABLE FOR CONSTRUCTING THE STEREOGRAPHIC PROJECTION CENTERED ON 10°

(D = 1)

Parallels	Upper		Lower
North pole		0.83910	
80°	1.00000		0.70021
70°	1.19175		0.57735
60°	1.42815		0.46631
50°	1.73205		0.36397
40°	2.14451		0.26795
30°	2.74748		0.17633
20°	3.73205		0.08749
10°	5.67128		0.00000
0°	11.43005		−0.08749
10°	−0.17633	−0.17633	−0.17633
20°	−0.26795		−11.43005
30°	−0.36397		−5.67128
40°	−0.46631		−3.73205
50°	−0.57735		−2.74748
60°	−0.70021		−2.14451
70°	−0.83910		−1.73205
80°	−1.00000		−1.42815
South pole		−1.19175	

$$H = -0.17633$$

Meridians	Bow	Center
10°	0.08884	5.75876
20°	0.17905	2.78986
30°	0.27208	1.75877
40°	0.36958	1.21014
50°	0.47350	0.85204
60°	0.58626	0.58626
70°	0.71101	0.36958
80°	0.85204	0.17905
90°	1.01543	0.00000

TABLE F.3

TABLE FOR CONSTRUCTING THE STEREOGRAPHIC
PROJECTION CENTERED ON 20°

$(D = 1)$

Parallels	Upper		Lower
North pole		0.70021	
80°	0.83910		0.57735
70°	1.00000		0.46631
60°	1.19175		0.36397
50°	1.42815		0.26795
40°	1.73205		0.17633
30°	2.14451		0.08749
20°	2.74748		0.00000
10°	3.73205		−0.08749
0°	5.67128		−0.17633
10°	11.43005		−0.26795
20°	−0.36397	−0.36397	−0.36397
30°	−0.46631		−11.43005
40°	−0.57735		−5.67128
50°	−0.70021		−3.73205
60°	−0.83910		−2.74748
70°	−1.00000		−2.14451
80°	−1.19175		−1.73205
South pole		−1.42815	

$H = -0.36397$

Meridians	Bow	Center
10°	0.09310	6.03526
20°	0.18764	2.92381
30°	0.28515	1.84321
40°	0.38733	1.26824
50°	0.49624	0.89295
60°	0.61440	0.61440
70°	0.74515	0.38733
80°	0.89295	0.18764
90°	1.06418	0.00000

TABLE F.4

TABLE FOR CONSTRUCTING THE STEREOGRAPHIC
PROJECTION CENTERED ON 30°

$(D = 1)$

Parallels	Upper		Lower
North pole		0.57735	
80°	0.70021		0.46631
70°	0.83910		0.36397
60°	1.00000		0.26795
50°	1.19175		0.17633
40°	1.42815		0.08749
30°	1.73205		0.00000
20°	2.14451		−0.08749
10°	2.74748		−0.17633
0°	3.73205		−0.26795
10°	5.67128		−0.36397
20°	11.43005		−0.46631
30°	−0.57735	−0.57735	−0.57735
40°	−0.70021		−11.43005
50°	−0.83910		−5.67128
60°	−1.00000		−3.73205
70°	−1.19175		−2.74748
80°	−1.42815		−2.14451
South pole		−1.73205	

$H = -0.57735$

Meridians	Bow	Center
10°	0.10103	6.54863
20°	0.20360	3.17251
30°	0.30940	2.00000
40°	0.42028	1.37295
50°	0.53845	0.96891
60°	0.66667	0.66667
70°	0.80853	0.42028
80°	0.96891	0.20360
90°	1.15470	0.00000

TABLE F.5

TABLE FOR CONSTRUCTING THE STEREOGRAPHIC PROJECTION CENTERED ON 50°

(D = 1)

Parallels	Upper		Lower
North pole		0.36397	
80°	0.46631		0.26795
70°	0.57735		0.17633
60°	0.70021		0.08749
50°	0.83910		0.00000
40°	1.00000		−0.08749
30°	1.19175		−0.17633
20°	1.42815		−0.26795
10°	1.73205		−0.36397
0°	2.14451		−0.46631
10°	2.74748		−0.57735
20°	3.73205		−0.70021
30°	5.67128		−0.83910
40°	11.43005		−1.00000
50°	−1.19175	−1.19175	−1.19175
60°	−1.42815		−11.43005
70°	−1.73205		−5.67128
80°	−2.14451		−3.73205
South pole		−2.74748	

$$H = -1.19175$$

Meridians	Bow	Center
10°	0.13611	8.82296
20°	0.27432	4.27432
30°	0.41686	2.69460
40°	0.56624	1.85404
50°	0.72545	1.30541
60°	0.89820	0.89820
70°	1.08933	0.56624
80°	1.30541	0.27432
90°	1.55572	0.00000

TABLE F.6

TABLE FOR CONSTRUCTING THE STEREOGRAPHIC PROJECTION CENTERED ON 60°

(D = 1)

Parallels	Upper		Lower
North pole		0.26795	
80°	0.36397		0.17633
70°	0.46631		0.08749
60°	0.57735		0.00000
50°	0.70021		−0.08749
40°	0.83910		−0.17633
30°	1.00000		−0.26795
20°	1.19175		−0.36397
10°	1.42815		−0.46631
0°	1.73205		−0.57735
10°	2.14451		−0.70021
20°	2.74748		−0.83910
30°	3.73205		−1.00000
40°	5.67128		−1.19175
50°	11.43005		−1.42815
60°	−1.73205	−1.73205	−1.73205
70°	−2.14451		−11.43005
80°	−2.74748		−5.67128
South pole		−3.73205	

$$H = -1.73205$$

Meridians	Bow	Center
10°	0.17498	11.34230
20°	0.35265	5.49495
30°	0.53590	3.46410
40°	0.72794	2.38351
50°	0.93262	1.67820
60°	1.15470	1.15470
70°	1.40042	0.72794
80°	1.67820	0.35265
90°	2.00000	0.00000

TABLE F.7

TABLE FOR CONSTRUCTING THE STEREOGRAPHIC PROJECTION CENTERED ON 70°

(D = 1)

Parallels	Upper		Lower
North pole		0.17633	
80°	0.26795		0.08749
70°	0.36397		0.00000
60°	0.46631		−0.08749
50°	0.57735		−0.17633
40°	0.70021		−0.26795
30°	0.83910		−0.36397
20°	1.00000		−0.46631
10°	1.19175		−0.57735
0°	1.42815		−0.70021
10°	1.73205		−0.83910
20°	2.14451		−1.00000
30°	2.74748		−1.19175
40°	3.73205		−1.42815
50°	5.67128		−1.73205
60°	11.43005		−2.14451
70°	−2.74748	−2.74748	−2.74748
80°	−3.73205		−11.43005
South pole		−5.67128	

$$H = -2.74748$$

Meridians	Bow	Center
10°	0.25580	16.58172
20°	0.51555	8.03309
30°	0.78343	5.06418
40°	1.06418	3.48446
50°	1.36339	2.45336
60°	1.68806	1.68806
70°	2.04727	1.06418
80°	2.45336	0.51555
90°	2.92381	0.00000

TABLE F.8

TABLE FOR CONSTRUCTING THE STEREOGRAPHIC PROJECTION CENTERED ON 80°

(D = 1)

Parallels	Upper		Lower
North pole		0.08749	
80°	0.17633		0.00000
70°	0.26795		−0.08749
60°	0.36397		−0.17633
50°	0.46631		−0.26795
40°	0.57735		−0.36397
30°	0.70021		−0.46631
20°	0.83910		−0.57735
10°	1.00000		−0.70021
0°	1.19175		−0.83910
10°	1.42815		−1.00000
20°	1.73205		−1.19175
30°	2.14451		−1.42815
40°	2.74748		−1.73205
50°	3.73205		−2.14451
60°	5.67128		−2.74748
70°	11.43005		−3.73205
80°	−5.67128	−5.67128	−5.67128
South pole		−11.43005	

$$H = -5.67128$$

Meridians	Bow	Center
10°	0.50383	32.65958
20°	1.01543	15.82208
30°	1.54306	9.97447
40°	2.09602	6.86303
50°	2.68536	4.83228
60°	3.32483	3.32483
70°	4.03233	2.09602
80°	4.83228	1.01543
90°	5.75877	0.00000

TABLE F.9

TABLE FOR CONSTRUCTING THE STEREOGRAPHIC PROJECTION CENTERED ON 90°

(D = 1)

Parallels	Upper	Lower	Parallels	Upper	Lower
North pole	0		30°	1.73205	−1.73205
80°	0.08749	−0.08749	40°	2.14451	−2.14451
70°	0.17633	−0.17633	50°	2.74748	−2.74748
60°	0.26795	−0.26795	60°	3.73205	−3.73205
50°	0.36397	−0.36397	70°	5.67128	−5.67128
40°	0.46631	−0.46631	80°	11.43005	−11.43005
30°	0.57735	−0.57735	South pole	∞	∞
20°	0.70021	−0.70021			
10°	0.83910	−0.83910		$H = \infty$	
0°	1.00000	−1.00000			
10°	1.19175	−1.19175	Meridians are straight lines through the center		
20°	1.42815	−1.42815	with equal angles between them.		

Lettering Magnification Tables

Tables G.1 to G.7 provide equivalent lettering sizes for projected maps that are magnified from 2 to 15 times their original size and are viewed at various distances from a screen. Equivalent sizes are expressed to the nearest even or common point size in the smaller ranges, with some clear intermediates noted, and in the larger sizes they are approximate to the nearest even or common point size. The tables are used by permission of *Surveying and Mapping,* in which they originally appeared.

Notes: (1) Approximate equivalent letter heights *in inches* of point sizes appear in Table 13.2, Article 13.5. (2) For magnifications intermediate to those shown in the tables the data may be determined for all practical purposes by a linear interpolation.

TABLE G.1
LINEAR MAGNIFICATION, 2
(Blank spaces indicate nonlegibility)

Point size on original	Approximate equivalent size in points viewed at distance (feet) from screen									
	10	20	30	40	50	60	70	80	90	100
6										
8										
10										
12	3									
14	4									
16	4–5									
18	5									
24	7	4								
30	9	4–5	3							
36	10	5	4							

TABLE G.2
LINEAR MAGNIFICATION, 3
(Blank spaces indicate nonlegibility)

Point size on original	Approximate equivalent size in points viewed at distance (feet) from screen									
	10	20	30	40	50	60	70	80	90	100
6										
8	3									
10	4–5									
12	5									
14	6	3								
16	7	4								
18	8	4–5								
24	10	5	4							
30	12	6	4–5	3–4						
36	16	8	5	4	3					

TABLE G.3
LINEAR MAGNIFICATION, 4
(Blank spaces indicate nonlegibility)

Point size on original	Approximate equivalent size in points viewed at distance (feet) from screen									
	10	20	30	40	50	60	70	80	90	100
6	3									
8	4–5									
10	6	3								
12	7	4								
14	8	4–5								
16	9	4–5	3							
18	10	5	4							
24	14	7	4–5	3–4						
30	18	9	6	4–5	3–4	3				
36	22	11	8	5–6	4–5	4	3			

TABLE G.4
LINEAR MAGNIFICATION, 6
(Blank spaces indicate nonlegibility)

Point size on original	Approximate equivalent size in points viewed at distance (feet) from screen									
	10	20	30	40	50	60	70	80	90	100
6	5									
8	7	4								
10	9	4–5	3							
12	10	5	4							
14	12	6	4–5	3						
16	14	7	4–5	3–4						
18	16	8	5	4	3					
24	22	11	8	5–6	4–5	4	3			
30	28	14	9	7	5–6	4–5	4	3		
36	33	16	10	8	6	5–6	5	4	3–4	3

TABLE G.5
LINEAR MAGNIFICATION, 9
(Blank spaces indicate nonlegibility)

Point size on original	Approximate equivalent size in points viewed at distance (feet) from screen									
	10	20	30	40	50	60	70	80	90	100
6	8	4–5	3							
8	10	5	4							
10	12	6	4–5	3–4						
12	16	8	5	4	3					
14	18	9	6	5	4	3				
16	22	11	8	5–6	4–5	4	3			
18	24	12	8	6	5	4	3–4	3		
24	32	16	10	8	6	5–6	5	4	3–4	3
30	42	21	14	11	9	7	6	5–6	5	4–5
36	48	24	16	12	10	8	7	6	5–6	5

TABLE G.6
LINEAR MAGNIFICATION, 12
(Blank spaces indicate nonlegibility)

Point size on original	Approximate equivalent size in points viewed at distance (feet) from screen									
	10	20	30	40	50	60	70	80	90	100
6	10	5	4							
8	14	7	4–5	3–4						
10	18	9	6	4–5	3–4	3				
12	22	11	8	5–6	4–5	4	3			
14	24	12	8	6	5	4	3–4	3		
16	30	14	10	8	6	5	4	3–4		
18	32	16	10	8	6	5–6	5	4	3–4	3
24	42	21	14	11	9	7	6	5–6	5	4–5
30	54	27	18	14	12	9	8	7	6	5–6
36	68	34	24	16	13	11	9	8	7	6

TABLE G.7
LINEAR MAGNIFICATION, 15
(Blank spaces indicate nonlegibility)

Point size on original	Approximate equivalent size in points viewed at distance (feet) from screen									
	10	20	30	40	50	60	70	80	90	100
6	13	6–7	4–5	3						
8	18	9	6	4–5	3–4	3				
10	24	12	8	6	5	4	3			
12	28	14	9	7	5–6	4–5	4	3		
14	32	16	10	8	6	5	4–5	4	3–4	3
16	36	18	12	9	8	6	5	4–5	4	3–4
18	42	21	14	11	9	7	6	5–6	5	4–5
24	54	27	18	14	12	9	8	7	6	5–6
30	68	34	23	17	13	12	10	9	8	7
36	80	40	27	20	16	14	12	10	9	8

Tabular Aid to Consistency When Estimating Values of Fractional Areas

The table below, devised by John K. Wright, enables one to solve without multiplication or division the fundamental equation required to estimate densities of fractional areas referred to in Article 8.9. The explanation and tables are here presented by permission of *The Geographical Review,* published by the American Geographical Society of New York.

The basic equation is

$$D_n = \frac{D}{1 - a_m} - \frac{D_m a_m}{1 - a_m}$$

in which D_n = the density in area n.

D = average density of the area as a whole (number of units ÷ area).

D_m = estimated density in part m of area.

a_m = the fraction (0.1 to 0.9) of the total area comprised in m.

$1 - a_m$ = the fraction (0.1 to 0.9) of the total area comprised in n.

Values of $\dfrac{D}{1 - a_m}$ and $\dfrac{D_m a_m}{1 - a_m}$ may be extracted from the table as follows. The table is entered at the top with a_m and entered at the side with D or D_m as arguments. When D is the argument, the left-hand column under the particular value of a_m gives values of $\dfrac{D}{1 - a_m}$. When D_m is the argument, the right-hand column under the particular value of a_m gives values of $\dfrac{D_m a_m}{1 - a_m}$.

In order to obtain D_n, subtract the value obtained from entering the table with D_m as argument from the value obtained from entering the table with D as argument. (If this value is a minus quantity, then the value of D_m is too large to be consistent with the values of D and of a_m.)

For example: $D = 100$, $D_m = 10$, $a_m = 0.8$. From row 100 and the left-hand column under 0.8 extract value 500; from row 10 and the right-hand column under 0.8 extract value 40; $500 - 40 = 460 = D_n$.

TABLE H.1
TABULAR AID TO CONSISTENCY IN ESTIMATING DENSITIES OF PARTS

Each pair of columns under a given a_m value gives D and $D_m a_m$ for the condition $1 - a_m$.

D or D_m	D (0.1)	$D_m a_m$ (0.1)	D (0.2)	$D_m a_m$ (0.2)	D (0.3)	$D_m a_m$ (0.3)	D (0.4)	$D_m a_m$ (0.4)	D (0.5)	$D_m a_m$ (0.5)	D (0.6)	$D_m a_m$ (0.6)	D (0.7)	$D_m a_m$ (0.7)	D (0.8)	$D_m a_m$ (0.8)	D (0.9)	$D_m a_m$ (0.9)	D or D_m
1	1	0.1	1	0.3	1	0.4	2	0.7	2	1	2	1.5	3	2.3	5	4	10	9	1
2	2	0.2	3	0.5	3	0.9	3	1.3	4	2	5	3.0	7	4.7	10	8	20	18	2
3	3	0.3	4	0.8	4	1.3	5	2.0	6	3	7	4.5	10	7.0	15	12	30	27	3
4	4	0.4	5	1.0	6	1.8	7	2.7	8	4	10	6.0	13	9.3	20	16	40	36	4
5	6	0.6	6	1.3	7	2.2	8	3.3	10	5	12	7.5	17	11.7	25	20	50	45	5
6	7	0.7	8	1.5	9	2.7	10	4.0	12	6	15	9.0	20	14.0	30	24	60	54	6
7	8	0.8	9	1.8	10	3.1	12	4.7	14	7	17	10.5	23	16.3	35	28	70	63	7
8	9	0.9	10	2.0	12	3.6	13	5.3	16	8	20	12.0	27	18.6	40	32	80	72	8
9	10	1.0	11	2.3	13	4.0	15	6.0	18	9	22	13.5	30	21.0	45	36	90	81	9
10	11	1.1	13	2.5	14	4.4	17	6.7	20	10	25	15.0	33	23.3	50	40	100	90	10
11	12	1.2	14	2.8	16	4.9	18	7.3	22	11	27	16.5	37	25.6	55	44	110	99	11
12	13	1.3	15	3.0	17	5.3	20	8.0	24	12	30	18.0	40	28.0	60	48	120	108	12
13	14	1.4	16	3.3	19	5.8	22	8.7	26	13	32	19.5	43	30.3	65	52	130	117	13
14	16	1.6	18	3.5	20	6.2	23	9.3	28	14	35	21.0	47	32.6	70	56	140	126	14
15	17	1.7	19	3.8	22	6.7	25	10.0	30	15	37	22.5	50	35.0	75	60	150	135	15
16	18	1.8	20	4.0	23	7.1	27	10.7	32	16	40	24.0	53	37.3	80	64	160	144	16
17	19	1.9	21	4.3	24	7.5	28	11.3	34	17	42	25.5	57	39.6	85	68	170	153	17
18	20	2.0	23	4.5	26	8.0	30	12.0	36	18	45	27.0	60	41.9	90	72	180	162	18
19	21	2.1	24	4.8	27	8.4	32	12.7	38	19	47	28.5	63	44.3	95	76	190	171	19
20	22	2.2	25	5.0	29	8.9	33	13.3	40	20	50	30.0	67	46.6	100	80	200	180	20
21	23	2.3	26	5.3	30	9.3	35	14.0	42	21	52	31.5	70	48.9	105	84	210	189	21
22	24	2.4	28	5.5	32	9.8	37	14.7	44	22	55	33.0	73	51.3	110	88	220	198	22
23	26	2.6	29	5.8	33	10.2	38	15.3	46	23	57	34.5	77	53.6	115	92	230	207	23
24	27	2.7	30	6.0	35	10.7	40	16.0	48	24	60	36.0	80	55.9	120	96	240	216	24
25	28	2.8	31	6.3	36	11.1	42	16.7	50	25	62	37.5	83	58.3	125	100	250	225	25
26	29	2.9	33	6.5	37	11.5	43	17.3	52	26	65	39.0	87	60.6	130	104	260	234	26
27	30	3.0	34	6.8	39	12.0	45	18.0	54	27	67	40.5	90	62.9	135	108	270	243	27
28	31	3.1	35	7.0	40	12.4	46	18.6	56	28	70	42.0	93	65.2	140	112	280	252	28
29	32	3.2	36	7.3	42	12.9	48	19.3	58	29	72	43.5	97	67.6	145	116	290	261	29
30	33	3.3	38	7.5	43	13.3	50	20.0	60	30	75	45.0	100	69.9	150	120	300	270	30
31	34	3.4	39	7.8	45	13.8	51	20.6	62	31	77	46.5	103	72.2	155	124	310	279	31
32	36	3.6	40	8.0	46	14.2	53	21.3	64	32	80	48.0	107	74.6	160	128	320	288	32
33	37	3.7	41	8.3	48	14.7	55	22.0	66	33	82	49.5	110	76.9	165	132	330	297	33
34	38	3.8	43	8.5	49	15.1	56	22.6	68	34	85	51.0	113	79.2	170	136	340	306	34
35	39	3.9	44	8.8	50	15.5	58	23.3	70	35	87	52.5	117	81.6	175	140	350	315	35
36	40	4.0	45	9.0	52	16.0	60	24.0	72	36	90	54.0	120	83.9	180	144	360	324	36
37	41	4.1	46	9.3	53	16.4	61	24.6	74	37	92	55.5	123	86.2	185	148	370	333	37
38	42	4.2	48	9.5	55	16.9	63	25.3	76	38	95	57.0	127	88.5	190	152	380	342	38
39	43	4.3	49	9.8	56	17.3	65	26.0	78	39	97	58.5	130	90.9	195	156	390	351	39
40	44	4.4	50	10.0	58	17.8	66	26.6	80	40	100	60.0	133	93.2	200	160	400	360	40
41	46	4.6	51	10.3	59	18.2	68	27.3	82	41	102	61.5	137	95.5	205	164	410	369	41
42	47	4.7	53	10.5	60	18.6	70	28.0	84	42	105	63.0	140	97.9	210	168	420	378	42
43	48	4.8	54	10.8	62	19.1	71	28.6	86	43	107	64.5	143	100.2	215	172	430	387	43
44	49	4.9	55	11.0	63	19.5	73	29.3	88	44	110	66.0	147	102.5	220	176	440	396	44
45	50	5.0	56	11.3	65	20.0	75	30.0	90	45	112	67.5	150	104.9	225	180	450	405	45
46	51	5.1	58	11.5	66	20.4	76	30.6	92	46	115	69.0	153	107.2	230	184	460	414	46
47	52	5.2	59	11.8	68	20.9	78	31.3	94	47	117	70.5	157	109.5	235	188	470	423	47
48	53	5.3	60	12.0	69	21.3	80	32.0	96	48	120	72.0	160	111.8	240	192	480	432	48
49	54	5.4	61	12.3	71	21.8	81	32.6	98	49	122	73.5	163	114.2	245	196	490	441	49

50	450	500	200	250	116.5	167	75.0	125	50	100	33.3	83	22.2	72	12.5	63	5.6	56	50
51	459	510	204	255	118.8	170	76.5	127	51	102	34.0	85	22.6	73	12.8	64	5.7	57	51
52	468	520	208	260	121.2	173	78.0	130	52	104	34.6	86	23.1	75	13.0	65	5.8	58	52
53	477	530	212	265	123.5	177	79.5	132	53	106	35.3	88	23.5	76	13.3	66	5.9	59	53
54	486	540	216	270	125.8	180	81.0	135	54	108	36.0	90	24.0	78	13.5	68	6.0	60	54
55	495	550	220	275	128.2	183	82.5	137	55	110	36.6	91	24.4	79	13.8	69	6.1	61	55
56	504	560	224	280	130.5	187	84.0	140	56	112	37.3	93	24.9	81	14.0	70	6.2	62	56
57	513	570	228	285	132.8	190	85.5	142	57	114	38.0	95	25.3	82	14.3	71	6.3	63	57
58	522	580	232	290	135.1	193	87.0	145	58	116	38.6	96	25.8	84	14.5	73	6.4	64	58
59	531	590	236	295	137.5	197	88.5	147	59	118	39.3	98	26.2	85	14.8	74	6.5	65	59
60	540	600	240	300	139.8	200	90.0	150	60	120	40.0	100	26.6	86	15.0	75	6.7	67	60
61	549	610	244	305	142.1	203	91.5	152	61	122	40.6	101	27.1	88	15.3	76	6.8	68	61
62	558	620	248	310	144.5	207	93.0	155	62	124	41.3	103	27.5	89	15.5	78	6.9	69	62
63	567	630	252	315	146.8	210	94.5	157	63	126	42.0	105	28.0	91	15.8	79	7.0	70	63
64	576	640	256	320	149.1	213	96.0	160	64	128	42.6	106	28.4	92	16.0	80	7.1	71	64
65	585	650	260	325	151.5	217	97.5	162	65	130	43.3	108	28.9	94	16.3	81	7.2	72	65
66	594	660	264	330	153.8	220	99.0	165	66	132	44.0	110	29.3	95	16.5	83	7.3	73	66
67	603	670	268	335	156.1	223	100.5	167	67	134	44.6	111	29.7	96	16.8	84	7.4	74	67
68	612	680	272	340	158.4	227	102.0	170	68	136	45.3	113	30.2	98	17.0	85	7.5	75	68
69	621	690	276	345	160.8	230	103.5	172	69	138	46.0	115	30.6	99	17.3	86	7.7	77	69
70	630	700	280	350	163.1	233	105.0	175	70	140	46.6	116	31.1	101	17.5	88	7.8	78	70
71	639	710	284	355	165.4	237	106.5	177	71	142	47.3	118	31.5	102	17.8	89	7.9	79	71
72	648	720	288	360	167.8	240	108.0	180	72	144	48.0	120	32.0	104	18.0	90	8.0	80	72
73	657	730	292	365	170.1	243	109.5	182	73	146	48.6	121	32.4	105	18.3	91	8.1	81	73
74	666	740	296	370	172.4	247	111.0	185	74	148	49.3	123	32.9	107	18.5	93	8.2	82	74
75	675	750	300	375	174.8	250	112.5	187	75	150	50.0	125	33.3	108	18.8	94	8.3	83	75
76	684	760	304	380	177.1	253	114.0	190	76	152	50.6	126	33.7	109	19.0	95	8.4	84	76
77	693	770	308	385	179.4	257	115.5	192	77	154	51.3	128	34.2	111	19.3	96	8.5	85	77
78	702	780	312	390	181.7	260	117.0	195	78	156	52.0	129	34.6	112	19.5	98	8.7	87	78
79	711	790	316	395	184.1	263	118.5	197	79	158	52.6	131	35.1	114	19.8	99	8.8	88	79
80	720	800	320	400	186.4	267	120.0	200	80	160	53.3	133	35.5	115	20.0	100	8.9	89	80
81	729	810	324	405	188.7	270	121.5	202	81	162	53.9	134	36.0	117	20.3	101	9.0	90	81
82	738	820	328	410	191.1	273	123.0	205	82	164	54.6	136	36.4	118	20.5	103	9.1	91	82
83	747	830	332	415	193.4	277	124.5	207	83	166	55.3	138	36.9	120	20.8	104	9.2	92	83
84	756	840	336	420	195.7	280	126.0	210	84	168	55.9	139	37.3	121	21.0	105	9.3	93	84
85	765	850	340	425	198.1	283	127.5	212	85	170	56.6	141	37.7	123	21.3	106	9.4	94	85
86	774	860	344	430	200.4	287	129.0	215	86	172	57.3	143	38.2	124	21.5	108	9.5	95	86
87	783	870	348	435	202.7	290	130.5	217	87	174	57.9	144	38.6	125	21.8	109	9.7	97	87
88	792	880	352	440	205.0	293	132.0	220	88	176	58.6	146	39.1	127	22.0	110	9.8	98	88
89	801	890	356	445	207.4	297	133.5	222	89	178	59.3	148	39.5	128	22.3	111	9.9	99	89
90	810	900	360	450	209.7	300	135.0	225	90	180	59.9	149	40.0	130	22.5	113	10.0	100	90
91	819	910	364	455	212.0	303	136.5	227	91	182	60.6	151	40.4	131	22.8	114	10.1	101	91
92	828	920	368	460	214.4	307	138.0	230	92	184	61.3	153	40.8	132	23.0	115	10.2	102	92
93	837	930	372	465	216.7	310	139.5	232	93	186	61.9	154	41.3	134	23.3	116	10.3	103	93
94	846	940	376	470	219.0	313	141.0	235	94	188	62.6	156	41.7	135	23.5	118	10.4	104	94
95	855	950	380	475	221.4	317	142.5	237	95	190	63.3	158	42.2	137	23.8	119	10.5	105	95
96	864	960	384	480	223.7	320	144.0	240	96	192	63.9	159	42.6	138	24.0	120	10.7	107	96
97	873	970	388	485	226.0	323	145.5	242	97	194	64.6	161	43.1	140	24.3	121	10.8	108	97
98	882	980	392	490	228.3	327	147.0	245	98	196	65.3	163	43.5	141	24.5	123	10.9	109	98
99	891	990	396	495	230.7	330	148.5	247	99	198	65.9	164	44.0	143	24.8	124	11.0	110	99
100	900	1,000	400	500	233.0	333	150.0	250	100	200	66.6	166	44.4	144	25.0	125	11.1	111	100

Proof of Tissot's Law
of Deformation

The law of deformation was developed by M. A. Tissot and appears in full in his *Mémoire sur la représentation des surfaces et les projections des cartes géographiques,* Paris, 1881, which includes sixty pages of deformation tables for various projections. The late Oscar S. Adams, a noted authority on the mathematics of map projections, included an account of it in his "General Theory of Polyconic Projections," U. S. Coast and Geodetic Survey *Special Publication 57,* Washington, D.C. 1934, pp. 153–163.

The following demonstration of the proof of the law of deformation consists of slightly reworded extracts taken from the above source with the permission of the Director, United States Coast and Geodetic Survey. The modifications are those of the author.

To represent one surface upon another it is necessary to imagine that each surface is composed of two systems of lines which divide them into infinitesimal parallelograms. To each line of the first surface is made to correspond one of the lines of the second. The intersection of two lines of the different systems upon the one surface and the intersection of the two corresponding lines upon the other, therefore, determine two corresponding points. The totality of the points of the second surface which correspond to the points of the first forms the

representation or the projection of the first surface. Different methods of representation are obtained by varying the two series of lines which form the graticule upon one of the surfaces.

If two surfaces are not applicable to each other, that is, cannot be transformed without compression or expansion, it is impossible to choose a method of projection where there is similarity between every figure traced upon the first and the corresponding figure upon the second. On the other hand, whatever the two surfaces may be, there exists an infinity of systems of projection which preserve the angles; consequently, each *infinitely small* figure and its representation are similar to each other. There is also an infinity of systems which preserve the areas. These two classes of projections are exceptions, however. In a method of projection being taken by chance, the angles will be generally changed, except possibly at particular points, and the corresponding areas will not have a constant ratio to each other. The lengths on the one surface will thus be altered on the second.

Consider two curves, one on one surface and one on the other, which correspond to each other. In Fig. I.1 let O and M be two points of the one, O' and M' the corresponding points of the other, and let OT be

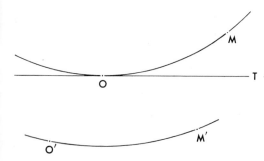

FIGURE I.1. A curve (above) and its projection (below).

the tangent at O to the first curve. If the point M lies infinitely close to the point O, then point M' will approach infinitely close to the point O'. The ratio of the length of the arc $O'M'$ to that of the arc OM will therefore tend toward a certain limit; this limit is what is called the ratio of lengths at the point O upon the curve OM or in the direction OT. In a system of projection preserving the angles, the ratio of lengths thus defined has the same value for all directions at a given point; but it varies with the position of this point, unless the two surfaces are applicable to each other. When the representation does not preserve the angles except at particular points, the ratio of lengths at all other points changes with the direction.

The deformation produced around each point is subjected to a law which depends neither upon the nature of the surfaces nor upon the method of projection.

Every representation of one surface upon another can be replaced by an infinity of orthogonal projections, each made upon a suitable scale.

It is noted, first, that there always exists at every point of the first surface two tangents perpendicular to each other such that the directions which correspond to them upon the second surface also intersect at right angles. In Fig. I.2 let CE and OD be two tangents perpendicular to each other at

the point O on the first surface; let $C'E'$ and $O'D'$ be the corresponding tangents on the second surface. Suppose, further, that of the two angles $C'O'D'$ and $D'O'E'$ the first is acute, and imagine that a right angle having its vertex at O turns from left to right around this point in the plane CDE starting from the position COD and arriving at the position DOE. The corresponding angle in the plane tangent at O to the second surface will first coincide with $C'O'D'$ and will be acute; in its final position it will coincide with $D'O'E'$ and will be obtuse; within the interval it will have passed through a right angle. Therefore, there exists a system of two tangents satisfying the condition stated, except at certain singular points. From this property it may be concluded that in every system of representation there is upon the first of the two surfaces a system of two series of orthogonal curves whose projections upon the second surface are also orthogonal. The two surfaces are thus divided into infinitesimal rectangles which correspond the one to the other.

With this fact established, let M be a point in Fig. I.3 infinitely near to O upon the first

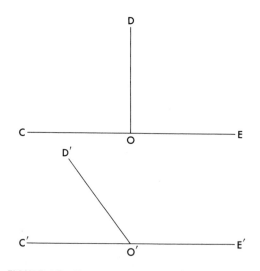

FIGURE I.2. Two tangents at right angles and their projections.

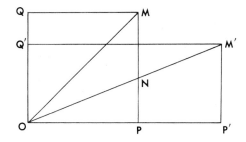

FIGURE I.3. Projection of infinitely near points.

surface and let $OPMQ$ be that one of the infinitesimal rectangles which has just been described that has OM as a diagonal. Then let $O'P'M'Q'$ be the rectangle on the second surface which corresponds to $OPMQ$ on the first. Move the second surface and place it in such a position that O on each surface coincides, and that the sides OP' and OQ' on the second surface fall upon the sides OP and OQ on the first surface. Designate as N the point of intersection of the lines OM' and PM. This point can be considered as the orthogonal projection of the point if the plane of the rectangle $OPMQ$ were turned through a suitable angle with OP as an axis. But this angle, which depends only upon the ratio of the two lines NP and MP. is the same whatever point M may be; for denoting, respectively, by a and b the ratios of the lengths in the directions OP and OQ —that is, on setting

$$\frac{OP'}{OP} = a \text{ and } \frac{OQ'}{OQ} = b$$

then

$$\frac{NP}{M'P'} = \frac{OP}{OP'} = \frac{1}{a}, \text{ and } \frac{MP}{M'P'} = \frac{OQ}{OQ'} = \frac{1}{b}$$

and, consequently,

$$\frac{NP}{MP} = \frac{b}{a}$$

Thus if M moves on an infinitesimal curve traced around O, the locus described by N is obtained by turning this curve through a certain angle around OP as an axis and by

then projecting orthogonally upon the plane tangent at O. On the other hand,

$$\frac{OM'}{ON} = \frac{OP'}{OP} = a$$

so that the locus of the points M' is homothetic to that of the points N; the center of similitude is O, and the ratio of similitude has the value a. The representation of the infinitesimal figure described by the point M is then in reality an orthogonal projection of this figure made on a suitable scale, or the figure formed by the points N and that formed by the points M' are formed by parallel sections of the same cone. Any map projection can therefore be considered as produced by the juxtaposition of orthogonal projections of the surface elements of the earth sphere, provided that, from one element to the other, both the scale of the reduction and the position of the element with respect to the plane of the map are varied.

Of all the right angles which are formed by the tangents at the point O, those of the lines OP and OQ and their prolongations are the only ones one side of which remains parallel to the tangent plane after the rotation which was just described. These are, therefore, the only right-angled tangents which are projected into right angles. An addition to the proposition which has just been proved can now be stated, and the whole can be expressed in the following form: at every point of the surface which is to be represented (the earth) there are two perpendicular tangents, and, if the angles are not preserved, there are only two, such that those which correspond to them upon the other surface (the map plane) also intersect at right angles. Thus, upon each of the two surfaces, there exists a system of orthogonal trajectories, and, if the method of representation does not preserve the angles, there exists only one of them, the projections of which upon the other surface are also orthogonal.

The two perpendicular tangents, the angle between which is not altered by the projection, are designated as first and second principal tangents. The ratio of lengths in the directions of these two tangents is designated respectively by a and b. Ratio a is assumed to be greater than b.

If the infinitesimal curve drawn around the point O is a circumference of which O is the center, the representation of this curve will be an ellipse, the axes of which will fall upon the principal tangents, and these will have the values $2a$ and $2b$ when the radius of the circle is taken as unity. This ellipse constitutes at each point a sort of indicatrix of the system of projection.

In place of (1) projecting orthogonally the circumference (the locus of the points M in Fig. I.3), which gives the ellipse (the locus of the points N), and (2) then increasing this in the ratio of a to unity (which gives the locus of the points M'), one may perform these two operations in the inverse order. Then, in Fig. I.4 the point M' of the elliptic indicatrix can be obtained which corresponds to a given point M of the circle. This is done by prolonging the radius OM until it meets at R the circumference described upon the major axis as diameter, and then by dropping

a perpendicular from R upon OA, the semi-major axis, and finally, by reducing this perpendicular RS, starting from its foot S in the ratio of b to a. The point M' thus determined is the required point.

If in Fig. I.4 OM' is drawn, then the angles AOM and AOM' which correspond upon the two surfaces may be designated, respectively, as U and U'. Inasmuch as the second is the smaller of the two, it may be seen that the representation diminishes all the acute angles, one side of which coincides with the first principal tangent. Between U and U' there is, moreover, the relation

$$\tan U' = \frac{b}{a} \tan U$$

since

$$\tan U = \frac{RS}{OS}$$

$$\tan U' = \frac{M'S}{OS}$$

and, consequently,

$$\tan U' = \frac{M'S}{RS} \tan U = \frac{b}{a} \tan U$$

Prolong the line RS to R' and then join O and R'. The two triangles ORM' and $OR'M'$ give

$$\sin (U - U') = \frac{a - b}{a + b} \sin (U + U')$$

which is obtained by equating two expressions for the ratio of the areas of the triangles. The same relation follows at once analytically from the tangent relation first given. The angle U increasing from zero to $\pi/2$, its alteration $U - U'$ increases from zero up to a certain value ω, then decreases to zero. The maximum is produced at the moment when the sum $U + U'$ becomes equal to $\pi/2$. From the tangent formula the following are their values:

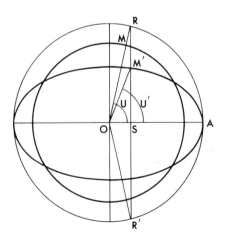

FIGURE I.4. Tissot's indicatrix.

$$\tan U = \frac{\sqrt{a}}{\sqrt{b}} \text{ and } \tan U' = \frac{\sqrt{b}}{\sqrt{a}}$$

The quantity ω can be computed by any one of the formulas

$$\sin \omega = \frac{a - b}{a + b}$$

$$\cos \omega = \frac{2\sqrt{ab}}{a + b}$$

$$\tan \omega = \frac{a - b}{2\sqrt{ab}}$$

$$\tan \frac{\omega}{2} = \frac{\sqrt{a} - \sqrt{b}}{\sqrt{a} + \sqrt{b}}$$

$$\tan \left(\frac{\pi}{4} + \frac{\omega}{2}\right) = \frac{\sqrt{a}}{\sqrt{b}} \text{ and } \tan\left(\frac{\pi}{4} - \frac{\omega}{2}\right) = \frac{\sqrt{b}}{\sqrt{a}}$$

If one wishes to calculate directly the alteration which any given angle U is subject to, he may use one of the two formulas

$$\tan (U - U') = \frac{(a - b) \tan U}{a + b \tan ^2 U'}$$

$$\tan (U - U') = \frac{(a - b) \sin 2U}{a + b + (a - b) \cos 2U}$$

which follow immediately from the previous formulas.

Consider now an angle MON in Figs. I.5 and I.6, which has for sides neither one nor the other of the principal tangents OA and OB. Assume the two directions OM and ON to be to the right of OB and the one of

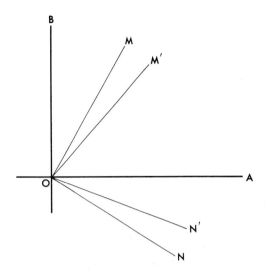

FIGURE I.6. **Angular change in projections, second case.**

them OM above OA. According to whether the other ON will be above OA (Fig. I.5) or below OA (Fig. I.6), the corresponding angle $M'ON'$ can be calculated by taking the difference or the sum of the angles AOM' and AON', which would be given by the formula stated above. The alteration $MON - M'ON'$ would also in the first case be the difference, and in the second case would be the sum of the alterations of the angles AOM and AON. When the angle AON (Fig. I.5) is equal to the angle BOM', its alteration is the same as that of the angle AOM, so that the angle MON will then be reproduced in its true magnitude by the angle $M'ON'$. Thus to every given direction another can be joined and only one other, such that their angle is preserved in the projection. However, the second direction will coincide with the first when it makes with OA the angle which has been denoted by U.

The angle the most altered is that which this direction forms with the point symmetric to it with respect to $OA;$ it is represented upon the projection by its supplement. The maximum alteration thus produced is equal to 2ω. This can never be found applicable

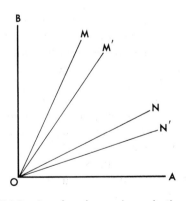

FIGURE I.5. **Angular change in projections, first case.**

to two directions that are perpendicular to each other.

The length OM in Fig. I.4 having been taken as unity, the ratio of lengths in the direction OM is measured by OM'. If this ratio is designated as r, it may be calculated by one of the formulas

$$r \cos U' = a \cos U$$
$$r \sin U' = b \sin U$$

or

$$r^2 = a^2 \cos{}^2 U + b^2 \sin{}^2 U.$$

There is also among r, U, and the alteration $U - U'$ of the angle U the relation

$$2r \sin (U - U') = (a - b) \sin 2U$$

which expresses that, in the triangle ORM', the sines of two of the angles are to each other as the sides opposite.

The maximum and the minimum of r correspond to the principal tangents and are, respectively, a and b.

If r and r_1 are the ratios of lengths in two directions at right angles to each other and if θ is the alteration that the right angle formed by these two directions is subjected to, then from the properties of conjugate diameters in the ellipse

$$r^2 + r_1{}^2 = a^2 + b^2$$
$$rr_1 \cos \theta = ab$$

In terms of the scale along a parallel (h) and along a meridian (k) at a point on a projection, the semi-axes are given by the equations

$$a^2 + b^2 = h^2 + k^2$$
$$ab = hk \cos \theta$$

Bibliography

SELECTED LIST OF GENERALLY AVAILABLE MATERIALS USEFUL FOR ADDITIONAL READING

The following list includes references to only those items which are in English, and which are readily available or easily secured. They will be found useful for reference or for further reading in the topics under which they have been included.

GENERAL REFERENCES

T. W. Birch, *Maps, Topographical and Statistical,* Oxford University Press, London, 1949.

David Greenhood, *Down to Earth,* Holiday House, New York, 1951.

A. L. Kaminstein, "Copyright and Registration of Maps," *Surveying and Mapping,* Vol. 13, 1953.

F. J. Monkhouse and H. R. Wilkinson, *Maps and Diagrams: Their Compilation and Construction,* Methuen and Co., Ltd., London, 1952.

Erwin Raisz, *General Cartography,* 2nd Ed., McGraw-Hill Book Co., New York, 1948.

World Cartography, Vols. 1–4, United Nations, New York (available through International Documents Service, Columbia University Press).

Leo J. Zuber, "What's a Map Worth?," *Surveying and Mapping,* Vol. 12, 1952.

HISTORICAL BACKGROUND

Lloyd A. Brown, *The Story of Maps,* Little, Brown and Co., Boston, 1949.

G. R. Crone, *Maps and Their Makers,* Hutchinson's University Library, London, 1953.

H. G. Fordham, *Maps, Their History, Characteristics and Uses,* Cambridge University Press, Cambridge, England, 1943.

W. W. Jervis, *The World in Maps,* Oxford University Press, New York, 1938.

J. Keuning, "The History of Geographical Map Projections until 1600," *Imago Mundi,* Vol. 12, 1955.

Edward Lynam, *The Map Maker's Art, Essays on the History of Maps,* The Batchworth Press, London, 1953.

Erwin Raisz, *General Cartography.*

Arthur H. Robinson, "The 1837 Maps of Henry Drury Harness," *The Geographical Journal,* Vol. 121, 1955.

R. A. Skelton, *Decorative Printed Maps of the 15th to 18th Centuries,* Staples Press, London, 1952.

John K. Wright, "Highlights in American Cartography, 1939–1949," *Compte rendu du XVIᵉ congrès international de géographie,* Lisbon, 1949.

COORDINATE SYSTEMS, SCALE, AND MEASUREMENT

Harry P. Bailey, "A Grid Formed of Meridians and Parallels for the Comparison and Measurement of Area," *The Geographical Review,* Vol. 46, 1956.

W. G. V. Balchin, "The Representation of True to Scale Linear Values on Map Projections," *Geography,* Vol. 36, 1951.

Clement L. Garner, "Geodesy—A Framework for Maps," *Surveying and Mapping,* Vol. 17, 1957.

John W. Gierhart, "Evaluation of Methods of Area Measurement," *Surveying and Mapping,* Vol. 14, 1954.

John A. O'Keefe, "The Universal Transverse Mercator Grid and Projection," *The Professional Geographer,* Vol. 4, 1952.

M. Proudfoot, "The Measurement of Geographic Area," Bureau of the Census, Washington, D.C., 1946.

Erwin Raisz, *General Cartography.*

The Universal Grid Systems, TM 5-241 (Army) TO 16-1-233 (Air Force) Government Printing Office, Washington, D.C., 1951.

MAP PROJECTIONS

W. G. V. Balchin, "The Choice of Map Projections," *Empire Survey Review,* Vol. 12, 1954.

Wellman Chamberlin, *The Round Earth on Flat Paper,* The National Geographic Society, Washington, D.C., 1947.

C. H. Deetz and O. S. Adams, "Elements of Map Projection," U. S. Coast and Geodetic Survey *Special Publication* 68, Washington, D.C. (latest edition available).

Irving Fisher and O. M. Miller, *World Maps and Globes,* Essential Books, New York, 1944.

B. Goussinsky, "On the Classification of Map Projections," *Empire Survey Review,* Vol. 11, 1951.

A. R. Hinks, *Map Projections,* Cambridge University Press, Cambridge, England (latest edition available).

L. P. Lee, "The Oblique Mercator Projection," *New Zealand Geographer,* Vol. 10, 1954.

John Leighly, "Extended Use of Polyconic Projection Tables," *Annals of the Association of American Geographers,* Vol. 46, 1956.

F. J. Marschner, "Structural Properties of Medium and Small Scale Maps," *Annals of the Association of American Geographers,* Vol. 34, 1944.

O. M. Miller, "Notes on Cylindrical Map Projections," *The Geographical Review,* Vol. 32, 1942.

Arthur H. Robinson, "An Analytical Approach to Map Projections," *Annals of the Association of American Geographers,* Vol. 39, 1949.

Arthur H. Robinson, "The Use of Deformational Data in Evaluating Map Projections," *Annals of the Association of American Geographers,* Vol. 41, 1951.

Arthur H. Robinson, "Interrupting a Map Projection: A Partial Analysis of Its Value," *Annals of the Association of American Geographers,* Vol. 43, 1953.

William J. Sear, "Map Projection by Transformation," *Cartography,* Vol. 2, 1957.

J. A. Steers, *An Introduction to the Study of Map Projections,* University of London Press, London, 1957.

J. Q. Stewart, "The Use and Abuse of Map Projections," *The Geographical Review,* Vol. 33, 1943.

THE CARTOGRAPHIC METHOD

S. W. Boggs, "Mapping the Changing World: Suggested Developments in Maps," *Annals of the Association of American Geographers,* Vol. 31, 1941.

S. W. Boggs, "Cartohypnosis," *Scientific Monthly,* Vol. 64, 1947.

Max Eckert, "On the Nature of Maps and Map Logic,"

Bulletin of the American Geographical Society, Vol. 40, 1908 (translated by W. L. G. Joerg).

J. Ross Mackay, "Geographic Cartography," *The Canadian Geographer,* Vol. 4, 1954.

Arthur H. Robinson et. al., "Geographical Cartography," Chapter 26 in *American Geography Inventory and Prospect,* Syracuse University Press, Syracuse, 1954.

Allen K. Philbrick, "Toward a Unity of Cartographical Forms and Geographical Content," *The Professional Geographer,* Vol. 5, 1953.

Morris M. Thompson, "How Accurate Is That Map?," *Surveying and Mapping,* Vol. 16, 1956.

John K. Wright, "Map Makers Are Human. Comments on the Subjective in Maps," *The Geographical Review,* Vol. 32, 1942.

PROCESSING AND REPRESENTING QUANTITATIVE DATA

David I. Blumenstock, "The Reliability Factor in the Drawing of Isarithms," *Annals of the Association of American Geographers,* Vol. 43, 1953.

William G. Byron, "Use of the Recording Densitometer in Measuring Density from Dot Maps," *Surveying and Mapping,* Vol. 18, 1958.

O. D. Duncan, "The Measurement of Population Distribution," *Population Studies,* Vol. 11, 1957.

J. Ross Mackay, "Dotting the Dot Map," *Surveying and Mapping,* Vol. 9, 1949.

J. Ross Mackay, "Some Problems and Techniques in Isopleth Mapping," *Economic Geography,* Vol. 27, 1951.

J. Ross Mackay, "Percentage Dot Maps," *Economic Geography,* Vol. 29, 1953.

J. Ross Mackay, "A New Projection for Cubic Symbols on Economic Maps," *Economic Geography,* Vol. 29, 1953.

J. Ross Mackay, "An Analysis of Isopleth and Choropleth Class Intervals," *Economic Geography,* Vol. 31, 1955.

E. Mather, "A Linear Distance Map of Farm Population in the United States," *Annals of the Association of American Geographers,* Vol. 34, 1944.

F. J. Monkhouse and H. R. Wilkinson, *Maps and Diagrams.*

Erwin Raisz, "The Rectangular Statistical Diagram," *The Geographical Review,* Vol. 24, 1934.

Erwin Raisz, *General Cartography.*

Calvin F. Schmid and E. H. MacCannell, "Basic Problems, Techniques, and Theory of Isopleth Mapping," *Journal of the American Statistical Association,* Vol. 50, 1955.

John Q. Stewart and William Warntz, "Macrogeography and Social Science," *The Geographical Review,* Vol. 48, 1958.

E. C. Wilcox and W. H. Ebling, "Presentation of Agri-

cultural Data in the States," *Journal of Farm Economics,* Vol. 31, 1949.

John K. Wright, "A Proposed Atlas of Diseases, Appendix I, Cartographic Considerations," *The Geographical Review,* Vol. 34, 1944.

John K. Wright, "The Terminology of Certain Map Symbols," *The Geographical Review,* Vol. 34, 1944.

STATISTICAL TECHNIQUES

H. J. Allcock and J. R. Jones, *The Nomogram,* Pitman and Sons, London, 1938.

C. E. P. Brooks and N. Carruthers, *Handbook of Statistical Methods in Meteorology,* Her Majesty's Stationery Office, London, 1953.

M. J. Hagood and D. O. Price, *Statistics for Sociologists,* Rev. Ed., Henry Holt and Company, New York, 1952.

Alexander Levens, *Nomography,* 2nd Ed., John Wiley and Sons, New York, 1959.

W. A. Neiswanger, *Elementary Statistical Methods,* The Macmillan Company, New York, 1943.

Arthur H. Robinson and Reid A. Bryson, "A Method for Describing Quantitatively the Correspondence of Geographical Distributions," *Annals of the Association of American Geographers,* Vol. 47, 1957.

Alfred R. Sumner, "Standard Deviation of Mean Monthly Temperatures in Anglo-America," *The Geographical Review,* Vol. 43, 1953.

W. Allen Wallis and Harry V. Roberts, *Statistics: A New Approach,* The Free Press, Glencoe, Illinois, 1956.

REPRESENTATION OF TERRAIN

R. B. Batchelder, "Application of Two Relative Relief Techniques to an Area of Diverse Landforms: A Comparative Study," *Surveying and Mapping,* Vol. 10, 1950.

Wesley Calef and Robert Newcomb, "An Average Slope Map of Illinois," *Annals of the Association of American Geographers,* Vol. 43, 1953.

John E. Dornbach, "An Approach to Design of Terrain Representation," *Surveying and Mapping,* Vol. 16, 1956.

Edwin H. Hammond, "Small Scale Continental Landform Maps," *Annals of the Association of American Geographers,* Vol. 44, 1954.

Armin K. Lobeck, *Block Diagrams,* 2nd Ed., Emerson-Trussell Book Company, Amherst, Mass., 1958.

Captain H. G. Lyons, "Relief in Cartography," *The Geographical Journal,* Vol. 43, 1914.

Erwin Raisz, "The Physiographic Method of Representing Scenery on Maps," *The Geographical Review,* Vol. 21, 1931.

Erwin Raisz, *General Cartography.*

Arthur H. Robinson and Norman J. W. Thrower, "A New Method of Terrain Representation," *The Geographical Review,* Vol. 47, 1957.

Guy-Harold Smith, "The Relative Relief of Ohio," *The Geographical Review,* Vol. 25, 1935.

John R. Stacy, "Terrain Diagrams in Isometric Projection-Simplified," *Annals of the Association of American Geographers,* Vol. 48, 1958.

K. Tanaka, "The Relief Contour Method of Representing Topography on Maps," *The Geographical Review,* Vol. 40, 1950.

Joseph E. Williams, "The Relief Map," *The Professional Geographer,* Vol. 5, 1953.

GRAPHIC TECHNIQUES AND DESIGN

Army Technical Manual 5-230, *Topographic Drafting,* Washington, D.C.

Faber Birren, *The Story of Color,* The Crimson Press, Westport, Connecticut, 1941.

Lavoi B. Davis, "Design Criteria for Today's Aeronautical Charts," *Surveying and Mapping,* Vol. 18, 1958.

E. De Lopatecki, *Advertising Layout and Typography,* Ronald Press, New York, 1935.

Higgins Ink Company, *Techniques,* 5th Ed., Brooklyn, New York, 1948.

International Printing Ink Corporation, *Three Monographs on Color,* New York, 1935.

Edwin H. Land, "Color Vision and the Natural Image, Parts I and II," *Proceedings of the National Academy of Sciences,* Vol. 45, Numbers 1 and 4, 1959. See also "Symposium on New Developments in the Study of Color Vision" preceding Part I in Vol. 45.

R. R. Lutz, *Graphic Presentation Simplified,* Funk and Wagnalls Co., New York, 1949.

Richard W. Philbrick, "New Design Features for the World Aeronautical Chart," *Surveying and Mapping,* Vol. 17, 1957.

Walter W. Ristow, "Journalistic Cartography," *Surveying and Mapping,* Vol. 17, 1957.

Arthur H. Robinson, *The Look of Maps, An Examination of Cartographic Design,* University of Wisconsin Press, Madison, Wisconsin, 1952.

Walter Sargent, *The Enjoyment and Use of Color,* Charles Scribner's Sons, Chicago, 1923.

John C. Sherman and Waldo R. Tobler, "The Multiple Use Concept in Cartography," *The Professional Geographer,* Vol. 9, 1957.

U. S. Government Printing Office, *Typography and Design,* Washington, D.C., 1951.

Robert L. Williams, *Statistical Symbols for Maps: Their Design and Relative Values,* Yale University Map Laboratory, New Haven, Connecticut, 1956.

Robert Lee Williams, "Equal-Appearing Intervals for Printed Screens," *Annals of the Association of American Geographers,* Vol. 48, 1958.

MAP LETTERING

Higgins Ink Company, *Lettering,* 2nd Ed., Brooklyn, New York, 1949.

Ross F. George, *Speedball Text Book,* 17th Ed., Hunt Pen Co., Camden, New Jersey, 1948.

Merideth F. Burrill, "U. S. Board on Geographical Names," *Surveying and Mapping,* Vol. 6, 1946.

John S. Keates, "The Use of Type in Cartography," *Surveying and Mapping,* Vol. 18, 1958.

Charles E. Riddeford, "On the Lettering of Maps," *The Professional Geographer,* Vol. 4, 1952.

Arthur H. Robinson, *The Look of Maps.*

Arthur H. Robinson, "The Size of Lettering for Maps and Charts," *Surveying and Mapping,* Vol. 10, 1950.

Daniel B. Updike, *Printing Types, Their History, Forms, and Use; a Study in Survivals,* Harvard University Press, Cambridge, Mass., 1922.

U. S. Government Printing Office, *Typography and Design.*

J. G. Withcombe, "Lettering on Maps," *The Geographical Journal,* Vol. 73, 1929.

MAP REPRODUCTION

Inter-Agency Committee on Negative Scribing, *Report on Scribing, Part I,* Map Information Office, U. S. Geological Survey, Washington, D.C., 1957. (Parts II and III scheduled for publication.)

L. H. Joachim (editor), *Seventh Production Yearbook,*

The Reference Manual of the Graphic Arts, Colton Press, New York, 1941.

M. S. Kantrowitz, "Printing Papers," *Surveying and Mapping,* Vol. 10, 1950.

The Lithographer's Manual (compiled by W. E. Soderstrom), Waltwin Publishing Co., New York, 1940.

Lynn R. Wickland, "Evolution of Paper and Plastics as Related to Mapping," *The Professional Geographer,* Vol. 4, 1952.

GOVERNMENT PUBLICATIONS

Branches of the U. S. Government have issued a large number of useful publications concerning many aspects of cartography. Publications in series, such as the *Technical* or *Training Manuals* of the Departments of the Army and Air Force, the *Special Publications* of the Coast and Geodetic Survey and the Geological Survey, etc., are published by the Government Printing Office, from which listings are available. In addition, the major mapping agencies, such as the Army Map Service, the Hydrographic Office, and the Aeronautical Chart and Information Service, themselves publish *Technical Bulletins,* etc., which are ordinarily obtainable directly from the issuing agency.

Index

Adams, Oscar S., 324
Aeronautical charts, 10
Air photography, 10
Albers projection, 72
   construction of, 104
   deformation on, 73
Albumin lithography, 271
Alphabet, freehand forms of, 258
Ames lettering instrument, 256
Angular alteration in map projections, 56
Angular deformation in map projections, 61
Arc, formula for chord of, 47
Arcs, drawing of, 46
Area, alteration of, by projections, 57, 61
   measurement of, 61
Area measurement, 26, 48
Area symbols, for terrain maps, 219
   qualitative, 138–139, 141
   quantitative, 138–139, 142, 171
Arithmetic progression, 191
Art in cartography, 222
Artype, 44
Authalic latitude, 97
Average, arithmetic, *see* Mean
Azimuth, 24
Azimuthal equidistant projection, 84, 86
   construction of, 115
   deformation on, 85
Azimuthal projections, 59
   comparison of, 83, 111
   construction of, 110
   employment of, 83
   transformation of, 117
Azimuthality, definition of, 69

Balance, 234
Barch-Payzant pens, 38–39, 160
Barnes, James A., 312

Base data, 11, 121
Base map, changing scale of, 125
   coastlines on, 128
   hydrography on, 131
   importance of, 11, 122
   indexing of source maps for, 124
   political boundaries on, 129
Ben Day patterns, 273
Bias on isarithmic maps, 189
Block diagrams, 206
Block pile symbols, 170
Blue-line board, 279–280
Blueprint process, 266–267
Blumenstock, David I., 189
Board on Geographical Names, 261
Bonne projection, 73
   construction of, 104
   deformation on, 74
Boundaries, along rivers, 131
   compiling of, 129
   drafting of, 130
   political, 129
   symbols for, 130–131
Braddock-Rowe lettering angle, 256
Brightness, *see* Value
B-W process of map reproduction, 267

Cadastral maps, 2, 122–123
Capital letters, 249
Cartesian coordinate system, 18
Cartography, art of, 15
   convention in, 14, 233
   definition of, 11
   history of, 2–10
   principles of, 14
   science of, 13
   techniques of, 12
Center, optical of a map, 235